D1598204

# Characterization of Heterogeneous Catalysts

CHEMICAL INDUSTRIES

*A Series of Reference Books and Text Books*

*Consulting Editor*
HEINZ HEINEMANN
*Heinz Heinemann, Inc.,*
*Berkeley, California*

*Volume 1:* Fluid Catalytic Cracking with Zeolite Catalysts, *Paul B. Venuto and E. Thomas Habib, Jr.*

*Volume 2:* Ethylene: Keystone to the Petrochemical Industry, *Ludwig Kniel, Olaf Winter, and Karl Stork*

*Volume 3:* The Chemistry and Technology of Petroleum, *James G. Speight*

*Volume 4:* The Desulfurization of Heavy Oils and Residua, *James G. Speight*

*Volume 5:* Catalysis of Organic Reactions, *edited by William R. Moser*

*Volume 6:* Acetylene-Based Chemicals from Coal and Other Natural Resources, *Robert J. Tedeschi*

*Volume 7:* Chemically Resistant Masonry, *Walter Lee Sheppard, Jr.*

*Volume 8:* Compressors and Expanders: Selection and Application for the Process Industry, *Heinz P. Bloch, Joseph A. Cameron, Frank M. Danowski, Jr., Ralph James, Jr., Judson S. Swearingen, and Marilyn E. Weightman*

*Volume 9:* Metering Pumps: Selection and Application, *James P. Poynton*

*Volume 10:* Hydrocarbons from Methanol, *Clarence D. Chang*

*Volume 11:* Foam Flotation: Theory and Applications, *Ann N. Clarke and David J. Wilson*

*Volume 12:* The Chemistry and Technology of Coal, *James G. Speight*

*Volume 13:* Pneumatic and Hydraulic Conveying of Solids, *O. A. Williams*

*Volume 14:* Catalyst Manufacture: Laboratory and Commercial Preparations, *Alvin B. Stiles*

*Volume 15:* Characterization of Heterogeneous Catalysts, *edited by Francis Delannay*

Additional Volumes in Preparation

# Characterization of Heterogeneous Catalysts

Edited by

FRANCIS DELANNAY
*Université Catholique de Louvain*
*Louvain-la-Neuve, Belgium*

MARCEL DEKKER, INC. New York and Basel

Library of Congress Cataloging in Publication Data

Main entry under title:

Characterization of heterogeneous catalysts.

(Chemical industries: v. 15)
Includes bibliographies and index.
1. Catalysts. I. Delannay, F. (Francis), [date]
II. Series.
QD505.C46 1984 541.3'95 83-26256
ISBN 0-8247-7100-1



MARCEL DEKKER, INC.
270 Madison Avenue, New York, New York 10016

Current printing (last digit):
10 9 8 7 6 5 4 3 2 1

PRINTED IN THE UNITED STATES OF AMERICA

# Preface

Catalytic research has come to involve the cooperative efforts of people having fairly different scientific backgrounds, training, and points of view, such as chemists, physicists, and engineers. This cooperation necessitates that workers in the field properly understand one another. Efforts aimed at improving this mutual understanding appear especially necessary today, considering the wealth of experimental techniques that are presently dealt with in the literature on catalysis.

The editing of a book requires in the first instance a definition of objectives which, as far as possible, should comply with particular requests of potential readers. The primary objective assigned to this book was to provide readers, regardless of their primary training, with basic information that would allow them to improve their knowledge of techniques with which they may not already be fully familiar. Although reference is made to the most recent literature, the aim is thus not to write exhaustive reviews of recent advances for specialists in the field. Rather, chapters have been written so as to be sufficiently informative for inexperienced people. Practical details relating to various techniques have been included where appropriate and are intended for potential users who may wish to begin working with a new technique. In this respect, most chapters might be used as a basis for student texts in advanced courses on catalysis. It is the hope of the editor that this book will be recognized both as a research monograph and as an advanced textbook.

Nobody could hope to cover, in a single volume, all the experimental techniques that are presently used for characterizing catalysts. The scope of this book is centered around the study of *practical catalysts* as they are used in industrial processes. This has necessitated that we exclude all techniques whose application has up to now been limited essentially to the study of model systems (e.g., single crystals). Practical catalysts are usually finely divided synthetic mineral mixtures. The application of modern physicochemical methods to the study of such materials requires special care. The chapters of this book have been written by experienced researchers able to evaluate in a critical way the actual potentialities and limitations of their particular technique for the characterization of practical catalysts. We expect that this approach will be appreciated by scientists and engineers involved both in fundamental research and in industrial application problems, especially in the fields of catalyst preparation, deactivation, regeneration, and so on.

The choice of the topics to receive detailed presentation was governed by the following arguments.

First, the emphasis of the book is on the techniques for study of the solid itself and of its surface. This means that we omitted techniques more related to the characterization of the adsorbed phase and its bonding, diffusion, and reactions on the catalyst surface. Although most useful for the characterization of some solids, such major techniques as NMR, infrared, and Raman spectroscopies have not been covered. Space for a comprehensive presentation of their multiple capabilities might be given them in a future second volume.

Second, some techniques, such as X-ray diffraction, scanning electron microscopy, and the BET method, are today practiced quite routinely. They did not appear to deserve an updated description of their application to catalysts. For a similar reason, it did not appear useful to review again the application of Mössbauer spectroscopy to the characterization of catalysts because this subject has been dealt with in several recent reviews.

Third, techniques such as neutron diffraction, EXAFS, and ISS seemed still to be in too early a stage of development to permit evaluation of their actual prospects with regard to future catalytic research.

The general structure of this book follows from the overview presented in Chapter 1. For a summary, the reader is referred to Sec. IV of that chapter.

The editor gratefully acknowledges the encouragement and advice of Professor B. Delmon and of his colleagues of the Groupe de Physico-Chimie Minérale et de Catalyse during the course of the preparation of this book. The preparation of the manuscript was partially supported by a grant from the Ministère de l'Education Nationale et de la Culture Française (Belgium).

*Francis Delannay*

# Contributors

**Camille Defossé** Research Laboratory, Cementation Services, Laboratoire Dowell-Schlumberger, Saint-Etienne, France

**Francis Delannay** Groupe de Physico-Chimie Minérale et de Catalyse, Université Catholique de Louvain, Louvain-la-Neuve, Belgium

**Bernard Delmon** Groupe de Physico-Chimie Minérale et de Catalyse, Université Catholique de Louvain, Louvain-la-Neuve, Belgium

**Peter A. Jacobs** National Fund of Scientific Research and Centrum voor Oppervlaktescheikunde en Colloidale Scheikunde, Katholieke Universiteit Leuven, Leuven (Heverlee), Belgium

**Jacques L. Lemaitre** Groupe de Physico-Chimie Minérale et de Catalyse, Université Catholique de Louvain, Louvain-la-Neuve, Belgium

**P. Govind Menon** Laboratorium voor Petrochemische Techniek, Rijksuniversiteit Gent, Gent, Belgium

**Robert A. Schoonheydt** National Fund of Scientific Research and Centrum voor Oppervlaktescheikunde en Colloidale Scheikunde, Katholieke Universiteit Leuven, Leuven (Heverlee), Belgium

**Jacques C. Védrine** Institut de Recherches sur la Catalyse, Centre National de la Recherche Scientifique (CNRS), Villeurbanne, France

# Contents

# 1

# Methods of Catalyst Characterization: An Overview

FRANCIS DELANNAY and BERNARD DELMON Université Catholique de Louvain, Louvain-la-Neuve, Belgium

## I. INTRODUCTION

Being intended primarily for the nonspecialist, an overview necessarily involves the recalling of quite elementary principles. Experienced readers will forgive the present authors if some of these principles appear too general or repetitive.

Heterogeneous catalysis deals with the transformation of molecules at the interface between a solid (the catalyst) and the gaseous or liquid phase carrying these molecules. This transformation involves a series of phenomena, the understanding and hence control of which requires the study of:

1. How the catalyst is constituted in its bulk and at its surface and what transformations it suffers (chemical reactions, exchange of atoms between surface and bulk, sintering, etc.)
2. How the gaseous or liquid phase is modified (composition, kinetics, etc.)
3. The nature of the interface (adsorbed species and bonds between these species and the catalyst surface)

Of course, these three fields of knowledge are closely interrelated and can often only be investigated simultaneously. For example, many properties of the surface of the solid are best determined by studying the binding of "probe" molecules on the surface.

In an attempt to classify the approaches to catalyst characterization, one may divide, somewhat arbitrarily, the catalytic studies in the literature between those making use of simplified (model) catalysts, such as single crystals or films (so as to reduce the number of parameters affecting the interpretation of the experiments), and those dealing with real (practical) catalysts or at least with catalysts similar in their texture and composition to those used in industrial plants.

According to the objectives defined in the foreword of this book, this chapter focuses on the characterization of the solid [i.e., the characteristics classified above in (1)] and is centered around methods that can be applied to practical catalysts.

Scientifically, this choice is justified by the fact that, if relevant studies of the catalytic mechanisms operating in real systems are to be made (on the basis of kinetics and/or the spectroscopy of adsorbed species), a detailed knowledge of the catalyst itself is required (a prerequisite not always respected, even in recent publications). The development of powerful investigation methods (essentially physicochemical, i.e., based on well-understood physical or physicochemical phenomena) for the characterization of catalysts has been a major advance in recent years. It follows that no catalytic study, even a kinetic study, should be presented to the scientific community without a description of the major features of the catalyst. This trend toward a more exhaustive characterization of catalysts is apparent when examining the proceedings of successive International Congresses on Catalysis.

Practically, the characterization of solids is a major concern in many industrial activities, such as the manufacturing of the catalysts (where control of the various steps of preparation necessitates the study of the successive catalyst precursors), the development of catalysts better resistant to aging and deactivation, and the activation, reactivation, and regeneration of catalysts.

The development of a more active catalyst gives large energy savings by allowing operation at lower temperatures. In certain cases, reduction by only a few degrees corresponds to significant savings of money. An increase of selectivity saves feeds and reduces purification costs. It is therefore not surprising that companies devote costly research and development efforts for a gain of even 1% or less in yield. Such gains may correspond to a 10,000-ton/year increase in output in the huge plants of the modern petroleum and chemical industries. This has prompted all the companies involved in the development of catalysts to equip their laboratories with a large variety of sophisticated physicochemical instruments.

Extending the life of catalysts is probably as important as developing more active or selective catalysts; a deactivated catalyst, indeed, usually requires a higher operating temperature and may be less selective. Some industrial engineers estimate that roughly 50% of the expense of catalyst development is concerned with aging and deactivation problems. This involves the use of a great variety of techniques for detecting the symptoms and, hopefully, identifying the causes of aging and deactivation. Because a detailed knowledge of the catalyst at each stage of its work is so essential, devices have been designed for routinely taking samples of catalyst out of the industrial reactor. Despite their high cost, such devices are beginning to be used for platinum reforming catalysts, which are undoubtedly the most sophisticated and fragile catalysts in large-scale operations. These catalysts require careful regeneration treatments at frequent intervals, thus justifying easy access to the catalyst for frequent characterization.

Because detailed knowledge of the characteristics of catalysts is as important for the science of catalysis as for the efficient and economical operation of industrial processes, it is not surprising that several scientific assemblies (e.g., Refs. 1 and 2) have recently emphasized the need to continue the effort toward both the acquisition of specialized equipment and the development (or improvement) of characterization methods specifically adapted to the nature of catalysts. The latter aspect requires special care. Originally, many physicochemical techniques were designed for quite different types of solids, namely monocrystals or ideal surfaces in ultrahigh vacuum. The interpretation of the results provided by these techniques when applied to highly dispersed solids such as catalysts often requires special care, and much experience is needed before it is possible to assess the actual usefulness of a given technique for catalytic research. It is the aim of the subsequent chapters to provide such a critical evaluation of selected characterization methods.

Present catalytic research more frequently involves the cooperation of people of quite different backgrounds: chemists, physicists, and engineers, who may feel overwhelmed by the wealth of techniques available today for the study of solids and surfaces. The aim of this chapter is to clarify ideas in this respect. In Sec. II, the various "characteristics" of a catalyst that should be known are discussed. In Sec. III we propose a selection of methods best adapted to the study of these characteristics. This selection will be evaluated according to both practical and scientific criteria. An overview of various techniques presently used in material and surface science laboratories is given in the chapter appendix.

## II. ESSENTIAL CHARACTERISTICS OF CATALYSTS

Before examining the characterization techniques it is worthwhile to indicate briefly the various "characteristics" that should be known about a practical catalyst. Obviously, the first feature is the nature of the basic "building units" constituting the solid [i.e., the overall (or average) bulk atomic composition]. Then comes the arrangement of these basic "building units" (i.e., the "architecture" of the catalyst). The determination of this architecture should logically go from the most macroscopic or average features toward the most microscopic or localized ones. Figure 1 is an attempt to summarize these various characteristics and to suggest some paths along which the study should proceed.

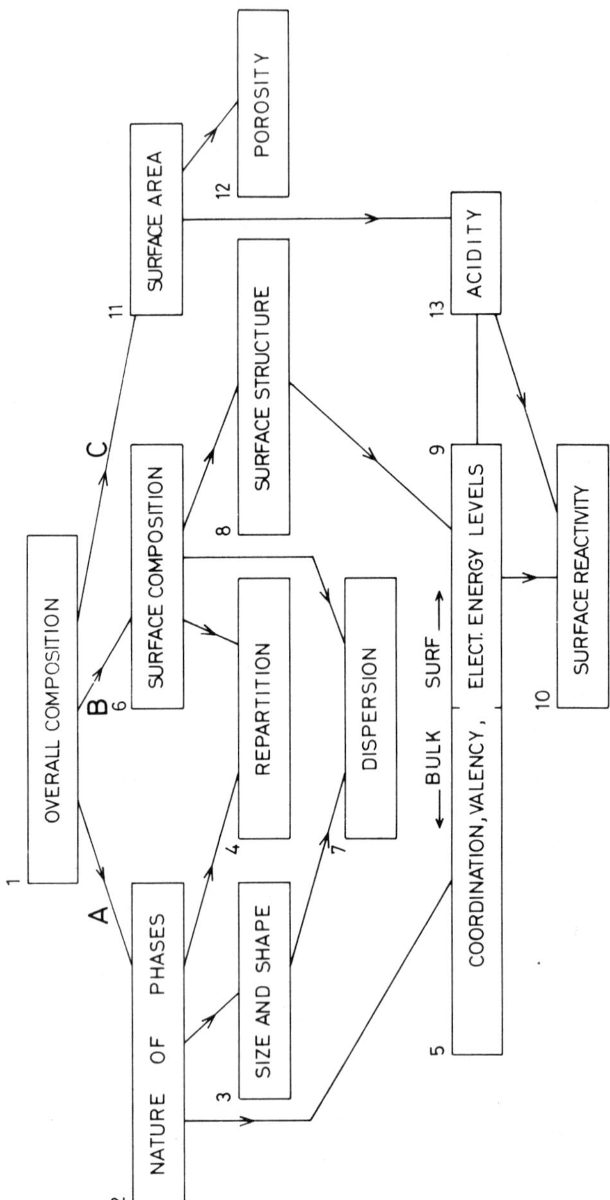


FIG. 1. General scheme of the characterization of practical catalysts.

Path A concerns the nature of the bulk of the solid. The individual building blocks (atoms) are grouped and often organized to form a limited number of phases (amorphous or crystalline) which can be characterized macroscopically by features such as crystal structure or reactivity. Knowing the *overall composition* of the solid (box 1 in the figure), the first step is to discover the *nature* of these phases (box 2). The investigation may then proceed both toward the description of the *size and shape* of the particles of each phase (box 3) (e.g., size and crystal habit of metal particles on a silica support) and toward the study of the mutual position or distribution of the phases within the solid (box 4). We call this the *repartition* (or *distribution in space*) of the phases. Measurement of repartition includes the determination of the distribution of the atomic composition, especially when no separate phase can be distinguished. Along a third direction, path A may proceed toward a more microscopic description of the environment (*coordination*) and chemical state (*valency, electron energy levels*, etc.) of the individual atoms (box 5). Obviously, the coordination (octahedral, tetrahedral) of an individual atom is directly related to the nature of the phase to which it belongs. As the chemical state of the atom is determined largely by its environment, these two features are strongly interrelated.

Path B deals with the nature of the surface of the solid. The first step is necessarily the measurement of the atomic *composition of the surface* (box 6). It is also desirable to get information on the *repartition* of this surface composition. Obviously, this repartition is related to the repartition of the bulk composition (box 4). The knowledge of both bulk and surface compositions allows the measurement of the *dispersion* of the various phases constituting the catalyst, in particular, of the active phase (box 7). The approach to the evaluation of dispersion is discussed at length in Chap. 7. One should remember that, in some favorable cases, dispersion may also be determined from the size and shape of the particles belonging to the various phases. Path B may also proceed toward the study of long-range atomic arrangement, that is, the *crystal structure at the surface* (box 8) and, afterwards, of the more local arrangement (*coordination*) and *chemical state* of the surface atoms (box 9). The latter features may often be investigated by use of the same techniques as those used for the corresponding bulk properties (box 5). In particular, this occurs if the atom being studied is located exclusively at the surface of the catalyst.

Presently, the properties of surfaces are often most easily determined by studying their interaction with selected molecules. This is the reason we have distinguished, as a last step along path B, the study of what we call the *reactivity of surfaces*, which includes selective adsorption (chemisorption) and surface chemical transformations (as determined, for example, by thermoprogrammed reaction techniques). The reactivity of a surface is a direct consequence of the features mentioned above, but its characterization requires specific investigation methods (box 10).

Path C concerns a series of characteristics which are usually considered separately, although they are not completely independent of those already considered. The first step is the measurement of the *surface area* (box 11). The study of the *shape and distribution of the pores* follows logically (box 12). (The arrow that should connect this box to box 3 has been omitted.) A further step is the study of the *surface acid and basic sites* (which normally requires previous knowledge of the surface area of the sample) (box 13). This subject is covered in detail in Chap. 8. Clearly, the coordination, chemical state, and reactivity of surfaces have a strong bearing on the existence and nature of such surface sites.

The reader should realize that the scheme presented in Fig. 1 constitutes nothing more than a general framework, the details of which cannot correspond to all practical situations. For example, the study of coordination may, in some cases, lead to the discovery of a macroscopic phase which could otherwise not be detected. The numerous interconnections drawn in this figure illustrate, however, how tightly the various characteristics of the architecture of the catalysts are related. This stresses the need for an approach involving many techniques, each complementing the other.

## III. TECHNIQUES FOR CATALYST CHARACTERIZATION: AN EVALUATION

Table 1 presents a list of a large variety of techniques which are used for the characterization of solids and surfaces. (This list should not be considered as exhaustive.) A summary of the information provided by each of these techniques is given in the chapter appendix. In Fig. 2, these techniques have been classified according to the nature of the information, and thus correspond to the numbered boxes of Fig. 1. (For the sake of simplicity, in Fig. 2, the initials AEM refer to all the techniques related to transmission electron microscopy: TEM, CTEM, STEM, EELS, and AEM.)

It is noticeable that the present literature shows only a limited number of techniques commonly selected for characterizing practical catalysts. The following discussion aims at evaluating this selection and suggests future trends in the use of other techniques.

### A. Practical Considerations

#### 1. Nature of the Specimen

As indicated at the beginning of this chapter, the first criterion is that the technique be applicable to practical catalysts. It should

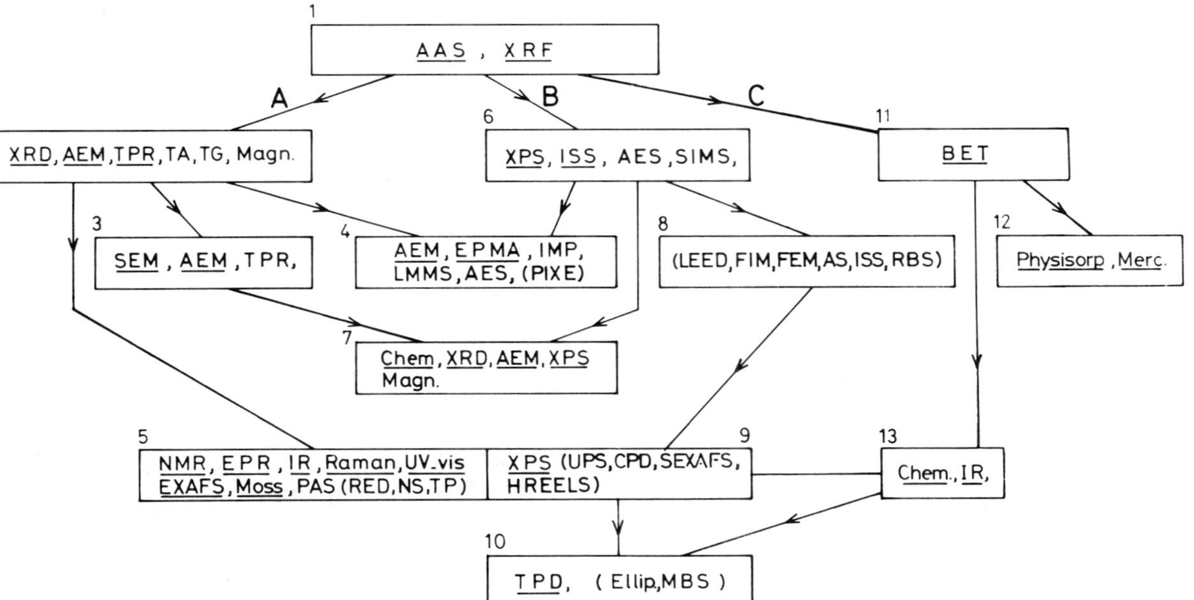


FIG. 2. The characterization methods are classified according to the information they provide, following the scheme of Fig. 1. The significance of the abbreviations and acronyms is given in Table 1.

TABLE 1 Techniques for Characterization of Solids and Surfaces

| Abbreviation in Figs. 2 and 3 | Name | Number in the appendix |
|---|---|---|
| AAS | Atomic absorption spectroscopy | 17 |
| AEM | Analytical electron microscopy | 29 |
| AES | Auger electron spectroscopy | 30 |
| AS | Atom scattering | 38 |
| BET | BET method | 1 |
| Chem. | Chemisorption | 2 |
| CPD | Contact potential difference measurements | 9 |
| CTEM | Conventional transmission electron microscopy | 29 |
| EELS | Electron energy loss spectroscopy | 29 |
| Ellip. | Ellipsometry | 16 |
| EPMA | Electron probe microanalysis | 33 |
| EPR | Electron paramagnetic resonance | 12 |
| EXAFS | Extended X-ray absorption fine structure | 23 |
| FEM | Field emission microscopy | 10 |
| FIM | Field ion microscopy | 10 |
| HREELS | High-resolution electron energy loss spectroscopy | 32 |
| IMP | Ion microprobe | 35 |
| IR | Infrared spectroscopy | 13 |
| ISS | Ion scattering spectrometry | 34 |
| LEED | Low-energy electron diffraction | 31 |
| LMMS | Laser microprobe mass spectrometry | 27 |
| Magn. | Magnetic susceptibility measurements | 8 |
| MBS | Molecular beam scattering | 38 |
| Merc. | Mercury porosimetry | 6 |
| Micr. | Optical microscopy | 15 |
| Moss. | Mössbauer spectroscopy | 24 |
| NMR | Nuclear magnetic resonance | 11 |
| NS | Neutron scattering | 39 |
| PAS | Photoacoustic spectroscopy | 19 |
| Physisorp. | Physisorption | 1 |
| PIXE | Proton-induced X-ray emission | 37 |
| Raman | Raman spectroscopy | 14 |
| RBS | Rutherford backscattering | 35 |
| RED | Radial electron distribution | 21 |
| SEM | Scanning electron microscopy | 28 |
| SEXAFS | Surface-sensitive extended X-ray absorption fine structure | 26 |

Table 1 (Continued)

| Abbreviation in Figs. 2 and 3 | Name | Number in the appendix |
|---|---|---|
| SIMS | Secondary ion mass spectroscopy | 35 |
| STEM | Scanning transmission electron microscopy | 29 |
| TA | Thermal analysis methods | 3 |
| TEM | Transmission electron microscopy | 29 |
| TG | Thermogravimetric methods | 4 |
| TP | Transport properties | 7 |
| TPD | Temperature-programmed desorption | 5 |
| TPR | Temperature programmed reduction | 5 |
| UPS | UV photoelectron spectroscopy | 25 |
| UV-vis | UV-visible spectroscopy | 18 |
| XRF | X-ray fluorescence spectroscopy | 22 |
| XPS | X-ray photoelectron spectroscopy | 25 |
| XRD | X-ray diffraction | 20 |

obviously not be restricted to monocrystals and should also, potentially at least, accept samples in powder form.

This restriction typically concerns FIM and FEM, which require a sharply pointed specimen, and also LEED, atom scattering, and ellipsometry, which require a single-crystal surface. The use of ISS for surface structure studies is also restricted to single crystals.

Some other methods that could in principle be applied to any type of specimen cannot be in practice, because interpretation of the results is too difficult for complex solids or surfaces. This is the case for the measurement of transport properties of solids (TP) and for surface analysis methods, such as HREELS, UPS, and MBS. The latter methods usually require "clean" surfaces and, consequently, ultrahigh-vacuum conditions, which are hardly compatible with the presence, in the vacuum chamber, of a highly porous catalyst specimen.

### 2. Accessibility

The second criterion for the selection of a technique is that it should be reasonably accessible to people working in catalytic research laboratories. Some methods require large, complex equipment which thus is limited (and will remain so in the foreseeable future) to a few large research centers. This applies to methods using neutrons, which require a high-flux nuclear reactor, and also, to a lesser extent, for the EXAFS and SEXAFS methods, which need a high-intensity continuous X-ray source (such as the synchrotron radiation produced by particle storage rings). Fortunately, the development of rotating anode X-ray emitters provides a possible alternative that will permit EXAFS measurements in smaller-scale laboratories.

The accessibility of a technique depends directly on the cost of the equipment it requires. It is evident, however, that some costly methods may develop if their potentialities for catalytic research appear sufficiently rewarding. For instance, it is unlikely that many laboratories become equipped with a Van de Graaf accelerator for the purpose of applying PIXE and RBS to catalysts. In contrast, the promise of analytical electron microscopy has recently prompted several groups to purchase a STEM microscope. As regards the use of costly techniques in catalyst research, another factor has to be accounted for: the strong tendency presently observed toward better collaboration between research groups. This trend more than compensates for the restricted number of costly instruments that can be available in each laboratory.

Another practical consideration concerning the accessibility of a given method is the existence of commercial instruments, it not being reasonable that investigators in the field of catalysis divert a large fraction of their effort to the design and construction of special equipment. Usually, a method finds widespread application in chemistry only when a commercial instrument becomes available. The reason a particular method succeeds commercially instead of another is not always purely scientific. It could be a matter of proper advertising, patent protection, or even fashion. For example, one could wonder if some of these reasons partially explain the limited development of ISS (compared with AES or SIMS).

#### 3. Ease of Interpretation

Because of fundamental limitations, some methods cannot deal with solids containing more than two or three elements or having two or more different phases. A similar argument has already been mentioned for methods which are, in practice, restricted to single crystals. Another example is the radial electron distribution (RED) technique, where usable information can be obtained only if only two elements (exceptionally three) are present, because RED gives the weighted average of the electronic densities around all the atoms of the solid. RED has become progressively superseded by EXAFS, which provides the advantage of selectively probing the environment of each element, by choosing at will the central atom (see the chapter appendix for details). A similar limitation explains the limited success of contact potential difference (CPD) measurements on complex solids.

### B. Selection of the Most Appropriate Methods

Table 2 summarizes the practical considerations that render some methods unsuitable for extended use in practical catalyst studies.

TABLE 2 Practical Considerations Preventing the Use of Some Techniques for Catalyst Characterization

| Technique | Only for monocrystals | Limited accessibility | Difficult interpretation |
|---|---|---|---|
| AS | X | | |
| CPD | | | X |
| Ellip. | X | | |
| FEM | X | | |
| FIM | X | | |
| HREELS | X | | |
| LEED | X | | |
| MBS | X | | |
| NS | | X | |
| PIXE | | X | |
| RBS | | X | |
| RED | | | X |
| TP | X | | |
| UPS | X | | |

These methods are shown in parentheses in Fig. 2. Further selection is necessary, however. Figure 2 indicates that, in many cases, several methods remain qualified for measuring approximately the same feature. Although every technique is likely to bring its own insight, one can hardly imagine that laboratories become equipped with all the possible equipment or that the researcher duplicates his or her measurements by using all techniques allowing characterization of the same factor.

A further selection is a matter of personal appreciation. The methods preferred by the authors are underlined in Fig. 2. Let us justify this choice by reviewing the successive characterization steps sketched in Figs. 1 and 2.

### 1. Bulk Composition

AAS and XRF both have their own merits, which makes it difficult to propose a definitive selective advantage between them. The choice will often be a matter of accessibility of equipment.

### 2. Nature of Phases

XRD and AEM appear to be indispensible tools for the study of crystalline phases. XRD gives average information, whereas AEM allows more local investigations [down to the scale of the individual lattice planes when performing high-resolution electron microscopy (see Chap. 3)]. Complementing these crystal structure determinations, the study of the reactivity of the solid offers a very sensitive tool for revealing the nature of the phases. The most common techniques for this are (differential) thermal analysis (TA), (differential) thermogravimetry (TG), and temperature-programmed reduction (TPR). Although all three methods provide different insights, TPR tends to be preferred by virtue of (1) its better sensitivity for the detection of small transformations of the solid and (2) the fact that TPR equipment is merely an adapted chemical reactor which can be built fairly easily in the research laboratory. For more details, the reader is referred to Chap. 2.

Magnetic susceptibility measurement cannot be considered as a major method, as its use is restricted essentially to the study of some catalysts, mostly those containing nickel.

### 3. Size and Shape

For sufficiently large scale features (⩾100 nm), SEM is more usable than TEM (AEM), as it does not require the preparation of electron transparent specimens. AEM allows study of the size and shape of particles down to a scale of about 0.5 to 5 nm (depending on the contrast, which is determined essentially by the atomic weights) (see Chap. 3). TPR is sensitive to the size of the particles being reduced, but the interpretation is not straightforward (see Chap. 2).

### 4. Repartition

There are two scales at which the repartition of a phase or the heterogeneity of composition must be studied: the macroscopic and the microscopic scale. The distribution of composition across a catalyst pellet is a typical large-scale characteristic. Four microanalytical techniques are available for measuring this distribution: EPMA, IMP, LMMS, and PIXE. All these methods potentially provide a lateral resolution of the order of 1 μm. As discussed above, the use of PIXE is limited by the requirement for a Van de Graaf accelerator. Compared to IMP and LMMS, the greater success of EPMA is probably due to the fact that this method presently allows better quantitative precision, as a result of the development of computer-aided correction procedures. In addition, EPMA is often combined as an attachment of SEM, which itself is a standard tool of material research laboratories. However, it should be remembered that IMP and LMMS are sensitive to hydrogen, whereas EPMA is not.

Features at a smaller, more microscopic scale should also be considered. Supported catalysts are usually made of a microporous solid such as alumina, silica, or zeolite, on which an amount of active species has been deposited. This microporous solid is made up of elementary grains of size 1 to 100 μm, eventually joined together to form a pellet. The behavior of the catalyst will be strongly influenced by the location of these active species (in the form of isolated atoms, clusters, or several-nanometer-size particles). This location may be outside the elementary grains, at the mouth of the pores, or deeper into the microporosity. Analytical electron microscopy has emerged as a major tool for studying repartition of composition at this scale. It allows measurement of the local composition with a spatial resolution of about 10 nm (see Chap. 3). There is no doubt that studies using this technique will receive increasing interest in the near future.

### 5. Coordination, Valency, and Electron Energy Levels

Unfortunately, there exists no universal method allowing the characterization of the structure of the outer electronic shells and of the immediate environment of the atoms of all elements. One has usually, therefore, to resort to a variety of techniques, each of which is quite often adapted to a particular case or gives only partial insight.

EXAFS, in this respect, is exceptional, as it is quite a general method and can, in principle, be applied to any element, hence justifying its retention in our list despite its limited accessibility. However, present experience of the application of EXAFS to catalysts is still very limited and does not allow a definite evaluation of its prospects.

NMR, EPR, and Mössbauer spectroscopy are highly sensitive techniques for studying the environment of specific individual atoms: atoms having a nuclear magnetic moment for NMR; paramagnetic species for EPR; availability of an emitter-adsorber pair for Mössbauer spectroscopy (see the appendix). Obviously, therefore, the usefulness of these methods will vary according to the composition of the catalyst under investigation.

The main domain of application of ultraviolet (UV)-visible spectroscopy is the study of the coordination of transition metal atoms. Unfortunately, quantitative interpretation of UV-visible spectra is complex, which means that most present studies are very qualitative (see Chap. 4).

Infrared and Raman spectroscopy are most frequently used for the study of the nature of adsorbed molecules and of their binding with catalyst surface. The application of these methods to the study of vibration modes within the solid itself is restricted to a limited number of systems (e.g., molybdenum oxide compounds [3,4]).

Photoacoustic spectroscopy [which is merely a particular way of performing infrared (IR) and UV-visible spectroscopy (see the appendix)] undoubtedly offers some promise. More experience is needed, however, before proper evaluation of the method is possible.

It may be noticed that all methods which have been underlined in box 5 of Fig. 2 may, at least potentially, be used for in situ measurements (i.e., for measurements during the course of the catalytic reaction). Such studies require only the design of a specially adapted analysis cell within which the catalytic reaction may proceed. There are numerous examples of such in situ measurements with the techniques outlined above.

6. Surface Composition

Table 3 summarizes the respective advantages of the four major techniques for surface analysis (XPS, AES, ISS, SIMS), according to seven criteria: (1) number of monolayers probed; (2) detection yield (or sensitivity); (3) possibility of using the data for obtaining the quantitative composition of the surface; (4) possibility of studying the chemical state of surface atoms; (5) damage caused to the surface; (6) problems induced by the electrical charge accumulating on insulating samples; and (7) lateral resolution. (In Table 3, the question marks indicate either the existence of a major difficulty or the need for future development.) Both XPS and AES analyze the same "moderately thick" surface layer. There is no doubt that XPS is to be preferred to AES for the study of practical catalysts: it is more directly sensitive to chemical states; it is not destructive (whereas electron bombardment may induce much chemical transformation of the surface); and it is better adapted than AES to the study of insulating samples (see Chap. 6). The only advantage of AES is its remarkable lateral resolution; however, the achievement of such a resolution requires a conducting surface. The potential resolution in the study of the repartition of surface composition of complex insulating samples should be evaluated. Because of the lack of such an evaluation, the prospects for high-resolution AES study of practical catalysts cannot

TABLE 3 Comparison of Surface Analysis Techniques

| Criterion | XPS | AES | ISS | SIMS |
|---|---|---|---|---|
| (1) Depth sampled (monolayers) | 2–20 | 2–20 | 1 | 1–3 |
| (2) Detection yield | 0.1–1% | 0.1–1% | 0.1–1% | 1–10 ppm |
| (3) Quantitative analysis | Yes | Yes | ? | No |
| (4) Chemical state | Yes | ? | No | ? |
| (5) Damage | No | Yes | Yes | Yes |
| (6) Charging problems | Little | Yes | Yes | Yes |
| (7) Lateral resolution | 5 mm | 0.1 μm | 50 μm | 10 μm |

be estimated. This is the reason AES has not been underlined in box 4 in Fig. 2.

Although the usefulness of XPS is very wide ranging, it seems desirable to complement this technique by a method, such as ISS or SIMS, which is more selective with respect to the topmost surface monolayer. Experience of the application of these methods to practical catalysts is at present very limited. ISS appears very promising because of its theoretically ideal surface selectivity. The large variation of peak intensities as a function of oxygen content of the surface hinders accurate quantitative interpretation of SIMS data. However, ISS and SIMS are, in some respect, complementary, as the sensitivity of ISS is higher for heavy atoms, whereas that of SIMS is higher for light atoms (especially hydrogen).

### 7. Dispersion

Dispersion may be defined as the fraction of potentially active atoms which are effectively on the surface of the solid (i.e., exposed to the gas or liquid reactant phase). It is clearly, therefore, the most important property of a catalyst. Its characterization is essential both for researchers involved in the study of reaction kinetics (measurement of turnover number) and for those concerned with practical aspects of catalysts, such as preparation, aging, sintering, poisoning, and so on.

It is well known that, using still largely empirical experimental recipes, the dispersion of some metals (Pt, Ni, and some noble metals of group VIII) can be measured by chemisorption methods (see Chap. 7 for details). Nonmetal catalysts, however, represent an important fraction of the catalysts used in industry: about 85% when weight sold is considered, or more than 55% of the sales value. In addition, control of the various steps of catalyst manufacture demands measurement of the dispersion of nonmetal precursors even in the case of metal catalysts. The solids to be characterized for dispersion are, for example, those obtained after impregnation (metal salts), after drying (dehydrated or partially decomposed salts), and after calcination (oxides). It is unlikely that selective chemisorption methods can be developed in the near future for measuring the surface areas of the majority of such nonmetallic phases. When these phases form sufficiently large particles, one can resort to electron microscopy or X-ray line broadening analysis for the determination of the mean particle size and, in turn, the dispersion. Another method is to determine dispersion from surface composition, as measured by a surface-sensitive technique such as XPS. However, such a method is considerably influenced by the repartition of the components of the catalyst and it is often necessary to combine XPS measurements with AEM studies (i.e., determining dispersion and repartition together). For a more detailed discussion, the reader is referred to Chaps. 6 and 7.

### 8. Surface Structure

Unfortunately, it appears that no method is presently available for determining the long-range two-dimensional arrangement of the atoms (i.e., the crystal structure) at the surface of, for example, a crystallite in a powdered (or finely divided) sample. Practically, only the bulk structure can be known, by use of electron microdiffraction in the transmission electron microscope.

It often occurs that the active species (or precursors at intermediate preparation steps) merely cover the surface of the catalyst, by forming one-atom (or one-molecule)-thick two-dimensional layers ("rafts" or complete monolayers). Poisons may also be deposited in the form of such thin layers. It is thus absolutely essential to obtain information on the composition of each of the successive atomic layers near the surface. This particular aspect of surface structure may be investigated by use of a method such as ISS, which allows the recording of the in-depth composition profile, due to the progressive "peeling off" of the successive topmost layers under the impact of the ion beam (e.g., Ref. 5).

### 9. Coordination and Chemical State at the Surface

As mentioned in Sec. II, these aspects can be investigated by use of the same methods as those for the corresponding bulk properties, but on the condition that the particular atom being studied is exclusively present at the surface. Apart from these methods, XPS is the only technique allowing a selective study of the valency of near-surface atoms. SEXAFS might also offer some promises for this type of investigation.

### 10. Surface Reactivity

Temperature-programmed desorption is a fairly convenient tool which reveals the presence of different "surface phases" from their different reactivities (see Chap. 2). This information is especially useful as a complement of other characterization studies.

### 11. Surface Area, Porosity, and Acidity

The methods used for investigating these important aspects have been well established over the years and therefore deserve no special discussion.

## IV. CONCLUSIONS

The previous paragraphs have emphasized the importance of accumulating as much information as possible concerning the catalyst. Such information, although diverse, is closely interrelated. (These relations are clearly illustrated in Figs. 1 and 2.) The characterization of practical catalysts thus always requires the joint use of several techniques, an aspect that cannot be overemphasized.

A more detailed examination of Fig. 2 indicates that some techniques are more complementary because they study features which are directly related to each other. This is the case of AEM (which is mentioned in boxes 2, 3, 4, and 7) and XPS (which is mentioned in boxes 6, 7, and 9). The development of the application of these two techniques in catalysis research is certainly one of the major advances in recent years. This is why two chapters of this book (Chaps. 3 and 6) are devoted to them.

In the scope of this book, it would have been impossible to devote a special chapter to each of the techniques underlined in Fig. 2. That some of these techniques were omitted was justified by the following arguments.

1. Some techniques are presently practiced quite routinely and do not therefore deserve an updating description of their applications to catalysts. This is the case for AAS, XRF, XRD, SEM, EPMA, BET, physisorption isotherms, and mercury porosimetry.
2. Three major techniques (NMR, IR, Raman) have been omitted because it was difficult to deal with their application to the characterization of the solid without also detailing their multiple capabilities for the investigation of the nature, bonding, and diffusion of the molecules adsorbed onto the surface of the catalyst. This deliberate restriction of the scope of this book has been mentioned in the preface and in Sec. I of the present chapter.
3. The number of works dealing with the use of ISS or EXAFS for the study of practical catalysts presently remains too limited to allow a comprehensive evaluation of the present prospects of these promising techniques.
4. The application of Mössbauer spectroscopy to the characterization of catalysts has been reviewed several times in recent years [16, 29,46-48]. It did not appear useful to review it again.

The succession of the subsequent chapters follow approximately the same scheme as that used in Secs. II and III. The topics of catalyst dispersion and acidity (boxes 7 and 13 of Figs. 1 and 2) are dealt with in separate chapters aimed at a comprehensive presentation and comparison of the various methods that can be used for their determination.

## ACKNOWLEDGMENTS

The authors gratefully acknowledge the advice of Dr. M. O'Callaghan in improving the manuscript.

## APPENDIX: TECHNIQUES FOR THE CHARACTERIZATION OF SOLIDS AND SURFACES

The aim of this appendix is to describe very briefly the techniques mentioned in Table 1. This rapid review should provide the reader having little or no knowledge of a given technique with some information and thus enable him or her to follow more easily the discussion of Sec. III.

An attempt has been made to classify the techniques according to the phenomena studied. Three main classes have been distinguished: (1) chemical techniques, (2) static physicochemical techniques, and (3) spectroscopy and related methods. The techniques are outlined below by numbers in parentheses, with cross-references to the corresponding boxes in Fig. 2. For the techniques that are not dealt with in a subsequent chapter, the literature cited has been restricted to one or two basic references where the reader can find more details.

### A. Chemical Techniques

1. *Based on gas adsorption experiments*
   - (1) [Boxes 11 and 12 of Fig. 2] The interpretation of the physisorption isotherm of an inert gas is used for determining the surface area of the solid (BET method) and/or the distribution of pore sizes [6,7].
   - (2) [Boxes 7 and 13 of Fig. 2.] The chemisorption of reactive gases is a standard method for measuring the surface area of certain metallic phases (see Chap. 7) or the basicity of the surface (see Chap. 8).
2. *Based on the measurement of the reactivity of solids*
   - (3) [Box 2 of Fig. 2.] *Thermal analysis* (TA). The technique consists in measuring heat evolution or absorption as a function of increasing/decreasing temperature. The detection of exothermic or endothermic effects due to phase transformations or chemical reactions allows the identification of the sample [8-10].
   - (4) [Box 2 of Fig. 2.] *Thermogravimetry* (TG). The measurement of weight loss (or gain) as a function of temperature is a standard tool for the study of reactions of solids and hence for giving insight into their nature [8].
   - (5) [Boxes 2, 3, and 10 of Fig. 2.] *Temperature-programmed desorption or reduction* (TPD, TPR). The measurement of the rate of desorption or reduction as a function of temperature allows the study of the reactivity of the surface of a solid and of its bulk (see Chap. 2).

### B. Static Physicochemical Techniques

These techniques consist in measuring the response of the solid when submitted to a static field of forces.

1. *Mechanical force*
   (6) [Box 12 of Fig. 2.] Somewhat arbitrarily, perhaps, mercury porosimetry is included in this section. The method consists in measuring the distribution of pore sizes by forcing mercury to penetrate into the porous volume. The pressure applied compensates the capillary forces, the latter depending on the size of the pores [7].
2. *Electromagnetic forces*
   (7) [Box 15 of Fig. 2.] The study of transport properties (TP) of solids (usually single crystals) (electrical conductivity, thermal conductivity, Hall effect, Seebeck effect, etc.) is a major tool for understanding their bulk physicochemical properties [11].
   (8) [Boxes 2 and 7 of Fig. 2.] The nature and particle size of some metallic phases (especially nickel) may be investigated by magnetic susceptibility measurements [12].
   (9) [Box 9 of Fig. 2.] The physicochemical state of solid surfaces is reflected by the appearance of a surface potential [or contact potential difference (CPD)] which is commonly determined by capacity measurements (vibrating capacitor) [13].
   (10) [Box 8 of Fig. 2.] *Field emission microscopy* (FEM) and *field ion microscopy* (FIM). The creation of a very intense electrical field at the tip of a very sharp-pointed specimen brings about the projection of electrons (FEM) or ions (FIM) along radial directions, thus bringing about a very large magnification. This allows the formation of an image of the atomic arrangement at the surface of the tip [14].

## C. Spectroscopy and Related Techniques

These techniques consist in measuring the response of the solid when submitted to radiation, either an electromagnetic wave or particles. This response may be merely the scattering or absorption of this radiation or it may also involve absorption followed by emission of another type of radiation. The techniques may be classified according to the nature of the incident radiation versus nature of the response studied. Figure 3 summarizes this classification.

1. *Photons/photons*
   The methods are classified by order of increasing incident photon energy.
   (11) [Box 5 of Fig. 2.] *Nuclear magnetic resonance* (NMR). The interaction of the nuclear spins with an external magnetic field causes a splitting of the corresponding energy levels. For nuclei having a magnetic moment, transitions between these levels occur when this splitting corresponds

| Excitation | Response | | | |
|---|---|---|---|---|
| | Photons | Electrons | Ions | Neutrals |
| Photons | NMR<br>EPR<br>IR<br>Raman<br>Micr.<br>Ellip.<br>AAS<br>UV-Vis<br>PAS<br>XRD<br>RED<br>EXAFS<br>Moss. | UPS<br>XPS<br>SEXAFS | LMMS | |
| Electrons | EPMA | SEM<br>TEM(CETM, STEM)<br>AEM<br>EELS<br>AES<br>LEED<br>HREELS | | |
| Ions | PIXE | | ISS<br>IMP<br>SIMS<br>RBS | |
| Neutrals | | | | AS<br>MBS<br>NS |

FIG. 3. The spectroscopic techniques are classified according to the combination: nature of excitation/response. The significance of the abbreviations and acronyms is given in Table 1.

to the energy of the incident wave [typically 100 MHz (frequency) or 3 m (wavelength)]. This phenomenon allows the study of the environment of these nuclei and of their motion within the solid [15,16].

(12) [Box 5 of Fig. 2.] *Electron paramagnetic resonance* (EPR). In this case, the frequency of the wave is typically 9.5 GHz (wavelength 30 mm) and the transition occurs between

electron spin energy levels of paramagnetic ions. This transition is affected by the environment of these ions (see Chap. 5 for an extensive discussion).

(13) [Boxes 5 and 13 of Fig. 2.] *Infrared spectroscopy* (IR). The incident electromagnetic wave (typical wavelength 2.5 to 25 μm) is absorbed upon excitation of molecular vibration modes. The frequency of these vibrations depends on the nature and binding of the molecules [16,17]. A similar spectrum is also obtained by infrared emission spectroscopy, which studies the IR radiations emitted by a solid when the temperature is increased [18].

(14) [Box 5 of Fig. 2.] *Raman spectroscopy*. Radiation in the visible frequency range (typically laser beams of wavelength 500 to 650 nm) is inelastically scattered as a result of the excitation of molecular vibration modes. The information provided by this method is similar to that given by infrared spectroscopy [16]. The use of a focused laser beam allows spatial resolution down to about 1 μm in special instruments (Raman microprobe) [19].

(15) *Optical microscopy*. The resolution limit of the best optical microscopes is of the order of 0.2 μm [20].

(16) [Box 1 of Fig. 2.] *Ellipsometry*. A polarized beam of visible light is reflected from a surface. The change of its amplitude and phase upon adsorption of a gas is measured. This technique permits the measurement of adsorption isotherms on single-crystal surfaces [21].

(17) [Box 1 of Fig. 2.] *Atomic absorption spectroscopy* (AAS). Transition between electronic energy levels of atoms is induced by the absorption of photons in the visible frequency range (typical wavelengths 200 to 1000 nm). These absorption lines are typical of each atom. AAS is a very common technique for quantitative measurements of atomic composition [22].

(18) [Box 5 of Fig. 2.] *UV-visible reflectance spectroscopy*. This method allows the study of the absorption of UV-visible radiations by finely divided solids. The environment (coordination) of transition metal atoms within the solid may be studied from the position and intensity of the absorption bands (see Chap. 4).

(19) [Box 5 of Fig. 2.] *Photoacoustic spectroscopy* (PAS). This method differs from infrared and UV-visible spectroscopy merely by the way the absorption is detected. By modulating the intensity of the incident radiation, the temperature increase induced by absorption produces an acoustic wave that may be recorded by a microphone [23].

(20) [Boxes 2 and 7 of Fig. 2.] *X-ray diffraction* (XRD). The characterization of crystal structure by X-ray diffraction is

literally the basic technique of any material science laboratory [24,25]. The dispersion of a phase may be investigated by analysis either of the broadening of the diffraction peaks or of the X-ray distribution at a low angle (see Chap. 7).

(21) [Box 5 of Fig. 2.] *Radial electron distribution* (RED) is a particular application of XRD. In this case, the study of the angular distribution of X-rays scattered by amorphous solids allows a determination of the mean distances between neighboring atoms [25,26].

(22) [Box 2 of Fig. 2.] *X-ray fluorescence spectroscopy.* The incident X-ray radiation can eject electrons from inner levels of the atoms. The following deexcitation involves a transition of electrons from upper levels, with emission of "characteristic" X ray photons. This radiation may be used for analyzing the composition of the solid. Like AAS, XRF is a standard method for this purpose [24].

(23) [Box 5 of Fig. 2.] *Extended X-ray absorption fine structure* (EXAFS). Absorption of X-rays may involve the transmission of the photon energy to an inner electron and allow it to escape the atomic potential well. Interaction between the wave associated with this excited electron and the neighboring atoms produces a fine structure in the X-ray spectrum within an energy domain 50 to 1000 eV higher than the energy of the absorption edge. Observation of the fine structure requires a high-intensity X-ray source such as that provided by synchroton radiation. In the case of amorphous solids, the technique allows the determination of local structural parameters around the excited atom, such as coordination numbers and interatomic distance [27,28].

(24) [Box 5 of Fig. 2.] *Mössbauer spectroscopy.* A $\gamma$-ray photon from a radioactive nucleus (the emitter) may be absorbed by another nucleus (the absorber) if the corresponding transition energies are properly matched. This matching is obtained by varying the relative velocities of the two atoms (Doppler effect). The energy of this resonance is affected by the interaction of the nucleus with its surroundings. This phenomenon allows the study of the environment of the emitter or the absorber in the case of atoms for which an emitter-absorber pair is available (e.g., $^{57}Fe$-$^{57}Co$; $^{195}Pt$-$^{195}Au$, $^{119}Sn$-$^{119m}Sn$, etc.) [16,29].

2. *Photons/electrons*

(25) [Boxes 6, 7, and 9 of Fig. 2.] *UV-photoelectron spectroscopy* (UPS) and *X-ray photoelectron spectroscopy* (XPS). The principle of photoelectron spectroscopy follows from the relation $h\nu = E_b + E_k$, where $h\nu$ is the energy of the incident photon, $E_b$ the binding energy in the solid, and

$E_k$ the kinetic energy of the electron escaping from the solid (which is the response recorded by the spectrometer). UPS allows the study of valence and conduction bands [30], whereas XPS is a powerful tool for determining the nature and binding of the atoms from the analysis of core electron photoemission peaks (see Chap. 6). As the mean free path of the photoelectrons is typically within the range 0.5 to 5 nm, these techniques are especially sensitive for the 2 to 20 uppermost atomic layers of the surface.

(26) [Box 9 of Fig. 2.] *Surface-sensitive extended X-ray absorption fine structure* (SEXAFS). The principle of the technique is the same as in EXAFS, but the signal studied is in this case the fine structure observed in the yield of, for example, a particular Auger electron line when the energy of the incident X-ray photons is varied. The information thus originates only from the surface layers [31].

3. *Photons/ions*

(27) [Box 4 of Fig. 2.] *Laser microprobe mass spectrometry* (LMMS). The impact of a (pulsed) laser beam on a solid brings about the emission of ionized species which may be identified by analysis in a mass spectrometer. This method allows measurement of the composition of the sample with a resolution down to the range 1 to 10 μm. The in-depth resolution may vary from a few nanometers, (laser desorption) to several tens of micrometers, depending on the incident power density [32].

4. *Electrons/electrons*

(28) [Box 3 of Fig. 2.] *Scanning electron microscopy* (SEM). This technique allows essentially the imaging of the topography of a solid surface by use of backscattered or secondary electrons, with a resolution, at present, of better than 5 nm [33].

(29) [Boxes 2, 3, 4, and 7 of Fig. 2.] *Transmission electron microscopy* and related techniques. Transmission electron microscopy (TEM) involves a variety of imaging techniques: bright field, dark field, or high resolution. It allows the determination of the microtexture and microstructure of electron transparent samples (typical thickness less than 100 nm) with a resolution presently better than 0.5 nm. The method of irradiation of the sample distinguishes conventional transmission electron microscopy (CTEM) from scanning transmission electron microscopy (STEM) (see Chap. 3).

Analytical electron microscopy (AEM) allows comprehensive structural and chemical microanalysis of an electron transparent sample due to the combination of TEM with electron microdiffraction, X-ray microanalysis (see below), and electron energy loss spectroscopy (EELS, which involves the study of the energy loss suffered by the transmitted electrons) (see Chap. 3).

(30) [Boxes 4 and 8 of Fig. 2.] *Auger electron spectroscopy* (AES). Like X-rays, energetic electrons (1000 to 5000 eV) may eject electrons from inner levels of the atoms. As a result of the deexcitation process, a second electron (Auger electron) may be ejected, the energy of which is characteristic of the energy-level separations in the atom, and therefore of its nature. Owing to the limited mean free path of the electrons, this phenomenon allows the analysis of the atomic composition of the surface. Auger electrons lines are also observed in XPS spectra. AES designates specifically the study of Auger electrons excited by an impinging electron probe. This probe may be rastered on the surface so as to allow the formation of an image (sometimes called scanning Auger microprobe, SAM). The spatial resolution of such an image may presently be of the order of 0.1 μm when using a high-density, focused electron probe [34].

(31) [Box 8 of Fig. 2.] *Low-energy electron diffraction* (LEED). Low-energy electrons (in the range 10 to 500 eV) are diffracted by the topmost layers of a single-crystal surface. By a proper (but rather difficult) interpretation of the diffracted intensities, the structure of the surface and/or of the absorbed overlayer can be deduced [35].

(32) [Box 9 of Fig. 2.] *High-resolution electron energy loss spectroscopy* (HREELS). When scattered on a surface, electrons can lose energy by the excitation of vibrational modes of surface atoms and molecules. Observation of this effect requires a highly monochromatic (maximum energy spread, ±10 meV) low-energy (1 to 10 eV) electron beam. This method has emerged as a powerful tool for the investigation of the adsorption of molecules on single-crystal surfaces [36]. [Note that HREELS should not be confused with EELS (28), which deals with high-energy electrons transmitted through a thin foil.]

5. *Electrons/photons*

(33) [Box 4 of Fig. 2.] The deexcitation of atoms ionized upon the impact of high-energy electrons (10 to 100 keV) brings about the emission of "characteristic" X-ray photons having energies equal to the energy-level separation of the ionized atoms. This phenomenon is exploited in the popular electron probe microanalysis (EPMA) method, which allows quantitative measurement of the composition of solids with a spatial resolution (both lateral and in depth) of the order of 1 μm

[37]. This resolution may be improved to values of about 10 nm in the case of electron transparent specimens (see Chap. 3). Today, X-ray spectrometers are common attachments of scanning and transmission electron microscopes.

6. *Ions/ions*

(34) [Boxes 6 and 8 of Fig. 2.] *Ion scattering spectrometry* (ISS). When scattered by a surface, low-energy ions (typically 0.5 to 5 keV) transmit some part of their kinetic energy to the atoms of the surface. As this lost energy depends on the mass of the target atom, and of the scattering angle, analysis of the energy of the ions scattered provides an atomic mass spectrum of the components at the surface. This method is presently the most "selective" method for the measurement of the atomic composition of the surface. The signal, indeed, originates only from the topmost atomic layer. On single-crystal surfaces, shadowing effects are observed which allow the study of fine details of the surface structure [38,39].

(35) [Boxes 4 and 6 of Fig. 2.] *Ion microprobe* (IMP) and *secondary ion mass spectrometry* (SIMS). The erosion of a solid surface under the impact of an ion beam (1 to 10 keV) brings about the emission of a variety of ionized species from the solid. The composition of the solid can be measured by simply analyzing these ions through a mass spectrometer. The sensitivity of this method is high enough to allow nearly nondestructive analysis of the one to three topmost surface layers by use of a low-density ion beam (SIMS) [40,41]. A lateral resolution of the order of 1 $\mu$m may also be obtained by bombarding the solid with a higher density, finely focused ion probe [ion microprobe (IMP)]. The depth resolution, however, is then of the order of 5 to 10 nm. IMP has a high sensitivity (down to the ppm level), but unfortunately, the accuracy of quantitative measurements is rather poor [41].

(36) [Box 8 of Fig. 2.] *Rutherford backscattering* (RBS). In contrast with ISS, RBS makes use of high-energy (1 to 3 MeV) ions. Information concerning deeper layers is thus obtained. The major application of RBS is the study of the nature and distribution of heavy impurities in a light matrix (e.g., copper within a silicon matrix) [42].

7. *Ions/photons*

(37) [Box 4 of Fig. 2.] As with electrons, the impact of high-energy protons (1 to 3 MeV) upon a solid causes the emission of characteristic X-rays, which can be used for quantitative composition analysis. This method is known as *proton-induced X-ray emission* (PIXE). Its advantage over EPMA or the ion microprobe is that it does not require

introduction of the specimen into a vacuum chamber. Spatial resolution of the order of a few micrometers is possible at present [43].

8. *Neutral particle/neutral particle*

(38) [Boxes 8 and 10 of Fig. 2.] *Atom and molecular beam scattering* (AS, MBS). The structure and reactivity of single-crystal surfaces can be investigated by directing onto them a monoenergetic beam of atoms or molecules and studying the angular distribution of the number of scattered particles [44].

(39) [Box 5 of Fig. 2.] *Neutron scattering* (NS). As for X-rays or electrons, the scattering of neutrons is used for investigating various properties of the solid. The technique is especially sensitive to hydrogen (as the scattering cross section for hydrogen is considerably greater than for any other atom). It is possible to study the crystal structure (diffraction), the vibrational transitions (inelastic scattering), the atomic and molecular diffusion (quasielastic scattering), and the particle (or pore) sizes (small-angle scattering) [45].

## REFERENCES

1. B. C. Gates, J. R. Katzer, and G. L. Schrader, eds., *National Science Foundation Workshop on Research Needs and Instrumental Requirements in Catalysis*, University of Maryland, College Park, Md., 1978.
2. S. Basalo and R. F. Burwell, Jr., eds., *Catalysis—Progress in Research*, Plenum Press, London, 1973.
3. F. Cariati, J. C. J. Bart, and A. Sgamellotti, *Inorg. Chimi. Acta, 48*: 97 (1981).
4. H. Jeziorowski and H. Knözinger, *J. Phys. Chem., 83*: 1166 (1979).
5. F. Delannay, E. N. Haeussler, and B. Delmon, *J. Catal., 66*: 469 (1980).
6. S. J. Gregg and K. S. W. Sing, *Adsorption, Surface Area and Porosity*, Academic Press, New York, 1967.
7. W. B. Innes, in *Experimental Methods in Catalytic Research* (R. B. Anderson, ed.), Academic Press, New York, 1968, p. 44.
8. J. Sestak, V. Satava, and W. W. Wendlandt, *Thermochim. Acta, 7*: 333 (1973).
9. R. C. Mackenzie, *Differential Thermal Analysis—Fundamental Aspects*, Academic Press, New York, 1970.
10. R. C. Mackenzie, *Differential Thermal Analysis—Applications*, Academic Press, New York, 1972.

11. F. J. Blatt, *Physics of Electronic Conduction in Solids*, McGraw-Hill, New York, 1968.
12. L. J. H. Hofer, in *Experimental Methods in Catalytic Research* (R. B. Anderson, ed.), Academic Press, New York, 1968, p. 402.
13. P. M. Gundry and F. C. Thompkins, in *Experimental Methods in Catalytic Research* (R. B. Anderson, ed.), Academic Press, New York, 1968, p. 100.
14. E. W. Müller and T. T. Tsang, *Field Ion Microscopy*, American Elsevier, New York, 1969.
15. A. Carrington and A. D. McLachlan, *Introduction to Magnetic Resonance*, Harper & Row, New York, 1967.
16. W. N. Delgass, G. L. Haller, R. Kellerman, and J. H. Lunsford, *Spectroscopy in Heterogeneous Catalysis*, Academic Press, New York, 1979.
17. M. L. Hair, *Infrared Spectroscopy in Surface Chemistry*, Marcel Dekker, New York, 1967.
18. P. R. Griffiths, *Am. Lab.*, March: 37 (1975).
19. W. F. Murphy, ed., *Proc. 7th Int. Conf. Raman Spectrosc.*, NRCC, Ottawa, 1980.
20. V. E. Cosslett, *Modern Microscopy*, Cornell University Press, Ithaca, N.Y., 1966.
21. J. M. Morabito, Jr., R. H. Muller, R. F. Steiner, and G. A. Somorjai, *Surf. Sci.*, *16*: 234 (1969).
22. B. Welz, *Atomic Absorption Spectroscopy*, Verlag Chemie, Weinheim, West Germany, 1976.
23. A. Rosencwaig and A. Gersho, *J. Appl. Phys.*, *47*: 64 (1976).
24. B. D. Cullity, *Elements of X-ray Diffraction*, Addison-Wesley, Reading, Mass., 1956.
25. H. Klug and L. Alexander, *X-ray Diffraction Procedures for Polycristalline and Amorphous Materials*, Wiley, New York, 1974.
26. P. Ratnasamy and A. J. Léonard, *Catal. Rev.*, *6*: 293 (1972).
27. R. W. Joyner, in *Characterization of Catalysts* (J. M. Thomas and R. M. Lambert, eds.), Wiley, New York, 1980, p. 237.
28. R. F. Pettifer, in *Characterization of Catalysts* (J. M. Thomas and R. M. Lambert, eds.), Wiley, New York, 1980, p. 264.
29. H. Topsoe, J. A. Dumesic, and S. Morup, in *Applications of Mossbauer Spectroscopy* (R. L. Cohen, ed.), Academic Press, New York, 1980.
30. W. C. Price, in *Electron Spectroscopy: Theory, Techniques and Applications*, Vol. 1 (C. R. Brundle and A. D. Baker, eds.), Academic Press, New York, 1977, p. 152.
31. P. H. Citrin, P. Eisenberger, and H. C. Hewitt, *J. Vac. Sci. Technol.*, *15*: 449 (1978).
32. R. A. Bingham and P. L. Salter, *Anal. Chem.*, *48*: 1735 (1976).
33. J. I. Goldstein and H. Yakowitz, eds.), *Practical Scanning Electron Microscopy*, Plenum Press, New York, 1975.

34. T. A. Carlson, *Photoelectron and Auger Spectroscopy*, Plenum Press, New York, 1975.
35. J. B. Pendry, *Low Energy Electron Diffraction*, Academic Press, London, 1974.
36. H. Ibach, *Phys. Rev. Lett.*, *24*: 1416 (1970).
37. S. J. B. Reed, *Electron Microprobe Analysis*, Cambridge University Press, Cambridge, 1975.
38. E. Taglauer and W. Heiland, *Appl. Phys.*, *9*: 261 (1976).
39. H. H. Brongersma and T. M. Buck, *Nucl. Instrum. Methods*, *149*: 569 (1978).
40. A. Benninghoven, *Surf. Sci.*, *35*:427 (1973).
41. J. A. McHugh, in *Methods of Surface Analysis* (A. W. Czanderna, ed.), Elsevier, Amsterdam, 1975, p. 223.
42. J. M. Poate and T. M. Buck, in *Experimental Methods in Catalytic Research*, Vol. 3 (R. B. Anderson and P. T. Dawson, eds.), Academic Press, New York, 1976, p. 175.
43. S. A. E. Johansson and T. B. Johansson, *Nucl. Instrum. Methods*, *132*: 473 (1976).
44. S. T. Ceyer, R. J. Gale, S. L. Bernasek, and G. A. Somorjai, *J. Chem. Phys.*, *64*: 1934 (1976).
45. C. J. Wright, in *Characterization of Catalysts* (J. M. Thomas and R. M. Lambert, eds.), Wiley, New York, 1980, p. 169.
46. M. M. Gager and M. C. Hobson, Jr., *Catal. Rev.*, *11*: 117 (1975).
47. M. C. Hobson, Jr., in *Experimental Methods in Catalytic Research*, Vol. 2 (R. B. Anderson and P. T. Dawson, eds.), Academic Press, New York, 1976, p. 187.
48. J. A. Dumesic and H. Topsoe, in *Advances in Catalysis*, Vol. 26 (D. D. Eley, H. Pines, and P. B. Weisz, eds.), Academic Press, New York, 1979.

# 2

# Temperature-Programmed Methods

JACQUES L. LEMAITRE Université Catholique de Louvain, Louvain-la-Neuve, Belgium

## I. INTRODUCTION

### A. Characterization of Solids by Thermal Methods

Those analytical investigation techniques, relating some characteristic property of a sample to its temperature in the course of a temperature-programmed heating, are commonly included in the field of thermal analysis. Le Châtelier [1] in 1887 first used the measurement of temperature difference between the wall of a furnace and a clay sample placed in it, versus the temperature of the furnace in the course of a heating program, for the purpose of clay minerals identification. Later, the method was implemented by Roberts-Austen [2] in 1889, who identified phase transitions in iron by measuring the temperature difference between the iron sample and a platinum block placed in the same furnace as a reference. Differential thermal analysis was born and, since that time, a number of thermoanalytical techniques have been developed.

The use of thermal analysis in characterizing solid materials rests on the fact that, provided that the temperature interval is properly chosen, any solid will undergo characteristic phase transformations. Exchanges of matter and/or energy with the surroundings are always involved in such transformations and are used by the thermoanalyst to detect them. Various thermoanalytical techniques are thus possible according to the way phase transformations are detected. The most common ones are summarized in Table 1. Detailed descriptions of those techniques are given in Refs. 3 to 5.

The characteristic temperature at which a thermal change will occur in a given sample will depend (1) on the *nature* of the system under study (phase composition of the sample *and* composition of the surrounding atmosphere) and (2) on any factors affecting the *kinetics* of the transformation. Some such kinetic factors are related to the experimental arrangement used for thermal analysis (flow rate of

TABLE 1 Thermal Analysis Techniques: Symbols, Names, and Mode of Detection

| Symbol | Name | Characteristic factor detected |
|---|---|---|
| DTA | Differential thermal analysis | Temperature difference between sample and reference |
| TG | Thermogravimetry | Weight of sample |
| DTG | Differential thermogravimetry | Rate of weight changes |
| TMA | Thermomechanical analysis (dilatometry) | Specific volume (true or apparent) of a solid sample |
| TMA | Thermomagnetic analysis | Magnetic susceptibility |
| DMC | Differential microcalorimetry | Enthalpy difference between sample and reference |

gaseous reactants, effectiveness of heat and matter transfer between the solid and its surroundings, temperature program), while others are related to the solid sample itself (particle size, pore structure, state of dispersion in an inert material, presence of trace impurities, crystallinity). A thermogram is, therefore, in the most complex situations, a piece of information mixing in an intricate way data about the nature and the reactivity of the phases present in the sample under study.

As a result of the remarks above, thermal analysis may be useful at two different levels: (1) As a tool for qualitative and quantitative analysis, and (2) as a way of evaluating the influence of various factors on the reactivity of a known substance. The identification of the constituents in a sample is usually made by comparing its thermogram with that of a reference material, obtained in the same experimental conditions; this procedure has been used with success in many mineralogical studies [6]. It will be effective for all samples consisting of mixtures of phases exhibiting a small degree of variation in their thermal behavior, as a function of secondary characteristics such as particle size, crystallinity, presence of trace impurities, and the like.

In the field of heterogeneous catalysis, thermal analysis is often used as a tool for investigating changes of surface and/or bulk reactivity of samples toward the atmosphere, as a result of variations in composition, preparation method, preliminary treatment, and the like. Murray and White [7] and Sewell [8] were the first investigators to deduce activation energies of heterogeneous reactions from thermoanalytical data. The procedure for deducing formal orders of reaction, activation energies, and frequency factors from variations of differential thermal analysis (DTA) peak position versus rate of temperature rise was developed later by Kissinger [9]. An extensive review of the use of thermoanalytical methods for the study of the kinetics of heterogeneous reactions has been published recently by Šesták et al. [10].

## B. Temperature-Programmed Desorption and Reduction Techniques

Since these two thermoanalytical techniques have become so popular among catalyst scientists, special attention will be devoted to them in the remainder of this chapter. The basic idea of the two techniques is to monitor surface or bulk reactions of solid catalysts with their gaseous environment by performing a continuous analysis of the gas phase. This principle was first applied to pyrolysis studies by Rogers et al. [11] in 1960.

Temperature-programmed desorption (TPD) was developed in 1963 by Amenomiya and Cvetanović [12] and effectively was an extension to powdered solids of the "flash desorption" technique developed by Ehrlich [13] for the study of the desorption of gases from heated metallic filaments in high vacuum. In TPD studies a solid previously equilibrated with an adsorbing gas in well-defined conditions is submitted to a programmed temperature rise and the amount of desorbing gas is continuously monitored. Possible experimental techniques are presented in Sec. II.

Temperature-programmed reduction (TPR) was first proposed in its present form by Robertson et al. [14] in 1975. An oxidic catalyst precursor is submitted to a programmed temperature rise, while a reducing gas mixture is flowed over it (usually, hydrogen diluted in some inert gas). The rate of reduction is continuously measured by monitoring the composition of the reducting gas at the outlet of the reactor. Experimental arrangements are presented in Sec. II.

## C. Aims of This Chapter

The basic aim of this chapter is to present the basic principles for the interpretation of TPD and TPR patterns. Some possible experimental arrangements relating to TPD and TPR experiments are discussed in Sec. II. Section III is devoted to an examination of theoretical TPD and TPR patterns obtained by computer simulation, to show what their general aspect in the case of model situations relevant to catalyst studies would be. The effect of experimental variables is also demonstrated. Finally, experimental studies selected from the literature are presented in Sec. IV to show some possible uses of information derived from TPD and TPR.

## II. EXPERIMENTAL TECHNIQUES

### A. General Comments

An extensive review of the numerous experimental setups that have been used for performing TPD and TPR studies is not within the scope of this chapter. Therefore, only the TPD and TPR arrangements most commonly used today for characterizing real heterogeneous catalysts (in the form of powdered solids) are considered in detail here. Table 2 presents a general review of different possible experimental configurations. The reader interested in more details may consult Refs. 4, 5, 10, and 15. The use of calorimetry for characterizing heterogeneous catalyst has recently been reviewed by Gravelle [16].

### B. Current Experimental Arrangement for TPD and TPR

Some early TPR studies of catalyst precursors were made using a conventional thermobalance through which a fresh reducing gas was continuously flowed [17,18]. Others used an arrangement of the type "closed, recirculated atmosphere through a fixed-bed reactor"; the progress of the reaction was monitored by total hydrogen pressure measurement (thermomanometric method), the water produced by the reduction being condensed into a liquid-nitrogen trap [19]. Since the work of Robertson et al. [14] it has become common practice to use an experimental arrangement first proposed by Rogers et al. [11] for studying the pyrolysis of various solid materials. The same arrangement has been proposed by Cvetanović and Amenomiya for TPD studies [20]. A schematic representation of a TPD-TPR apparatus is presented in Fig. 1. It is of the type "dynamic flow through a fixed bed" and the progress of the reaction is monitored by a continuous analysis of the effluent gas, using a katharometer (thermal conductivity detector). During TPD experiments, the solid sample is swept by an inert gas (helium or argon). In TPR work, a reducing gas mixture ($H_2$ in Ar or, sometimes, $N_2$) is used instead and dried in a cold trap just before reaching the katharometer. The progress of the reduction is then monitored by the decrease in $H_2$ concentration in the effluent gas. Some characteristics of the arrangement presented in Fig. 1 are compared in Table 3 to those of the thermogravimetric and thermomanometric methods.

The very good general performances of the Rogers-Amenomiya-Robertson arrangement, and the fact that it gives directly a signal proportional to the reaction rate, explain why it has become the most widely used experimental arrangement today. The other arrangements will therefore not be considered further below.

### C. Thermal Conductivity Detector

In TPD or TPR experiments, effluent gases are most commonly monitored using a thermal conductivity detector, also called a katharom-

TABLE 2 Various Possible Experimental Arrangements for TPD and TPR

| Arrangement | Comments |
|---|---|
| A. Type of atmosphere | |
| 1. Closed | |
| 1.1. Static vacuum | For TPD only, self-generated atmosphere |
| 1.2. Static gas | Reaction rate controlled by diffusion in the gas phase |
| 1.3. Recirculated gas | Variable gas composition |
| 2. Open | |
| 2.1. Dynamic vacuum | For TPD only |
| 2.2. Dynamic flow | |
| B. Type of reactor | |
| 1. Fixed bed | |
| 1.1. Flow over | Poor contact between solid and gas |
| 1.2. Flow through | |
| 2. Agitated bed | Special shaking device necessary |
| 3. Fluidized bed | Precise condition (flow rate, particle size) necessary for proper working |
| C. Monitoring of reaction progress | |
| 1. Calorimetry | |
| 2. Gravimetry | Possible only with (1.1)-type reactor |
| 3. Total pressure | Possible only in a closed atmosphere |
| 4. Partial pressure | |
| 4.1. Gas chromatography detectors | Better suited for (2.2)-type atmosphere |
| 4.2. Mass spectrometry | Very expensive: better suited for (2.1)-type atmosphere |

eter. It is therefore justifiable to describe here in some detail the basic features of the katharometer and to discuss the factors determining its sensitivity. The basic principle of the method is that heat is transferred from a hot wire, situated in a gas, at a rate proportional to the thermal conductivity of the gas, other factors being constant.

A typical katharometer is presented in Fig. 2. It consists of two sets of twin filaments (Fig. 2a) axially mounted in spaces containing the gas to be analyzed. The spaces are drilled in a metallic block, in contact with the gas line. One set of filaments is in contact with a stream of reference gas (unreacted gas in TPR or pure carrier gas in TPD experiment) while the second is in contact with the gas to be analyzed. The filaments are electrically mounted in a Wheatstone bridge circuit, as illustrated in Fig. 2b. They are made of some metal having a high temperature coefficient of electrical resistance.

The filaments are heated by a constant electric current. The thermal conductivity of the gas surrounding each filament is a factor determining its temperature and consequently also its resistance. So

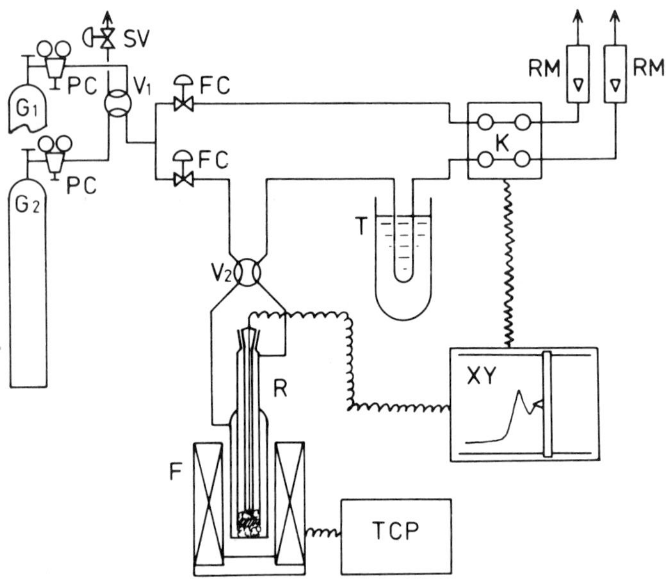


FIG. 1. Schematic of the Rogers-Amenomiya-Robertson arrangement for TPD and TPR studies. $G_1$ and $G_2$, gas cylinders (1, pure gas; 2, reducing gas mixture); SV, shutoff valve; $V_1$, four-way valve for gas selection; FC, flow controls; $V_2$, four-way valve for shunting the reactor; R, quartz made reactor, stoppered with a quartz thermowell; F, furnace; TCP, temperature controller-programmer; T, cold trap; K, katharometer; XY, recorder; RM, rotameters.

TABLE 3 Comparison of the Thermogravimetry and Thermomanometry Methods with the Rogers-Amenomiya-Robertson Arrangement

| Characteristics of the TPR analysis | Thermogravimetry | Thermomanometry | Rogers-Amenomiya-Robertson-Arrangement |
|---|---|---|---|
| Gas-solid contact | Poor (unless very small sample) | Good | Excellent |
| Gas composition around solid | Constant | Variable | Constant |
| Analysis sensitivity | High | High[a] | High[b] |
| Kinetic parameter measured | Conversion | Conversion | Reaction rate |
| Selectivity for reduction reaction | Not selective (all weight losses are recorded) | Selective | Selective |

[a]Depends on the volume of gas/weight of solid ratio.
[b]Depends on the gas flow rate/weight of solid ratio.

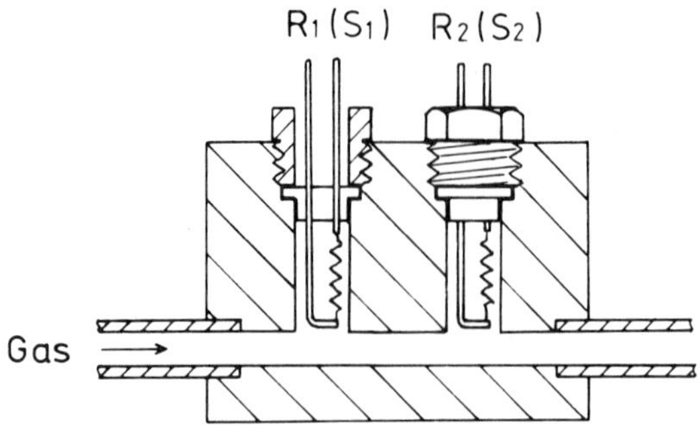


(a)

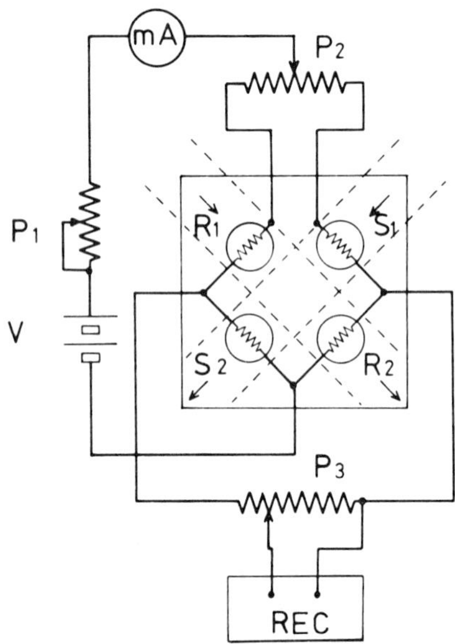


(b)

FIG. 2. (a) Typical katharometer design. $R_1$ and $R_2$, twin set of filaments in contact with the reference gas; $S_1$ and $S_2$, twin set of filaments in contact with the sample gas (see the text). (b) Bridge circuit for meter. $R_1$, $R_2$, $S_1$, $S_2$ are the same as in part (a); V, power supply; $P_1$, current adjustment; mA, milliammeter; $P_2$, zero potentiometer; $P_3$, attenuator; REC, recorder.

any small compositional difference dx (mole fraction, or volume fraction) between the reference and analyzed gases will result in an imbalance of the resistance bridge (Fig. 2b); a potential will be measured between A and B, which is given by

$$V = k_s \, dx \tag{1}$$

where $k_s$ is the *sensitivity* of the katharometer. The following subsection examines in more detail how $k_s$ is related to other experimental variables.

## D. Factors Determining the Sensitivity of a Katharometer

From the data of Tree and Leidenfrost [21], it may be shown that the thermal conductivity $\lambda$ of a binary mixture of gases is related to the thermal conductivities of the pure gases, $\lambda_1$ and $\lambda_2$, and the molar fraction of the second, X, by

$$\ln \lambda = \ln \lambda_1 + X \ln \frac{\lambda_2}{\lambda_1} \tag{2}$$

Equation (2) holds for a given temperature provided that the total pressure remains constant and the gas mixture behaves ideally. Differentiating Eq. (2), the effect on $\lambda$ of a small composition change dx is obtained:

$$\frac{d\lambda}{\lambda} = \varepsilon = \ln \frac{\lambda_2}{\lambda_1} \, dx \tag{3}$$

in which $\varepsilon$ is the relative change in thermal conductivity of the mixture. Values of $\lambda$ are given in Table 4 for various gases. If an electrically heated wire is placed in the axis of a cylindrical space filled with gas, the heat transported by the gas from the wire to the walls of the cylinder, at equilibrium, is equal to the heat generated in the wire [22]:

$$i^2 R(t_w) = a\lambda_m (t_w - t_c) \tag{4}$$

where i is the current in the wire; $R(t_w)$ is the resistance of the wire at its own temperature, $t_w$; $t_c$ is the temperature of the wall; $\lambda_m$ is the thermal conductivity of the gas mixture at a mean temperature [approximated, for practical purposes, at $(t_w + t_c)/2$]; and a is an instrument constant. The temperature dependence of R is given by

TABLE 4 Thermal Conductivity $(\lambda)^a$ of Gases and Vapors

| Gas or vapor | $\lambda \times 10^{-3}$ [W/(cm·K)] 4.4°C | 48.9°C |
|---|---|---|
| Air | 0.245 | 0.277 |
| Ammonia | 0.223 | 0.270 |
| Argon | 0.163 | 0.190 |
| Carbon dioxide | 0.149 | 0.183 |
| Carbon monoxide | 0.234 | 0.267 |
| Helium | 1.437 | 1.574 |
| Hydrogen | 1.747 | 1.972 |
| Hydrogen sulfide | 0.131 | 0.161 |
| Methane | 0.311 | 0.374 |
| Nitrogen | 0.244 | 0.275 |
| Nitrous oxide | 0.155 | 0.193 |
| Oxygen | 0.249 | 0.285 |
| Water | 0.163 | 0.195 |

[a]At 1 atm.
*Source*: Ref. 23.

$$R(t) = R_0(1 + \alpha t) \tag{5}$$

$\alpha$ being the temperature coefficient of the resistance. Values of $R_0$ and $\alpha$ are given for various metals in Table 5.

If the value of $\lambda$ now changes to a small extent of $d\lambda$, owing to a small change in the gas composition, assuming that the total energy generated in the wire is approximately constant and that the variation of $\lambda$ due to temperature changes is negligible, the corresponding change in $t_w$ is obtained by differentiating Eq. (4):

TABLE 5 Electrical Resistivity and Temperature Coefficients of Metals at 20°C

| Metal | Resistivity ($10^{-6}$ ohm·cm) | Temperature coefficient ($K^{-1}$) |
|---|---|---|
| Nickel | 6.84 | 0.0069 |
| Tungsten | 5.6 | 0.0045 |
| Platinum | 10.6 | 0.0039 |
| Gold | 2.44 | 0.0034 |

*Source*: Ref. 24.

$$dt_w = \frac{d\lambda}{\lambda_m}(t_w - t_c) \qquad (6)$$

Differentiating Eq. (5) and introducing the result in Eq. (6) gives, successively

$$dR = \alpha R_0 dt_w \qquad (7)$$

and

$$dR = \alpha R_0 \varepsilon (t_w - t_c) \qquad (8)$$

Now, applying the rule of the Wheatstone bridge,

$$V = \frac{dR\ I}{2} \qquad (9)$$

where I is the total current flowing through the bridge. Substituting for dR the value taken from Eq. (8) and introducing Eq. (3), it follows that

$$V = \frac{\alpha R_0 I}{2}(t_w - t_c)\ \ln \frac{\lambda_2}{\lambda_1}\ dx \qquad (10)$$

The factor $(t_w - t_c)$ may be calculated from Eq. (4), using the same assumption as above and taking into account the fact that if the bridge is perfectly symmetric, $i = I/2$,

$$t_w - t_c = \frac{I^2 R_0}{4a\lambda_m - \alpha I^2 R_0}(1 + \alpha t_c) \qquad (11)$$

Introducing Eq. (11) in Eq. (10) and recalling Eq. (1), the expression, of the sensitivity of the katharometer is finally found to be

$$k_s = \frac{\alpha I^3 R_0^2 (1 + \alpha t_c)}{2(4a\lambda_m - \alpha I^2 R_0)} \ln \frac{\lambda_2}{\lambda_1} \qquad (12)$$

Equation (12) shows that the sensitivity of katharometer measurements is increased if:

1. The gas is a mixture of components having very different thermal conductivities (high $\lambda_2/\lambda_1$ ratio).
2. The nominal composition of the gas is chosen so as to obtain the lowest thermal conductivity ($\lambda_m$).
3. The highest possible bridge current I is used. The limitation of this is that higher bridge currents will result in shorter filament life.
4. Whenever possible, a katharometer cell having the lowest possible instrument constant a should be chosen, the filament being made of a metal having the highest possible temperature coefficient $\alpha$ and the highest possible nominal resistance $R_0$.

Of course, criteria other than sensitivity may be of importance in the choice of the filament material, such as the avoidance of corrosion when in contact with reactive gases (e.g., $O_2$, NO, CO, $CO_2$, $H_2O$, and $H_2S$).

## III. THEORETICAL BASIS FOR INTERPRETING TPD AND TPR PATTERNS

### A. Theory of TPD: The Langmuir Adsorption Model

The simplest theoretical model describing gas-solid adsorption is the well-known Langmuir adsorption isotherm. This model will be recalled briefly in the case of both nondissociative and dissociative adsorption. In each case, sets of theoretical TPD curves, obtained by computer simulation, will be presented in such a way as to visualize qualitatively the effect of the kinetic parameters of the desorption phenomena. The effect of instrumental variables, such as heating rate and carrier gas flow rate, will also be illustrated. Finally, the effect of diffusional limitations will be stressed.

#### 1. Nondissociative (First-Order) Adsorption

The adsorption process of a gas G on a solid S may be considered as a chemical reaction between a gaseous molecule or atom with some adsorption sites S* present at the solid surface:

$$S^* + G \rightleftarrows S\text{-}G \tag{13}$$

The Langmuir model is based on the hypotheses that a fixed number of sites N ($F/cm^{-2}$) are present on the solid and that the enthalpy of adsorption $\Delta H_a$ is independent of the fraction of occupied adsorption sites. It is also assumed that both N and $\Delta H_a$ are temperature independent.

If N is the number of sites occupied at a given time t, the rate of adsorption is given by

$$\frac{dN}{dt} = pkn_a(N^* - N) - k_d N \tag{14}$$

where p is the adsorbate pressure over the solid and $kn_a$ and $k_d$ are, respectively, the kinetic constant of adsorption and desorption. The constant k is derived from the kinetic theory of gases:

$$k = \sigma(2\pi MRT)^{-1/2} \tag{15}$$

where $\sigma$ is the surface area occupied by one adsorption site ($cm^{-2}$/mol), M the molecular weight of the adsorbate (g/mol), R the gas constant [J/(K·mol)], and T the absolute temperature (K). If C is the absorbate concentration in the gas phase (mol/$cm^{-3}$), then

$$p = CRT \tag{16}$$

The constant $n_a$ is the fraction of adsorbate molecules reacting with an adsorption site upon their collision with the adsorbent. If the adsorption process is thermally activated, $n_a$ will obey an Arrhenius equation:

$$n_a = A_a \exp\left(\frac{-E_a}{RT}\right) \tag{17}$$

where $A_a$ is the entropy factor, $E_a$ the activation energy of the adsorption process, and the other symbols have their usual meanings. Similarly, the kinetic constant $k_d$ ($s^{-1}$) is related to temperature as follows:

$$k_d = A_d \exp\left(\frac{-E_d}{RT}\right) \tag{18}$$

where $A_d$ ($s^{-1}$) is the frequency factor and $E_d$ is the activation energy of the desorption process. Note here that

$$\Delta H_a = E_a - E_d \tag{19}$$

Equation (14) expresses the overall rate of adsorption as a balance between two competitive processes: the adsorption process, which is assumed here to be proportional to the number of vacant sites ($N^* - N$) (first-order adsorption), and the desorption process, assumed to be proportional to the number of adsorbed molecules N (first-order desorption). First-order adsorption corresponds generally to nondissociative adsorption. The case of dissociative adsorption, resulting in second-order adsorption, will be considered later.

In the course of a TPR investigation, the measured quantity is the adsorbate concentration C in the carrier gas sweeping the sample (see Sec. II.C). In the case of an ideal reactor (in which no axial or lateral concentration gradients exist), C is related to the adsorption rate by the equation

$$C = -\frac{S}{F}\frac{dN}{dt} \tag{20}$$

where S is the specific surface area ($cm^2/g$) of the solid and F the specific flow rate of the carrier gas [$cm^3$ STP/(s·g)]. Then combining (14) and (20), the following equation is obtained:

$$C(t) = \frac{SNk_d}{F + S\sigma(RT/2\pi M)^{1/2} n_a(N^* - N)} \tag{21}$$

If the TPD experiment is conducted using a linear heating schedule, the actual temperature T is given by

$$T = T_0 + \beta T \tag{22}$$

where $\beta$ is the heating rate (K/s) and $T_0$ is the starting temperature of the run.

It is customary to express the degree of occupancy of adsorption sites in terms of surface coverage $\theta$:

$$\theta = \frac{N}{N^*} \tag{23}$$

Combining Eqs. (20) to (23) and expressing the result as a function of temperature, the following equations are obtained:

$$C(T) = \frac{SN^*\theta Ad \exp(-E_d/RT)}{F + SN^*(1 - \theta)\sigma(RT/2\pi M)^{1/2} A_a \exp(-E_a/RT)} \tag{24}$$

$$\frac{d\theta}{dT} = -\frac{F}{S\beta N^*} C(T) \tag{25}$$

These equations are basically equivalent to those derived previously by Cvetanović and Amenomiya [20]. From this starting point these authors developed an analytical procedure that allowed the deduction of the kinetic parameters of the desorption process, or the enthalpy of adsorption, in the two following limiting cases: (1) the flow F is very much larger than $SN^*k_a(1 - \theta)$, so that readsorption occurs only to a negligible extent (kinetic control); and (2) F is very much smaller than the term above, so that the sample is in thermodynamic equilibrium with the surrounding gas (thermodynamic control). The use of such analytical procedures will not be considered here in greater detail, since they have been presented at length in the literature [20,27]. Equations (24) and (25) can serve to construct theoretical TPD curves, without further simplifying assumptions, using an iterative numerical procedure easily programmed on a minicomputer. Such model patterns, in which C is plotted versus temperature, are presented in Fig. 3. They were computed using typical values of kinetic and experimental variables, which are presented in Table 6.

Figure 3a shows the effect of varying $E_d$ at a fixed value of $H_a$ ($-36.6$ kJ/mol); curve (1) correspond to the lowest $E_d$ and, according to Eq. (19), also to the lowest $E_a$, so that, due to very fast adsorption and desorption reactions, the entire TPD run takes place under

TABLE 6 Typical Values of Kinetic and Experimental Parameters Used in TPD Simulation (Langmuir Model)

| Parameter | Value | Dimension |
|---|---|---|
| S | $1 \times 10^{6}$ | $cm^2/g$ |
| N* | $1 \times 10^{-9}$ | $mol/cm^2$ |
| $\sigma$ | $9.8 \times 10^{8}$ | $cm^2/mol$ |
| M | 28[a] | g/mol |
| | 2[b] | g/mol |
| R | 8.314 | J/(K·mol) |
| F | 10 | $cm^3/s \cdot g)$ |
| $\beta$ | 0.1 | K/s |
| Ea[c] | $10.0 \times 10^{3}$ | J/mol |
| $A_a$[c] | 1[a] | —[a] |
| | $1 \times 10^{9}$[b] | $cm^2/mol$[b] |
| $E_d$[c] | $60.0 \times 10^{3}$ | J/mol |
| $A_d$[c] | $1 \times 10^{10}$ to $1 \times 10^{13}$ | $s^{-1}$[a] |
| | $1 \times 10^{19}$ to $1 \times 10^{22}$ | $cm^2/(s \cdot mol)$[b] |

[a]Corresponds to nitrogen and first-order adsorption.
[b]Corresponds to hydrogen and second-order adsorption.
[c]Typical values taken from Refs. 25 and 26.

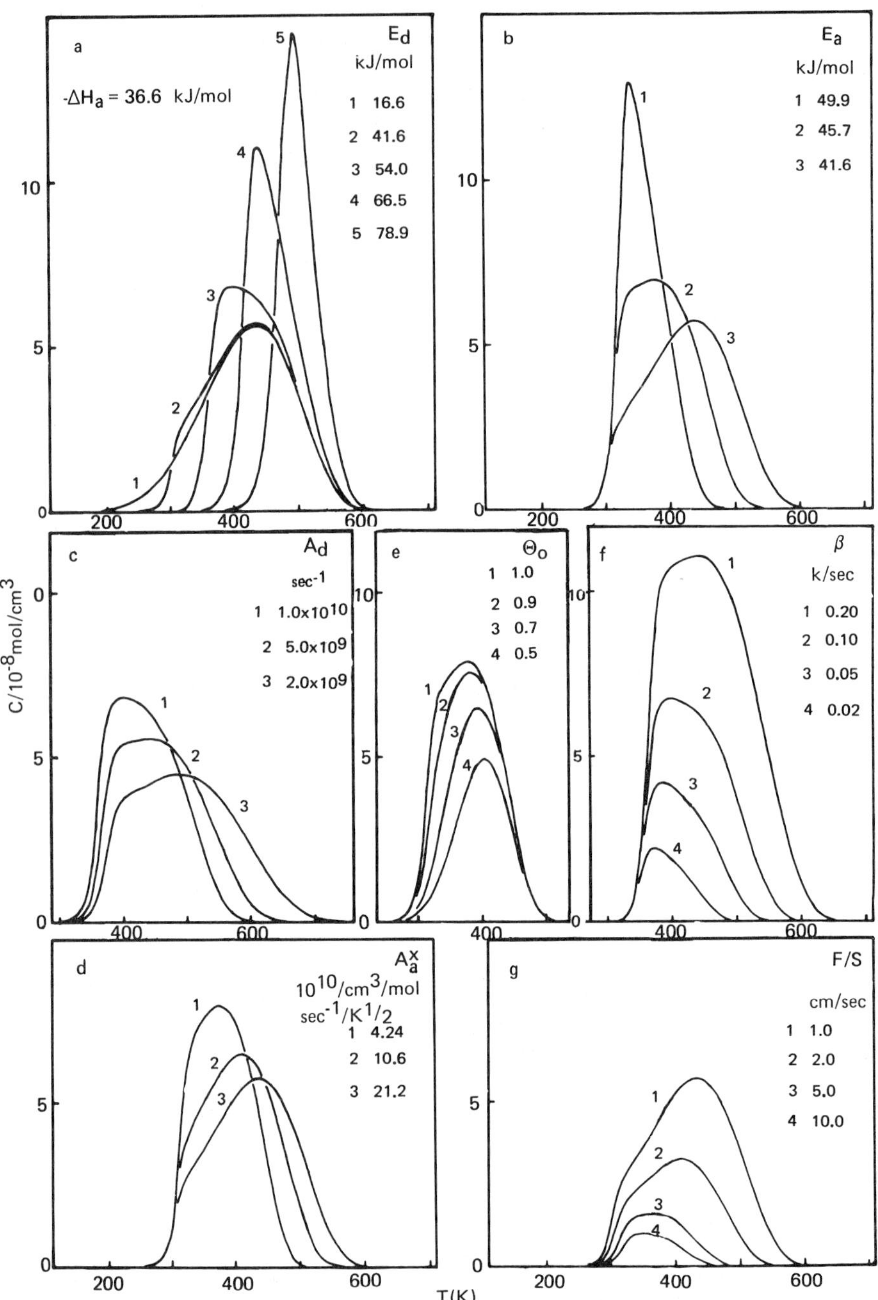


FIG. 3. Theoretical TPD patterns in the case of a Langmuir first-order adsorption model. $A_a^x$ stands for $\sigma(R/2\pi M)^{1/2}A_a$ (see the text).

thermodynamic control. This situation corresponds to the limiting case "with readsorption freely occurring" according to the classification of Cvetanović and Amenomiya [20]. When $E_d$ is increased, the left-hand tail of the TPD peak is progressively displaced toward higher temperatures, resulting in a marked deformation of the peak shape: a shoulder appears (curve 2) and develops (curve 3) until the TPD curve becomes skewed to the right. Curve (5) is closer to the situation where the desorption process is entirely under kinetic control.

Figure 3a stresses that intermediate situations between the two limiting cases emphasized by Cvetanović and Amenomiya are quite to be expected. Moreover, they could give way to serious misinterpretations of TPD patterns: for instance, curve (2) could have been interpreted as the superimposition of two peaks, ascribed to two distinct adsorbed states. The quite unexpected skewness of curve (3) would have been rather puzzling. The effect of $E_a$ is illustrated in Fig. 3b. Two main features are apparent here: (1) the main peak maximum moves toward *higher* temperatures when $E_a$ is *decreased*, the general shape of the peak approaching more closely that of a process under thermodynamic control; and (2) the left-hand tail of the peak is not affected by changes in $E_a$. The same observations are valid when considering the effect of increasing $A_a$ (Fig. 3d). Decreasing $A_d$ (Fig. 3c) results in a displacement of the main peak maximum and, to a minor extent, of its left-hand tail toward higher temperatures; as a result, the process becomes more extensively controlled by thermodynamics.

The effect of decreasing the initial surface coverage is illustrated in Fig. 3e. The left-hand shoulder has completely disappeared for $\theta_0 = 0.7$; for lower coverages the shape of the TPD curve does not differ from the one that should be obtained under complete thermodynamic control. The influence of the heating rate $\beta$ (see Fig. 3f) is twofold: first, the overall surface area of the TPD band is proportional to $\beta$, and second, increasing $\beta$ results in a higher fraction of gas desorbing under thermodynamic control (consider the progressive growth of the right-hand shoulder of the curves when $\beta$ is increased). The trends above are reversed when F/S (the flow rate per unit surface area of the solid) is increased instead of $\beta$ (Fig. 3g).

### 2. Dissociative (Second-Order) Adsorption

The adsorption process of a gaseous molecule on a solid sometimes involves the dissociation of the adsorbate into two or more fragments (ions or radicals). These fragments are the species effectively found on the adsorbent. Their recombination is necessary before any desorption reaction can occur. The case of the dissociative adsorption of a diatomic molecule (e.g., $H_2$, $O2$, $N_2$ and the like) may be envisaged as a chemical reaction with adsorption sites:

$$2S^* + G_2 \rightleftarrows 2S\text{-}G \tag{26}$$

The other hypotheses are identical to those made in the preceding subsection. As a result, the following equation for the adsorption rate is obtained:

$$\frac{dN}{dt} = pkn_a(N^* - N)^2 - k_d N^2 \tag{27}$$

Equation (27) involves the *second power* of the number of free $(N^* - N)$ and occupied (N) adsorption sites to take into account that each adsorbing molecule occupies *two* adsorption sites. Exactly the same reasoning as that given in Sec. III.A.1 leads to the following set of equations of the TPD pattern:

$$C(T) = \frac{SN^{*2}\theta^2 A_d \exp(-E_d/RT)}{F + SN^{*2}(1-\theta)^2 \sigma(RT/2\pi M)^{1/2} A_a \exp(-E_a/RT)} \tag{28}$$

$$\frac{d\theta}{dT} = \frac{F}{S\beta N^*} C(T) \tag{29}$$

These equations are basically identical to those derived previously by Konvalinka et al. [27]. Those authors have developed a procedure for deriving the order of desorption together with the kinetic and/or thermodynamic parameters of the adsorption-desorption process in the same two limiting cases as above: complete kinetic or thermodynamic control of the process. Equations (28) and (29) will be used here, as in Sec. III.A.1, to construct theoretical second-order TPD curves and to show how they are affected by kinetic and experimental variables.

Theoretical second-order TPD patterns are presented in Fig. 4. They have been constructed on the basis of the kinetic and experimental data presented in Table 6. Figure 4 shows that, by varying $E_d$ at a fixed value of $H_a$, a variety of intermediate situations exists between the two limiting cases in which desorption is completely controlled either by kinetic or by thermodynamic factors: the former situation corresponds more closely to curve (4) (high values of $E_d$) in Fig. 4a, while the latter corresponds to curve (1) (low value of $E_d$). Intermediate situations are characterized by a secondary peak of which maximum temperature and intensity increase for increasing values of $E_d$. This situation is very similar to the one observed for the first-order desorption process, except that a shoulder rather than a peak appeared on the TPD curves.

This secondary peak, just like the shoulder observed in first-order desorption curves, should *not* be attributed to a distinct adsorption state or species. As above, it will disappear completely if the initial coverage is somewhat decreased (see Fig. 4e). It is character-

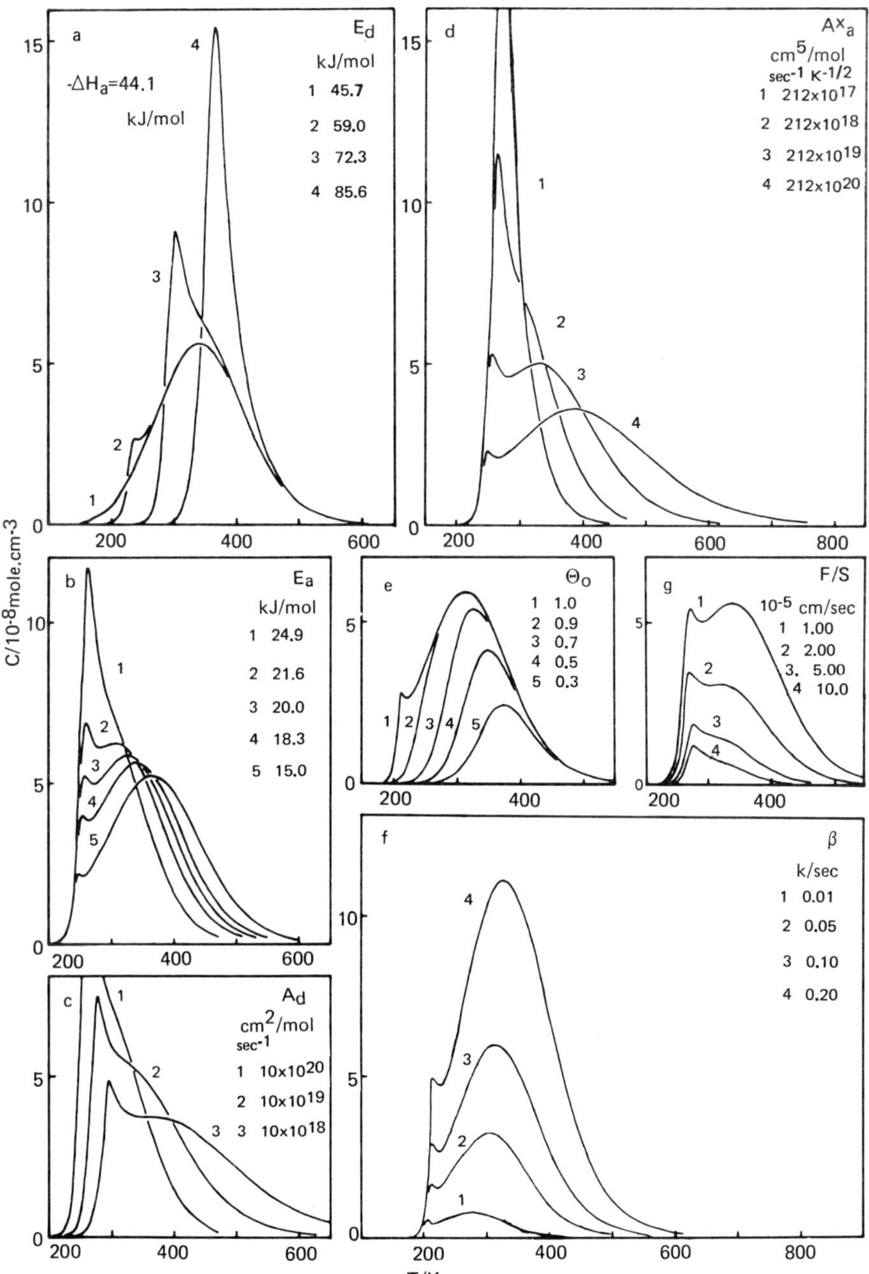


FIG. 4. Theoretical TPD patterns in the case of a Langmuir second-order adsorption model. $A_a^x$ stands for $\sigma(R/2\pi M)^{1/2}A_a$ (see the text).

istic of the fraction of adsorbed atoms, which, at the start of the thermal desorption process, will desorb under pure kinetic control. This fraction will depend, of course, on the experimental conditions of the TPD run; in particular, it will increase for decreasing $\beta$, the rate of temperature increase (see Fig. 4f), and for increasing F/S, the intrinsic flow rate (see Fig. 4g), in both cases at the expense of sensitivity.

The trends observed while varying the kinetic parameters are identical to those already reported for first-order desorption and therefore will not be discussed again in detail. They are illustrated in Figs. 4b to d.

### 3. Diffusion-Controlled Desorption

In all cases considered so far, diffusion of the adsorbate in the pores of the solid adsorbent has been neglected. However, slow diffusion in the pores might sometimes control the rate of desorption in highly porous materials. Unfortunately, a general mathematical treatment of diffusion in the pores of a solid is extremely difficult and will therefore not be presented here. Cvetanović and Amenomiya [20] have developed an equation for diffusion-controlled TPD curves, on the basis of a simplified model (straight pores of uniform lengths and radii). It appears that the shapes of the TPD curves obtained under either diffusion control, or pure kinetic control in the first-order desorption model, are practically identical. When the desorption process is controlled by diffusion $k_d$, the kinetic constant of desorption appearing in Eq. (21) must be replaced by the following constant:

$$k_d \simeq \frac{D_0 \pi^2 A^*}{\ell^2} \exp\left(\frac{-\Delta H}{RT}\right) \tag{30}$$

where $\ell$ is the length of the pores, $A^* = \exp(-\Delta S/R)$ ($\Delta S$ being the differential entropy of adsorption), and $D_0$ is the effective diffusion coefficient of the gas in the porous particles. The coefficient $D_0$ is related to $D_i$, the self-diffusion coefficient of the gas, as follows [28]:

$$D_0 = D_i \theta \chi \tag{31}$$

where $\theta$ is the specific pore volume (in cubic centimeters per cubic centimeter of adsorbent) and $\chi$ is the labyrinth factor ($\simeq 0.7$). The self-diffusion coefficient is calculated as follows [28]:

$$D_i = \frac{c\lambda}{3} \tag{32}$$

where $c = (8RT/\pi M)^{1/2}$ is the mean velocity of the gaseous molecule (cm/s) (M is the molecular weight, R is the gas constant, and T the absolute temperature) and

$$\lambda = \frac{3.065 \times 10^{-23} T}{pd^2}$$

is the mean free path (centimeters) [p is the gas pressure (atmospheres) and d is the effective molecular diameter (centimeters)].

Knudsen diffusion will occur in pores having diameters (2r) smaller than the mean free path:

$$2r < \lambda \tag{33}$$

In that case, the diffusion coefficient becomes independent of the gas pressure:

$$D_i = \frac{2cr}{3} \tag{34}$$

Since first-order desorption processes under kinetic control are not distinguishable from diffusion-controlled ones on the basis of the shapes of the TPD patterns, some other criterion that would allow the absence of diffusion problems to be checked would be useful. Such a criterion has been developed by Ibok and Ollis [29], and is expressed as follows:

$$R < R_{max} = \left[\frac{D_{0\,max} C_{max}}{(S/V_a)(dN/dt)_{max}}\right]^{1/2} \tag{35}$$

where R is the radius of the adsorbent particles, $c_{max}$ the bulk adsorbate concentration measured in the carrier gas at the peak temperatures ($T_{max}$), $D_{0\,max}$ the effective diffusion coefficient at $T_{max}$, $(dN/dT)_{max}$ the maximum rate of desorption, S the specific surface area, and $V_a$ the apparent specific volume of the adsorbent. Equation (35) is valid only if readsorption may be neglected. When readsorption is appreciable, the effective diffusion coefficient $D_0$ is reduced by a factor $(1 + K)$, where $K = pkn_a/k_d$ (see Eq. 14). Equation (35) stresses that diffusion will not control the desorption process provided that the adsorbent has been ground into particles having radii smaller than $R_{max}$. The higher the specific surface area (S) and the smaller the pore volume (included in $V_a$) of an adsorbent, the smaller will be the critical particle radius above which diffusion will control the desorption process. It is important to note that $\beta$, the rate of temperature increase, will also influence $R_{max}$, since

$$\frac{dN}{dt} = \beta \frac{dN}{dT} \tag{36}$$

Therefore, the higher $\beta$, the smaller $R_{max}$ will be. In other words, diffusion is more likely to control the desorption process when temperature is increased very rapidly.

## A. Theory of TPR

Gas-solid reactions are complex processes that can be decomposed in a succession of steps:

1. Transport of the gaseous reactant toward the solid-gas interface (diffusion)
2. Adsorption of the gaseous reactant
3. Interfacial processes
4. Desorption of the gaseous product
5. Transport of the gaseous product away from the solid-gas interface (diffusion)

Each of these steps may, in principle, control the overall rate of the process. Steps 2 and 4 have been considered in Secs. III.B.1 and III.B.2, and diffusional problems (steps 1 and 5) have been accounted for in Sec. III.B.3. The present section will therefore focus attention on step 3.

A number of mechanisms have already been proposed for the interfacial processes of gas-solid reactions, and extensive reviews have been published in the past [10,15]. In this section, only a limited number of reaction mechanisms, the most relevant to catalyst studies, will be considered. Theoretical TPR curves will be developed from the selected model mechanisms and used to illustrate the influence of kinetic and other experimental factors.

Let us consider the following solid-gas reactions:

$$R_{(solid)} + A_{(gas)} \rightarrow P_{(solid)} + B_{(gas)} \tag{37}$$

In the case of an ideal fixed-bed flow through the reactor, $\Delta C$, the difference in concentration of A between the inlet and the outlet of the reactor, will be related to the reaction rate as follows:

$$\Delta C = \frac{m}{F} \frac{d\alpha}{dt} \tag{38}$$

where F [$cm^3/(s \cdot g)$] is the specific flow rate of the reacting mixture m is the specific molar consumption (mol/g) and $\alpha$ is the fraction of solid reactant converted. In the following discussion, the experimental conditions will be assumed to be such that $\Delta C$ can be neglected with respect to C, the nominal concentration of the reacting mixture, and that the rate of the reverse reaction is negligible.

1. Phase-Boundary-Controlled Reaction

This model assumes that the reaction rate is proportional to the surface area of the unreacted solid. The reaction rate is then given, for one individual particle, by [10]

$$\frac{d\alpha}{dt} = ks \tag{39}$$

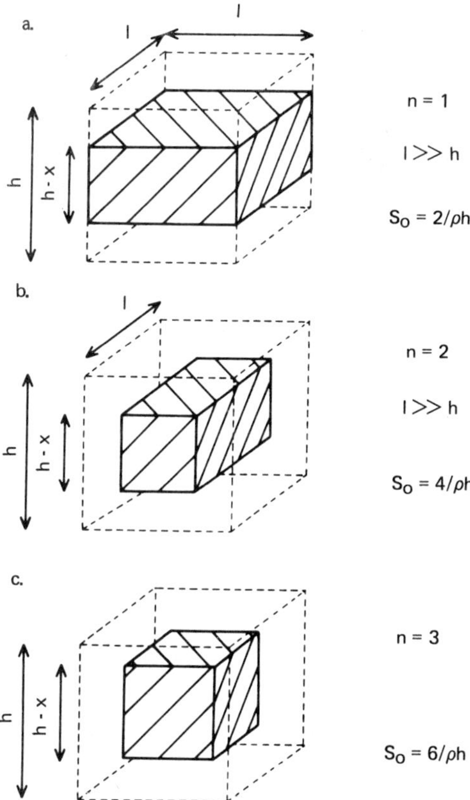


FIG. 5. Model for a solid-gas reaction controlled by phase boundary progression. (a) Monodirectional, (b) two-directional, and (c) three-directional phase boundary progression. [$\rho$ (g/cm$^3$), specific weight of the solid reactant].

where k is the kinetic constant $[g/(cm^2 \cdot s)]$ and S is the surface area of the unreacted core of the particle per unit weight of starting reactant.

It may be shown from pure geometric considerations that for a given conversion $\alpha$,S is related to $S_0$, the specific surface area of the starting reactant, by

$$S = S_0(1 - \alpha)^{(n-1)/n} \tag{40}$$

where n represents the number of independent directions along which the reaction interface moves toward the bulk of the solid (see Fig. 5). The case of a three-dimensional interface progress (Fig. 5c) will now be considered in more detail. Introducing the linear law of temperature increase (Eq. 22) into Eqs. (38) and (39), and assuming that the kinetic constant obeys the Arrhenius law, the following set of equations is obtained:

$$\frac{d\alpha}{dT} = \frac{S_0 A}{\beta}(1 - \alpha)^{2/3} \exp\left(\frac{-E}{RT}\right) \tag{41}$$

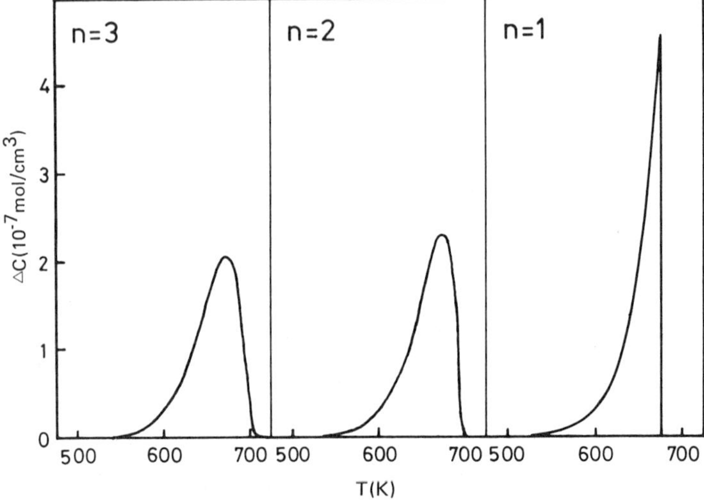


FIG. 6. Effect of n on the shape of the TPR patterns corresponding to a phase-boundary-controlled reaction [$A = 1.5 \times 10^4$ $g/(cm^2 \cdot s)$; E = 121 kJ/mol; h = 8800 nm corresponding to $S_0 = 10^3$ $cm^2/g$; $\beta$ = 0.2 K/s; m = $133 \times 10^{-2}$ mol/g; F = $2.0 \times 10^2$ $cm^3/(s \cdot g)$] (see the text).

$$\Delta C = \frac{m\beta}{F}\frac{d\alpha}{dT} \tag{42}$$

where E is the activation energy of the interfacial process and A is the preexponential factor. Equations (41) and (42) allow computation of theoretical TPR curves (Figs. 6 and 7). Figure 6 shows the effect on the shape of the resulting TPR pattern of changing n in Eq. (40). Lower n values result in higher and sharper peaks, other factors remaining constant. The effect of increasing E is illustrated in Fig. 7a; higher values of E result in broader peaks exhibiting their maxima at higher temperatures.

It is easy to realize, by considering Eq. (41), that any increase of the apparent preexponential factor ($S_0A/\beta$) will lower the peak maximum temperature. As a result, as the particle size of the solid reactant in inversely proportional to $S_0$, increasing it will result in increasing the peak temperature (Fig. 7b). Since $\Delta C$ is proportional to $\beta$ (Eq. 42), decreasing the latter factor will not only move the peak maximum toward lower temperatures, but will also decrease its intensity (Fig. 7c). Changing F, the specific flow rate, will affect only the intensity of the TPR peak, not its temperature, as F only appears in the expression of $\Delta C$ (Eqs. 41 and 42). However, the latter observa-

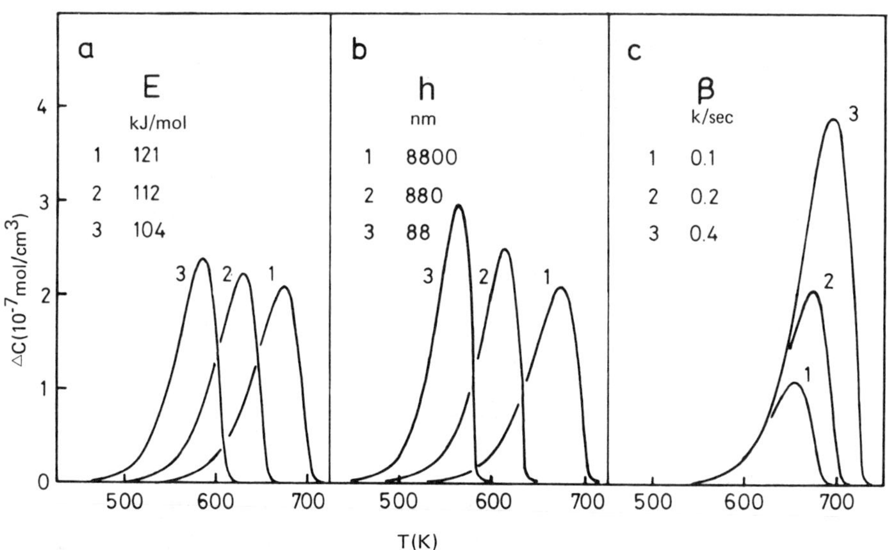


FIG. 7. Theoretical TPR patterns of a three-directional phase-boundary-controlled reaction (values of the parameters: see legend to Fig. 6, unless otherwise stated) (see the text).

tion is valid only provided that $\Delta C$ remains negligibly small with respect to the nominal concentration in the gaseous reactant, or if the reaction rate does not depend on the composition of the gas phase; unfortunately, there is no room in the present review to analyze more complex situations.

2. Reaction Controlled by Nucleation

The rate of a gas-solid reaction is sometimes controlled by the slow formation of the very first amounts of solid product. These cases are usually referred to as "nucleation-controlled reactions"; detailed theoretical descriptions may be found in the literature [10, 15]. The reduction of oxidic precursors of supported nickel catalysts has been reported to be nucleation controlled [30]. A simplified picture of nucleation-controlled gas-solid reactions, but one sufficient for our present purposes, will be presented here. In the present model, the solid reactant is supposed to consist of a large number of identical particles of size h.

Each individual particle is virtually completely converted as soon as it has developed one nucleus of the product solid. The probability of a nucleus appearing on an individual particle in a given time interval is assumed to be independent of time; it is supposed to depend on temperature according to an Arrhenius law. The probability of nucleus formation on an individual particle is likely to depend on its size. In the case of gas-solid reactions, nuclei may be assumed to appear with the same probability all over the gas-solid interface; the probability that one individual particle will nucleate will therefore be proportional to its surface area (i.e., to $h^2$). These hypotheses are summarized in the equation

$$\frac{d\alpha}{dt} = k_n h^2 (1 - \alpha) \tag{43}$$

where $\alpha$ is the number fraction of converted particles and $k_n$ ($cm^{-2}/s$) is the kinetic constant of the nucleation process. A derivation quite similar to that of Sec. III.B.1 gives

$$\frac{d\alpha}{dT} = \frac{h^2 A}{\beta}(1 - \alpha) \exp\left(\frac{-E}{RT}\right) \tag{44}$$

Equation (44) may be used together with Eq. (42) to compute theoretical TPR curves (Fig. 8). There are two principal differences between Eqs. (41) and (44): the first power in the factor $(1 - \alpha)$ (instead of the 2/3 power) results in a peak exhibiting more tailing toward higher temperatures; *increasing* h, the particle size, results in an *increase* in the reaction rate, and therefore in a *decrease* in the peak maximum temperature (Fig. 8b); this is due to the fact that the apparent preexponential factor is proportional to $h^2$.

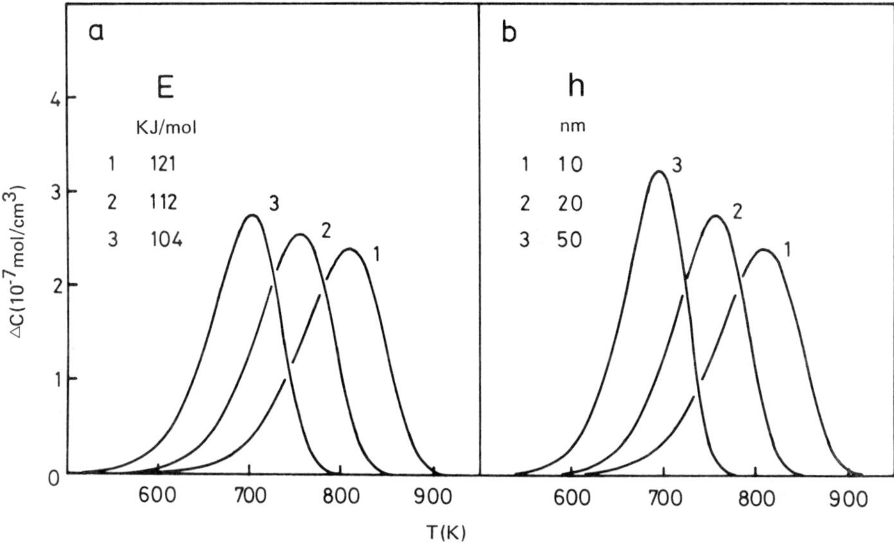


FIG. 8. Theoretical TPR patterns of a nucleation-controlled reaction. ($A = 5.45 \times 10^{17}$ cm$^{-2}$/s; E = 121 kJ/mol; h = 10 nm, $\beta = 0.4$ K/s; $m = 1.33 \times 10^{-2}$ mol/g; $F = 2.0 \times 10^{2}$ cm$^3$/(s·g) unless otherwise stated) (see the text).

### 3. Reactive Species in Solid Solution in an Inert Matrix

A representative example of the present situation is the reduction of transition metal ions in zeolites [19,31]. Other systems, such as transition metal aluminates, could behave similarly when reduced by hydrogen [32]. The starting point of this model is the same as for the phase boundary model developed in Sec. III.B.1. In this case, however, the surface area $S_0$ of the reacting particle does not change during the reaction. Instead, the reaction rate will progressively diminish due to depletion of the reactive species. A simple way to express this is to set the reaction rate to be proportional to $\chi$, the actual concentration of the reactive species (mol/cm$^3$):

$$\frac{d\alpha}{dt} = kS_0\chi \tag{45}$$

If $\chi_0$ is the initial concentration in active species, then

$$\chi = \chi_0(1 - \alpha) \tag{46}$$

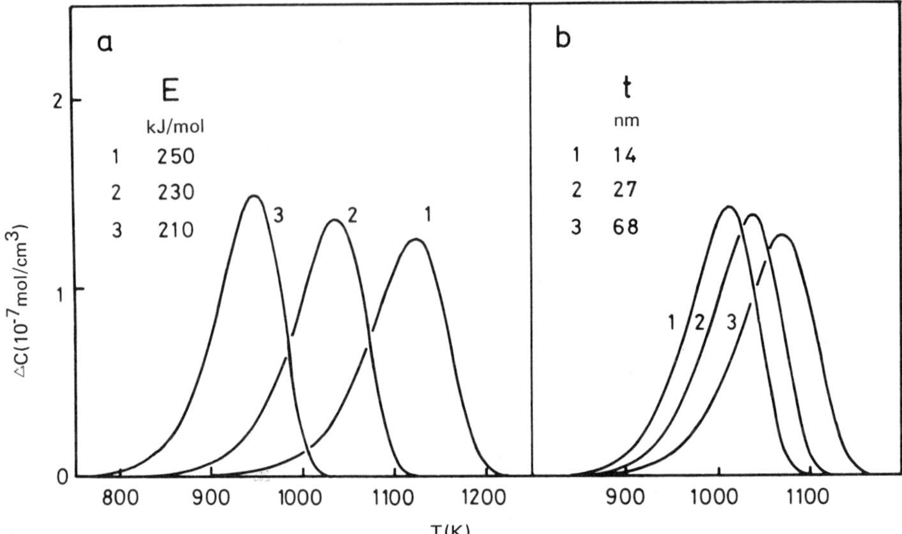


FIG. 9. Theoretical TPR patterns of a solid solution reaction. ($A = 1.26 \times 10^4$ g/(cm$^2$·s); $E = 230$ kJ/mol; $S_0 = 5 \times 10^5$ cm$^2$/g, corresponding to $h = 27$ nm; $\chi_0 = 0.33$ mol fraction; $\beta = 0.2$ K/s; $m = 5.67 \times 10^{-3}$ mol/g; $F = 85$ cm$^3$/(s·g) unless otherwise stated) (see the text).

Combining Eqs. (45) and (46) and introducing the temperature program through Eq. (22), the following equation is obtained:

$$\frac{d\alpha}{dT} = \frac{\chi_0 S_0 A}{\beta} (1 - \alpha) \exp\left(\frac{-E}{RT}\right) \tag{47}$$

Together with Eq. (42), Eq. (47) may be used to compute theoretical TPR curves (Fig. 9). Equation (47) is formally identical to Eq. (44), describing the nucleation-controlled process; therefore, nucleation-controlled processes will not be distinguished from reactions of species in solid solution on the basis of the *shape* of their TPR patterns. However, the apparent preexponential factor in Eq. (47) is proportional to $S_0$, so that, as was the case for phase-boundary-controlled reactions, *increasing* the particle size will result in an *increase* in the peak maximum temperature (Fig. 9b).

4. Conclusions

The three solid-gas reaction models presented above represent only a very limited selection of all conceivable situations. Unfortunately, an exhaustive review of these situations is not possible, were it even useful, in the framework of this review. A first conclusion thus emerges: the reader should never base conclusions about the mechanism of a solid-gas reaction on TPR evidence alone. The TPR technique can provide very interesting results and help toward a better understanding of the system under study, provided that other information, gained from other techniques, is available: for instance, an a priori knowledge of the chemical nature and of the state of dispersion of the reactive phase is a considerable help in limiting the choice among the possible reaction mechanisms.

A further complication of TPR patterns may arise if different rate-limiting steps happen to control the reaction rate. As was shown in the study of TPD (Sec. III.A), mixed control mechanisms will also probably result in TPR in complex patterns in which distinct peaks could be erroneously assigned to different reacting species. On the other hand, some reacting solids may undergo thermal changes during the TPR run and the associated changes in reactivity may result in complicated TPR patterns [33,34].

A very important factor governing the reactivity of a given material is its state of dispersion. Clearly, the simplified models presented above showed how strongly the particle size of a solid reactant could affect its TPR pattern. A further complication will come from the possible polydispersed character of the solid particles. The detailed shape of a TPR pattern is then expected to be affected by the particle size distribution of the solid reactant; the occurrence of multiple peaks may even be expected in the case of multimodal size distributions. Here again, separate knowledge of particle size (distribution) can be of considerable help in correctly interpreting TPR patterns.

In many cases, the intricate character of TPR patterns will not allow detailed quantitative treatment. In those cases, however, TPR analysis, like other thermoanalytical techniques, can help the investigator in delineating the actual complexity of the system under study. A complex sample will generally produce a characteristic TPR pattern which can be used as a fingerprint. Of course, reproducing such a fingerprint will neccessitate maintaining constant experimental conditions from one analysis to another. Thus the catalytic scientist may use TPR analysis as a quality control test, to check the reproducibility of a catalyst precursor preparation. Conversely, he or she may rapidly screen which preparative variables will actually affect the properties of a catalyst precursor.

## IV. EXPERIMENTAL TPD AND TPR STUDIES

The aim of this section is to present a few typical TPD and TPR studies in order to illustrate the use of these techniques in the field of catalyst characterization. An attempt will be made to interpret the original results in the light of the theoretical concepts given in the preceding section.

## A. TPD of $H_2$ from Nickel Catalysts

In a study by Konvalinka et al. [35], five different nickel catalysts, including a Raney nickel catalyst, were investigated for hydrogen TPD. The purpose of the work was to identify different hydrogen sites on metallic nickel particles and possibly to measure thermodynamic parameters (differential heat and entropy of adsorption).

Some characteristics of the catalysts are summarized in Table 7. The characteristic TPD patterns of catalysts 1 and 2 are presented in Fig. 10. In all cases the catalysts were first reduced in situ in highly purified hydrogen (166.7 ml/min) from room temperature up to 723 K (2 K/min). Reduction was contiued for 20 h at 723 K and for 3 h at 773 K. The catalyst was then cooled in hydrogen to 153 K, hydrogen was replaced by highly purified argon (16.7 ml/min), and the TPD spectrum was measured at a heating rate of 10 K/min. Dashed lines show the decomposition of the TPD patterns into elementary theoretical TPD curves. According to the authors, curves A and B corresponded to first-order desorption under thermodynamic control, and curves C to G corresponded to second-order desorption under thermodynamic control. The decomposition of the pattern was obtained as follows. The ascending part of curve A was fitted to a master curve presented in Ref. 20. The parameters of the best-fitting master curve were then used to calculate the whole peak A. After subtracting the contribution of peak A from the TPD pattern, the same procedure was used for calculating peak B and the other peaks in succession. The thermodynamic parameters of adsorption were calculated for each elementary peak assuming an initial coverage of 1 for the corresponding adsorption species and an entropy of the adsorbed state equal to zero: then,

TABLE 7 Characteristics of Some Ni Catalysts Investigated by $H_2$ TPD

| Catalysts | Ni content (wt %) | BET surface ($m^2/g$) | Metallic surface ($m^2/g$ Ni) | $\langle d_s \rangle$[a] (m) |
|---|---|---|---|---|
| 1 Ni-SiO-1 | 0.67 | 200 | 326 | 2.1 |
| 2 Ni-SiO-2 | 24.3 | 260 | 230 | 2.9 |
| 3 Ni-SiO-3 | 33.0 | — | 90 | 7.5 |
| 4 Ni-kaolinite | 52.5 | 110 | 54 | 12.5 |
| 5 Raney Ni | 76.2 | 58 | 23 | 29.3 |

[a]Surface average particle sizes derived from metallic surface area, assuming spherical particles.

*Source*: Ref. 35.

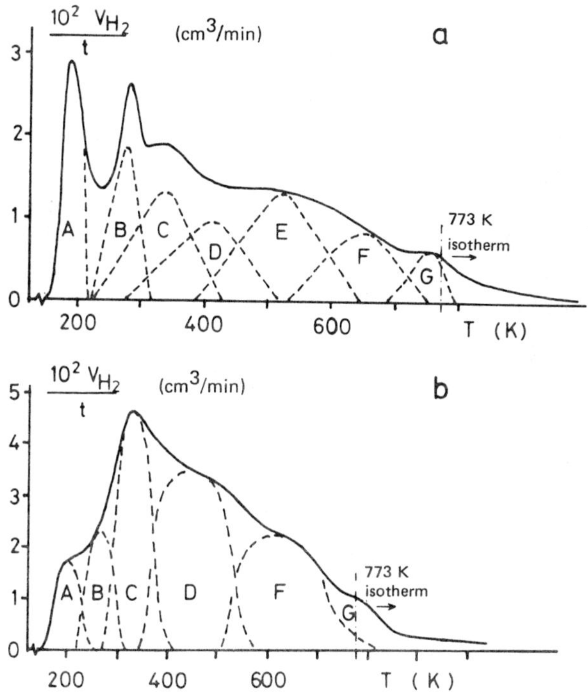


FIG. 10. TPD patterns of representative Ni catalysts: (a) catalyst 1 (0.97 g) and (b) catalyst 2 (0.080 g) (see the text). (From Ref. 35.)

in the calculation of the entropy factor $Ad/Aa = A^* = \exp(\Delta S/R)$, $\Delta S$ was taken as the standard entropy of hydrogen at the maximum temperature of the peak under study [36]. The thermodynamic parameters thus obtained for some of the catalysts are presented in Table 8. The agreement obtained among the three different catalysts is very good in view of the approximations and the simplifying assumptions made. Besides the assumption of zero entropy for the adsorbed state and full coverage for each adsorption state, Konvalinka et al. assumed that (1) the desorption process was entirely under thermodynamic control, (2) there were no diffusion problems, and (3) no thermal changes such as sintering occurred in the catalysts during the TPD runs. To check the existence of the last hypothesis would require measurement of the total and metallic surface areas of the catalysts *after* a TPD experiment.

Checking the second hypothesis is not possible here, since data for calculating the effective diffusion coefficient in the catalyst

TABLE 8 Enthalpies of Adsorption of Hydrogen on Nickel for Different Nickel Catalysts (kJ/mol)

| | Peaks | | | | | | |
|---|---|---|---|---|---|---|---|
| Catalyst | A | B | C | D | E | F | G |
| 1 | −32.9 | −52.3 | −65.6 | −82.6 | −106.9 | −138 | −170 |
| 2 | −35.9 | −48.0 | −60.8 | −85.4 | — | −123.4 | −170 |
| 3 | −37.9 | −51.8 | −71.0 | −93.7 | — | −127.4 | −162.2 |
| Type of chemisorption | Weak, first order | | Strong, second order | | | Very strong, second order | |

particle (e.g., the specific pore volume and the pore size distribution) and to test Eq. (35) (the radius of the catalyst particles) are not given. A tentative suggestion may be made concerning the first hypothesis, in order to lower the number of adsorbed states required to explain the TPD patterns of Fig. 10. As illustrated in Fig. 11, assuming mixed kinetic-thermodynamic control for the fraction of the TPD patterns covering the peaks C to G would result in only four distinct adsorption states, instead of seven, to explain the observed patterns. Unfortunately, the present state of knowledge does not allow a quantitative analysis of such complex TPD patterns to be made, taking into account possible desorption steps under mixed control. Therefore, the interpretation of the TPD experiments made by Konvalinka et al., although resting on an oversimplified assumption, is presently the best possible.

## B. Identification of Alloying Using TPR

The first application of TPR to catalyst investigation was devoted to the identification of alloying in supported copper-nickel catalysts [14].

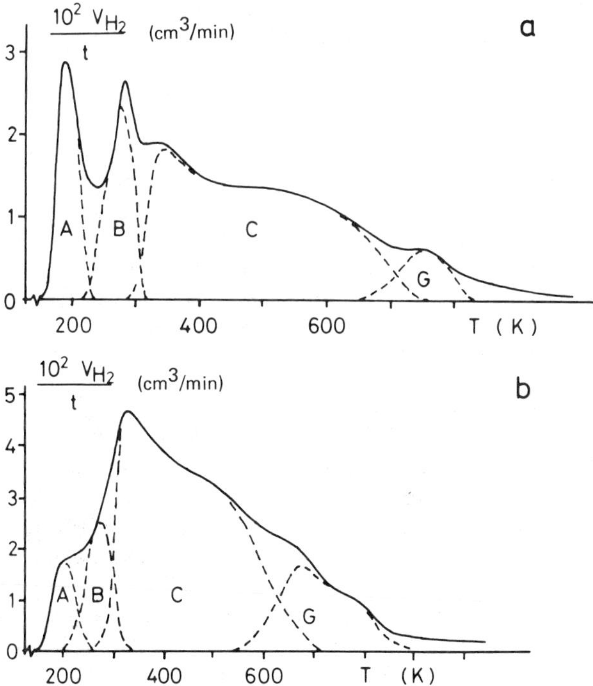


FIG. 11. Suggestion for an alternative decomposition in elementary TPD peaks of the TPD patterns presented in Fig. 10.

Since then, TPR has often been used in tentative identification of alloying in other bimetallic systems, such as Pt-Re [37] or Pt-Ir [38, 39], especially in the case of very highly dispersed bimetallic supported catalysts, for which other techniques of investigation, such as X-ray diffraction or electron microscopy, failed to give the information. The catalysts studied by Robertson et al. [14] were obtained by impregnation to incipient wetness of a Davison 70 silica (380 $m^2/g$) with a solution of Cu and Ni nitrate, followed by drying in vacuo at 100°C (2 h) prior to the TPR studies. The catalysts were in the form of particles 0.42 to 0.18 mm in diameter. A sample (350 mg of catalyst containing about 1% metal) was placed into a reactor whose temperature was increased at a constant rate (4.5 to 10°C/min) from −80 to 700°C. A reducing gas mixture (6 vol % $H_2$ in $N_2$) was flowed through the reactor (10 $cm^3$ STP/min). After passing through the sample, the gas was dried in a cold trap prior to reaching the katharometer, by which the hydrogen concentration was continuously monitored. Figure 12 presents the TPR patterns of a series of Cu-Ni/$SiO_2$ catalysts (10 wt % total metal loading) as a function of the Cu/Ni ratio. The samples were calcined in air for 1 h at 500°C prior to the TPR experiments. The surface area under each TPR patterns was found to correspond to a hydrogen consumption sufficient to reduce all the copper and the nickel from their oxides (CuO, NiO) to the metallic state. As Fig. 12 shows, increasing the Cu/Ni ratio results in a progressive displacement toward lower temperature of the TPR band at 380°C, ascribed to the reduction of NiO, and in a concurrent increase in the intensity of the peak at 240°C assigned to the reduction of CuO. At 5 wt % Cu in the catalyst, separate contributions of NiO and CuO are no longer discernible. The merging of the contribution of CuO and NiO was interpreted by the authors as an indication to the formation of nickel and copper species in very intimate contact, very much like a mixed oxide. They also observed that the reduction behavior of the copper-rich bimetallic catalyst was dependent on the thermal treatments prior to the TPR run; after calcination and subsequent cooling in pure nitrogen, the catalyst generated two discrete reduction peaks, while a single TPR peak at about 200°C was obtained when the cooling step was performed in open air. This second type of behavior was also observed when small amounts of hydrogen were added in the nitrogen atmosphere. The authors suggest that this behavior could be due to the adsorption of water facilitating the reduction of NiO while creating an induction period in the reduction of CuO.

The fact that the bimetallic catalyst (0.75% Cu-0.25% Ni) after reduction (500°C, 16 h) and subsequent recalcination (400°C, 0.5 h) afforded a single reduction peak at 200°C was proposed as a strong indication that alloying had occurred during the first reduction treatment. Another possible, and simpler, interpretation of the TPR patterns presented in Fig. 11, had been proposed in previous work by

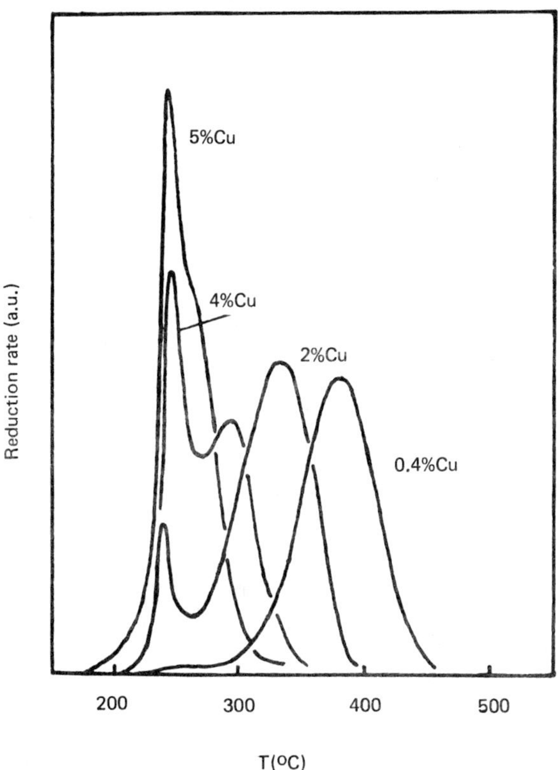


FIG. 12. Influence of the Cu content on the TPR pattern of a Ni-$Cu/SiO_2$ catalyst in its oxidic form (see the text). (From Ref. 14.)

Roman and Delmon [40]. The shape of the TPR peak of the low-Cu catalyst, in accordance with many investigations over the reduction of bulk or supported NiO, corresponds to a nucleation-controlled reaction. On another hand, the shape of the TPR peak corresponding to the reduction of CuO corresponds more closely to an interface-controlled reaction. According to Roman and Delmon [40], metallic copper particles in mere contact with NiO particles could act as nucleation centers and thus increase the reduction rate of NiO. Clearly, the effect would be proportional to the probability for the particles of copper and nickel oxide to be in contact with each other. Another interpretation is based on the possible effect of the presence of copper on the size of the NiO particles. As shown in Sec. III.B.2, the rate of a nucleation-controlled reaction is proportional to the square of the particle size of the solid reactant. Any increase of the size of the NiO particles brought about by some variation in the preparation method, presumably in the present case the addition of copper, would result in a decrease of the temperature of the corresponding TPR peak. Other possible explanations are that water produced by the early reduction of CuO serves as a nucleating agent for the subsequent reduction of NiO, or that metallic copper generates activated hydrogen, which can then more easily reduce the surrounding NiO particles. A review of "spillover hydrogen" phenomena may be found in [41].

A number of interpretations, distinct from the formation of a Cu-Ni alloy are thus possible. An important conclusion of the discussion above is thus that TPR analysis may give very interesting indications about the reactivity of catalyst precursors; unfortunately, TPR results alone cannot give all the requested information to reach a definitive explanation about the actual causes of the observed reactivity differences.

## C. Identification of Phases in Supported Catalyst Precursors, Using TPR

The study of the influence of the sodium content on the reactivity of NiO supported on $\gamma$-alumina is a good example of the use of TPR in conjunction with other characterization techniques for the purpose of phase identification in catalyst precursors [42,43]. A series of Na-modified aluminas were obtained by pore-volume impregnation of a powdered $\gamma$-$Al_2O_3$ (Houdry 0415; surface area, 140 $m^2/g$; pore volume, 0.45 $cm^3/g$; diameter of the grains, 5 to 100 $\mu m$) with a solution containing various concentrations of sodium nitrate. The samples were dried 2 h at 110°C and calcinated for 12 h at 600°C. The original

TABLE 9 Composition and Specific Surface Areas of the Modified Aluminas and of Supported NiO Catalysts (10 wt % NiO)

| Catalyst | Composition of the carrier (wt % $Na_2O$) | S (BET) carrier ($m^2/g$) | S (BET) NiO/Na-$Al_2O_3$ ($m^2/g$) |
|---|---|---|---|
| Na 0.5 | 0.7 | 142 | 124 |
| Na 1 | 1.1 | 150 | 122 |
| Na 2 | 1.6 | — | — |
| Na 3 | 2.5 | 127 | 143 |
| Na 5 | 4.7 | 99 | 111 |
| Na 7 | 7.1 | 72 | 73 |

*Source*: Ref. 44.

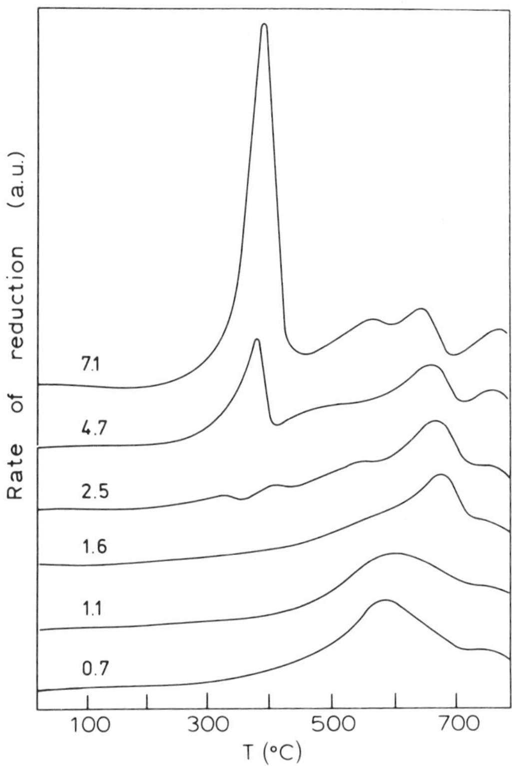


FIG. 13. Influence of the sodium content on the TPR pattern of a Ni/Na-$Al_2O_3$ catalyst in its oxidic form (see the text).

alumina contained 0.7 wt % $Na_2O$. A series of supported nickel oxides were obtained from the modified aluminas by pore volume impregnation with a solution of nickel nitrate. The impregnated samples were dried for 2 h at 110°C and calcinated for 6 h at 500°C. The nickel content was 10 wt % for each sample. Table 9 summarizes the compositions and surface areas of the samples, before and after the introduction of NiO.

The TPR experiments were performed using a constant weight of sample (50 mg). The reactor was flowed with a mixture of 5 vol% $H_2$ in Ar (35 $cm^3$/min) and its temperature was raised at a constant rate (10°C/min). Prior to the TPR run, each sample was heat-treated in situ in a pure oxygen flow (25 $cm^3$/min, 1 h at 400°C) to remove adsorbed water and to stabilize the oxidation state of the catalyst. The same catalysts have also been characterized by analytical electron microscopy (AEM) and X-ray photoelectron spectros-

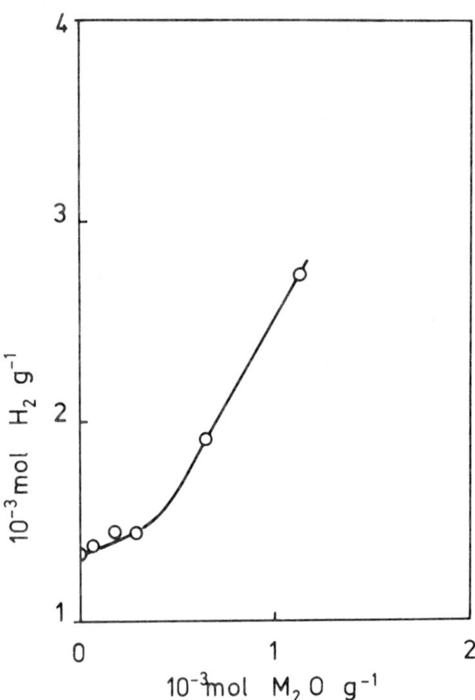


FIG. 14. Overall hydrogen consumption versus Na content of Ni/Na-$Al_2O_3$ catalysts.

copy (XPS); full experimental details can be found in the original paper [43]. The effect of increasing the Na content on the reducibility of NiO/Na-$Al_2O_3$ is illustrated in Fig. 13. The TPR patterns of samples Na-0.5 and Na-1 consist of two bands, having their respective peak maxima at 580 and 740°C. The second band has been found to correspond to the reduction of nickel aluminate ($NiAl_2O_4$) [45], while the first would correspond to free NiO in a highly dispersed state. Increasing the Na content of the alumina carrier above 2.5 wt % resulted in (1) the growth of a peak at 360°C, (2) a doubling of the band between 500 and 700°C, and (3) an increase in the intensity of the band characteristic of $NiAl_2O_4$. Figure 13 shows that, above about $0.3 \times 10^{-3}$ mol of $Na_2O$ per gram (2.5 wt %), increasing the Na content of the catalyst resulted in extra hydrogen consumption. This implied the formation of some reducible compound including Na and Ni in a higher oxidation state. The slope of the upper, straight part of the curve in Fig. 14 (2 extra moles of $H_2$ per mole of $Na_2O$ added) corresponds to the formation of sodium niccolate ($Na_2NiO_4$)

[46]. The niccolate would have been formed during the heat treatment of the samples under oxygen, according to the reaction

$$Na_2O + NiO + O_2 \rightarrow Na_2NiO_4 \tag{48}$$

Under reducing conditions, it would react with hydrogen as follows:

$$Na_2NiO_4 + 3H_2 \rightarrow Na_2O + Ni + 3H_2O \tag{49}$$

resulting in the consumption of two extra moles of $H_2$ per nickel atom. Equation (48) shows that $Na_2NiO_4$ was formed under strongly oxidizing conditions at the expense of free $Na_2O$, the amount of extra hydrogen consumed being a measure of the amount of free $Na_2O$ present in the catalyst. It has been shown by XPS measurements that in the Na-rich aluminas (>3 wt % NaO), sodium was partially present as a poorly dispersed phase, whereas it was atomically dispersed in Na-poor aluminas [43]. XPS examination of the NiO/Na-$Al_2O_3$ catalysts (Fig. 15) showed an increase in the $I_{Ni}/I_{Al}$ ratio for Na-rich catalysts (Na > 2.6 wt %). Such an increase may reflect two distinct phenomena: (1) an increase in the dispersion of the supported NiO and/or (2) an enrichment of the outer parts of the catalyst particles. The second hypothesis is strongly supported by AEM evidence (Fig. 16): measurements of the variation of the $I_{Ni}/I_{Al}$ intensity ratio across catalyst grains show that

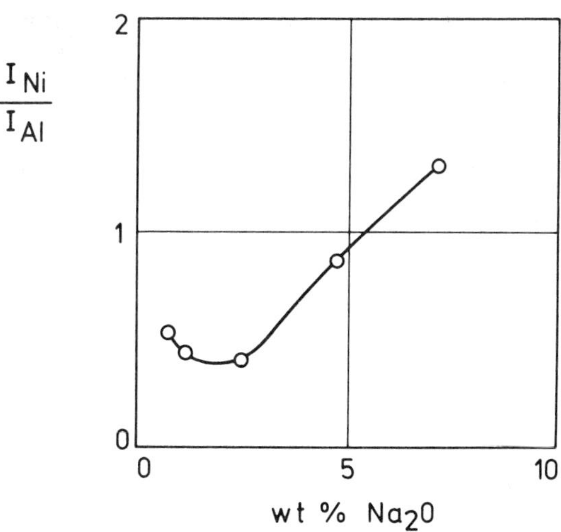


FIG. 15. Variation as a function of the $Na_2O$ content of the XPS intensity ratio $I_{Ni_{2p}}/I_{Al_{2s}}$. (From Ref. 43.)

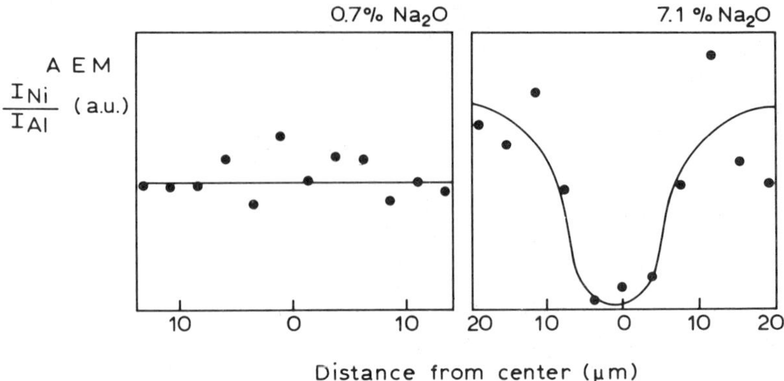


FIG. 16. Variation of the AEM $I_{Ni}/I_{Al}$ intensity ratio across thin sections of individual grains from the Na 0.5 and the Na 7 samples. (From Ref. 43.)

higher Na content promotes the segregation of Ni in the outer regions of the grains. The more extensive formation of $NiAl_2O_4$, also promoted by high Na contents, and clearly shown by the TPR analysis, is also expected to contribute to the increase of the XPS $I_{Ni}/I_{Al}$ ratio.

The doubling of the TPR band in the region 500 to 700°C is not yet fully understood; in connection with the AEM observation, it may be tentatively ascribed to a higher degree of heterogeneity in the sizes of NiO crystallites, as a result of the presence of excess sodium in the carrier.

As a conclusion, TPR results, in agreement with those obtained from XPS and AEM, show that NiO/Na-$Al_2O_3$ catalyst may contain mainly three different Ni species, depending on the amount of Na present: $NiAl_2O_4$, finely divided NiO, and nickel associated with free sodium in the form of $Na_2NiO_4$ after a strong oxidizing treatment. Furthermore, the quantitative use of TPR allows an estimation to be made of the amount of "free" sodium present in the catalyst, and of the repartition of Ni among the different species.

## ACKNOWLEDGMENT

The author gratefully acknowledges the assistance of Dr. B. K. Hodnett in improving the manuscript.

## REFERENCES


1. H. Le Châtelier, *Bull. Soc. Miner.*, *10*: 204 (1887).
2. W. C. Roberts-Austen, *Proc. Inst. Mech. Eng. (Lond.)*, *1*: 35 (1899).
3. W. W. Wendtlandt, *Thermal Methods of Analysis*, Wiley-Interscience, New York, 1964.
4. P. D. Garn, *Thermoanalytical Methods of Investigation*, Academic Press, New York, 1965.
5. A. P. Rollet and R. Bouaziz, *L'Analyse thermique*, Vol. 1: *Les changements de phase*, and Vol. 2: *L'examen des processus chimiques*, Gauthier-Villars, Paris, 1972.
6. R. C. MacKenzie and S. Caillère, in *Soil Components*, Vol. 2: *Inorganic Components* (J. E. Gieseking, ed.), Springer-Verlag, New York, 1975, p. 529.
7. P. Murray and J. White, *Trans. Br. Ceram. Soc.*, *54*: 204 (1955).
8. E. C. Sewell, *Clay Miner. Bull.*, *2*:233 (1955).
9. H. E. Kissinger, *Anal. Chem.*, *29*: 1702 (1957).
10. J. Šesták, V. Şavata, and W. W. Wendlandt, *Thermochim. Acta*, *7*: 333 (1973).
11. R. N. Rogers, S. K. Yasuda, and J. Zinn, *Anal. Chem.*, *32*: 672 (1960).
12. Y. Amenomiya and R. J. Cvetanović, *J. Phys. Chem.*, *67*: 144 (1963).
13. G. Ehrlich, *Adv. Catal.*, *14*:256 (1963).
14. S. D. Robertson, B. D. McNicol, J. M. De Baas, S. C. Kloet, and J. W. Jenkins, *J. Catal.*, *37*: 424 (1975).
15. B. Delmon, *Introduction à la cinétique hétérogène*, Technip, Paris, 1969, pp. 108-149.
16. P. C. Gravelle, *Catal. Rev. Sci. Eng.*, *16*: 37 (1977).
17. J. J. F. Scholten and A. M. Kiel, *J. Mater. Sci.*, *10*: 1182 (1975).
18. G. A. Martin, A. Renouprez, G. Dalmai-Imelik, and B. Imelik, *J. Chim. Physicochim. Biol.*, *67*: 1149 (1970).
19. P. A. Jacobs, M. Tielen, J. P. Linart, and J. B. Uytterhoeven, *J. Chem. Soc.*, *Faraday Trans. 1*, *72*: 2793 (1976).
20. R. J. Cvetanović and Y. Amenomiya, *Adv. Catal.*, *17*: 67 (1967).
21. D. R. Tree and W. Leidenfrost, in *Proceedings of the Eighth Conference on Thermal Conductivity* (C. Y. Ho and R. D. Taylor, eds.), Plenum Press, New York, 1969, pp. 101-124.
22. A. I. M. Keulemans, in *Gas Chromatography* (C. G. Verver, ed.), Reinhold, New York, 1959, pp. 85-91.
23. *Handbook of Chemistry and Physics* (R. C. Wheast, ed.), CRC Press, Cleveland, Ohio, 1976, p. E-2.

24. *Handbook of Chemistry and Physics* (R. C. Wheast, ed.), CRC Press, Cleveland, Ohio, p. F-170.
25. M. Smutek, S. Černý, and F. Busek, *Adv. Catal.*, *24*:353 (1975).
26. J. P. Candy, P. Fouillouy, and A. J. Renouprez, *J. Chem. Soc., Faraday Trans. 1*, *76*: 616 (1980).
27. J. A. Konvalinka, J. J. F. Scholten, and J. C. Rasser, *J. Catal*, *48*: 365 (1977).
28. D. Kalló, in *Contact Catalysis*, Vol. 1 (Z. G. Szabó and D. Kalló, eds.), Elsevier Scientific, New York, 1976, pp. 449-467.
29. E. E. Ibok and D. F. Ollis, *J. Catal.*, *66*: 391 (1980).
30. J. W. E. Coenen, in *Preparation of Catalysts II* (B. Delmon, P. Grange, P. Jacobs, and G. Poncelet, eds.), Elsevier Scientific, New York, 1979, pp. 89-108.
31. S. J. Gentry, N. W. Hurst, and A. Jones, *J. Chem. Soc., Faraday Trans. 1*, *75*: 1688 (1979).
32. M. Houalla, J. Lemaitre, and B. Belmon, *J. Chem. Soc., Faraday Trans. 1*, *78*: 1389 (1982).
33. J. Lemaitre and P. Gerard, *Bull. Miner.*, *104*: 655 (1981).
34. G. Ghesquière, J. Lemaitre, and A. J. Herbillon, *Clay Miner.*, *17*: 217 (1982).
35. J. A. Konvalinka, P. M. Van Oefelt, and J. J. F. Scholten, *Appl. Catal.*, *1*: 141 (1981).
36. I. Bairn and O. Knacke, *Thermochemical Properties of Inorganic Substances*, Springer-Verlag, Berlin, 1973, p. 316.
37. N. Wagstaff and R. Prins, *J. Catal.*, *59*: 434 (1979).
38. N. Wagstaff and R. Prins, *J. Catal.*, *59*: 446 (1979).
39. K. Foger and H. Jaeger, *J. Catal.*, *67*: 252 (1981).
40. A. Roman and B. Delmon, *J. Catal.*, *30*: 333 (1973).
41. P. A. Sermon and G. C. Bond, *Catal. Rev.*, *8*: 211 (1973).
42. J. Lemaitre and M. Houalla, unpublished results, 1980.
43. M. Houalla, F. Delannay, and B. Delmon, *J. Phys. Chem.*, *85*: 1704 (1981).
44. M. Houalla and B. Delmon, *C. R. Acad. Sci. Paris, Ser. C.*, *289*: 77 (1979).
45. M. Houalla, J. Lemaitre, and B. Delmon, *J. Chem. Soc., Faraday Trans. 1*, *78*: 1389 (1981).
46. J. Besson, in *Nouveau traité de chimie minérale*, Vol. XVII(2) (P. Pascal, ed.), Masson, Paris, 1963, pp. 729-759.

# 3

# Transmission Electron Microscopy and Related Microanalytical Techniques

FRANCIS DELANNAY Université Catholique de Louvain, Louvain-la-Neuve, Belgium

## I. INTRODUCTION

Over the last 30 years, one of the major advances in instrumental methods that have become available to materials scientists has undoubtedly been the development of electron microscopy and related microanalytical techniques. Practical catalysts usually consist of a porous material containing a mixture of highly dispersed "active" species or phases. Most applications of electron microscopic techniques in catalytic research have been centered around the assessment of particle shapes and size distributions in supported metal catalysts. However, recent works have illustrated the wealth of structural and chemical information that can be gained about practical catalytic systems by proper use of modern instrumentation.

The interaction of a high-energy electron beam with a solid specimen generates a variety of "signals" all of which yield information on the nature of the solid (Fig. 1). It would be impossible to present in a single chapter all the techniques that have been developed to exploit these "signals." Two classes of instruments may be distinguished according to the type of specimen studied: bulk samples or electron-transparent films.

The scanning electron microscope (SEM) is especially designed for the study of bulk samples. This instrument makes use essentially of the electrons emitted from the surface of a specimen exposed to the impinging electron beam. The low-energy electrons (secondary electrons) provide topographical contrast, allowing study of the relief of the surface, whereas the high-energy (backscattered) electrons give indications about variation in mean atomic weight across the specimen surface. A resolution down to less than 10 nm is now currently available with this technique. The capabilities of the SEM may be easily extended by the addition of attachments which allow the formation of images by collecting various other signals: absorbed electron

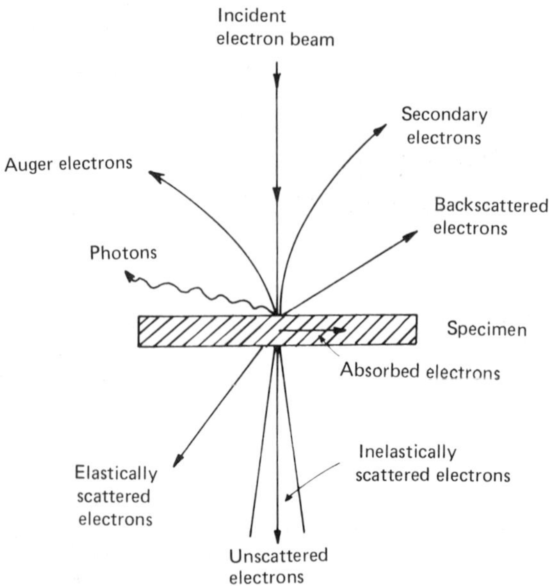


FIG. 1. Possible "signals" generated by the interaction of a high-energy electron beam with a thin solid specimen.

current, emitted optical photons (cathodoluminescence), Auger electrons (although this technique usually requires specially designed high-vacuum instruments) or emitted X-rays. The use of the electron-beam-induced characteristic X-ray emission for the analysis of bulk samples is often designated as electron probe microanalysis (EPMA). This technique was pioneered in the early 1950s [1] and is currently often combined with the SEM. Understanding of the physical phenomena governing X-ray emission is by now so well established that EPMA has become one of the most precise tools we have for the measurement of the atomic composition of solids.

SEM and EPMA today appear as well-documented techniques routinely used in material science research. Several reviews describing their basic principles and application for catalyst characterization may be found in the literature (e.g. Refs. 2 to 4).

The present chapter will be restricted to the second class of instruments, which deal with specimens prepared in electron transparent form. The transmission electron microscope (TEM) makes use of the information carried by transmitted electrons (either unscattered or elastically or inelastically scattered) in order to form high-resolution images of the specimen. Various technical improvements have progressively transformed the TEM into the "analytical electron microscope" (AEM), an instrument allowing comprehensive analysis of the structure and chemical composition of the specimen with a resolution on the order of 10 nm [5]. These developments undoubtedly deserve an updated discussion stressing the new prospects that are offered for the characterization of practical catalysts.

The present state of the art of TEM imaging of catalysts is reviewed in Sec. II. Section III discusses separately the three major microanalytical methods of the AEM: electron microdiffraction, thin-film X-ray microanalysis, and electron energy loss spectroscopy. Typical applications of AEM to practical catalysts are presented.

## II. TRANSMISSION ELECTRON MICROSCOPY

### A. Principles

#### 1. Scattering of Electrons by Solids

When interacting with the atoms of a solid, impinging electrons may suffer two types of scattering processes: elastic scattering, which does not involve transfer of energy to the atom, and inelastic scattering, which does involve such a transfer. Both elastically and inelastically scattered electrons carry useful information about the nature of the solid. Although transmission electron microscopy will make use of both of them, the major imaging techniques are based on the elastic processes, which deserves, consequently, a somewhat more detailed presentation (e.g., Refs. 6 and 7).

In quantum mechanics, the propagation of the incident electron along the z axis of the microscope may be represented by the plane wave exp $(2\pi i|\underline{k}|z)$. $|\underline{k}| = 1/\lambda$ is the length of the wave vector $\underline{k}$, which may be derived from the relation

$$|\underline{k}|^2 = \frac{E}{1.5031}\,(1 + 0.98 \times 10^{-6} E)\ \mathrm{nm}^{-2} \tag{1}$$

where E is the kinetic energy of the electron in electronvolts.

The problem of the elastic scattering of an electron by an isolated atom is that of solving the Schrödinger equation for the interaction potential between the electron and the atom. The solution of this equation is much simplified within the framework of the *kinematical approximation,* which assumes that the scattering is weak; that is, the amplitude of the scattered wave is much less than the amplitude of the incident wave. Although this approximation is most often invalid for electrons which are usually strongly scattered by the solid specimen being investigated, the kinematical theory allows a fairly simple approach to the understanding of the scattering phenomenon.

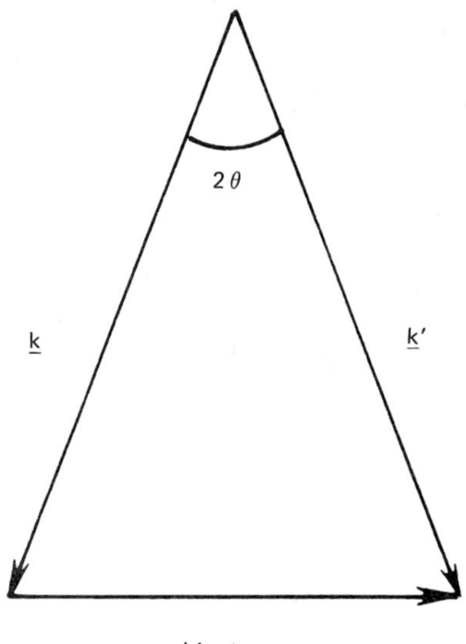


FIG. 2. Diagram illustrating scattering from an incident beam of wave vector $\underline{k}$ to a scattered beam of wave vector $\underline{k}'$. The scattering angle is defined as 2θ.

It is found that, at a large distance r from an isolated atom a, the amplitude $A_a$ of the scattered wave may be expressed as

$$A_a = f_a(\theta) \frac{\exp(2\pi i|\underline{k}|r)}{r} \tag{2}$$

As shown in Fig. 2, 2θ is the angle between the wave vectors $\underline{k}$ and $\underline{k}'$ of the incident and scattered waves, respectively, ($|\underline{k}| = |\underline{k}'|$ as the scattering is elastic). Tables of values of $f_a(\theta)$ (the atomic scattering amplitude) calculated for all the elements may be found in the literature [6].

In the case of a solid, the waves scattered from one atom interfere with the waves scattered from the other atoms. If the locations of the atoms were completely random, *incoherent* scattering would occur and the intensity scattered by the solid would be simply the sum of the intensities scattered by the individual atoms. Atomic positions are, however, never completely random (even in an amorphous sample). The *coherent* interference of the waves will then redistribute the scattered amplitude along privileged directions.

The geometry of the diffraction (coherent scattering) by crystalline solids is essentially the same whatever the nature of the incident

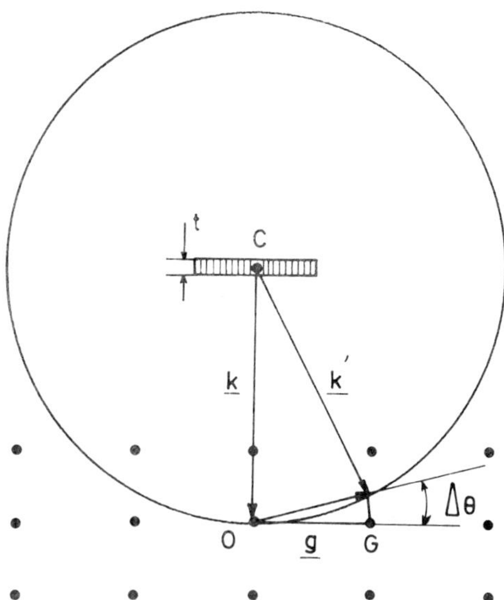


FIG. 3. The Ewald sphere construction for determining the direction of a diffracted wave. The crystal is misoriented by an amount $\Delta\theta$ from the exact Laue condition.

wave (electron, X-ray, neutron, etc.). It was established by von Laue, who derived the well-known "Laue condition":

$$\underline{k}' - \underline{k} = \underline{g} \tag{3}$$

where $\underline{g}$ is a vector of the reciprocal lattice of the crystal. The simplest expression of this condition is the Bragg law:

$$n\lambda = 2d \sin\theta \tag{4}$$

where d is the spacing of the set of lattice planes corresponding to $\underline{g}$. (For 100-keV electron diffraction, $\sin\theta \simeq \theta$ as $\lambda = 0.037$ Å $<< d$).

The Laue condition is readily interpreted geometrically when using the Ewald sphere (or reflection sphere) construction (Fig. 3): O being chosen as the origin of the reciprocal lattice, a sphere of radius $|\underline{k}|$ and center C is located in such a way that $\underline{CO} = \underline{k}$. It follows from the Laue condition (3) that if the end point G of the reciprocal lattice vector $\underline{g}$ is located on the sphere, a diffracted beam may appear along the direction $\underline{CG} = \underline{k}'$. In the case of Fig. 3, the appearance of such a diffracted beam would require a rotation $\Delta\theta$ of the crystal.

The Laue condition is strictly valid only in the case of an infinite crystal for which the interference of the waves is completely destructive in all directions except along the Bragg angle $2\theta$. As crystals studied in transmission electron microscopy are usually very thin, the interference is only partially destructive and some intensity will be diffracted even when $\Delta\theta \neq 0$.

This intensity may be calculated fairly easily assuming that the kinematical approximation remains valid. The amplitude $A_c$ scattered by one unit cell in the direction $\underline{k}' = \underline{k} + \underline{g}$ is obtained from (2) by summation of the amplitude scattered by the constituting atoms as

$$A_c = F(\underline{g}) \frac{\exp(2\pi i|\underline{k}|r)}{r} \qquad (5)$$

with

$$F(\underline{g}) = \sum_a f_a(\theta) \exp(-2\pi i \underline{g}\underline{r}_a) \qquad (6)$$

where $\underline{r}_a$ is the position of atom a in the unit cell ($\underline{g}\underline{r}_a$ is a scalar product). $F(\underline{g})$ is called the structure amplitude (or structure factor).

The amplitude scattered by the whole crystal is obtained by a similar summation over all the unit cells. Let us consider a flat crystal of thickness t perpendicular to the incident beam direction and misoriented by an amount $\Delta\theta$ from the exact Bragg orientation for the reflection $\underline{k}' = \underline{k} + \underline{g}$. It follows from the calculation that the fraction $I_{\underline{g}}/I_{in}$ of the incident intensity $I_{in}$ which is diffracted by the crystal is equal to

$$\frac{I_{\underline{g}}}{I_{in}} = \left[\frac{\pi t}{\xi(\underline{g})}\right]^2 \left(\frac{\sin \pi ts}{\pi ts}\right) \qquad (7)$$

with

$$\xi(\underline{g}) = \frac{\pi V_c \cos\theta}{\lambda F(\underline{g})} \qquad (8)$$

and

$$s = \frac{\Delta\theta}{d} \qquad (9)$$

where $\xi(\underline{g})$ is the extinction distance for vector $\underline{g}$ and $V_c$ is the volume of the unit cell.

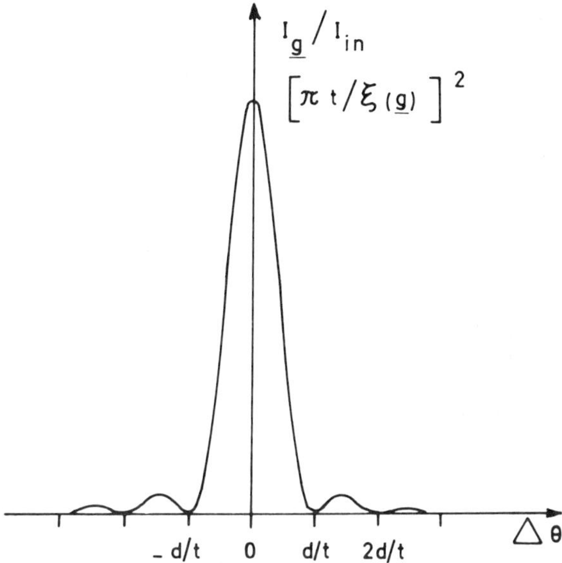


FIG. 4. Variation of the relative diffracted intensity $I_g/I_{in}$ as a function of the misorientation $\Delta\theta$, for a crystal of thickness t, assuming that the kinematical approximation is valid.

The variation of $I_g/I_{in}$ as a function of $\Delta\theta$ is shown in Fig. 4. It is noticeable that the range of misorientations $\Delta\theta$ where $I_g \neq 0$ increases when t decreases and that the maximum intensity $[\pi t/\xi(g)]^2$ which is obtained at the exact Bragg orientation ($\Delta\theta = 0$) increases as $t^2$. It follows that the *kinematical* approximation (which assumes that $I_g/I_{in} << 1$) becomes invalid above a limiting thickness. In fact, extinction distances are typically a few tens of nanometers for 100-keV electrons. Since usual specimen thicknesses are about 100 nm, it is clear that the exact diffracted intensities should be calculated by a *dynamical* theory which considers multiple scattering within the specimen (e.g., Refs. 6 and 7). However, the qualitative results obtained from the kinematical theory provide us with a sufficient basis for the following discussion of contrast effects in electron imaging.

## 2. Fundamentals of Imaging and Contrast

So far, the discussion has concerned only the interaction of the electron wave with the solid. Generally speaking, the result of this interaction is to form, at the exit surface, a transmitted wave which may be interpreted as being the sum of an unscattered (or, more exactly, forward scattered) wave plus a set of scattered waves. Let us

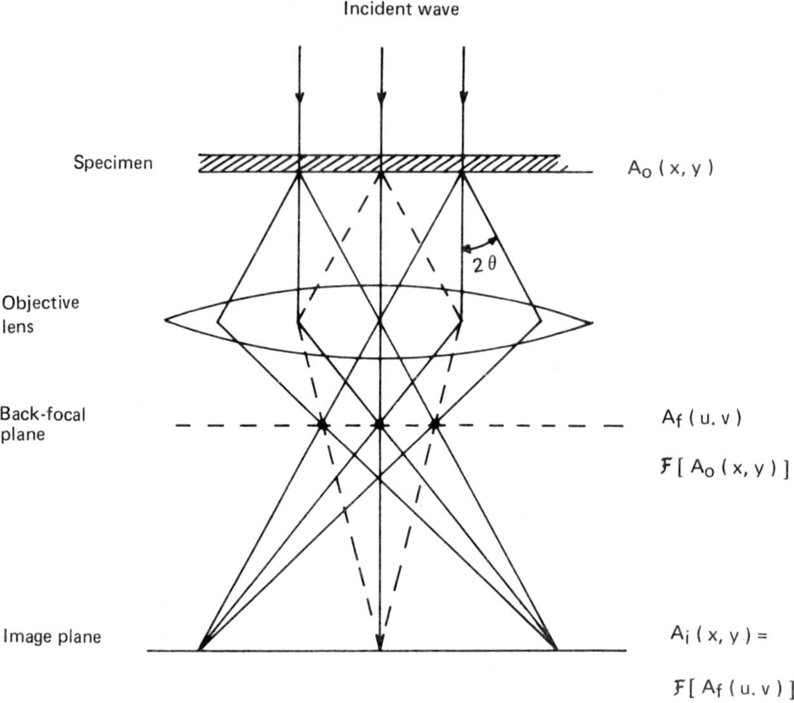


FIG. 5. Schematic diagram of the formation of an image by the objective lens in a transmission electron microscope. The mathematical formulations of the wave amplitudes in various planes along the optic axis are indicated.

now examine the second step of the process, which is the propagation of this transmitted electron wave along the optic axis of a magnetic lens: the objective lens of the microscope.

Figure 5 schematizes the formation of an image by the objective lens. The Abbe theory of imaging (which is applicable to both optical and electron microscopes) teaches that the unscattered wave amplitude will be transmitted to a sharp point on the axis at the back-focal plane of the lens. The amplitude of the wave scattered at an angle $2\theta$ to the optic axis is brought to a focus in the back-focal plane at a distance from the optic axis proportional to $\theta$. There results a distribution of the intensity in the back-focal plane which is called the *Fraunhofer diffraction pattern* of the specimen. If the lens was perfect, the wave amplitude in the plane conjugated to the exit plane of the specimen (the image plane) would be a faithful (magnified) reproduction of the transmitted wave.

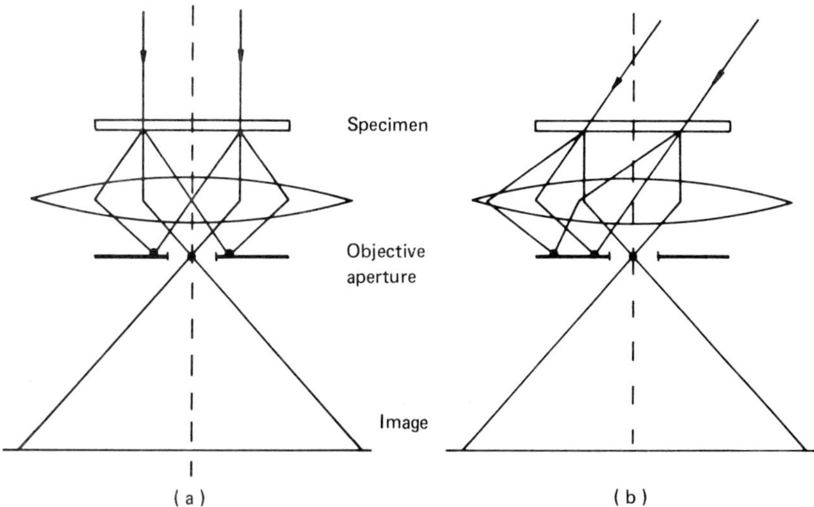


FIG. 6. (a) Bright-field and (b) dark-field imaging modes.

As the back focal plane cannot be infinite in practical instruments, one must consider the effect of inserting a physical aperture (the objective aperture) in this plane. This aperture is one of the major features of the electron microscope as it allows for the creation of contrast (the *amplitude contrast*) in the image by removing some of the scattered waves. As shown in Fig. 6a, *bright-field images* are formed when admitting only the unscattered wave. In this case, the darker parts of the image correspond to the more strongly scattering parts of the specimen. Inversely, these parts will appear brighter in *dark-field images* when the objective aperture is centered around the spot corresponding to the direction of the wave that they scatter (or diffract) more strongly. As indicated in Fig. 6b, such dark-field images are usually obtained by tilting the direction of the incident beam in order to keep the objective aperture centered around the optic axis so as to minimize instrumental aberration effects.

The Abbe theory of imaging may be conveniently translated into mathematical form (e.g., Ref. 8). As indicated in Fig. 5, the distribution of the wave amplitude $A_f(u,v)$ in the back-focal plane (the diffraction pattern) is related to the amplitude $A_o(x,y)$ of the transmitted wave at the exit surface of the specimen (object plane) by a Fourier transform

$$A_f(u,v) = \mathcal{F}[A_o(x,y)] \tag{10}$$

where x,y and u,v are coordinates perpendicular to the optic axis in the object and back-focal plane, respectively.

The waves will then propagate from the back-focal plane to the image plane, where they interfere to give the amplitude distribution $A_i(x,y)$. This interference may be represented by a second Fourier transform

$$A_i(x,y) = \mathcal{F}[A_f(u,v)] = \mathcal{F}\{\mathcal{F}[A_o(x,y)]\} \tag{11}$$

Stated differently, this formulation expresses that the distribution of the amplitude in the back-focal plane (the diffraction pattern) reproduces the distribution of the *spatial frequencies* in the transmitted wave. For a crystal at the exact Bragg orientation, the appearance of a sharp spot at g in the diffraction pattern (Fig. 5) reflects the periodic oscillation of the transmitted wave amplitude with a frequency 1/d. The oscillation reproduces the regular spacing of the set of diffracting planes. If both the unscattered wave and the diffracted wave are allowed to pass through the objective aperture, their interference in the image plane will bring about a periodic variation of the intensity in the form of fringes which may be interpreted as a (magnified) image of the lattice planes. This is the *phase contrast* effect, which governs the appearance of the image in the "high-resolution electron microscope" (HREM).

The effect of insertion of an objective aperture in the back-focal plane is to remove some of the spatial frequencies. As a result, the amplitude distribution in the image is no longer an exact reproduction of the transmitted wave. If the specimen is limited to a point, its image will not be a perfect point but a small disk (the Airy disk), of diameter $D_A$ with

$$D_A = 0.61\,\frac{\lambda}{\alpha_o} \tag{12}$$

where $\alpha_o$ is the maximum scattering angle that is admitted through the objective aperture. $D_A$ is the well-known resolution limit of any wave optical instrument in the absence of lens aberration.

Unfortunately, electron lenses are far from perfect. The main defect (aberration) is spherical aberration $C_s$. Its geometric effect is that the scattered waves are focused in slightly different image planes for different values of the scattering angle $2\theta$ (Fig. 7). It may be shown [9] that this phenomenon is identical to the introduction of a phase delay

$$\chi_s = -\frac{\pi}{2\lambda}C_s(2\theta)^4 \tag{13}$$

to the waves scattered by an angle $2\theta$.

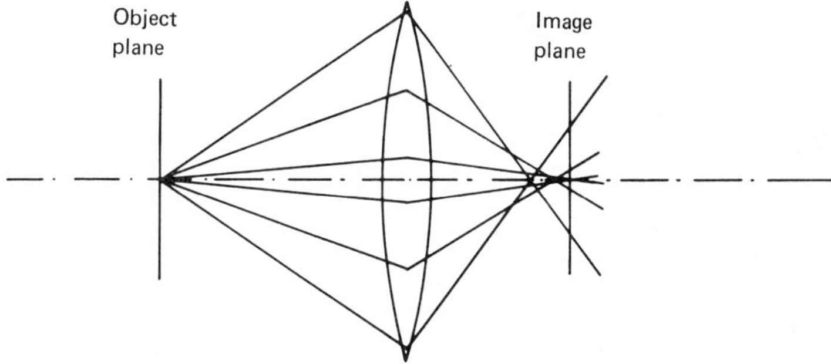


FIG. 7. Geometric effect of the spherical aberration on the focusing of a lens.

Another alteration of the phases of the waves must be considered. Indeed, if the focus of the objective is varied so that the image plane is shifted along the z axis by an amount $\Delta F$ (the defect of focus) from its former position, the distribution of the wave amplitude in this former image plane may be obtained by introducing a phase delay [9]

$$\chi_F = \frac{\pi}{\lambda}\,\Delta F(2\theta)^2 \tag{14}$$

As $2\theta = \lambda/d$ [Bragg law (Eq. 4)], the total phase delay becomes

$$\chi = \frac{\pi\lambda}{d^2}\left(\Delta F - \frac{C_s\lambda^2}{2d^2}\right) \tag{15}$$

If the unscattered and scattered waves are out of phase, their interference in the image plane will not give a faithful image of the wave transmitted by the specimen. If this transmitted wave contains only one spatial frequency 1/d, it is possible, by (15), to adjust $\Delta F$ to compensate for the phase delay introduced by $C_s$. The spacing of the fringes which are then obtained in the image plane corresponds to the spacing of the lattice planes. The problem of imaging together several different spatial frequencies is more complex. It may be demonstrated that these frequencies may be all faithfully reproduced on the image if $\sin\chi \simeq +1$ for all of them ($\sin\chi$ is called the contrast transfer function) [10].

Some examples of the variation of $\sin\chi$ as a function of the spatial frequency 1/d are shown on Fig. 8. One observes that there exists an optimum value of $\Delta F$ for which $\sin\chi \simeq 1$ within a fairly broad

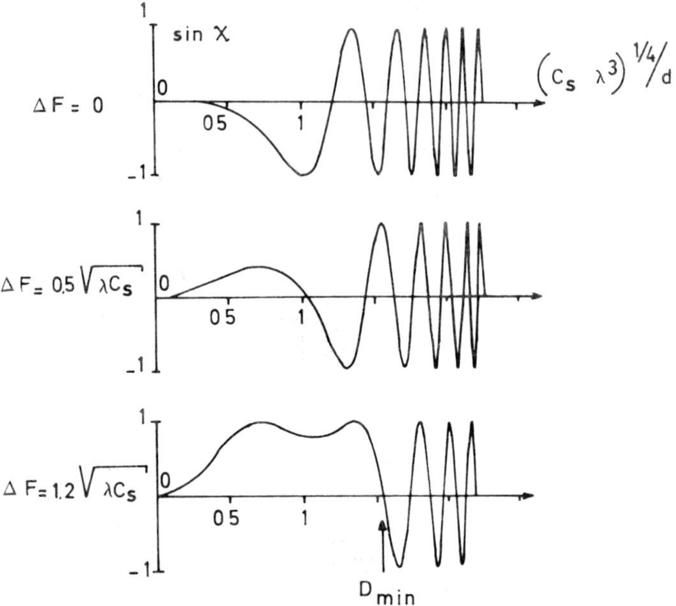


FIG. 8. Variation of the phase contrast transfer function sin $\chi$ at various values of underfocus as a function of the spatial frequencies 1/d. The position $1/D_{min}$ is indicated by an arrow.

range of 1/d frequencies. [$\Delta F = (\lambda C_s)^{1/2}$ is called the Scherzer focus [11].) It is around this defocus value that the most faithful image down to the smallest structural detail will be obtained. The objective lens may thus be considered as a "filter" which retains, for imaging, only the range of spatial frequencies within which sin $\chi \simeq +1$.

The resolution limit $D_{min}$ of the microscope is usually defined as the largest value of d for which sin $\chi = 0$ at the optimum defocus (see Fig. 8). Calculation gives

$$D_{min} = 0.65 C_s^{1/4} \lambda^{3/4} \tag{16}$$

It follows that the improvement of resolving power requires reduction of $C_s$ (i.e., a more perfect lens) and of $\lambda$ (i.e., an higher operating voltage). Values of $D_{min}$ down to about 0.3 nm are now available with the most recent microscopes. It must be noticed that the imaging of only one spatial frequency being less demanding, lattice fringes may usually be obtained down to about $D_{min}/2$.

This discussion indicates that the phase contrast appearing on high-resolution images may, usually, not be interpreted in a straightforward way in terms of structural details of the specimen. In principle, such an interpretation requires comparison of the images obtained at different defocus values with images obtained by computer simulation of (1) the scattering of the electron wave through a model specimen and (2) the transformations suffered by this wave during its transfer to the image plane of the objective lens [8].

### 3. CTEM Versus STEM

In practice, the fundamental principles that have so far been discussed apply to two different types of instruments. The conventional transmission electron microscope (CTEM) today remains the most commonly used. In the CTEM (Fig. 9), the part of the specimen to be studied is uniformly irradiated by a more or less parallel electron beam of typically 100 keV energy. The angular spread of the beam is limited by an aperture (the condenser aperture), whereas deflection coils are provided in order to align the beam and to adjust the incidence angle (e.g., for dark-field imaging). The transmitted beam is focused

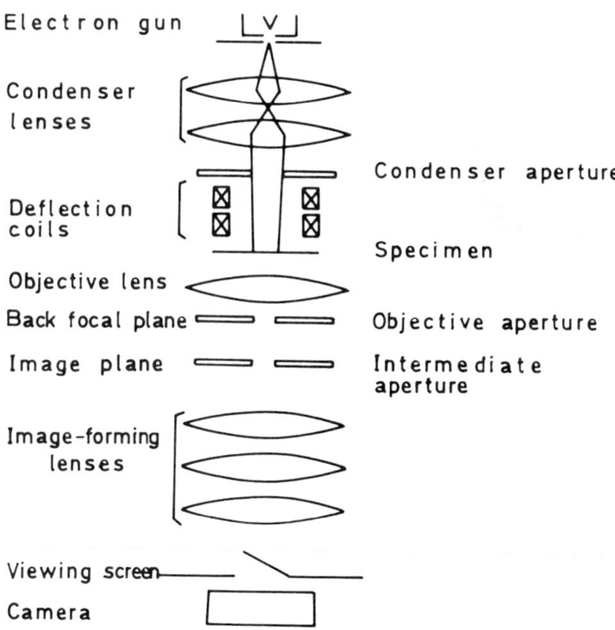


FIG. 9. Schematic diagram of a conventional transmission electron microscope (CTEM).

by the objective lens as shown in Fig. 5. It then propagates through several subsequent lenses (the image-forming lenses) which can be used to form, on a fluorescent screen (or a photographic plate) at the bottom of the column, the image either of the back-focal plane or of the image plane of the objective lens. This allows the observation (and recording) either of the diffraction pattern or of the image of the specimen. An aperture inserted in the image plane of the objective lens (intermediate aperture) allows the diffraction patterns from only a limited area of the specimen to be obtained [selected area diffraction (SAD), see below Fig. 18a]. The minimum area diameter that can be selected for SAD is about 0.5 μm.

In the last few years, there has been increasing interest in a new type of instrument: the scanning transmission electron microscope (STEM). In the STEM, whose operation is shown schematically in Fig. 10, the objective lens is located above the specimen and acts on the *incident* beam to form a very fine probe which is then scanned on the specimen. The transmitted beam is directly collected by various detectors and the resulting signal can then be used to modulate the intensity of a cathode-ray tube (CRT).

Two types of detectors are usually provided. The electrons at low angles from the optical axis are collected through the entrance aperture of an electron spectrometer which can be used to differentiate the electrons with respect to their energy. Bright-field images are obtained when the spectrometer filters the unscattered electrons (i.e., the incident energy). Deflection coils above the spectrometer aperture

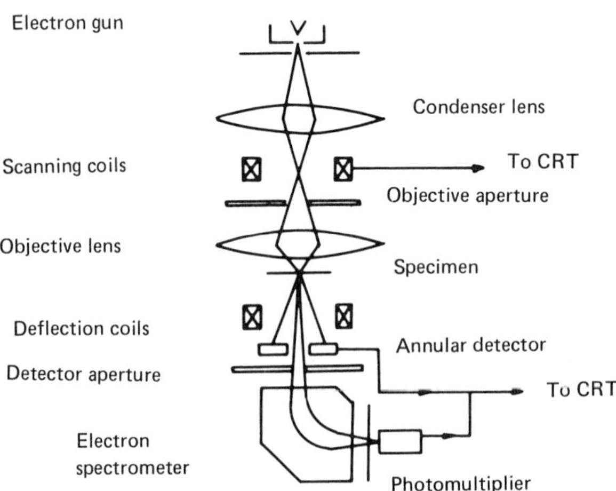


FIG. 10. Schematic diagram of a scanning transmission electron microscope (STEM).

allows dark-field imaging using some part of the *elastically* scattered (or diffracted) waves. These deflection coils moreover allow for successive scanning of all diffracted beams across the collector aperture so as to record the diffraction pattern of the irradiated area. Dark-field images using *inelastically* scattered electrons are obtained when the spectrometer filters the electrons which have suffered some energy loss.

The second type of detector is an annular detector which can collect all the electrons scattered within a certain range of $2\theta$ values. This allows the formation of a new type of dark-field image which is especially useful for observing noncrystalline specimen (e.g., biological materials) or for high-resolution imaging of isolated heavy atoms (see Sec. II.C.2.f).

The fundamentals of imaging and contrast which have been described in the preceding section apply in the case of the STEM by virtue of the reciprocity principle [12,13]. Indeed, as illustrated in Fig. 11, the modes of operation of the CTEM and the STEM may be considered as inverted with respect to each other. The reciprocity principle states that the images will be identical if the objective aperture angle in the CTEM is the same as the illumination angle in the STEM and if the illumination angle in the CTEM is the same as the detector angle in the STEM.

The resolution of STEM images is determined by the diameter $D_p$ of the electron probe incident on the specimen. Aberrations of the objective lens will affect this diameter in the same way as they

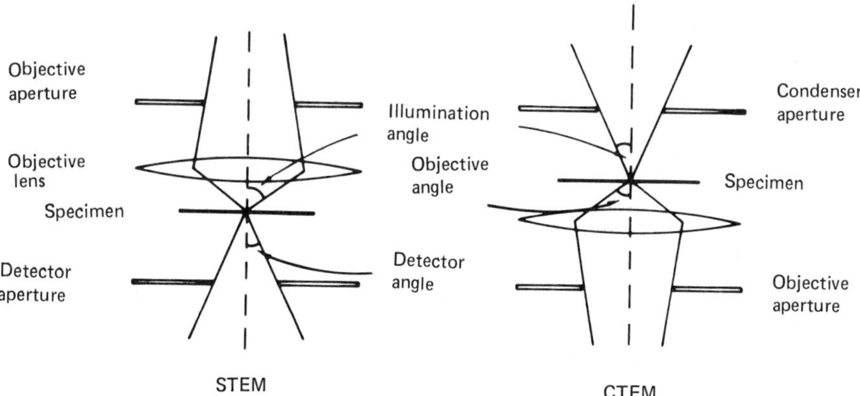


FIG. 11. Illustration of the reciprocity between the CTEM and the STEM. The objective angle and illumination angle of the CTEM correspond, respectively, to the illumination angle and detector angle of the STEM.

affect the resolution limit in CTEM (see above). However, it is further necessary that the signals collected by STEM detectors are strong enough to provide an adequate signal to noise ratio on the CRT. This means that the incident intensity $I_{in}$ in the probe should be high enough. Unfortunately, this intensity decreases with decreasing probe size according to the relation [14]

$$I_{in} \propto BD_p^{8/3} \tag{17}$$

where B is the brightness of the electron source. It follows that the optimum resolution allowed by the objective lens (16) can be reached only by use of a field emission source, the brightness of which is usually a factor of $10^3$ to $10^5$ larger than that of a conventional hot-filament source [15].

Most CTEM instruments today may be equipped with a scanning attachment and electron detectors (annular detector and spectrometer) in order to allow their use as a STEM. (The electron probe is then focused on the specimen by the prefield of the objective lens.) The highest resolution may, however, not be attained in STEM imaging on such instruments as the electron source and objective lens are not optimized for STEM operation. The best performances are provided by the "dedicated" STEM, which is housed in an ultrahigh-vacuum system (as UHV is required for optimum operation of the field emission source).

The potential advantage of the STEM over the CTEM is that the former provides a larger diversity of imaging modes thanks to the (possibly combined) use of the electron spectrometer and annular detector. In addition, the highly focused electron probe allows diffraction patterns to be obtained from much smaller volumes than in SAD (see Sec. III.A). The improved microanalytical capabilities brought about by the field emission gun will be discussed in more detail in Sec. III. Owing, however, to the requirement of ultrahigh vacuum, dedicated STEMs today remain more delicate to handle (and more expensive) than CTEMs that have been modified to allow operation in the STEM mode.

## B. Preparation of Electron Transparent Catalyst Specimens

The readiest way to prepare catalysts in a thin form suitable for transmission electron microscopy is to crush and grind the samples in a mortar. The fine powder thus obtained is dispersed in water or in any inert solvent by use of an ultrasonic vibrator, and a drop of the suspension is deposited on a thin carbon film supported on a standard electron microscope grid. To avoid the effect of the carbon film on the contrast at high magnification, it may be advantageous to make use of holey carbon films allowing observation of portions of the catalyst extending over the holes of the film.

More regular thicknesses can be obtained by use of ultramicrotomy. This method is also required when it is desired to retain some large-scale feature of the specimen (such as a composition gradient) which could be randomized by the grinding process. However, the method is fairly time consuming and costly as the hardness of many catalyst materials can damage the diamond knife that is used in this process.

Study of supported particles deposited on a carrier may be made easier by use of the extraction replication method [16]. The principle of this method is to evaporate a thin carbon film onto the catalyst in such a way that the particles on the surface of the sample are more or less encapsulated into the carbon. These particles will be retained by the film after separation of the film from the sample surface. This method allows improved imaging of the supported particles, as contrast effects from the support are completely avoided. However, care must be taken in ensuring that the extracted particles are truly representative of the particle lying deeper in the pores of the support.

A critical appraisal of various methods for the preparation of catalysts for TEM has been published by Sprys et al. [17].

## C. The Imaging of Supported Particles

The most widespread application of transmission electron microscopy in catalytic research is in measurement of size distributions of supported particles in order to determine from it the dispersion of the (usually metallic) active phase. As discussed already, the *resolving power* of modern instruments allows, in principle, detection of small isolated particles down to less than 0.4 nm size (see Eq. 16). However, the presence of the support will most often raise the detection limit. This latter limit depends on the *contrast* that can be obtained, on the image, between the particles and the support.

As pointed out by Flynn et al. [18], the drawing of a particle size distribution from electron images is based on three implicit assumptions: (1) the size of the particle is equal to the size measured on the micrograph (corrected for magnification); (2) for all measured sizes, the ratio of the number of observed particles to the true number of particles present is the same; and (3) contrast arising from the support cannot be confused with contrast arising from the particles. In addition to *size* measurements, it is often necessary to be able to assess the *shape* of particles as the existence of raftlike structures [19] or of multiple twinning [20] may be of great significance in relation to catalytic properties.

It is obvious that a proper interpretation of the image in terms of particle size and shape requires a proper understanding of the phenomena governing the contrast. The presentation above of the principles of TEM now enables us to discuss contrast effects relevant to the imaging of supported catalysts. The more widely used bright-field imaging will be dealt with first. A second section will describe complementary information that can be gained by use of the various dark-field techniques.

Electron microscopic investigations of supported metal particles have often been carried out on model specimens prepared by the evaporation of the metal on thin films of the support material. The use of such specimens alleviates to some extent some of the imaging problems that must be faced when studying practical catalyst samples. The following discussion is especially devoted to the latter type of material.

1. Contrast Effects in Bright-Field Imaging

*a. Amplitude Contrast.* As pointed out already in Sec. II.A.2, the simplest mechanism producing contrast on bright-field images is *amplitude contrast,* which arises because some part of the scattered electrons are stopped by the objective aperture. Consequently, the more strongly scattering parts of the specimen appear darker on the image.

Amorphous supports. Let us first assume that the support being studied is completely amorphous (as it is most often the case for silica and carbon black carriers). Such a support will give rise to some level of darkness on the image that is primarily due to the mostly incoherent elastic scattering. As a result of this effect, the fraction $\phi_e$ of the incident electron intensity that will be admitted through the objective aperture may be expressed as [21]

$$\phi_e = \exp\left(\frac{-t_s}{\Lambda_e}\right) \tag{18}$$

where $t_s$ is the support thickness and $\Lambda_e$ is a mean free path which can be calculated by integration of the intensity elastically scattered by the atoms outside the objective aperture.

If we consider supported crystalline particles, the main amplitude contrast arises from Bragg reflection (diffraction contrast). For small particles of general interest in catalysis ($\leqslant$10 nm size), it may be sufficient to consider, for the purpose of the present discussion, the results of the kinematical theory. It follows from Eq. (7) that, near the Bragg condition for a reflection $\underline{k}' = \underline{k} + \underline{g}$ stopped by the objective aperture, the fraction $\phi_{\underline{g}}$ of the intensity which remains within the image of the particle is

$$\phi_{\underline{g}} = 1 - \left[\frac{\pi t_p}{\xi(\underline{g})}\right]^2 \left(\frac{\sin \pi t_p s}{\pi t_p s}\right)^2 \tag{19}$$

where, as defined previously, $t_p$ is the thickness of the particle (or its size in the present case), $\xi(\underline{g})$ is the extinction distance (8), and $s = \Delta\theta/d$.

The contrast (i.e., the intensity difference between the images of the particle and of the support) varies as $\phi_e(1 - \phi_g)$. It is thus maximized in the case of thin specimens ($t_s$ minimum; that condition stresses the importance of careful preparation) for particles oriented as nearly as possible to the Bragg condition ($\Delta\theta$ minimum: see Fig. 3). The possibility of detecting a particle (or of determining its size and shape) depends thus both on the nature of the particle and on its orientation with respect to the electron beam.

The influence of the nature of the supported particle is illustrated on Table 1, which compares values of the extinction distances $\xi(\underline{g})$ (in the case of 100-keV electrons) for the most intense reflections of platinum and nickel oxide (NiO) [22]. [They have been calculated by use of the atomic scattering amplitudes proposed in Ref. 6]; the $\xi(\underline{g})$ values for NiO are approximate as they were computed assuming neutral atoms.] As the maximum diffracted intensity varies as $[t/\xi(\underline{g})]^2$ (see Eq. 7 and Fig. 4), Table 1 indicates that, on average, the limiting size for detection is more than twice larger for NiO particles than for Pt particles (supported on the same type of carrier).

The effect of orientation of the specimen is shown in Fig. 12 for Pt particles supported on $\gamma$-alumina. Arrows on the micrographs indicate particles that exhibit a large contrast change as a result of a small tilt (2°) of the specimen. Similar examples have been published elsewhere [23,24].

Figure 12 suggests, however, that some contrast between the particles and the support may remain observable even when the particles are oriented far from any Bragg reflection. This is mainly due to the thermal diffuse scattering of the electrons [6]. This effect is much weaker than the elastic scattering. It will induce removal, by

TABLE 1 Comparison of Extinction Distances

| | Extinction distances $\xi(\underline{g})$ (nm) | |
|---|---|---|
| Scattering vector $\underline{g}$ | Pt | NiO |
| 111 | 14.6 | 57.9 |
| 200 | 16.6 | 29.0 |
| 220 | 23.2 | 40.6 |
| 311 | 27.5 | 113.9 |
| 222 | 28.8 | 51.1 |

*Source*: Ref. 22.

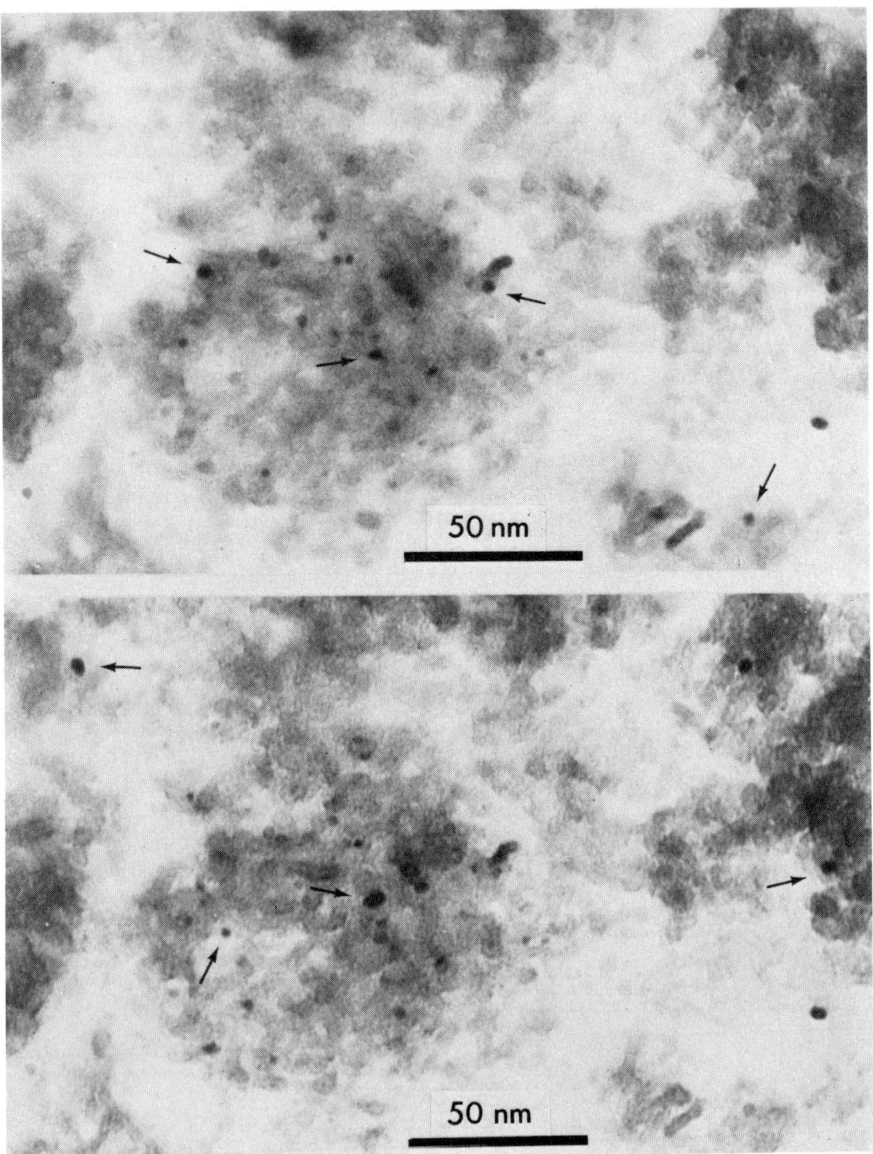


FIG. 12. Bright-field images of a 2% Pt/$\gamma$-$Al_2O_3$ catalyst, showing the influence of small tilts of the specimen on the contrast. The tilt angle between the top and bottom images is 2°. Arrows indicate particles that exhibit a large contrast change as a result of the tilt.

the objective aperture, of a small fraction of the electron intensity. As for incoherent elastic scattering, the fraction $\phi_{td}$ of the intensity within the image of the particle may be expressed as

$$\phi_{td} = \exp\left(\frac{-t_p}{\Lambda_{td}}\right) \qquad (20)$$

where the mean free path $\Lambda_{td}$ can be obtained by integration of the thermal diffuse scattering distribution over all scattering angles excluded by the objective aperture [25]. As $\Lambda_{td}$ decreases rapidly with increasing atomic number, the contrast $\phi_e(1 - \phi_{td})$ may be large enough for detection of small particles of an heavy element over a sufficiently thin support. In fact, most particles composed of heavy metals of size greater than 3 nm are generally visible on bright-field images of thin catalyst specimens [26].

It follows from this discussion that particular care must be exercised when interpreting contrast differences between particles on the same micrograph. Such observation should, indeed, generally not be taken as evidences of differing thicknesses among the particles as, for example, in the case of disk-shaped or raftlike structures [19,23].

Crystalline support. The interpretation of the image contrast is still more complex in the case of carriers such as $\gamma$-$Al_2O_3$ which are not completely amorphous. [The degree of crystallinity of $\gamma$-$Al_2O_3$ varies a great deal as a function of its origin (supplier) and surface area.] Diffraction patterns from $\gamma$-$Al_2O_3$ supports exhibit primarily two rings corresponding to the 400 and 440 reflections. Figure 13 presents a 400 dark-field micrograph of the same catalyst as shown in Fig. 12. The bright spots about 5 to 10 nm in size are images of $\gamma$-$Al_2O_3$ crystallites at about the Bragg orientation for g = 400. Bright-field images of such a support will exhibit diffraction contrast from these crystallites which could consequently be confused with crystallites of the supported phase. The extinction distance $\xi(g_{400})$ of $\gamma$-$Al_2O_3$ equals approximately 67 nm (for 100-keV electrons) [26]. This value should be compared with the data of Table 1. It appears that the probability of confusion is especially large for nonmetal particles as, for example, NiO.

For well-crystallized carriers such as, for example, $TiO_2$, the detection of small supported particles may be completely hindered by the large diffraction contrast arising from the support itself. More specialized imaging techniques such as dark field or Z contrast (see below) can be helpful in such cases. Alternatively, one may attempt to separate the particles from the support via an extraction replication method [16].

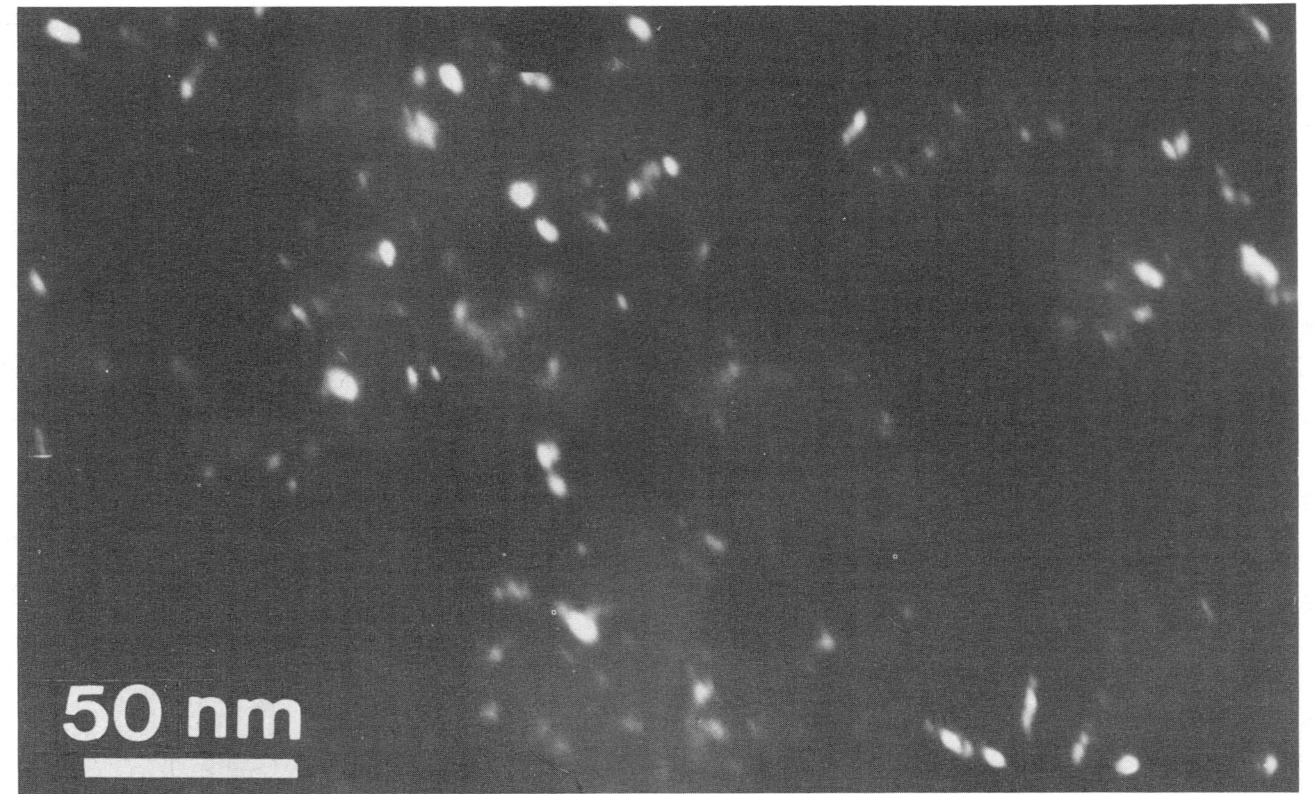


FIG. 13. 400 dark-field micrograph of a 2% Pt/$\gamma$-$Al_2O_3$ catalyst. The bright spots are images of $\gamma$-$Al_2O_3$ crystallites.

*b. Phase Contrast.* For very small particles or when a large objective aperture is used, contrast between the particle and the support may be governed by the phase contrast rather than by the amplitude contrast. As mentioned already, phase contrast arises from the interference between the unscattered and scattered waves when both are admitted through the objective aperture. As it depends on wave amplitude rather than on intensities, it is proportional to the thickness $t_p$ of the particles rather than to $t_p^2$ [24]. This explains that it may dominate for sufficiently small particles. However, it requires a very thin support, as scattering within the support will randomize the phases of the interfering waves.

It has been shown in Sec. II.A.2 that the phases of the waves and, consequently, the appearance of the image changes as a function of the defocus through the "contrast transfer function." Detailed calculations have been performed by Flynn et al. [18] to assess the influence of phase contrast on the imaging of small particles on supported catalysts. These authors concluded essentially that, for metal particles below about 2 nm in diameter, the apparent size is a sensitive function of defocus. It follows that identical particles may have different apparent sizes if they are positioned on the support at different elevations z along the axis of the microscope (as defocus varies with elevation).

This discussion indicates that the three implicit assumptions which form the basis of estimations of dispersion from particle size distribution measurements on *bright-field images* become invalid below some limiting size. For $Pt/\gamma\text{-}Al_2O_3$ catalysts, Flynn et al. [18] concluded that size distributions become increasingly subject to error as the fraction of particles with sizes below 2.5 nm increases. As a rule of thumb, the corresponding limiting size for other types of supported particles might be estimated by comparing, as in Table 1, the extinction distances with respect to platinum. These conclusions about the accuracy of size distributions do, however, not rule out the possibility of faithfully imaging supported particles down to less than 1 nm size when sufficient care is exercised by preparing thin samples and interpreting the contrast (e.g., Refs. 27 and 28).

### 2. Dark-Field Imaging Techniques

*a. General Method.* Dark-field images of supported particles may be obtained by tilting the incident electron beam so that the objective aperture excludes the unscattered electrons but accepts some of the electrons diffracted by a favorably oriented set of planes of the particle. Such images often exhibit very strong black and white contrast, allowing fairly easy measurement of particle sizes [29]. This imaging mode appears especially helpful in the case of partially crystalline supports such as $\gamma\text{-}Al_2O_3$. Indeed, problems arising from the diffraction contrast produced by the support are avoided if the tilt angle is chosen in such a way as to exclude the major reflections of the support. Dark-field imaging will also lead to an enhancement of the particle contrast in the case of insufficiently thin specimens.

*b. Hollow-Cone Illumination.* However, the number of particles observed on such dark-field images is only a small percentage of the total number of particles present within the observed area. Indeed, most particles are not in the Bragg orientation or, alternatively, diffract in another direction than the direction selected by the objective aperture. To circumvent this limitation, Freeman et al. [26] have proposed the use of an annular condenser aperture to produce "hollow-cone" illumination. As sketched in Fig. 14, a proper setting of the elevation of the specimen along the axis of the microscope allows adjustment of the tilt angle defined by the cone in such a way as to pick up major reflections of the supported crystallites. For Pd particles supported on $\gamma$-$Al_2O_3$, this technique typically allows observation, on a single dark-field micrograph, of about 70% of the particles present in the field of view [26].

Unfortunately, this method does not seem to have been used routinely up to the present time. The reason is probably that it requires a somewhat specialized instrument (annular aperture and variable elevation of the specimen). An alternative method has been described by Krakow and Howland [30], who proposed a method where-

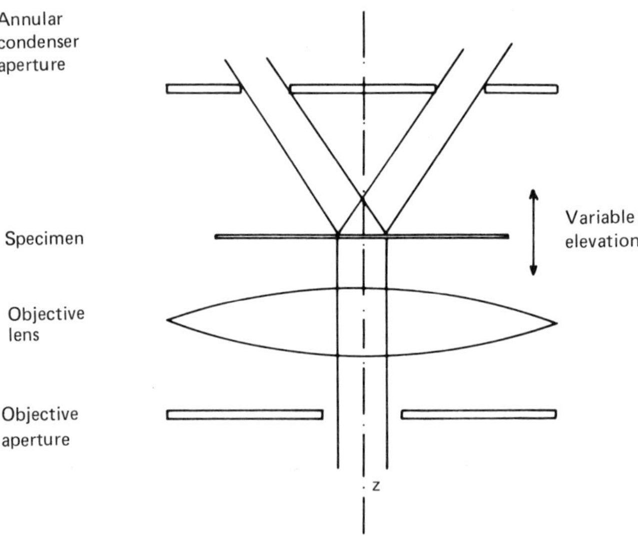


FIG. 14. Schematic diagram of the formation of a dark-field image using an annular condenser aperture (hollow-cone illumination).

by the hollow-cone illumination was generated by means of electronic control of the deflection coils.

*c. Detection Yield.* Figure 15 is a conventional tilted beam dark-field image of a thin amorphous $SiO_2$ support. The bright specks that appear on the image are formed by that part of the incoherently scattered electrons which are collected by the objective aperture. The origin of this speckled structure observed on amorphous materials has been the subject of many discussions over the last 10 years. Calculations have shown that these dots may arise from statistical effects and do not necessarily imply the presence of small crystalline

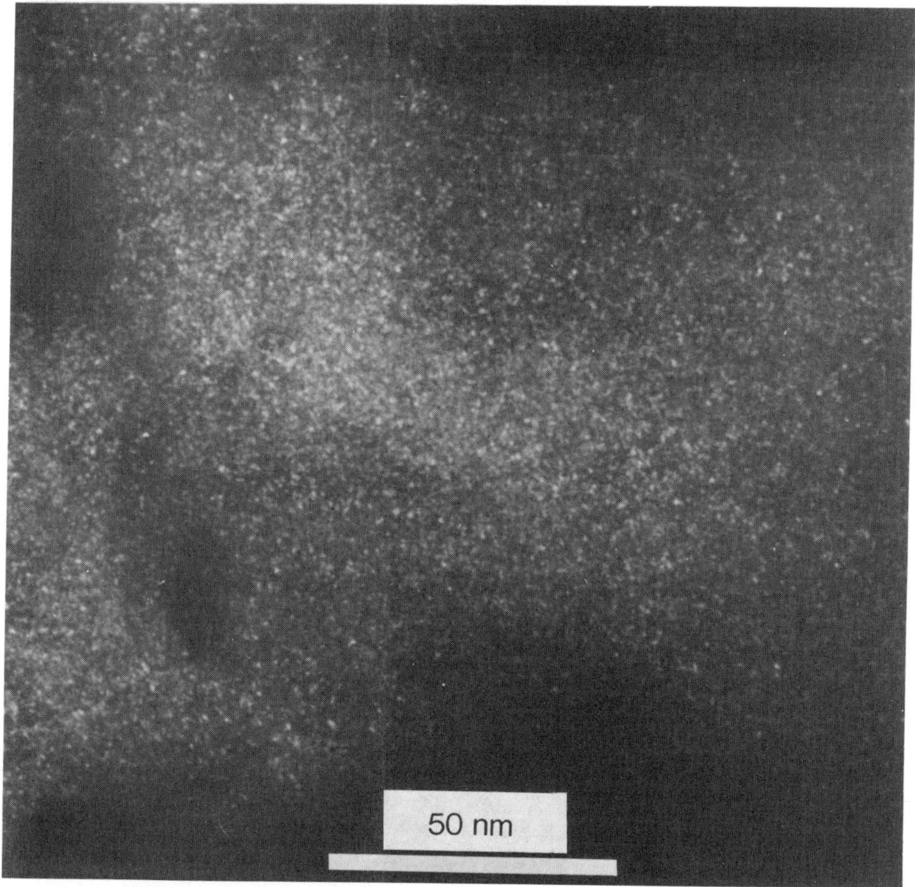


FIG. 15. Dark-field image of a thin amorphous $SiO_2$ support.

domains within the imaged area [31]. As a result of this effect, dark-field methods do not allow for observation of particles smaller than about 1.5 to 2.0 nm, as such particles could be confused with the unavoidable speckled image of the support.

*d. Selective Imaging in Mixtures of Phases.* Dark-field imaging may be especially useful for the study of samples containing a mixture of two (or more) different crystalline phases. Indeed, as suggested already, it is sometimes possible to adjust the tilt angle so as to admit within the objective aperture reflections from only one of these two phases. This method is illustrated in Fig. 16, which presents a dark-field micrograph of a CoMo/$\gamma$-$Al_2O_3$ hydrodesulfurization catalyst [32]. Both $MoS_2$ and $Co_9S_8$ crystallites were detected on this sample after catalytic work. As shown in Fig. 16, $MoS_2$ crystallites could be imaged alone when using, for dark-field imaging, the reflections corresponding to the $d_{002}$ = 6.15 Å lattice spacings of $MoS_2$. In a similar way, Mehta et al. [33] studied the epitaxial orientation of Cu crystallites on a Cu/ZnO catalyst.

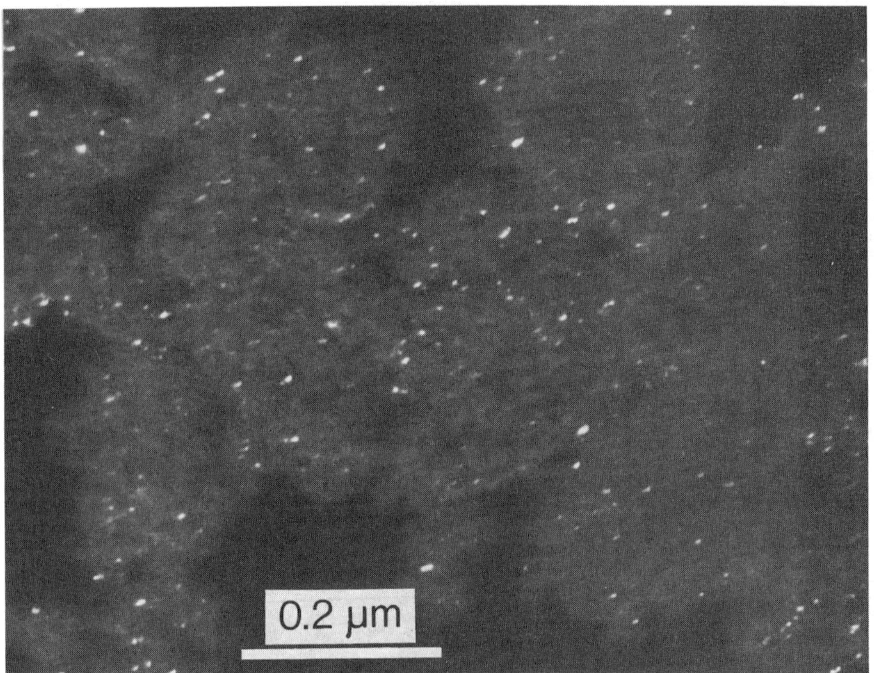


FIG. 16. Dark-field micrograph of a used CoMo/$\gamma$-$Al_2O_3$ hydrodesulfurization catalyst (precursor composition: 12.08% $MoO_3$, 2.52% $Co_3O_4$). The tilt angle corresponds to the $\underline{g}$ = 002 reflection of $MoS_2$.

However, the capabilities of this method are usually poor, owing to the finite size of the objective aperture. Indeed, the difference between the lattice spacings of the two phases is usually too small to allow picking up by the objective aperture of reflections corresponding to only one of these phases. A method has been proposed recently by Yacaman et al. [34] in order to distinguish the crystalline nature of different particles imaged in bright contrast on the same dark-field micrograph. This method is based on the fact that when defocus is varied by an amount $\Delta F$, the images of the particles are shifted along a distance

$$\Delta x = \frac{\lambda \, \Delta F}{d} \tag{21}$$

where $\lambda$ is the wavelength of the electrons and d is the spacing of the planes corresponding to the reflection $\underline{g}$ admitted by the objective aperture [35].

If the various crystallites imaged have sufficiently different d values, these differences may be detected by measuring the respective $\Delta x$ distances on doubly exposed micrographs. A careful calibration of the defocus value $\Delta F$ should, in turn, allow calculation of d from Eq. (21). This method has been applied by Yacaman et al. [34] to assess the nature of metal clusters on a Pt-Ir/$\gamma$-$Al_2O_3$ reforming catalyst.

*e. Observation of Inner Particle Structure.* It often occurs that supported particles are not single crystals but are made of several differently oriented crystallites joined by grain boundaries or twin planes. Dark-field imaging is probably the most straightforward way to study such inner structures, as each subcrystal may be imaged separately. (It follows from this effect that size distributions determined from X-ray line broadening are likely to be more comparable with distributions measured on dark-field than on bright-field images.)

In the case of supported metals, a particularly important inner structure is the occurrence of multiple twins, which induce formation of some well-defined polyhedral shapes (pentagonal bipyramid, icosahedron, etc.) instead of the cubic shape expected for a FCC structure [36]. The presence of such multiply twinned particles may have some bearing on the catalytic properties as they affect the nature of the exposed crystal faces and edges. The presence of such structures on Pd/$SiO_2$ catalyst has been shown by Avery and Sanders [20] using a conventional tilted beam dark-field technique. Similar observations were made recently by Marks and Howie [37] on Ag/$\alpha$-$Al_2O_3$ samples.

For the sake of completeness, let us mention that more sophisticated methods have been described for the study of these inner structures and particle shapes. Heinemann and Poppa [38] introduced the selected zone dark-field method (which involves the use of an annular objective aperture), whereas Yacaman and Ocana [39] proposed the use of the weak-beam dark-field technique. Up to the present time, these models appear to have been applied successfully only on model samples but not on practical catalysts.

*f. Z-Contrast Imaging.* Early work in this area by Lenz [40] has shown that the elastic scattering of electrons involves much larger scattering angles than inelastic scattering. Moreover, Lenz calculated that the ratio of the total elastic scattering cross section to the total inelastic scattering cross section is proportional to the atomic number Z. With proper setting of the experimental conditions, advantage may be taken of this phenomena to create a new contrast effect, the Z contrast.

In bright-field imaging, one may optimize the size of the objective aperture in order to maximize the removal of the electrons elastically scattered by the heavy atoms while minimizing the removal of the electrons (largely inelastically) scattered by the support material. In this way, Prestridge and Yates [27] succeeded in imaging isolated rhodium atoms supported on silica.

The Z-contrast effect is more efficiently exploited in dark-field imaging using an annular objective aperture in CTEM or an annular detector in STEM (which are equivalent in virtue of the reciprocity principle; see Fig. 11). Both of these techniques have allowed for imaging of single heavy atoms deposited on light substrates as bright spots over a dark background [41,42]. The use of the STEM allows still more powerful imaging. Indeed, a large part of the inelastically scattered electrons may be collected by setting the electron spectrometer at a low energy loss with respect to the unscattered wave. The Z contrast will be optimized on STEM images generated by taking the ratio of the elastic intensity collected by the annular detector to this inelastic intensity collected by the spectrometer [43].

The potentialities of this ratio method for the study of particles on supported catalysts have been assessed by Treacy et al. [21,44]. It appears that this method gives slightly better contrast than hollow-cone dark-field imaging with much shorter exposure times. However, this technique has only limited success with crystalline particles, as it execssively heightens contrast variations due to diffraction. Pennycook [45] has shown recently that this difficulty may be circumvented by use of a high-angle annular detector. There is no doubt that such methods will develop in the future as the use of STEM becomes more widespread.

## D. High-Resolution Electron Microscopy of Catalysts

The term high-resolution electron microscopy (HREM) commonly designates works based on the use of phase contrast effects. The resolution limit of presently available electron microscopes now stands at less than 0.4 nm. HREM appears thus as a method (the only method?) which permits examination of the catalyst nearly down to the scale of the "active site."

The use of phase contrast for imaging supported particles has already been discussed at length in the preceding section. As an example of the type of HREM work which could be anticipated in the future, it is worth mentioning the recent observation by Tesche et al. [46] of symmetrical shapes of less than 2-nm-sized rhodium clusters.

On crystalline specimens, HREM is usually synonymous of "lattice imaging." Recently, some workers have attempted to correlate the activity of catalysts with observations of specific lattice images (e.g., Ref. 47). Hydrodesulfurization (HDS) catalysts are especially suited for the type of study. Indeed, HDS catalysts are made of intricate mixtures of oxide and sulfide phases which usually cannot be characterized separately unless looked at on a near-atomic scale. $MoS_2$ or $WS_2$ are major components of active catalysts. These compounds have layered structures whose basal spacings (d = 0.615 nm for $MoS_2$) can be fairly readily imaged [32,48,49].

Figure 17 is a high-resolution micrograph of an activated CoMo/ $\gamma$-$Al_2O_3$ HDS catalyst. Lattice fringes corresponding to the stackings of the basal planes of $MoS_2$ can be clearly seen. (This micrograph should be related to the 002 dark-field picture shown in Fig. 16, where the $MoS_2$ crystallites appear as bright spots.)

The main debate about HDS catalysts concerns the role of the group VIII metal atoms (usually Co or Ni) in promoting the activity of molybdenum and tungsten sulfides. From Mössbauer studies, Topsoe and co-workers [50] have recently inferred that cobalt forms with molybdenum a mixed phase (Co-Mo-S phase) which is much more active than pure $MoS_2$. It might be expected that the formation of such a mixed phase would involve changes in the lattice spacings which could be detected by measurements on the micrographs. Indeed, it is known that local variations of composition in alloys may be detected as variations of the lattice spacings [51].

In fact, fairly large variations of spacings were observed on micrographs such as Fig. 17 (e.g., compare the two crystallites pointed to by the arrow). However, it must be remembered that the objective lens acts as a filter which removes some part of the structural information carried by the scattered electrons. When, as in the present case, crystals are limited to a few unit cells, the structural information extends over a relatively wide range of spatial frequencies. Faithful image will only be obtained, in such a case, at a certain value of the defocus which should be determined from computer simulations [52]. As the present specimens are fairly thick, the different defocus values resulting from the different positions of the individual crystallites within the specimen will affect the fringe spacings by an amount sufficient to smear out the effect expected

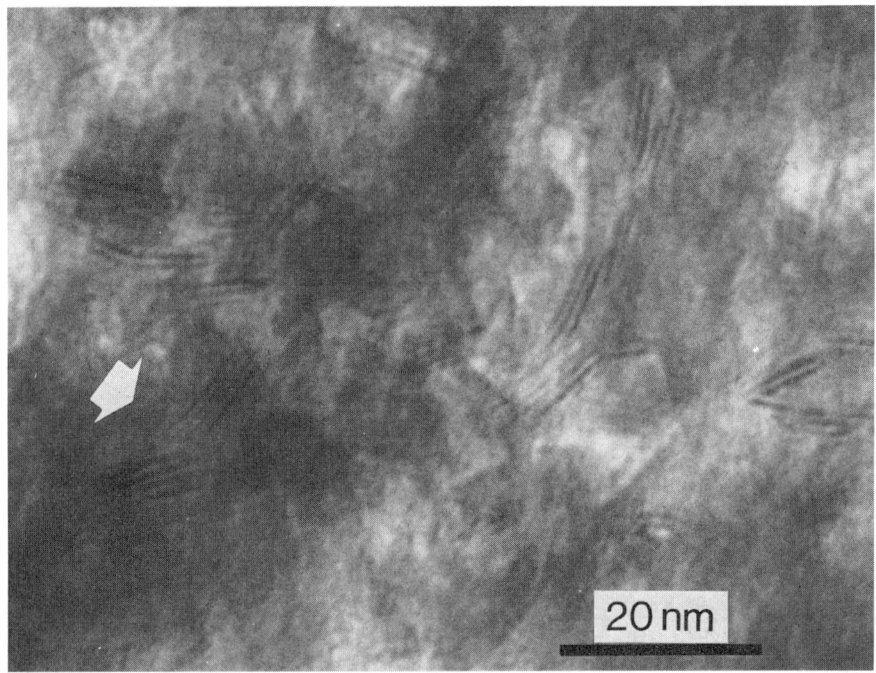


FIG. 17. High-magnification micrograph of the same CoMo/$\gamma$-$Al_2O_3$ catalysts as in Fig. 16, showing fringes corresponding to the basal spacings of the individual $MoS_2$ crystallites.

from the presence of cobalt in the crystallite. Moreover, as observed in the case of graphite [53], it may be expected that relaxation effects could appreciably modify the spacings on such small crystallites.

The example above was chosen as an illustration of the care that must be exercised when interpreting high-resolution images. The "prettiest" lattice image does not necessarily carry useful information. Major new insights into the structure of catalysts may, however, be expected from studies combining HREM and computer simulation and/or processing of the image.

## III. MICROANALYSIS IN THE TRANSMISSION ELECTRON MICROSCOPE

Today, the transmission electron microscope can no longer be considered only as an instrument providing *images*. Thanks to various technical improvements, it has now been promoted to the "analytical electron microscope" (AEM), that is, an instrument allowing comprehensive structural and chemical *analysis* of samples at a submicron scale. Historically, the first tool for "analyzing" a sample within the microscope was electron diffraction. Thin-film X-ray microanalysis (i.e., the combination of TEM and X-ray emission spectrometry) developed afterward, during the 1960s. More recently, electron energy loss spectrometry (EELS) has appeared as a suitable microanalytical tool providing new perspectives for the characterization of thin specimens.

This section will be devoted to a separate presentation of the principles of these three techniques. In conjunction with the problems of *resolution limit* and *image interpretation* which were discussed in the preceding sections, the important features to be considered about the microanalytical techniques will be, respectively, *spatial resolution* (which is often directly related to sensitivity and precision) and *quantitative interpretation* of the measurements. Typical examples illustrating the applications of AEM to the study of practical catalysts will be discussed in Sec. III.E.

## A. Electron Microdiffraction

### 1. Principle

The fundamentals of the scattering and diffraction of electrons by solids have been introduced in Sec. II.A.1. At the exact Bragg orientation, the fraction of the incident intensity that is diffracted by a crystal of thickness t was expressed in the framework of the kinematical theory as $I_{\underline{g}}/I_{in} = [\pi t/\xi(\underline{g})]^2$, where $\xi(\underline{g})$ is the extinction distance for reflection $\underline{g}$ (see Eqs. 7 to 9). It follows that about 10% of the incident intensity will be diffracted by a crystal of thickness $0.1\xi(\underline{g})$. As extinction distances are typically a few tens of nanometers for 100-keV electrons, electron diffraction should potentially provide crystallographic data down to the scale of a few nanometers if the diffracted electron intensity can be suitably recorded.

### 2. Electron Microdiffraction Methods: Spatial Resolution

It was mentioned in Sec. II.A.3 that electron diffraction patterns from selected parts of the specimen are most commonly obtained in the CTEM by the selected area diffraction technique (SAD) [54]. The principle of SAD is recalled in Fig. 18a. The portion of the specimen that contributes to the diffraction pattern is defined by an aperture (intermediate aperture) inserted in the image plane of the objective lens. Owing to the spherical aberration of this lens, it can be shown that the minimum area which may be selected in this way is approximately 0.5 μm in diameter.

The need to record diffraction patterns from smaller areas has motivated the development of various new diffraction methods [55,56]. A detailed description of all of them (which often require especially adapted CTEM or STEM instruments) would be outside the scope of this chapter. Techniques that allow electron diffraction work to be performed down to a resolution of a few nanometers are now available, but their use remains fairly limited at the present time.

The most straightforward and most routinely used improvement of the SAD technique is the "microdiffraction" method. As sketched in Fig. 18b, the diffraction area is limited by illuminating only a small spot of the specimen with a finely focused electron beam. The spatial resolution is then no longer limited by the spherical aberration of the objective lens and may be lowered down to about 20 nm in diameter when using a STEM equipped with a conventional hot-filament electron source.

As suggested in Fig. 19a, conventional electron diffraction patterns made of sharp spots are obtained by illuminating the specimen with a nearly parallel electron beam. In practice, the angular aperture (or convergence) $2\alpha_i$ of the incident beam (see Fig. 19) should be of the order of $10^{-4}$ rad for a fairly accurate determination of lattice spacings on a thin crystal. However, it may be shown that, for a given probe size $D_p$, the intensity decreases as $B\alpha_i^2$, where B is the brightness of the electron gun. Obtaining sufficiently sharp high-spatial resolution microdiffraction patterns within recording times compatible with the unavoidable drift of the specimen stage thus most

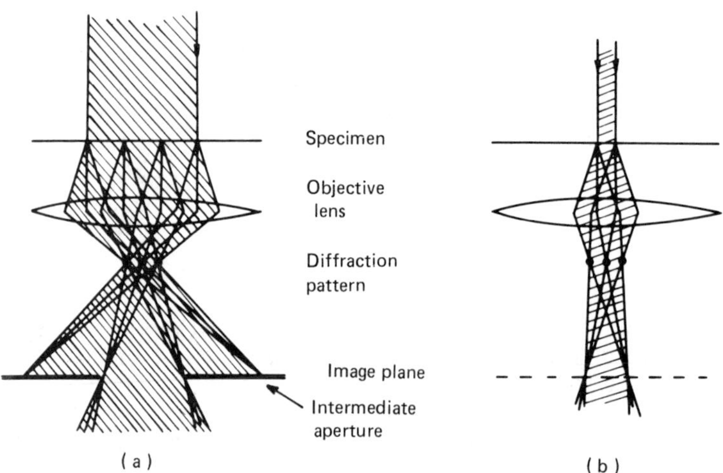


FIG. 18. Schematic diagram of (a) the selected area diffraction method (SAD) and (b) the microdiffraction method.

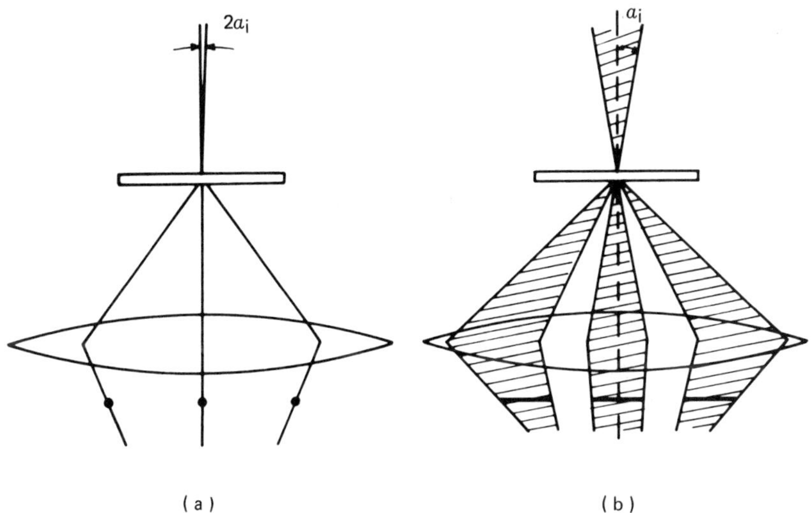


FIG. 19. Comparison of (a) conventional electron diffraction and (b) convergent beam electron diffraction.

often involves the use of a high-brightness gun, such as a field emission gun.

3. Interpretation of Electron Diffraction Patterns

From the Bragg law (4), the lattice spacings d may be easily determined by measurement, on the recorded spot pattern, of the distance R between the unscattered beam and the diffracted beam. This requires only calibration of the instrument on a specimen of known crystal structure. It is worth stressing that, owing to instrumental factors, the precision of such lattice spacing measurements on sharp spot patterns is usually only a few percent. The precision would be still worse when the angular aperture $\alpha_i$ has been increased to allow sufficient beam current for high-resolution microdiffraction. It is clear that electron diffraction cannot compete with X-ray diffraction in this respect.

As shown in Fig. 19b, if the angular aperture $\alpha_i$ increases, the direct and diffracted spots become extended into circles. This is the convergent beam pattern [57]. Each point inside the circles corresponds to one direction within the incident electron cone. The intensity distribution inside the circles may then be calculated and interpreted by the dynamical theory of electron diffraction. However, such an interpretation remains too complicated to be practiced routinely when studying catalyst samples. Nevertheless, it is worth noticing that properly interpreted convergent beam patterns provide much more information than conventional spot patterns: accurate crystal thickness and orientation, Fourier coefficients of lattice potential. This information undoubtedly offers new prospects for the study of crystal physical chemistry.

## B. Thin-Film X-ray Microanalysis

### 1. Principle

During their passage through a thin specimen, high-energy electrons may suffer various inelastic scattering phenomena. As sketched in Fig. 20, it may happen that enough energy is transferred to an inner-shell electron of an atom of the solid so as to displace this inner-shell electron from its atomic energy level. The transition of an outer-shell electron to the vacant site may then induce the emission of a X-ray photon with an energy equal to the energy difference between the excited and final atomic states. The energy (or wavelength) of the photon is thus "characteristic" of the emitting atom. Measurement of this energy on a X-ray spectrum such as shown in Fig. 20 allows identification of the nature of the atoms present in the sample.

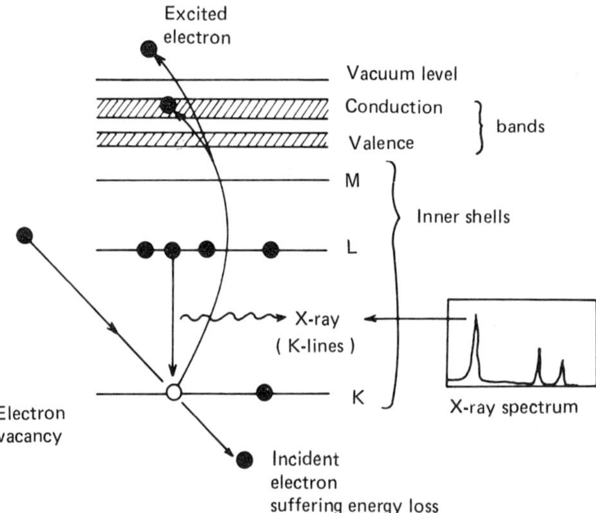


FIG. 20. Schematic representation of the formation of an electron vacancy in an inner shell with subsequent deexcitation and X-ray emission.

The combination of transmission electron microscopy and X-ray spectrometry was pioneered by Duncumb [58] and developed by the AEI Company under the commercial name of EMMA (electron microscope microprobe analyzer). These early instruments used crystal spectrometers based on Bragg diffraction on selected crystal planes (WDS: wavelength dispersive spectrometer). This spectrometer being fairly cumbersome suffers from poor overall collection efficiency. It has now been nearly completely superseded by the solid-state detector based on the conversion of the X-ray energy into electron-hole pairs in a perfectly intrinsic silicon crystal (EDS: energy dispersive spectrometer). The EDS has a lower resolution ($\simeq$150 eV) than the WDS, but it provides a much higher efficiency, as it can be readily positioned close to the specimen into the objective lens pole piece of the TEM. The specimen is usually separated from the silicon crystal by a thin beryllium window, allowing the latter to be maintained at liquid-nitrogen temperature within a protected vacuum chamber. Owing to the adsorption of the low-energy X-rays by this window, the domain of EDS analysis is restricted to elements of atomic number $Z \geqslant 11$.

Today, thin-film X-ray microanalysis is probably the most used microanalytical tool of the analytical electron microscope. Only major features will be outlined here. More details may be found in the recent literature (e.g., Ref. 5).

2. Spatial Resolution

On a thick specimen, the X-rays are emitted from a volume delimited by the scattering of the incident electrons within the solid. This phenomenon limits the spatial resolution of conventional EPMA to about 1 μm at best. On a thin specimen only minimal spreading of the focused electron beam occurs. Figure 21 displays the volume analyzed in a thin specimen relative to that in a thick target. The ultimate spatial resolution depends on the spreading b of the beam at the exit face of the specimen film.

Several ways of calculating beam spreading have been proposed. The most precise one involves simulation of the scattering phenomenon by Monte Carlo calculations [59]. These calculations have been shown to agree fairly well with experiment (for a review, see Ref. 60). However, Monte Carlo calculations are very computer time consuming. A more simple, although valuable, estimate of beam spreading was proposed by Goldstein et al. [61]. These authors considered only the Rutherford expression for Coulomb scattering and assumed a single scattering at a level equidistant from both faces of the specimen film. Assuming a parallel beam of infinitely small size, they derived the following expression for beam spreading at the exit face:

$$b = 625\left(\frac{\rho}{A}\right)^2 \frac{Z}{E}\, t^{2/3} \quad \text{centimeters} \tag{22}$$

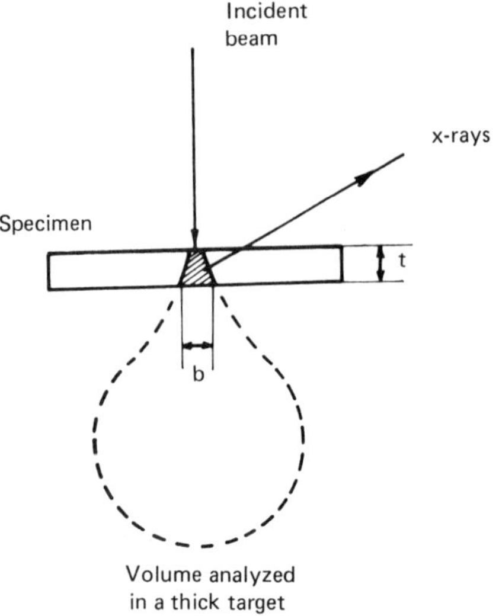


FIG. 21. Qualitative display of the volume analyzed in a thin specimen, relative to that analyzed in a thick target.

where $\rho$ is the specimen density in g/cm$^3$, A is the atomic weight, Z is the atomic number, E is the beam energy in keV, and t is the film thickness in centimeters. For sufficiently thin films, the results of this single scattering model are in good agreement with Monte Carlo calculations [60,62,63].

Figure 22 shows, for a beam energy of 100 keV, the variation of the beam spreading to be expected on alumina or silica catalyst supports as a function of the thickness of the analyzed area [22]. The apparent density has been assumed equal to 0.85 g/cm$^3$ for $\gamma$-$Al_2O_3$ and 0.45 g/cm$^3$ for $SiO_2$. It is shown that beam spreading of 20 nm is the upper limit if one restricts the analysis to areas thinner than 0.2 $\mu$m. Larger spreadings would, of course, be obtained for more dense and more heavy specimens such as metals. It is noteworthy that in all but the thinnest foils, spatial resolution is controlled by beam spreading rather than by incident probe size.

When studying practical catalysts, it would be desirable to be able to analyze the composition of a single particle, a few nanometers in size, observed on a support by TEM imaging. As detailed in Sec. II.A.3, the use of the STEM (either dedicated or as an attachment to a CTEM) allows a highly focused electron probe to be directed onto such a particle. The problem is then to detect enough characteristic X-ray radiation from the few atoms contained within the particle above the background radiation originating from the whole irradiated volume

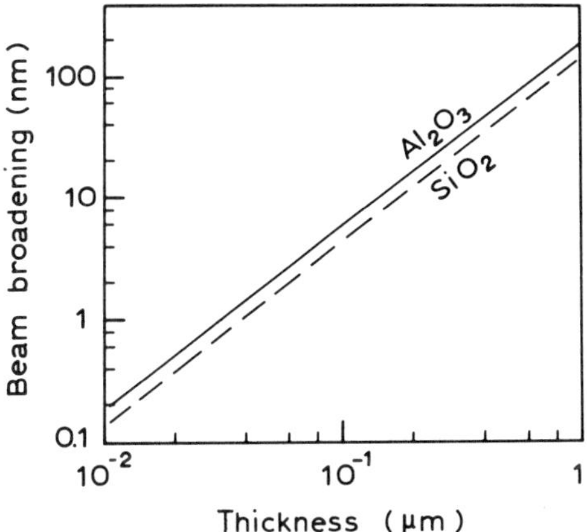


FIG. 22. Beam broadening b as a function of specimen thickness for $Al_2O_3$ and $SiO_2$ (calculated from relation 22). (From Ref. 22.)

(particle, carrier, and eventual supporting carbon film). This volume depends on the spreading suffered by the electron probe. The main source of background counts is the bremsstrahlung radiation, arising from the deflection of fast electrons by the electrostatic field of the nuclei [64].

Theoretical formulas are available to calculate the signal to background ratio to be expected from such experimental conditions [65, 66]. In this case, it is clear that the problem of spatial resolution becomes a problem of sensitivity. It has been shown by Joy and Maher [66] that the minimum mass (free standing or supported on a weakly scattering matrix) which can be detected varies as $(JT)^{-1}$, where J is the incident current density and T is the counting time. In practice, the counting time is often limited by contamination and specimen drift to a few hundred seconds. The only way to increase sensitivity is thus to increase current density (e.g., by use of an electron source of greater brightness). It appears that a spatial resolution of about 10 nm is a practical limit for conventional thermoionic electron emitters (as far as specimen thickness allows), whereas recent work has shown that the use of a dedicated STEM equipped with a field emission gun allows analysis of supported catalyst particles down to about 1 nm [67].

The spatial resolution of X-ray microanalysis in the transmission electron microscope is, unfortunately, also affected by instrumental limitations. Indeed, the specimen may be irradiated by spurious radiations (electrons and/or X-rays) which excite characteristic X-rays from areas of the sample which are not directly exposed to the electron probe. The two main sources of these spurious radiations are the X-rays generated at the condenser aperture system and the electrons backscattered from the sample itself [68,69]. The first of these sources today may be nearly completely suppressed on most microscopes by insertion of thick apertures preventing exposition of the sample to the spurious X-rays. The elimination of the second source is virtually impossible. The most noticeable result is the detection of X-rays which are characteristic of the surroundings of the electron-bombarded area. The worst case occurs when analyzing an element that is also present in the surroundings. Such a problem is often encountered on catalyst samples, where it may be desirable to detect traces of a finely dispersed element in the vicinity of larger aggregates containing the same element. Whereas the sensitivity of the technique is usually about 0.1% for detecting traces of one element within a matrix of another [65], this sensitivity will deteriorate by more than one order of magnitude in the presence of such problems. It is important to be aware of these limitations and to verify in each case which part, if any, of the detected X-ray counts could originate from areas of the specimen that are not directly bombarded by the electron beam.

### 3. Quantitative Interpretation of Characteristic X-ray Intensities

In conventional EPMA of thick samples, the measured characteristic X-ray intensity can be converted into composition data by comparison with the X-ray intensity recorded on suitable standards of known composition. The phenomena governing X-ray emission from thick samples have by now been sufficiently well understood to allow the design of a reliable correction procedure (the ZAF method). This procedure currently enables an accuracy better than a few percent in EPMA composition analysis.

In a thin specimen, the intensity of the characteristic X-rays is a function of thickness as well as of composition. Comparison with intensity obtained from thin standards is usually impracticable, owing to the difficulty of determining with precision the local thickness of the various parts of a thin specimen. However, the characteristic X-ray intensity ratio for any two elements will not be dependent on thickness if the specimen is sufficiently transparent to the characteristic X-rays produced by the electron beam so that the effects on X-ray intensity of absorption and fluorescence are negligible. If this so-called thin-film condition is satisfied, one may write [70]

$$\frac{C_A}{C_B} = k_{AB} \frac{N_A}{N_B} \tag{23}$$

where $C_A$ and $C_B$ are the concentrations of the elements A and B, $N_A$ and $N_B$ are the characteristic X-ray counts (intensity), and $k_{AB}$ is a factor that varies with incident electron energy but is independent of specimen thickness and composition.

In early works using this ratio method, the $k_{AB}$ factors were determined experimentally on multielement thin standards of known composition (e.g., Refs. 70 and 71). More recently, it has been shown that these factors could be fairly accurately calculated from theoretical models [61,62,65,69]. Zaluzec [69] has published tables allowing such standardless determination of $k_{AB}$ for all element pairs in various experimental conditions.

Figure 23 displays the Z variation of $k_{ZSi}$ (for atomic and weight composition ratio), as it can be derived from the calculations of Goldstein et al. [61] for the K X-ray lines at 100-keV beam energy. A maximum sensitivity (atomic) is observed for elements 24 (Cr) $\leqslant$ Z $\leqslant$ 28 (Ni).

In practice, the validity of the thin-film criterion must be checked in all experimental situations in order to warrant an accurate composition analysis. For specimens that are not too thick, Goldstein et al. [61] have proposed an expression for the correction to be carried out

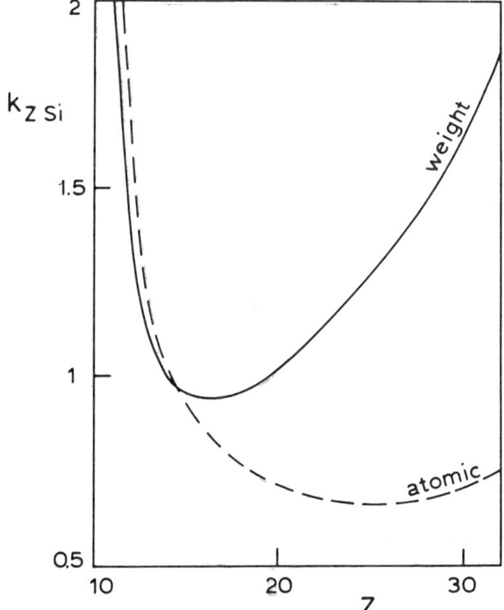


FIG. 23. Z variation of the relative sensitivity with respect to silicon. (From Ref. 22.)

on relation (23) when accounting for X-ray absorption in the sample. It may be shown [22] that this correction may be neglected in many cases when studying thin supported catalysts. The correction for fluorescence is still much smaller than that for absorption [72].

## C. Electron Energy Loss Spectrometry (EELS)

As discussed in Sec. II.A.3, the STEM is usually equipped with an electron spectrometer allowing analysis of the kinetic energy of transmitted electrons. The inelastic scattering phenomena suffered by the electrons when passing through the thin specimen may be studied when recording, as shown schematically in Fig. 24, the electron intensity I as a function of the energy loss $\Delta E$ with respect to the incident energy. Such an energy loss spectrum may be divided into three regions.

Region I around $\Delta E = 0$ corresponds to the "zero-loss" peak, which contains both unscattered and elastically scattered electrons. This peak is very intense and exhibits a width of a few electron volts, which is a convolution of the resolution of the spectrometer and of the energy spread of the electron gun.

Region II, which extends from the edge of the zero-loss peak out to about $\Delta E = 50$ eV, is usually called the "low-loss" region. The structure of the spectrum in this region is due to inelastic scattering phenomena involving transfer of energy to valence or conduction band electrons. The best known of these phenomena is the "plasmon" ex-

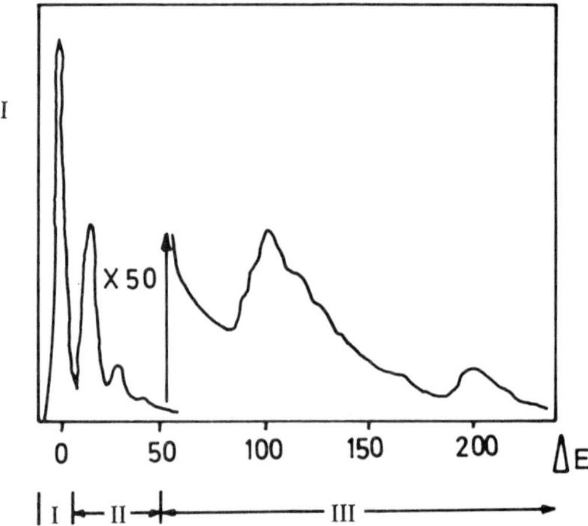


FIG. 24. Schematic representation of an electron energy loss spectrum, showing the three regions of interest.

citation, which can be used to study spatial fluctuations of electron density across a metal specimen [73].

Region III is that above $\Delta E = 50$ eV. As suggested in Fig. 24, the signal intensity has fallen by a factor of about 50 with respect to the zero-loss peak. The spectrum in this region has the form of a smoothly decreasing background on which quite abrupt "edges" are superimposed. These edges arise at an energy loss corresponding to the transfer of an inner-shell electron up to the vacuum level (as sketched in Fig. 20). They are thus identical to the edges displayed on X-ray absorption spectra. (The high-energy side of the edge may exhibit a structure similar to the structure studied in EXAFS.) The $\Delta E$ values of the various edges recorded in the spectrum are equal to the ionization energy of the corresponding shells of the appropriate atoms and may be used to identify the chemical components of the sample.

Although the information contained in region II may provide valuable insight into the electronic structure of the sample, it is the data contained in region III which today are most routinely used for microanalytical purposes. Indeed, EELS spectra display very efficiently K-shell edges for elements with atomic number 3 (Li) $\leqslant Z \leqslant$ 9 (F) which cannot be detected by energy dispersive X-ray spectrometry. Heavier elements may be identified by their L, M, and so on, edges but problems may arise from superposition with the strong K edges from light elements. EELS appears thus as very complementary to X-ray microanalysis.

There is no doubt that EELS offers promising prospects for the study of practical catalysts. Unfortunately, examples of applications of this technique to catalytic materials presently remain very scarce. In the present context, it thus appears premature to discuss the performances of this technique in too much detail. The reader may consult recent reviews [74,75]. Let us just summarize briefly some features of the technique.

The implicit assumption in the previous discussion was that the specimen must be thin enough so that each electron is scattered only once. Multiple scattering will cause additional losses, which may tend to smear out the edge beyond a limiting specimen thickness. In practice, the ideal thickness for EELS microanalysis should be about 30 to 50 nm [74]. In such cases it is possible to obtain quantitative compositional data from measurement of the magnitude of the characteristic edges. Various procedures have been proposed in this respect [75]. The spatial resolution of EELS should be less affected by beam spreading than in the case of X-ray microanalysis. Indeed, the spectrometer does not collect the electrons scattered at large angles (see Fig. 10). The sensitivity of the method for detecting light atoms (C, N, O, etc.) appears to be high enough to allow resolution in the nanometer range on sufficiently thin films.

## D. Radiation Damage and Contamination

It has been already stressed several times that high-resolution microanalysis often requires the use of high current densities and fairly long recording times. Such measurements suppose that the analyzed area can resist such an irradiation dose without significant damage. The first type of damage that may occur is the accumulation of contamination caused by a poor vacuum environment. Such contamination essentially causes a loss of spatial resolution (due to the increased sample thickness) and a fading out of the diffraction spots. The solution to this problem is obvious (i.e., improved vacuum conditions).

The most detrimental type of damage is modification of the specimen itself. Frequent phenomena that can occur are changes (or destruction) of the crystal structures, loss of mass (e.g., by evaporation), partial reduction of oxides, diffusion, and so on. Fortunately, these phenomena are rather rare in the case of catalyst samples, which are usually designed to resist fairly high working temperatures. The most frequent problem arises from the diffusion of species that are not sufficiently anchored to the support. Alkaline ions are espeically prone to move away from the positive space charge created through the impact of an electron beam.

A detailed discussion of radiation damage and contamination in analysis of inorganic solids may be found in Chapters 17 and 18 of Ref. 5.

## E. The Study of Practical Catalysts by AEM

This section aims at illustrating which types of information may be gained on catalysts by a proper use of the techniques described above. Only two examples will be given. A more detailed discussion focusing on thin-film X-ray microanalysis may be found in a recent review [22].

### 1. Introductory Remarks

Major catalysts are made of highly porous carriers on which an active phase has been deposited. In many cases this supported phase has the form of crystallites or amorphous aggregates whose (1) size and shape may be studied by TEM imaging (current resolution ~1 nm, see Sec. II), (2) crystal structure by electron microdiffraction (current resolution ~20 nm), and (3) elemental composition by X-ray microanalysis or EELS (current resolution ~10 nm). (These resolutions correspond roughly to what may be fairly easily obtained when using an instrument equipped with a thermoionic electron source and a STEM attachment.)

The supported phase may also have the form of finely dispersed species anchored to the surface of the carrier. These species cannot usually be distinguished from the support by imaging. As sketched in

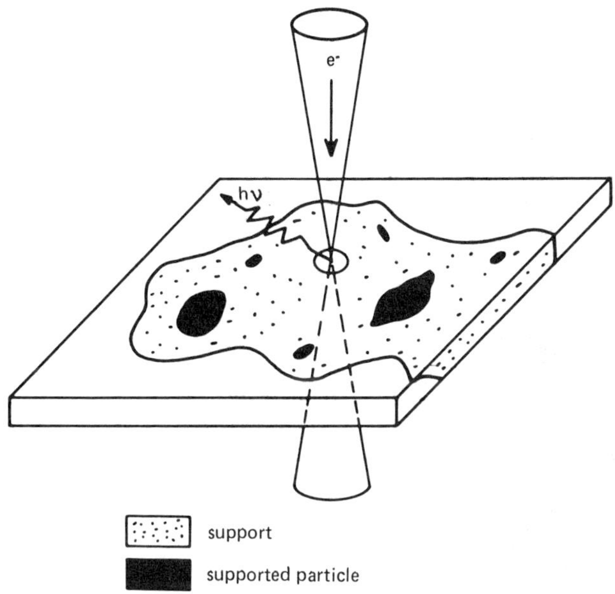


FIG. 25. Principle of the selective microanalysis of the most dispersed species on areas free of distinguishable supported particles. (From Ref. 22.)

Fig. 25, their concentration and distribution may be studied by X-ray microanalysis (or EELS) when directing the electron probe onto areas of the support where no supported particle or aggregate can be observed.

When combined with particle size distribution measurements, AEM thus appears as a powerful tool for characterizing the dispersion and distribution of the supported phase. This tool is especially useful when studying oxide or sulfide catalysts whose dispersion can usually not be assessed by selective chemisorption methods [76]. Recent works have demonstrated the wealth of information that can be gained when combining AEM with XPS intensity measurements [32,77-79].

The first example presented in the following sections is a typical study of a complex oxidic catalyst using the common CTEM with STEM attachment and thermoionic electron source. The second example illustrates the improved capabilities offered by presently available dedicated STEMs equipped with a field emission gun.

### 2. Selective Oxidation Catalyst Supported on $SiO_2$

Figure 26 summarizes the results of the characterization of a catalyst for selective oxidation of propene into acrolein. This catalyst

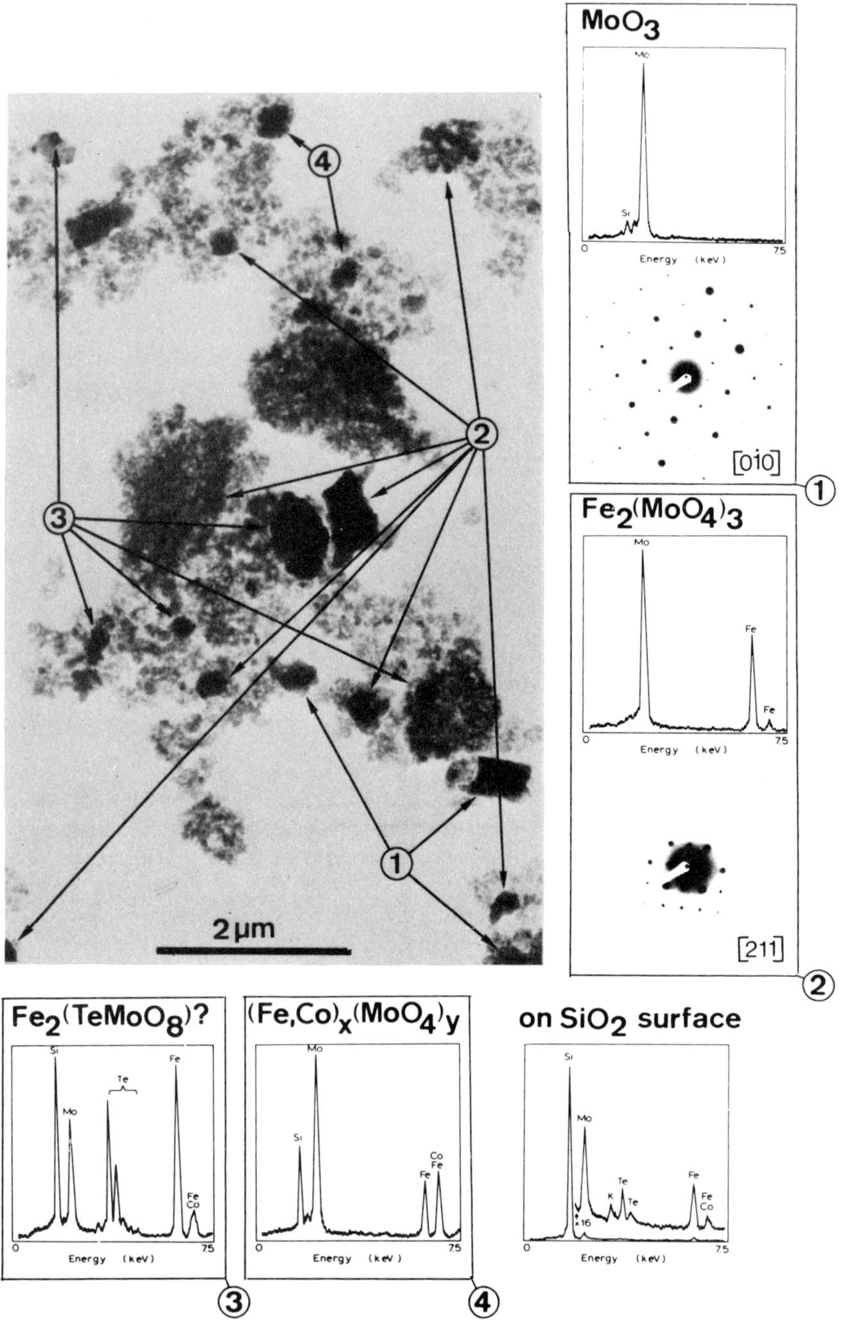


FIG. 26. AEM investigation of an oxidic $MoFeTeCo/SiO_2$ catalyst. The arrows point to grains belonging to the specific phases.

contains Mo, Fe, Te, and Co in oxidic form deposited on $SiO_2$ by impregnation from their salts and subsequent calcination. As seen on the micrograph, numerous particles of the supported phase could be distinguished from the carrier. These particles have been characterized by X-ray microanalysis and, when possible, by electron diffraction. As schematized on the figure, four different compounds can be characterized.

1. Well-crystallized orthorhombic $MoO_3$ crystals are identified by X-ray microanalysis and electron diffraction.
2. The most abundant phase was iron molybdate $Fe_2(MoO_4)_3$. The stoichiometry can be determined from the peak intensity ratio Mo/Fe on the X-ray spectrum and confirmed by the crystal structure deduced from the diffraction pattern.
3. Tellurium was always associated with Fe and Mo, forming a ternary oxide. The Te/Fe ratio seemed fairly constant for all the grains of this phase ($\simeq$0.5 atomic), whereas the Mo content varied appreciably. The X-ray spectrum displayed on Fig. 26 corresponds to the most frequent composition. The relative intensities of the X-ray peaks suggest the stoichiometry $Fe_2MoTeO_8$. These grains did not appear sufficiently crystalline as to allow recording of a useful diffraction pattern.
4. A mixed (iron + cobalt) molybdate can also be identified from the X-ray microanalysis spectra.

In addition to these aggregated compounds, the spectra recorded by directing the electron probe on areas where no particle could be detected established the presence of small peaks of Mo, Te, and Fe (spectrum on the lower right of Fig. 26). Although it cannot be excluded that some part of these signals might be due to a remotely excited radiation (see Sec. III.B.2), it appears, however, that a significant proportion of the supported phase was finely dispersed on the surface of the $SiO_2$ support.

This example does not involve very high resolution work or very precise quantitative interpretation of the data. It illustrates how AEM can be valuable for giving insight into the complexity of some practical catalysts. A similar illustration may be found in the study of $Cu/ZnO/Cr_2O_3$ catalysts by Mehta et al. [33].

### 3. $Ru/SiO_2$ Catalysts [45]

This study was performed on a dedicated STEM (VG Microscopes' HB5). The catalyst contains ruthenium clusters supported on amorphous $SiO_2$. All three microanalytical techniques were used. Figure 27a shows the X-ray spectrum after 300 s of analysis from a 7-nm-diameter ruthenium particle, whereas Fig. 27b is the spectrum obtained from the support at 7 nm from the center of the particle. (The

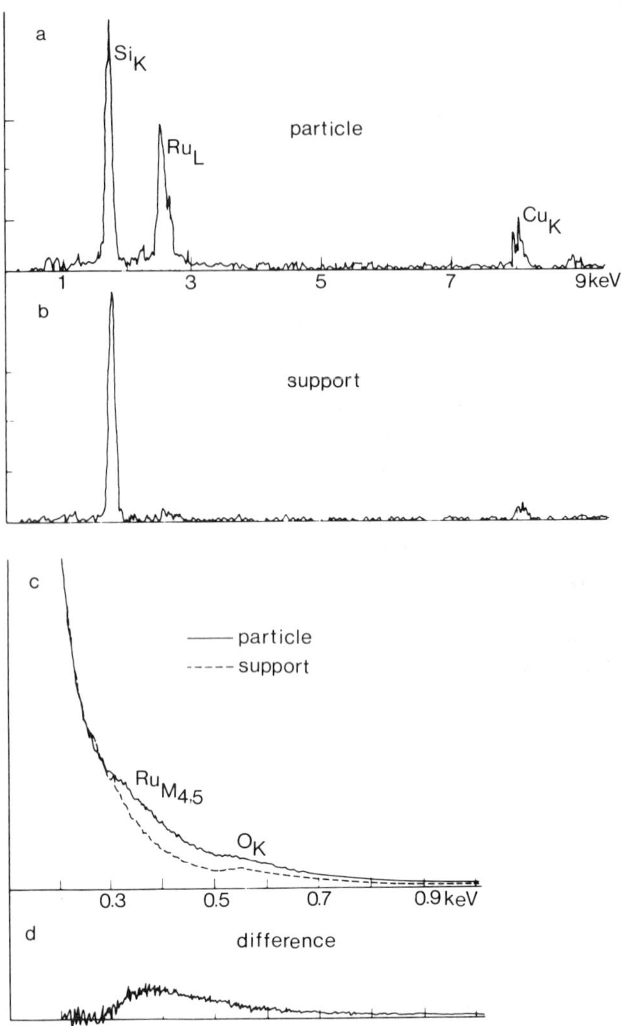


FIG. 27. (a) X-ray spectrum from a 7-nm ruthenium particle and (b) from the $SiO_2$ support 7 nm from the center of the particle; (c) EELS spectra recorded simultaneously with the X-ray spectra; (d) difference between the latter two spectra, showing clearly the ruthenium edge. (From Ref. 45 with permission.)

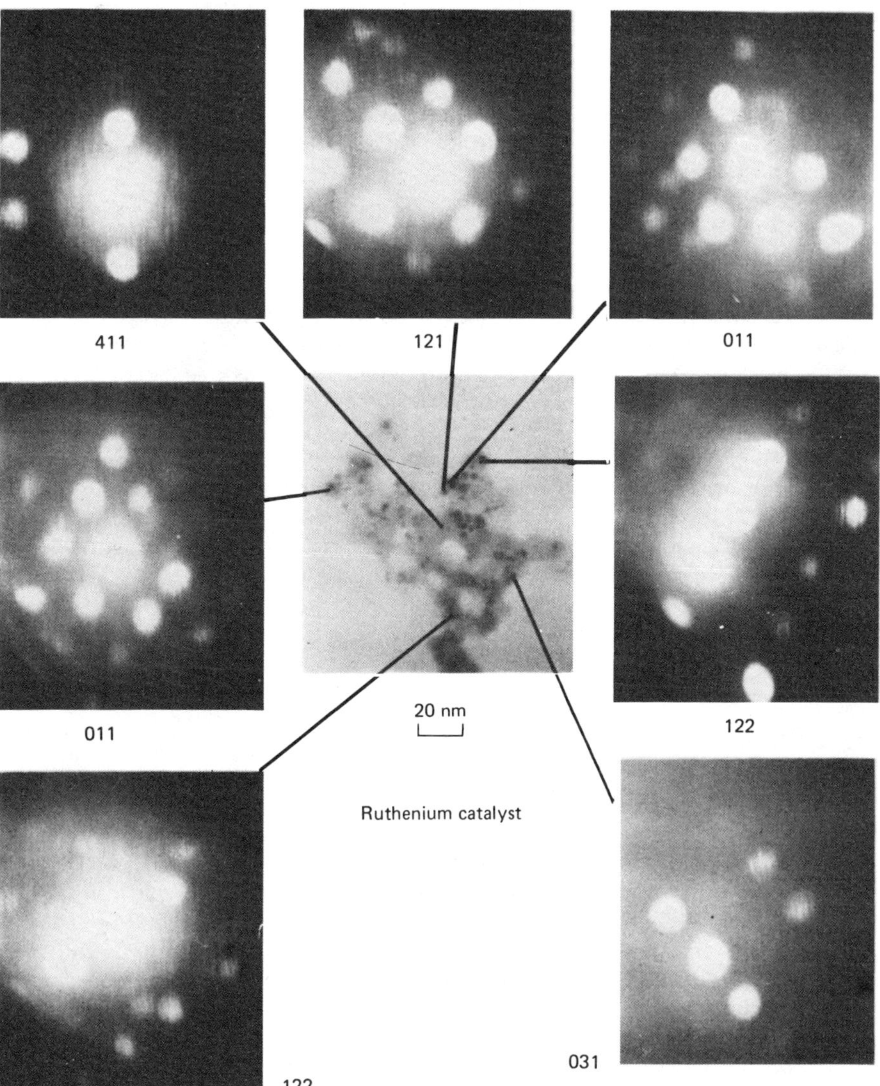


FIG. 28. Microdiffraction patterns from several ruthenium particles. (From Ref. 45 with permission.)

copper peak is a remote excitation from the supporting copper grid.) Figure 27c is a superposition of the corresponding EELS spectra recorded simultaneously with the X-ray spectra of Fig. 27a and b. Substracting the two spectra (Fig. 27d) clearly shows the ruthenium M edge. These results demonstrate strikingly the ability of such a dedicated STEM to analyze small supported particles by both X-ray microanalysis and EELS.

The presence of the $SiO_2$ support unfortunately prevented detection of the oxygen within the particles. However, the possible presence of ruthenium oxide (RuO) could be assessed by electron microdiffraction. Figure 28 shows a small fragment of catalyst and a selection of microdiffraction patterns obtained by pointing the electron probe onto individual particles. The patterns are characteristic of hexagonal ruthenium metal. They could not be confused with a ruthenium oxide pattern. Owing to the fairly large angular aperture $\alpha_i$ of the incident beam necessary to provide a sufficient electron current density, the diffraction spots are extended into small circles. It ensues that completely unknown particles could not have been identified with great accuracy from such patterns.

Ruthenium could also be detected in X-ray and EELS spectra from 3-nm particles after prolonged counting for 25 min. An optimum ultrahigh vacuum (requiring overnight baking) was necessary to prevent accumulation of contamination during such a long irradiation time. This illustrates the type of experimental constraints that have to be obeyed when ultimate resolution is required.

## IV. CONCLUSIONS

As shown in Chap. 1, the importance of transmission electron microscopy and related techniques for the characterization of practical catalysts is justified by the fact that AEM is involved in the investigation of many different features: nature of the phases, size and shape of particles, dispersion, and repartition of the supported species. The aim of this chapter was to provide the reader with the necessary bases, allowing him fully to appreciate the potentialities and limitations of AEM for such studies.

In summary, transmission electron microscopy presently allows the observation of structural details less than 0.3 nm in size. However, the observation of the size and shape of supported particles is governed by contrast effects which often raise the practical limit for the measurement of these features to about 2.0 nm. As concerns microanalysis by microdiffraction, X-ray spectrometry, and EELS, 10 nm seems to be the practical ultimate resolution limit for STEM instruments equipped with a conventional tungsten hairpin electron source. The use of a field emission gun in a dedicated ultrahigh-vacuum STEM allows the lowering of this limit to a few nanometers on sufficiently thin specimens (i.e., when the resolution is not governed by the spreading of the transmitted electron beam). As several catalysts research laboratories are now becoming equipped with the latter type of instrument, it is possible that a more precise evaluation of these new prospects will become possible soon.

## ACKNOWLEDGMENTS

The author is indebted to B. K. Hodnett and M. Genet for constructive comments about the manuscript.

## LIST OF SYMBOLS

| | |
|---|---|
| $z$ | coordinate (also called elevation) along the axis of the microscope column (beam direction) |
| $\underline{k}$ | wave vector of the incident electron |
| $\underline{k'}$ | wave vector of the scattered electron |
| $\lambda$ | wavelength of the incident electron |
| $E$ | kinetic energy of the incident electron |
| $A_{a,c,o,f,i}$ | amplitude of the electron wave |
| $2\theta$ | angle between directions of vectors k and k' |
| $f_a(\theta)$ | atomic scattering amplitude |
| $\underline{g}$ | vector of the reciprocal lattice |
| $d$ | spacing of lattice planes |
| $F(\underline{g})$ | structure factor |
| $r_a$ | vector position of the atom a in the unit cell |
| $t$, $t_{s,p}$ | thickness of the specimen (along z) |
| $I$, $I_{in,\underline{g}}$ | intensity of the electron wave |
| $V_c$ | volume of the unit cell |
| $\xi(\underline{g})$ | extinction distance |
| $x$, $y$ | coordinates perpendicular to the optic axis in the object and image planes |
| $u$, $v$ | coordinates perpendicular to the optic axis in the back-focal plane |
| $\alpha_o$ | maximum scattering angle admitted through the objective aperture |
| $D_{A,min}$ | resolution limit |
| $D_p$ | incident probe diameter |
| $\chi$, $\chi_{s,F}$ | phase delay between direct and scattered electron waves |
| $C_s$ | spherical aberration |
| $\Delta F$ | defect of focus |
| $\mathcal{F}$ | Fourier transform |
| $B$ | brightness of the electron source |

| | |
|---|---|
| $\phi_{e,\underline{g},td}$ | fraction of the electron intensity admitted through the objective aperture |
| $\Lambda_{e,td}$ | electron mean free path |
| $\alpha_i$ | angular aperture of the incident electron beam |
| b | beam spreading at the exit face of the specimen |
| $\rho$ | density of the specimen |
| J | incident current density |
| T | counting time |
| $C_{A,B}$ | concentration of elements A and B |
| $N_{A,B}$ | characteristic X-ray counts (intensity) for elements A and B |
| $k_{AB}$ | relative sensitivity factor for elements A and B |
| $\Delta E$ | energy loss of the transmitted electron |

## REFERENCES


1. R. Castaing, Ph.D. thesis, University of Paris, *ONERA Publ.* 55, 1951.
2. J. I. Goldstein and H. Yakowitz, eds., *Practical Scanning Electron Microscopy*, Plenum Press, New York, 1975.
3. F. Maurice, L. Meny, and R. Tixier, eds., *Microanalyse et microscopie electronique à balayage*, Les Éditions de Physique, Orsay, France, 1978.
4. G. R. Purdy and R. B. Anderson, in *Experimental Methods in Catalytic Research*, Vol. 2 (R. B. Anderson and P. T. Dawson, eds.), Academic Press, New York, 1976, p. 95.
5. J. J. Hren, J. I. Goldstein, and D. C. Joy, eds., *Introduction to Analytical Electron Microscopy*, Plenum Press, New York, 1979.
6. P. B. Hirsch, A. Howie, R. B. Nicholson, D. W. Pashley, and M. J. Whelan, *Electron Microscopy of Thin Crystals*, R. E. Krieger, New York, 1977.
7. C. J. Humphreys, *Rep. Prog. Phys.*, *42*: 1825 (1979).
8. J. M. Cowley, *Diffraction Physics*, Elsevier/North-Holland, Amsterdam, 1975.
9. R. D. Heidenreich, *Fundamentals of Transmission Electron Microscopy*, Wiley-Interscience, New York, 1964.
10. K. J. Hanzen, in *Advances in Optical and Electron Microscopy*, Vol. 4 (R. Barrer and V. E. Cosslett, eds.), Academic Press, New York, 1971, p. 1.
11. O. Scherzer, *J. Appl. Phys.*, *20*: 20 (1949).
12. E. Zeitler and M. G. R. Thomson, *Optik*, *31*: 258 (1970).
13. E. Zeitler and M. G. R. Thomson, *Optik*, *31*: 359 (1970).
14. K. C. A. Smith, in *Scanning Electron Microscopy 1972*, Vol. 3 (O. Johari, ed.), IIT Research Institute, Chicago, 1972, p. 1.

15. J. F. Hainfel, in *Scanning Electron Microscopy 1977*, Vol. 3 (Om Johari, ed.), IIT Research Institute, Chicago, 1977, p. 591.
16. G. Dalmai-Imelik, C. Leclercq, and I. Mutin, *J. Microsc.*, *20*: 123 (1974).
17. J. W. Sprys, L. Bartosiewicz, R. McCune, and H. K. Plummer, *J. Catal.*, *39*: 91 (1975).
18. P. C. Flynn, S. E. Wanke, and P. S. Turner, *J. Catal.*, *33*: 233 (1974).
19. E. B. Prestridge, G. H. Via, and J. H. Sinfelt, *J. Catal.*, *50*: 115 (1977).
20. N. R. Avery and J. V. Sanders, *J. Catal.*, *18*:129 (1970).
21. M. M. J. Treacy, A. Howie, and C. J. Wilson, *Philos. Mag.*, *A38*: 569 (1978).
22. F. Delannay, *Catal. Rev. Sci. Eng.*, *22*: 141 (1980).
23. M. M. J. Treacy and A. Howie, *J. Catal.*, *63*: 265 (1980).
24. A. Howie, in *Characterization of Catalysts* (J. M. Thomas and R. M. Lambert, eds.), Wiley, New York, 1980, p. 89.
25. C. R. Hall and P. B. Hirsch, *Proc. R. Soc.*, *A286*: 158 (1965).
26. L. A. Freeman, A. Howie, and M. M. J. Treacy, *J. Microsc.*, *111*: 165 (1977).
27. E. B. Prestridge and D. J. C. Yates, *Nature*, *234*: 345 (1971).
28. H. Knözinger, Y. Zhao, B. Tesche, R. Barth, R. Epstein, B. C. Gates, and J. P. Scott, *Faraday Discuss.*, *72*: in press (1981).
29. D. E. Fornwalt and K. Kinoshita, *Micron.*, *4*: 99 (1973).
30. W. Krakow and L. A. Howland, *Ultramicroscopy*, *2*: 53 (1976).
31. E. L. Thomas and E. J. Roche, *Polymer*, *20*: 1413 (1970).
32. F. Delannay, P. Gajardo, P. Grange, and B. Delmon, *J. Chem. Soc., Faraday Trans. 1*, *76*: 988 (1980).
33. S. Mehta, G. W. Simmons, K. Klier, and R. G. Herman, *J. Catal.*, *57*: 339 (1979).
34. M. J. Yacaman, J. Zenith, and J. L. Contreras, *Appl. Surf. Sci.*, *6*: 71 (1980).
35. K. Heinemann, *Optik*, *34*: 113 (1971).
36. S. Ino and S. Ogawa, *J. Phys. Soc. Jap.*, *22*: 1365 (1967).
37. L. D. Marks and A. Howie, *Nature*, *282*: 196 (1979).
38. K. Heinemann and H. Poppa, *Appl. Phys. Lett.*, *20*: 122 (1972).
39. M. J. Yacaman and T. Ocana, *Phys. Status Solidi*, *a42*: 571 (1977).
40. F. Lenz, *Z. Naturforsch.*, *9a*: 185 (1954).
41. A. V. Crewe, J. Wall, and J. P. Langmore, *Science*, *168*: 1338 (1970).
42. H. Hashimoto, A. Kumao, K. Hino, H. Yotsumoto, and A. Ono, *Jap. J. Appl. Phys.*, *10*: 1115 (1971).

43. A. V. Crewe, J. P. Langmore, and M. S. Isaacson, in *Physical Aspects of Electron Microscopy and Microbeam Analysis* (B. M. Siegel and D. R. Beaman, eds.), Wiley, New York, 1975, p. 47.
44. M. M. J. Treacy, A. Howie, and S. J. Pennycook, *Inst. Phys. Conf. Ser.*, *52*: 261 (1980).
45. S. J. Pennycook, *J. Microsc.*, *124*: 15 (1981).
46. B. Tesche, H. Knözinger, and B. C. Gates, *J. Catal.*, *64*: 232 (1980).
47. J. M. Cowley, J. C. Wheatley, and W. O. Kehl, *J. Catal.*, *56*: 185 (1979).
48. F. Delannay, D. S. Thakur, and B. Delmon, *J. Less-Common Met.*, *63*: 265 (1979).
49. J. V. Sanders and K. C. Pratt, *J. Catal.*, *67*: 331 (1981).
50. H. Topsoe, B. S. Clausen, R. Candia, C. Wivel, and S. Mørup, *J. Catal.*, *68*: 433 (1981).
51. R. Sinclair and G. Thomas, *Metall. Trans.*, *9A*: 373 (1978).
52. G. R. Millward and J. M. Thomas, *Carbon*, *17*: 1 (1979).
53. S. Iijima, *Chem. Scr.*, *14*: 117 (1978-1979).
54. J. B. Le Poole, *Philips Tech. Rev.*, *9*: 33 (1947).
55. L. Reimer, *Scanning*, *2*: 3 (1979).
56. J. B. Warren, in *Introduction to Analytical Electron Microscopy*, Plenum Press, New York, 1979, p. 369.
57. J. W. Steeds, in *Introduction to Analytical Electron Microscopy*, Plenum Press, New York, 1979, p. 387.
58. P. Duncumb, in *Proceedings of the Fifth International Congress on Electron Microscopy*, Academic Press, New York, 1962, p. KK4.
59. D. F. Kyser, in *Introduction to Analytical Electron Microscopy*, Plenum Press, New York, 1979, p. 199.
60. I. P. Jones and M. H. Loretto, *J. Microsc.*, *124*: 3 (1981).
61. J. I. Goldstein, J. L. Costley, G. W. Lorimer, and S. J. B. Reed, in *Scanning Electron Microscopy 1977*, Vol. 1 (Om Johari, ed.), IIT Research Institute, Chicago, 1977, p. 315.
62. D. R. Beaman, in *Environmental Pollutants* (T. Y. Toribara, J. R. Coleman, B. E. Dahneke, and I. Feldman, eds.), Plenum Press, New York, 1978, p. 255.
63. L. M. Brown, *J. Phys. F: Met. Phys.*, *11*: 1 (1981).
64. S. J. B. Reed, *Electron Microprobe Analysis*, Cambridge University Press, Cambridge, 1975.
65. J. I. Goldstein, in *Introduction to Analytical Electron Microscopy*, Plenum Press, New York, 1979, p. 83.
66. D. C. Joy and D. M. Maher, in *Scanning Electron Microscopy 1977*, Vol. 1 (Om Johari, ed.), IIT Research Institute, Chicago, 1977, p. 325.
67. G. Blanchard, H. Charcosset, H. Dexpert, E. Freund, C. Leclercq, and G. Martino, *J. Catal.*, *70*: 168 (1981).

68. J. Bentley, N. J. Zaluzec, E. A. Kenik, and R. W. Carpenter, *Scanning Electron Microscopy*, SEM Inc., AMF O'Hare, Ill., 1979, p. 581.
69. N. J. Zaluzec, in *Introduction to Analytical Electron Microscopy*, Plenum Press, New York, 1979, p. 121.
70. G. Cliff and G. W. Lorimer, *J. Microsc.*, *103*: 203 (1975).
71. A. J. Morgan, T. W. Davies, and D. A. Erasmus, *J. Microsc.*, *104*: 271 (1975).
72. C. Nockolds, C. Cliff, and G. W. Lorimer, *Micron*, *11*: 325 (1980).
73. D. B. Williams and J. W. Edington, *J. Microsc.*, *108*: 113 (1976).
74. D. C. Joy, in *Introduction to Analytical Electron Microscopy*, Plenum Press, New York, 1979, p. 223.
75. D. M. Maher, in *Introduction to Analytical Electron Microscopy*, Plenum Press, New York, 1979, p. 259.
76. F. Delannay, P. Gajardo, and P. Grange, *J. Microsc. Spectrosc. Electron.*, *3*: 411 (1978).
77. M. Houalla, F. Delannay, and B. Delmon, *J. Chem. Soc.*, *Faraday Trans. 1*, *76*: 1766 (1980).
78. M. Houalla, F. Delannay, and B. Delmon, *J. Phys. Chem.*, *85*: 1704 (1981).
79. F. Delannay, M. Houalla, D. Pirotte, and B. Delmon, *Surf. Interface Anal.*, *1*: 172 (1979).

# 4

# Diffuse Reflectance Spectroscopy

ROBERT A. SCHOONHEYDT National Fund of Scientific Research and Katholieke Universiteit Leuven, Leuven (Heverlee), Belgium

## I. INTRODUCTION

The interaction of light with catalysts' particles has been and is used as a major tool in the characterization of catalysts. On these high-surface-area solids severe difficulties arise due to light scattering, expecially in the near infrared (NIR), visible, and ultraviolet (UV) regions of the spectrum. They are largely overcome by the application of diffuse reflectance spectroscopy (DRS) and photoacoustic spectroscopy (PAS). The latter technique has been commercialized in the last 5 years and a few papers on the characterization of catalysts have already appeared. This technique will not be discussed here. Recent publications on PAS include a book [1], a review paper in which PAS and DRS are compared [2], and a paper on its application in clay mineral research [3]. The interested reader is referred to these references.

DRS covers the infrared (IR), visible, and UV regions of the spectrum and in principle bulk and surface properties of the catalysts can be studied. Kortüm has discussed the technique in great detail in his book [4]. For quantitative work a comprehensive theory for the interaction of light with a medium that absorbs, emits, and scatters radiation is necessary. It can be found in Kortüm's book, but the latest advancements have been discussed by Klier [5].

Table 1 summarizes the properties and components of both the support and the adsorbed phase which can be studied by DRS. The frequency range is 5000 to 50,000 $cm^{-1}$. In this range information about the catalysts' properties can be obtained from vibrational and electronic transitions in adsorbed molecules, from electronic transitions within the d-orbital manifold of transition metal ions (TMI), from

TABLE 1 Catalyst Properties Studied by Diffuse Reflectance Spectroscopy

| Bulk and surface | Wavenumber range | Adsorbed phase | Wavenumber range |
|---|---|---|---|
| Band gap | UV 30,000–50,000 $cm^{-1}$ | Transition metal ions | NIR, visible, UV 5000–50,000 $cm^{-1}$ |
| Defects | UV 30,000–50,000 $cm^{-1}$ | Molecules with chromophoric groups | UV, visible 14,000–50,000 $cm^{-1}$ |
| Transition metal ions | NIR, visible, UV 5000–50,000 $cm^{-1}$ | Vibrational overtone and combination bands | NIR 5000–14,000 $cm^{-1}$ |

electronic transitions between ligands and TMI, and from electronic transitions involving defects and the band gap of the catalysts. The band gap is the energy difference between the (empty) conduction band and the (filled) valence band and presents itself as a continuum absorption starting from a characteristic frequency and extending to higher wavenumbers.

It is not possible to give a detailed description of the state of the art of the technique and the interpretation of the spectra in this chapter. It is not absolutely necessary for a beginner. Therefore, only the principles of the technique are explained in the next section, together with some technical considerations about recording and manipulation of spectra. In the third part, the physical basis of the interpretation of the various spectral bands which can show up in a DRS spectrum is qualitatively explained. For the quantitative aspects the reader is referred to the specialized literature. References are given. In the following three parts the DRS spectra of catalysts are reviewed. The emphasis is placed on transition metal oxides and TMI supported on oxidic carriers. The application of DRS to zeolites and clay minerals is not included because recent reviews have appeared [2,5,7].

## II. DIFFUSE REFLECTANCE SPECTROSCOPY

### A. Theory

The dimensions of the catalyst particles are comparable to the wavelength. This makes it impossible to distinguish the phenomena of reflection, refraction, and diffraction: the light is scattered. In DRS the light intensity scattered at a given wavelength from an "infinitely thick" closely packed catalyst layer is compared with that scattered from an infinitely thick layer of a nonabsorbing (white) reference. The ratio of the light intensity scattered from the catalyst to that from the reference is recorded as a function of the wavelength. This constitutes the diffuse reflectance spectrum. There are two ways to illuminate sample and reference. In the first mode a direct, dispersed light beam impinges perpendicularly on the sample and on the reference. The first layer of randomly oriented particles scatters the light in all directions, independently of the angle of incidence, and ensures diffuse illumination of the other particles. The light scattered from sample and reference is collected in an integration sphere and detected by a PbS cell (NIR) or a photomultiplier (visible UV) on top of the integration sphere. Because the integration sphere must scatter the light and not absorb it, it is coated with a perfectly white coating [2,4]. In the second mode of operation sample and reference are illuminated with diffuse, undispersed radiation, its diffuse character being ensured by the integration sphere. In principle, measurements on luminescent samples present no difficulties. In mode 1 the absorption spectrum is obtained, whereas in mode 2 both the absorption and luminescence are registered. By substraction the luminescence spectrum is obtained.

The experimental spectrum contains an absorption part and a scattering part. For closely packed particles the light beam undergoes multiple scattering on a great number of particles. If, at the same time, phase relations and interferences among the scattered light beams arise, a general quantitative solution to the problem of multiple scattering is impossible. There are two approaches. In the continuum approach—by far the most popular—the characteristics of the individual particles are not taken into account. In the statistical approach the individual particles are characterized. The validity of this approach depends on the accuracy with which these particles can be characterized.

The most popular continuum theory is the Schuster-Kubelka-Munk (SKM) theory. The monochromatic diffuse illumination flux I and the diffusively scattered light flux J are approximated by two opposite fluxes, perpendicular to the surface of the infinitely thick catalyst as shown in Fig. 1. The SKM equation is

$$F(R_\infty) = \frac{(1 - R_\infty)^2}{2R_\infty} = \frac{K}{S} \tag{1}$$

$$R_\infty = \frac{\text{light intensity reflected from the sample}}{\text{light intensity reflected from the reference}}$$

is directly obtained from the output of the spectrometer. K and S are the SKM absorption and scattering coefficients, respectively, and are characteristic of the material under investigation. The true absorption coefficient $\alpha_\nu$ and true scattering coefficient $\sigma_\nu$ at frequency $\nu$ are related to K and S through

$$\alpha_\nu = \eta K \quad \text{and} \quad \sigma_\nu = \chi S \tag{2}$$

It follows from (2) and (1) that

$$\frac{\alpha_\nu}{\sigma_\nu} = \frac{(1 - R_\infty)^2}{2R_\infty} \frac{\eta}{\chi} \tag{3}$$

Equations (2) and (3) are due to Klier [5,6]. The ratio $\eta/\chi$ is fairly constant and equal to 3/8 for values of K/S between 0 and 0.3. For strongly absorbing samples ($K/S > 0.3$ or $R_\infty < 0.5$) ($\eta/\chi$) decreases. Values are tabulated by Klier [6]. Thus at low concentrations of absorbing centers the SKM equation (1) is a good representation of the absorption spectrum.

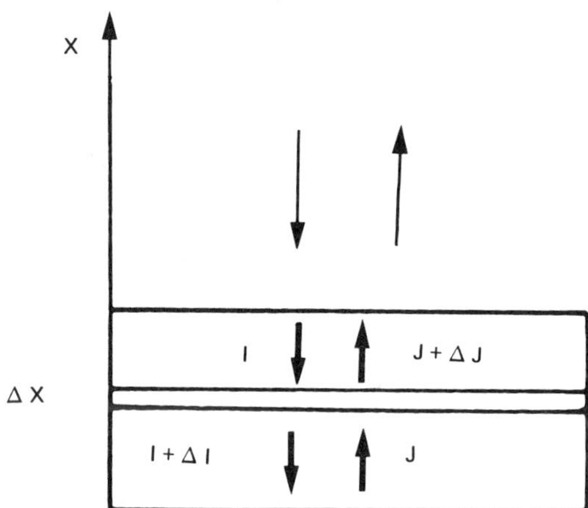


FIG. 1. The Schuster-Kubelka-Munk approximation in diffuse reflectance spectroscopy. The incident and remitted light fluxes are approximated by two opposite fluxes, perpendicular to the surface of the infinitely thick sample layer.

When Eq. (3) is calculated with the aid of the experimental $R_\infty$ values at different frequencies, a spectrum is obtained which is amenable to quantitative interpretation provided that $\sigma_\nu$ is constant over the experimental wavelength range and that the conditions of isotropic scattering, infinitely thick sample and reference layers, and diffuse illumination are fulfilled. Isotropic scattering can be obtained on randomly oriented, loosely packed, irregular particles, very much smaller than the layer thickness, with an average interparticle distance which is smaller than the average particle size.

The scattering coefficient S depends on the wavelength and is inversely proportional to the particle size. The wavelength dependence is usually a monotonous function:

$$S = \nu^\alpha \tag{4}$$

$\alpha$ approaches 0 for particle sizes much larger than the wavelength. It is approximately 1 for particle sizes of the order of the wavelength. It attains values between 2 and 4, increasing with decreasing particle size, which is in any case smaller than the wavelength. $\alpha = 4$ corresponds to single scattering at small particles [4]. If $\alpha \neq 0$, a shift of the maxima of the absorption bands to lower wavenumbers can be calculated:

$$\frac{\Delta\nu}{\nu} = \frac{1 - [1 - C^2\alpha(\alpha + 2)]^{1/2}}{\alpha + 2} \qquad (5)$$

with $C = b/2\nu$ and b is the width at half of the maximum band intensity. For very broad bands and $\alpha$ approaching 4, $\Delta\nu$ can attain a few hundred $cm^{-1}$. Also, the absorption band flattens toward the short-wavelength range due to the $\nu^{\alpha}$ dependence of S [4]. In most cases these extreme conditions are not met and a true representation of the absorption spectrum can be obtained.

## B. Practice

The conditions of isotropic scattering and diffuse illumination are most closely met when the medium consists of densily packed, randomly shaped particles whose sizes are comparable with or smaller than the wavelength of the light. Catalyst layers ~5 mm thick are sufficient for the infinite thickness criterion. For work in vacuum, adsorption studies or catalytic experiments specially designed cells are necessary with silica windows with extremely low OH and $H_2O$ contents. It is advisable to sieve the catalyst and to work with fractions of the same size range. The scattering properties are strongly influenced by adsorbed layers on the external surfaces. Thus the $H_2O$ combination and overtone bands intensities are not linearly dependent on the amount adsorbed from complete dehydration up to full saturation because of adsorption on the external surface in the latter case.

The same remarks hold for the reference materials. In addition, they must be totally reflecting over as wide a frequency range as possible. The most widely used standards are MgO and $BaSO_4$. They are also used to cover the inner surface of the integration sphere. Specially purified $BaSO_4$ standards are commercially available (Merck $BaSO_4$ Weissstandard Din 5033, Eastman white reflection standard No. 6091). When the standards and catalysts are in the same type of cells, effects due to these cells are eliminated. All the standards suffer from aging. They must be regularly checked and replaced.

The investigation of surface species is hampered by light absorption by the support. This is especially the case in the UV range. To eliminate this, DRS spectra can be recorded with the pure support as a reference. The drawback of this method is that the light intensity, diffusively reflected from sample and reference, is too small to record a physically meaningful spectrum. Thus the UV range, which can be covered with such a setup, does not extend down to 200 nm.

In Fig. 2 several types of cells currently in use in our laboratories are shown. Type A is designed for measurements in vacuum or static atmospheres. Type C allows pretreatment of the samples with the desired gas flow through the catalyst bed. With type B, DRS spectra and EPR spectra can be recorded on the same catalyst bed.

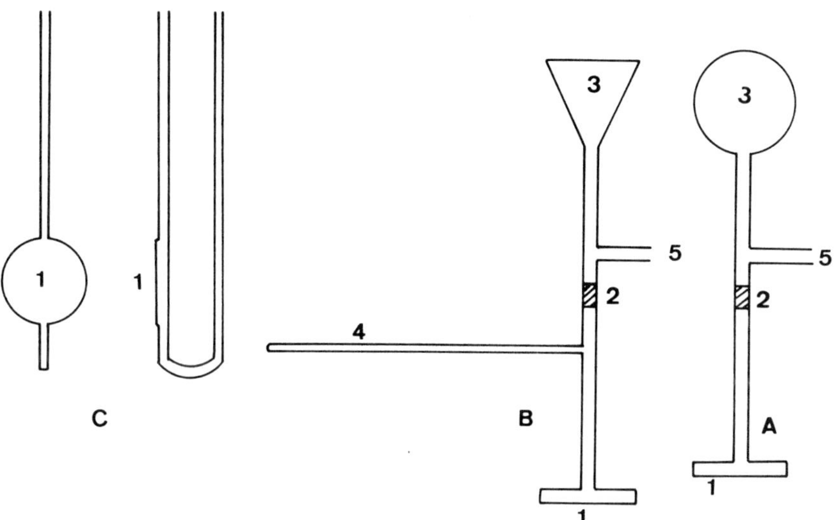


FIG. 2. Reflectance cells: 1, Suprasil windows; 2, quartz-Pyrex transitions; 3, pretreatment volumes; 4, EPR quartz tube; 5, exits to vacuum line.

Spectrometers of the major companies have DRS attachments. If the spectrometer is equipped with a digital slide wire, it can be connected to a desk computer and plotter for calculation of the SKM function and a plot of this function versus wavenumber. A block diagram of the setup in our laboratories is given in Fig. 3. The computer program developed in our laboratories allows subtraction of the baseline, calculation of the SKM function, storage of spectra on tape, plot of the spectra with a linear or logarithmic ordinate scale, editing of spectra, and plot of preselected spectral regions in the linear or

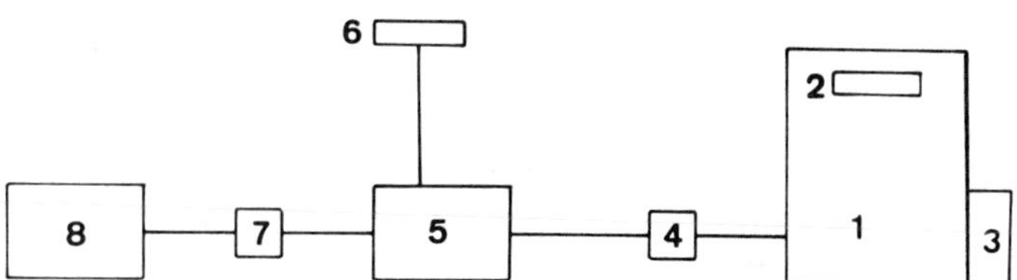


FIG. 3. Block diagram of spectrometer setup in our laboratories: 1, Cary 17 spectrometer; 2, digital slide wire; 3, reflectance attachment; 4, interface; 5, Hewlett-Packard desk computer 9825B; 6, tape; 7, interface; 8, Hewlett-Packard plotter 9872B.

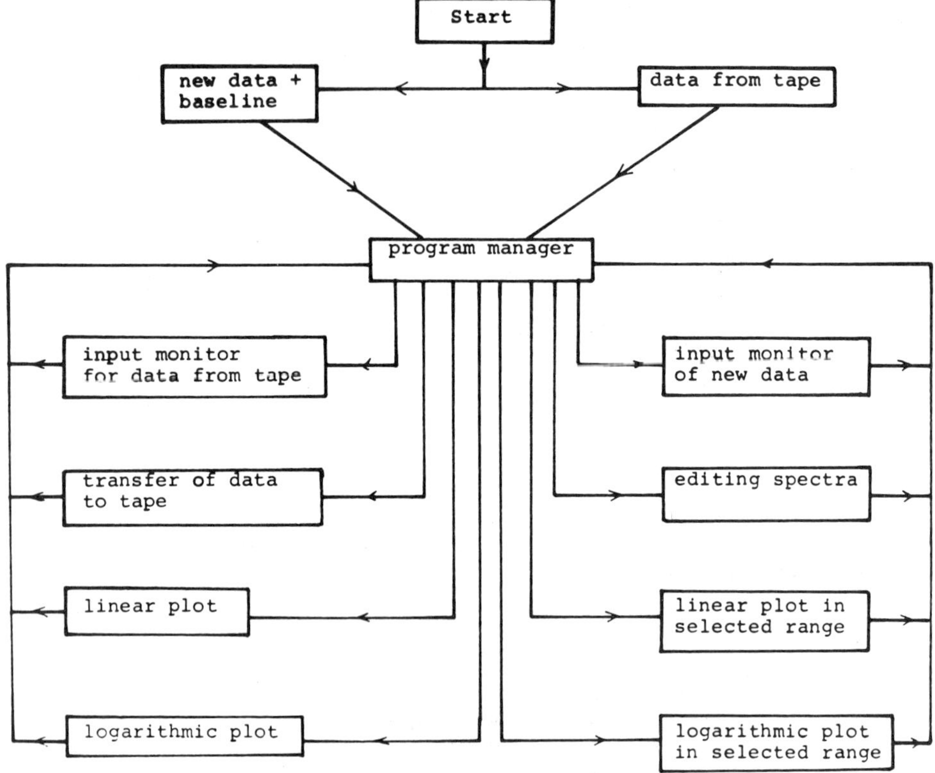


FIG. 4. Block diagram of the computer programs used for manipulation of reflectance spectra.

logarithmic ordinate scale. A block diagram showing the organizing of all these possibilities around a central program manager is shown in Fig. 4.

## III. INTERPRETATION OF SPECTRA

In this section the physical basis for the interpretation of spectra is summarized with the main emphasis on the spectra of transition metal ions. The problem is approached in the framework of the ligand field (LF) theory. For vibrational spectroscopy and electronic spectroscopy of adsorbed molecules only those aspects that are of direct use for understanding the spectra are treated.

## A. Ligand Field Theory

Ligand field (LF) theory is an adapted form of crystal field (CF) theory. In the latter theory the ligands are thought to be bonded to the TMI by coulombic forces. The corresponding energy is the CF potential:

$$V(\underline{r}_i) = \sum_{j=1}^{n} \frac{e^2}{|\underline{R} - \underline{r}_i|} \tag{6}$$

where $\underline{R}$ is the distance TMI nucleus-ligand, $\underline{r}_i$ is the distance TMI nucleus-electron i, and n is the number of ligands. The ligands are represented as point charges, −e, but they may be replaced by charge distributions. For m electrons the CF potential is

$$V_{CF} = \sum_{i=1}^{m} V(\underline{r}_i) \tag{7}$$

The effect of $V_{CF}$ on the d orbitals is that orbitals pointing toward the ligands are destabilized (increase in energy) and orbitals directed away from the ligands are stabilized (decrease in energy). This is illustrated in Fig. 5 for octahedral and tetrahedral fields. Figure 5 shows that the splitting is reversed in the two cases and that

$$10Dq_{tet} = \frac{4}{9}\, 10Dq_{oct} \tag{8}$$

10Dq is the splitting parameter, characteristic for the TMI and the ligands. The weaker crystal field of tetrahedral complexes is due primarily to the difference in number of ligands and the differences in positions of the ligands with respect to the d orbitals. In real systems the conversion factor is different from 4/9 due to differences in bond lengths and ionic character of the bonds. The dashed line in Fig. 5 is the energy level of the five d orbitals in a spherically symmetric potential field. It is traced to show the center of weight rule: the number of stabilized orbitals × their stabilization energy = number of destabilized orbitals × destabilization energy.

Group theory is very useful for predicting the d-orbital splitting. Indeed, the d orbitals transform as irreducible representations of the point group to which the TMI complex belongs. These irreducible representations and the corresponding d orbitals have been tabulated [8]. For octahedral and tetrahedral complexes the symbols of the irreducible representations are given at the left side of the orbital levels in Fig. 5. For one-electron systems (e.g., $Ti^{3+}$) the octahedral electron configuration in the ground state is $(t2g)^1$ and in the excited

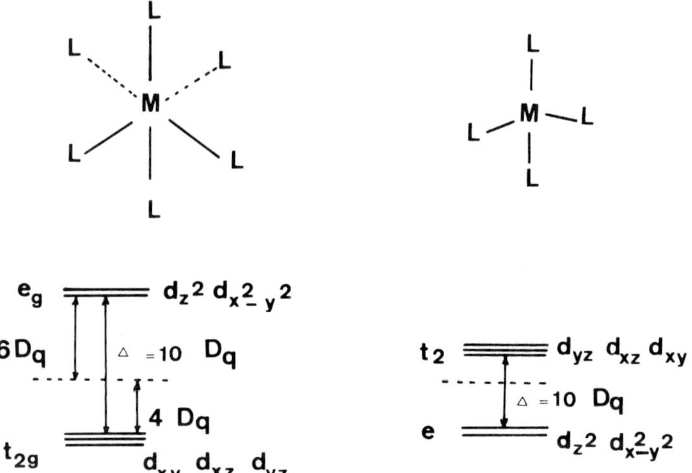


FIG. 5. Octahedral (left) and tetrahedral (right) complexes and their d-orbital splitting diagrams. The group theoretical symbols of the orbitals are indicated on the left. The energy levels splitting parameters 10Dq are indicated.

state $(t2g)^0(eg)^1$. Such a transition within the d-orbital manifold is a d-d transition. The energy of the transition $t2g^1eg^0 \rightarrow t2g^0eg^1$ equals $10Dq_{oct}$.

For many electron systems, electron-electron repulsion, $V_r$, within the d-orbital manifold and the CF potential determine the energy levels associated with all the possible electron configurations. In the weak-field approximation, $V_r > V_{CF}$, the crystal field energy levels are calculated as perturbations of the energy levels obtained after application of $V_r$. In the strong-field approach, $V_{CF} > V_r$, the calculations are performed in the reversed order. Mathematically the two approaches must give the same results. For details of the calculations the reader is referred to Refs. 9 to 11.

Some ligands create weak fields; others, strong fields. Calculations on complexes with weak-field ligands have been preferentially done in the weak-field approach. Calculations on complexes with strong-field ligands have been performed preferentially in the strong-field approach. The ordering of the ligands in a series of increasing CF potential is the spectrochemical series: $I^- < Br^- < S^{2-} < SCN^- < Cl^- < NO_3^- < F^- < OH^- < H_2O < NC5 < NH_3 <$ en $< NO_2^- < CN^- < CO$. In the ground state of weak-field complexes, the electrons distribute themselves as much as possible over the five d orbitals with parallel spins to minimize the electron-electron repulsion. These complexes are of the high-spin type. In the strong-field complexes the electrons scramble together as much as possible in the energetically most favorable d orbitals. They are low-spin complexes.

The crystal field stabilization energy (CFSE) is the energy gain of the ground-state TMI in the CF potential of the ligands with respect to their ground-state energy in a spherical symmetrical potential. The octahedral CFSEs for $d^1$-$d^9$ systems both in weak and strong fields are given in Fig. 6. The CFSE of tetrahedral complexes is much smaller because of Eq. (8). In normal spinels the divalent ions occupy the tetrahedral sites and the trivalent ions the octahedral sites. The oxygens are weak ligands, so the ions have a high-spin configuration. The larger CFSE of octahedral coordination is sufficient to invert the spinel. The theoretical predictions of the spinel structure based on the octahedral site preference are compared to the experimental structures in Table 2 [12]. The agreement is remarkably good in view of the fact that many other factors not considered here come into play.

There is now ample evidence that the CF approximation is an oversimplification. The TMI-ligand bond has a large amount of covalent character. The d electrons occupy molecular orbitals (MOs) composed of metal orbitals and ligand orbitals. Therefore, the volume occupied by these electrons is larger than in the free ion. This is electron cloud expansion, or the nephelauxetic effect. For a given cation it depends on the nature of the ligands. Ligands can be arranged in a nephelauxetic series, wherein the nephelauxetic effect increases from

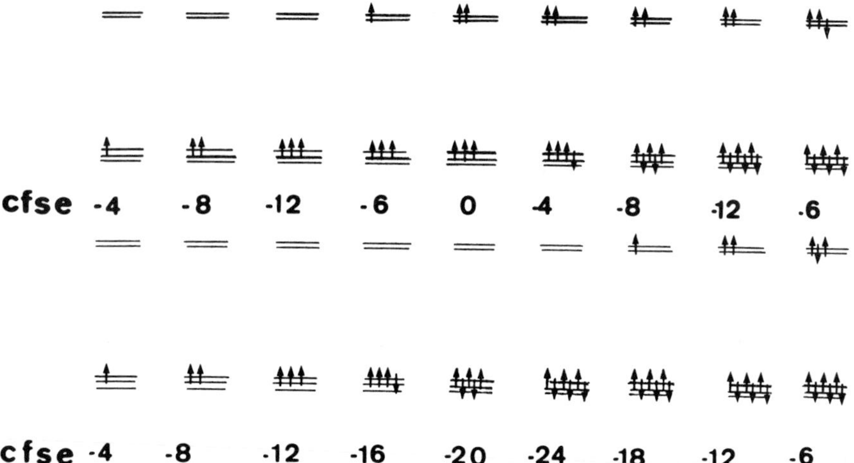


FIG. 6. Arrangements of d electrons in weak (upper) and strong (lower) crystal fields. The corresponding crystal field stabilization energies are given in units of Dq. There, where electrons with antiparallel spins are present this CFSE is counteracted by the electron-pair repulsion energy times the number of electron pairs.

TABLE 2 Site Preferences in Spinels $A^{2+}B^{3+}O_4$ [a]

| A | d-Electron configuration | B | | | | | | | | | | | |
|---|---|---|---|---|---|---|---|---|---|---|---|---|---|
| | | $Al^{3+}$ | | $Fe^{3+}$ | | $Cr^{3+}$ | | $Mn^{3+}$ | | $V^{3+}$ | | $Co^{3+}$ | |
| | | exp | th | exp | th | exp | th | exp | th | exp | th | exp | th |
| $Mn^{2+}$ | $d^5$ | N | — | I | — | N | N | N | N | N | N | — | N |
| $Fe^{2+}$ | $d^6$ | N | I | I | I | N | N | — | — | N | I + N | — | N |
| $Co^{2+}$ | $d^7$ | N | I | I | I | N | N | — | — | — | I + N | N | N |
| $Ni^{2+}$ | $d^8$ | $\frac{3}{4} + \frac{1}{4}$ N | I | I | I | N | N | — | — | — | I | — | I |
| $Cu^{2+}$ | $d^9$ | I | I | 0,86 I, T | I | N | N | — | — | — | I | — | N |
| $Zn^{2+}$ | $d^{10}$ | N | — | N | — | N | N | N, T | N | N | N | — | N |

[a] N, normal; I, inverted; T, tetragonal distortion; exp, experimental; th, theoretical.

*Source*: Based on Table 4.2, "Theoretical and Experimental Cation Distributions" (p. 86), in *Some Aspects of Crystal Field Theory* by Thomas M. Dunn, Donald S. McClure, and Ralph G. Pearson. 

left to right: $F^-$ < $H_2O$ < $NH_3$ < en < $Cl^-$ < $CN^-$ < $Br^-$ < $I^-$. To take account of this effect in CF theory the electron repulsion is expressed in terms of parameters that are adjustable so as to obtain the best fit between theory and experiment. This is, in fact, LF theory. Racah's electron repulsion parameter B is most widely used. When its free ion value is $B_0$, the ratio $B/B_0$ is a measure of the nephelauxetic effect or the covalent character of the bonding. The limiting value is, of course, $B = B_0$ [9-11].

In the framework of the LF theory all the d-d transitions can be rationalized. However, a consequence of the existence of MOs is also the occurrence of charge transfer (CT) bands in the spectrum. They are due to the transition of an electron from a molecular orbital with mainly ligand character to a MO with mainly metal d character. If the ligand have empty, low-energy antibonding orbitals (CO, unsaturated organic molecules), a CT transition from a MO with mainly d character to a MO with mainly ligand character is also possible. The former case is called ligand-to-metal charge transfer (LMCT), and the latter metal-to-ligand charge transfer (MLCT). In the charge transfer the ligand is formally oxidized and the metal reduced (or vice versa). The ease of electron transfer shows up in the position of the CT band and depends on the difference in electronegativity of TMI and ligand. With this knowledge Jörgensen was able to calculate optical electronegativies for a series a ligands and TMSs from the position of the CT bands [9]. Duffy [13] has used this concept for a classification of metal oxides. Table 3 is extracted from his work. A good prediction of the band gap of transition metal oxides is possible when $\chi_{opt}(O^{2-}) = 2.3$ for dipositive cations and when $\chi_{opt}(O^{2-})$ is between 2.3 and 3 for tripositive cations.

For octahedral and tetrahedral symmetries, explicit ligand field calculations can be found in every standard textbook [9-11]. For low-symmetry sites, such as typically occur on the surface of catalysts, the d-orbital energy levels can be calculated and fitted to experimental spectra in exactly the same way. Such a calculation has been performed by Klier and co-workers for $d^1$-$d^9$ ions in a $C_{3v}$ ligand field made up by three lattice oxygens of a crystalline zeolite [14]. The site is shown in Fig. 7, together with the corresponding d-orbital splitting diagram and the symbols of the irreducible representations.

Two parameters, $\Delta_2$ and $\Delta_3$, are needed to describe the LF potential. There are also two electron repulsion parameters. Therefore four d-d transitions must be observed for their determination. The results of the calculations are shown in Fig. 8 for $d^1$-$d^9$ systems [14]. This figure shows that in most cases the number of observable bands is less than 4. For that reason the diagrams of the type of Fig. 8 are plotted in units of Racah's repulsion parameter B and a suitable value is taken for the ratio of the two interelectronic repulsion parameters. This eliminates these repulsion parameters in the calculations.

TABLE 3 Optical Electronegativities and Comparison Between the Predicted Charge Transfer and the Experimental Band Gap of Transition Metal Oxides

| | | $\chi_{opt}$ ($O^{2-}$) 3.0 | $\chi_{opt}$ ($O^{2-}$) 2.3 | |
|---|---|---|---|---|
| Metal oxide | $\chi_{opt}$ ($M^{n+}$) | $\nu$ ($cm^{-1}$) | $\nu$ ($cm^{-1}$) | Band gap ($cm^{-1}$) |
| MnO | 1.4 | 48,000 | 27,000 | 23,000-31,000 |
| CoO | 1.4 | 48,000 | 27,000 | 22,000 |
| NiO | 1.4 | 48,000 | 27,000 | 30,000 |
| CuO | 1.9-2.0 | 30,000-33,000 | 9,000-12,000 | 5,000 |
| ZnO | 1.4 | 48,000 | 27,000 | 24,000 |
| CdO | 1.3-1.4 | 48,000-51,000 | 27,000-30,000 | 19,000 |
| HgO | 1.5 | 45,000 | 24,000 | — |
| $V_2O_3$ | 2.0 | 30,000 | 9,000 | 800 |
| $Cr_2O_3$ | 1.6 | 42,000 | 21,000 | 27,000 |
| $Mn_2O_3$ | 2.2 | 24,000 | 3,000 | — |
| $Fe_2O_3$ | 2.2 | 24,000 | 3,000 | 16,000 |
| $Co_2O_3$ | 1.8 | 36,000 | 15,000 | 44,000-48,000 |
| $Sc_2O_3$ | ~ 1.2 | ~ 54,000 | ~ 33,000 | 25,000-27,000 |
| $TiO_2$ | 2.0 | 30,000 | 9,000 | |

*Source*: After Ref. 13.

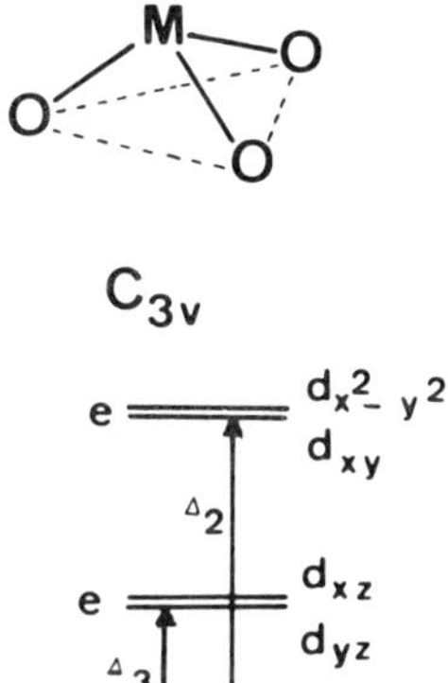


FIG. 7. A trigonal site of the surface oxygens of zeolites and the corresponding d-orbital splitting diagram.

From a fit of the experimental spectra to these diagrams it follows that the oxygens of the zeolitic lattice are weak ligands. All the TMIs are in their high-spin state. The experimental data for oxidic and supported catalysts (see following sections) agree with this conclusion. Some cations ($d^4$, $d^9$) have a doubly degenerate ground state. The site becomes distorted so as to remove this degeneracy. This is the Jahn-Teller effect. It is operative for $Cu^{2+}$ in octahedral, tetrahedral, and trigonal symmetries and for $Co^{2+}$ in tetrahedral symmetry. So far, spin-orbit coupling has not been included in this qualitative discussion. Its effect is—at least for 3d ions—small and cannot be resolved in most diffuse reflectance spectra taken at room temperature (RT).

An exception is $Cu^{2+}$ in the trigonal site symmetry of zeolites (Fig. 9). The three d-d bands at 10,800, 12,500, and 15,000 $cm^{-1}$ can be fitted to the theoretical spectrum only if the Jahn-Teller effect and spin-orbit coupling are taken into account [15]. Also, the typical tetrahedral band spectrum of $Co^{2+}$ consists of two groups of three equally spaced bands, one in the NIR and one in the visible. The three components are due to spin-orbit coupling. If they are not equally spaced, a $C_{2v}$ field is operative or, if there are two components only, the LF disturbing the tetrahedral symmetry is trigonal ($C_{3v}$).

The final remarks of this section are concerned with selection rules and band intensities. There are two selection rules: (1) spin selection rule: only those transitions are allowed between states of the same spin ($\Delta S = 0$), and (2) symmetry selection rule: those transitions for which the transition moment integral is different from zero

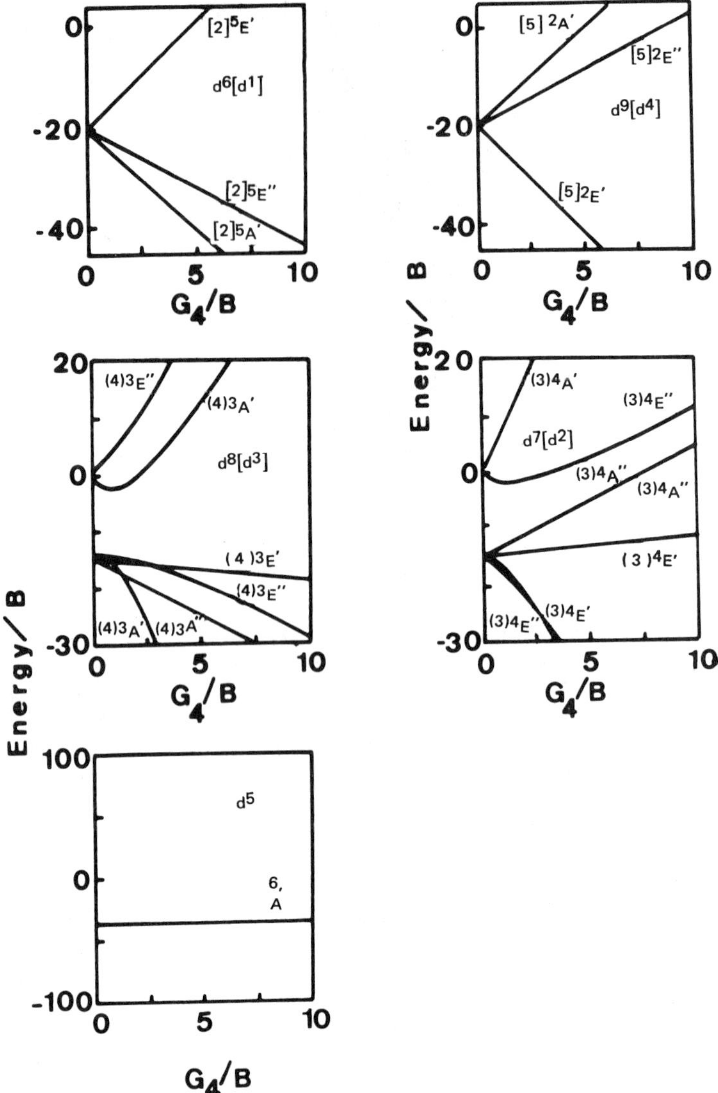


FIG. 8. Energy-term diagrams for $d^n$ ions in a trigonal site for C/B = 4. The terms are labeled by spin multiplicity and irreducible representations of the $D_{3h}$ group. The symbols in parentheses refer to the $d^n$ ions and the symbols without parentheses to the $d^{n+5}$ ions. (From K. Klier, P. J. Hutta, and R. Kellerman, in *Molecular Sieves II* Jim Kotrer, Ed., ACS Symposium Series No. 40, American Chemical Society, Washington, D.C. 1977, p. 113.)

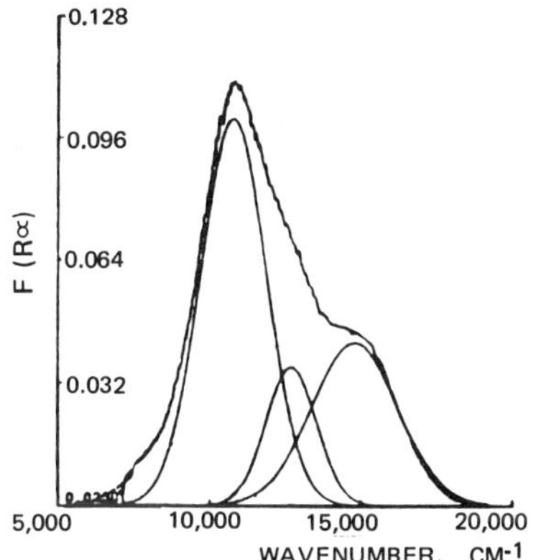


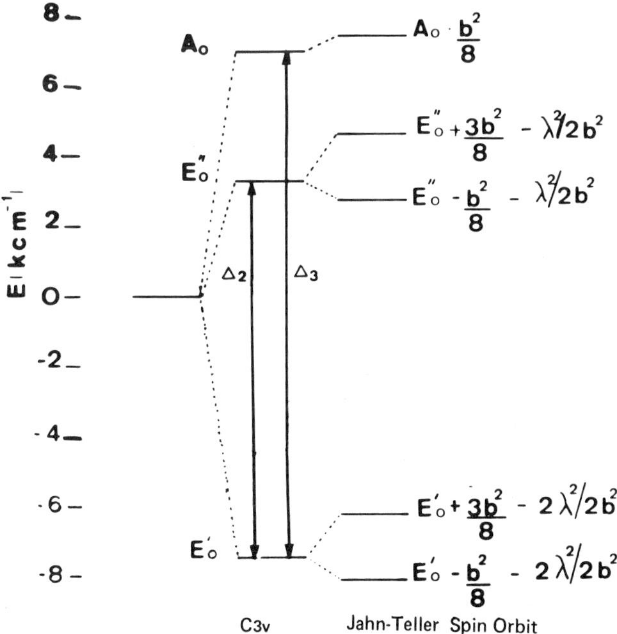


FIG. 9. Experimental spectrum of trigonal $Cu^{2+}$ in a CuA-zeolite and the corresponding d-orbital energy diagram with inclusion of the Jahn-Teller effect ($b^2$ = 3600 $cm^{-1}$) and spin-orbit coupling ($\lambda$ = 400 $cm^{-1}$). The labels are those of the irreducible representations of the $D_{3h}$ group. (Adapted from Ref. 15.)

are allowed. The transition moment integral is $<\psi_g|\Delta\mu|\psi_e>$, where $\psi_g$ is the wavefunction of the ground state, $\psi_e$ the wavefunction of the excited state, and $\Delta\mu$ is the operator of the dipole moment change. Group theory is very useful here because the integral is different from zero when the direct product of the irreducible representations of $\psi_g$, $\Delta\mu$, and $\psi_e$ contains the totally symmetric representation of the point group of the TMI complex. Thus a simple inspection of the character tables is sufficient to decide about the allowed transitions [8].

Let us as an example examine the band intensities of octahedral and tetrahedral complexes. The ground state and excited states of octahedral complexes are represented by even functions. $\Delta\mu$ transforms as the x, y, and z coordinates, which are uneven functions. The product of two even with one uneven function is uneven and the integration of an uneven function over the total space is zero. All d-d transitions in octahedral complexes are symmetry forbidden. This can be generalized to all complexes with a symmetry center. Tetrahedral complexes have no symmetry center and are not subjected to this rule.

The bands of tetrahedral complexes are at least two orders of magnitude more intense than those of octahedral complexes. If both coordination geometries occur simultaneously (a situation often encountered with catalysts), the tetrahedral bands dominate the spectrum even if the most abundant species is the octahedral one. Nevertheless, complexes with a symmetry center gain intensity through vibronic coupling, or coupling between the electronic states and normal modes of vibration of appropriate symmetry. Similarly, spin-forbidden transitions may become partially allowed by spin-orbit coupling, connecting states with $\Delta S = \pm 1$. The relaxation of the spin selection rule by spin-orbit coupling is much less than for the symmetry selection rule by vibronic coupling. Thus vibronically allowed bands are more intense than spin-forbidden bands, and the symmetry-forbidden transitions of octahedral complexes are always seen in the spectra. These arguments apply to d-d transitions as well as to CT bands. Usually, CT bands are more intense than d-d bands and less resolved. This makes it difficult to assign CT bands to specific transitions and to use them for diagnostic purposes.

### B. Electronic Spectroscopy of Adsorbed Molecules

Figure 10 shows a general orbital-energy ordering diagram. In the UV-visible region (200 to 700 nm) only $n \rightarrow \pi^*$ and $\pi \rightarrow \pi^*$ transitions are detected. Thus only molecules with nonbonding electrons and unsaturated molecules can be studied. The groups in the molecules carrying the nonbonding electrons or the unsaturation are called chromophores. Their electronic transitions are subjected to the same symmetry and spin selection rules as those of the TMI complexes. Except for paramagnetic molecules, the spin degeneracy (= 2S + 1)

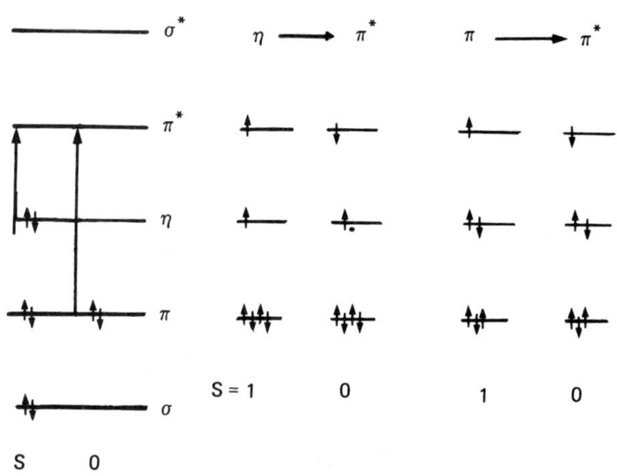


FIG. 10. Ground-state and excited-state electron configurations for molecules with nonbonding electrons and multiple bonds. S is the spin multiplicity.

of the ground state is 1. It is therefore a singlet. Thus for $n \to \pi^*$ and for $\pi \to \pi^*$ transitions, only singlet-singlet transitions are spin-allowed (Fig. 10).

The positions of the band maxima on the surface of a catalyst are determined by many factors, such as steric effects, polarity of the medium, H bonding to surface oxygens, and surface acidity. $n \to \pi^*$ transitions undergo shifts to shorter wavelengths (blue shifts) with increasing polarity; $\pi \to \pi^*$ transitions shift to larger wavelengths (red shifts) [16]. Special attention has been given to surface acidity because protonation of an adsorbed base drastically changes its electronic spectrum. By applying a series of bases with different $pK_B$ values, the strength of the acidity of the catalyst can be probed [17].

## C. Vibrational Spectroscopy

Bands observed in the NIR region (5000 to 12,000 $cm^{-1}$) of diffuse reflectance spectra are mainly combination and overtone bands of OH, NH, and CH vibrations. These bands are of low intensity and result from the anharmonicity of the vibrations of the atoms in the molecules [18]. For anharmonic vibrations the energy levels are expressed as a power series of the vibrational quantum number n, wherein only the first two terms are retained:

$$E = h\nu_f\left(n + \frac{1}{2}\right) - x_a h\nu_f\left(n + \frac{1}{2}\right)^2 \tag{9}$$

where $\nu_f$ is the vibrational frequency in the harmonic oscillator approximation and $x_a$ is the anharmonicity constant. It equals 0 in the harmonic oscillator approximation. In that case only transitions between energy levels with $\Delta n = \pm 1$ are allowed. At RT only the ground state (n = 0) is populated and the vibrational frequency $\nu_f$ corresponds to the energy difference between the levels with n = 1 and with n = 0. That is the fundamental.

The consequences of the anharmonicity are:

1. The occurrence of overtone bands (i.e., transitions corresponding to $\Delta n = \pm 2, \pm 3, \ldots$).
2. The occurrence of combination bands: transitions corresponding to the sum or the difference of fundamental vibrational frequencies.
3. The observed fundamental frequency $\nu_{exp}$ is always smaller than $\nu_f$.
4. In order to determine both $x_a$ and $\nu_f$, at least the fundamental and the first overtone must be experimentally observed.

As an example, Table 4, extracted from Kazansky's work [19], gives the experimentally observed fundamental and first overtone of free silanol groups in $SiO_2$ and their perturbation after adsorption of various molecules. The corresponding harmonic frequencies $\nu_f$ and anharmonicity constants $x_a$, calculated with the aid of Eq. (9), are also given. It is shown that the perturbation by adsorbed molecules increases the anharmonicity of the vibration.

Overtones and combination bands may be composed of forbidden fundamental transitions. Their observation makes it possible to locate these fundamentals. For hydrated samples it is particularly easy to distinguish between $H_2O$ and surface OH groups. On silica the latter can be seen as a sharp overtone band in the region 7300 to 7350 $cm^{-1}$. Its frequency increases with increasing pretreatment temperature. The overtone $2\nu$ of adsorbed $H_2O$ occurs around 6800 $cm^{-1}$, and is always accompanied by a combination band ($\nu + \delta$) at 5200 $cm^{-1}$.

A final application comes from band intensity analysis. With the true vibrational band shape the Fourier transformation of the band intensities on the time base gives the time development of the molecular reorientation. One can then determine whether the adsorbed molecules are fixed, rotate freely, or are hindered in their rotational mobility [5]. As far as the author is aware, this method has been applied only for $H_2O$ on silicas, zeolites, and micas. One of the reasons is the doubt of the researchers about the experimental band shape as a representation of the true vibrational band shape [5].

TABLE 4 Experimental Frequencies, the Fundamental Frequency, and the Anharmonicity Constant of Free and Perturbed Silanol Groups of $SiO_2$

| | $\nu_{exp}$ ($cm^{-1}$) | First overtone ($cm^{-1}$) | Fundamental ($cm^{-1}$) | Anharmonicity constant |
|---|---|---|---|---|
| Free SiOH | 3749 | 7325 | 3921 | $2.3 \times 10^{-2}$ |
| Perturbed by: | | | | |
| $C_6H_{12}$ | 3720 | 7220 | 3943 | $3 \times 10^{-2}$ |
| $(CH_3)_2CO$ | 3460 | 6400 | 3979 | $76 \times 10^{-2}$ |
| $NH_3$ | 2960 | — | 3670 | $12 \times 10^{-2}$ |

*Source*: After Ref. 19.

## IV. TRANSITION METAL OXIDES

A physicochemical study of oxides as a basis for the understanding of their catalytic properties involves the characterization of their bulk properties (coordination and bonding, valence state of the cation, stoichiometry) and their surface properties (coordinatively unsaturated cations, surface defects, and charge transfer properties) [20]. Any detailed investigation involves a combination of techniques, as shown by the beautiful study of the $Cu/ZnO/M_2O_3$ (M = Al, Cr) catalyst for methanol synthesis from synthesis gas [21]. DRS or other spectroscopic techniques in the same frequency range have been used mainly to probe the bulk or overall properties of the oxides. Surface properties were investigated by DRS after adsorption of gases.

In the early 1960s it was suggested that bonding and ligand field strength of TM ions in oxides is determined both by the nearest-neighboring oxygens and the next nearest neighbors [22,23]. The ligand field parameters Dq and Racah's repulsion parameter B for octahedral coordination, summarized in Table 5, illustrate the point. In the compounds of Table 5 the TMI-ligand distances are the same, yet the Dq values differ appreciably for the same cation. This is due not only to the effects of next-nearest-neighboring ligands, but also to the charge distribution in the complex, in other words, the nature of the bonding. Indeed, the B values of Table 5 show increasing covalent character with decreasing Dq.

On the surface, coordinatively unsaturated ions exist whose properties cannot be rationalized in terms of the bulk properties dis-

TABLE 5 Ligand Field Parameter Dq and the Electronic Repulsion Parameter B for Octahedral Coordination

| Oxide | Dq ($cm^{-1}$) | B ($cm^{-1}$) | $B/B_0$ |
|---|---|---|---|
| CoO | 920 | 835 | 0.75 |
| Co/MgO | 920 | 835 | 0.85 |
| $CoWO_4$ | 690 | 770 | 0.69 |
| $NiWO_4$ | 710 | — | — |
| Ni/MgO | 860 | — | — |
| $CrF_6$ | 750 | 920 | 0.89 |
| $K_2NaCrF_8$ | 1650 | 680 | 0.66 |

*Source*: Data from Refs. 22 and 23.

cussed above. Thus on the surface of a thoroughly outgassed MgO surface, absorptions are observed with bands at 37,000 and 46,000 $cm^{-1}$. They are due to coordinatively unsaturated oxygen ions. These ions are preferential chemisorption sites [24]. The same oxygen ions can be excited at 254 nm to give an emission band at 415 nm, while the OH groups are excited at 365 nm and emit at 470 nm [25].

On $ThO_2$, luminescence is excited during CO oxidation [26,27]. This phenomenon, called "cataluminescence," involves the same transitions as in the photoluminescence, that is, excited states of the $4f^8$ ($Th^{3+}$) electron configuration.

The luminescence of tracer ions ($Fe^{3+}$, $Cr^{3+}$, $Mn^{2+}$, $Mn^{4+}$) incorporated into the structure of catalysts is structure sensitive and characteristic of the host lattice. Compound formation even at very low concentration, structural changes, and diffusion from the surface to the bulk can be studied [28-31]. Some characteristic emission bands in typical host lattices are summarized in Table 6.

Recently, DRS has been applied quantitatively on the low pressure methanol synthesis catalysts, Cu/ZnO, $Cu/ZnO/Al_2O_3$, and $Cu/ZnO/Cr_2O_3$ [21,32]. Figure 11 shows the representative spectra

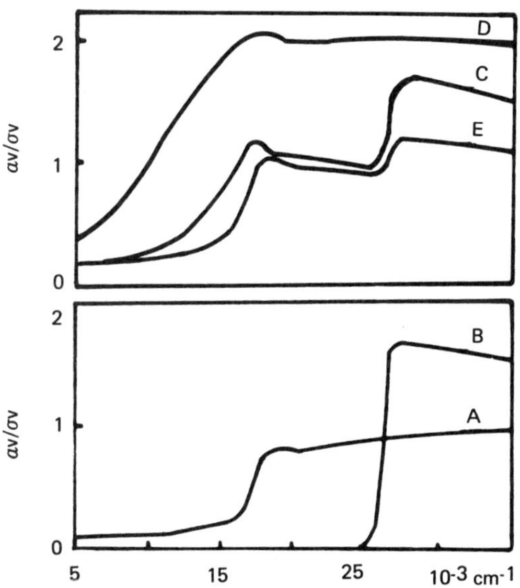


FIG. 11. Reflectance spectra of Cu/ZnO catalysts and reference compounds: A, pure Cu; B, pure ZnO; C, Cu/ZnO with composition 5/95 wt %; D, Cu/ZnO with composition 30/70 wt %; E, Cu/ZnO with composition 67/33 wt %. The experimental spectrum is calculated with the aid of Eq. (3) and plotted. (From Ref. 32.)

TABLE 6 Emission Band Maxima and Their Assignment

| Compound | Emission maximum (nm) |
|---|---|
| $Mn^{4+}$ | |
| In $Li_2CO_3/\gamma$-$Al_2O_3$ | 700 (bread) |
| In $Li_2CO_3/\alpha$-$Al_2O_3$ | 676 (sharp) |
| In Li-$\beta$-$Al_2O_3$ | 725 |
| In $\alpha$-$LiAlO_2$ | 667, 674 (sharp) |
| In ordered $LiAl_5O_8$ | 716 (sharp) |
| In disordered $LiAl_5O_8$ | 661 (sharp) |
| $Cr^{3+}$ | |
| In $Al_2(MoO_4)_3$ | 740 (doublet), 820 (broad) |
| In $\gamma$-$Al_2O_3$ | 703, 720 (shoulder) |
| $Mn^{2+}$ | |
| On surface of $\gamma$-$Al_2O_3$ | 515 |
| On surface of $SiO_2$ | 510 (weak) |
| $Fe^{3+}$ | |
| In silicoaluminates | |
| In the bulk | 690 |
| At the surface | 720 |
| $Fe^{3+}$ in silicoaluminates heated above 573 K | |
| tetrahedral $Fe^{3+}$ sharing edges | 790 |
| In amorphous $Al_2O_3$ phase | 770 |
| $Fe^{3+}$ | |
| In ordered $LiAl_5O_8$ | 656 |
| In disordered $LiAl_5O_8$ | 727 |
| In $\beta$-$NaAlO_2$ | 704 |
| In sodalite | 699 |
| In Na-silicate glass | 699 |

*Source*: Data from Refs. 28 to 31.

of the Cu/ZnO system. Equation (3) is plotted against the wavenumber. Three features are clearly visible: the ZnO absorption edge at 25,800 $cm^{-1}$, the d hump of metallic Cu at 17,500 $cm^{-1}$, and a broad absorption peaked at 17,500 $cm^{-1}$, due to the charge transfer between $Cu^+$, dissolved into the ZnO lattice and $Zn^{2+}$ [21].

Equation (3) allows a quantitative measurement of every component of the system, provided that the scattering coefficient is independent of the chemical composition of the catalyst [32]. This assumption is expected to hold whenever a single component dominates the light scattering, in this case ZnO. The ZnO absorption edge (Fig. 10) does not overlap with the other bands. Thus below 24,000 $cm^{-1}$ the absorption is due to $Cu^+$/ZnO and metallic Cu. At high Cu contents the metallic Cu band dominates the spectrum. Below 15 wt % CuO the $Cu^+$ band is predominant. Thus difference spectra can be obtained which allow the spectrum of $Cu^+$/ZnO to be obtained in the presence of metallic Cu.

## V. SUPPORTED CATALYSTS

The characteristic of a TMI at the surface of a diamagnetic carrier, which does not have an absorption of its own, is its coordinative unsaturation. This is especially evident at small loadings ($<1\%$). Coordinative unsaturation means that the symmetry of the first coordination shell is lower than octahedral or the number of ligands is less than 6. The most common symmetries are tetrahedral, trigonal, and square-pyramidal [19]. In most cases even these low-symmetry sites are distorted, but this distortion does not always show up in the DRS spectra taken at RT. The low symmetry affects the spectroscopic properties of the TMIs at the level of both the d-d transitions and the CT bands. It results in a change of CFSE with respect to the octahedral one and a difference in the electron distribution over the d orbitals. As a consequence, the chemical reactivity of these coordinatively unsaturated transition metal ions is affected. This is experimentally verified by (1) the ease with which the coordinatively unsaturated TMI adsorb ligands to complete their coordination to the octahedral case; (2) by their redox properties or electron transfer from the surface to adsorbed electron-accepting molecules [19]; and (3) the catalytic activity. Dowden has presented a ligand field model of catalysis over coordinatively unsaturated surface TMI more than 10 years ago [33].

The support is not always indifferent toward the transition metal. The interaction support-transition metal ion may ultimately lead to compound formation. Less drastic interaction are support-induced coordination symmetries: on MgO, octahedral symmetry predominates; on $SiO_2$, tetrahedral symmetry; and on $Al_2O_3$, both can occur simultaneously. How far this is due to compound formation in the surface layer of the support or to a support effect on the adsorbed TMI is difficult to establish.

It is clear that these supported catalysts are complicated materials. A multitude of coordination geometries exists, often simultaneously, depending on the type of support, the starting TMI complex, the loading, and the pretreatment. The DRS spectra are usually complex, and in most cases only a qualitative analysis in terms of idealized coordination geometries is possible. Here the most recent literature will be reviewed. It involves the 3d TM ions $Cu^{2+}$, $Ni^{2+}$, $Co^{2+}$, and $Cr^{x+}$; some 4d and 5d TM, such as Mo, Pd, and Ir; and a combination of these ions.

## A. $Cu^{2+}$

The DRS spectra of $Cu^{2+}$ on oxidic supports are dominated by broad bands in the regions expected for octahedral and tetrahedral coordination, 12,000 and 7000 $cm^{-1}$, respectively. On MgO only octahedral $Cu^{2+}$ is found, absorbing at 11,500 $cm^{-1}$. It is axially distorted on the surface. This results in supplementary shoulders around 9500 and 14,500 $cm^{-1}$ [34]. For $Cu^{2+}/Al_2O_3$ and $Mg_xCu_{1-x}Al_2O_4$ spinels the octahedral band maxima are around 13,300 and 12,000 $cm^{-1}$, respectively; the tetrahedral band has its maximum at 7000 $cm^{-1}$ but it extends from 8000 to 6000 $cm^{-1}$ [35,36]. These broad bands, typical for $Cu^{2+}$, encompass several components because both the octahedral and tetrahedral ground states are degenerated and subjected to the Jahn-Teller effect. As a result of the absence of an symmetry center in tetrahedral $Cu^{2+}$, the absorption coefficient of the d-d bands is at least an order of magnitude higher than that of octahedral $Cu^{2+}$. Thus in $Cu/Al_2O_4$ with 60% octahedral and 40% tetrahedral $Cu^{2+}$, only the latter shows up clearly in the spectrum [35].

The CT bands may also reveal information on the environment of $Cu^{2+}$. Boreskov reports an $O^{2-} \rightarrow Cu^{2+}$ band at 36,500 $cm^{-1}$ for isolated $Cu^{2+}$ ions on MgO and a band at 28,000 $cm^{-1}$ for $(Cu\text{-}O\text{-}Cu)_n$ clusters [34]. This means that the oxygens of the clusters are better electron donors than the surface oxygens of MgO. The difference in optical electronegativity of both types of oxygens calculated from these frequencies is 0.3. The $(Cu\text{-}O\text{-}Cu)_n$ clusters, however, do not yet resemble bulk CuO, whose band gap is only 5000 $cm^{-1}$ (Table 3).

## B. $Ni^{2+}$

When annealed at sufficiently high temperatures $Ni^{2+}$ forms true solid solutions with high surface area MgO. The coordination of $Ni^{2+}$ is then octahedral. For $Ni^{2+}$ in the surface layers a square-pyramidal coordination has been suggested [37].

On silica, small loadings of $Ni^{2+}$ (<1%) calcined at 928 K give a well-resolved tetrahedral spectrum with the typical bands at 6000 and 14,000 $cm^{-1}$ and a CT band at 35,000 $cm^{-1}$ [38]. However, the attribution of the supplementary bands at 18,000 to 19,000 $cm^{-1}$ to spin-forbidden transitions and at 24,000 to 25,000 $cm^{-1}$ to charge transfer transitions of tetrahedral $Ni^{2+}$ is doubtful. For instance, the latter band is also found as a d-d transition of trigonal $Ni^{2+}$ in zeolites [39]. In any case these spectra indicate isolated or well-dispersed $Ni^{2+}$, whereas above 1 wt % loading, NiO is the predominant phase on the surface of $SiO_2$. The typical octahedral band of $Ni^{2+}$ in NiO is at 13,500 to 14,000 $cm^{-1}$. In excess oxygen, $Ni^{3+}$ is formed with its characteristic band at 18,500 $cm^{-1}$.

Both bands have been observed on Ni-loaded silicoaluminas with high $SiO_2$ content [40]. At high alumina content, bands of octahedral and tetrahedral $Ni^{2+}$ are found, the latter being indicative for the formation of a surface spinel [40]. Surface spinels are also formed on pure aluminas together with a NiO phase [41,42]. The spinel formation is proportional to the surface area: $\eta\text{-}Al_2O_3 > \theta\text{-}Al_2O_3 > \alpha\text{-}Al_2O_3$. The characteristic bands of octahedral and tetrahedral Ni in $NiAl_2O_4$ are at 16,400 $cm^{-1}$ (tetrahedral) and 24,700 $cm^{-1}$ (octahedral).

## C. $Co^{2+}$

High-surface-area $Co_xMg_{1-x}O$ is characterized by tetrahedral-like $Co^{2+}$ species at the surface [34,37]. The spectrum consists of a band at 7000 $cm^{-1}$ with a shoulder around 9000 $cm^{-1}$, a band at 13,500 $cm^{-1}$, and a triplet: 16,800, 18,300, and 19,500 $cm^{-1}$ [37]. The 13,500-$cm^{-1}$ band is not characteristic for tetrahedral symmetry. However, it is found as a characteristic band of dehydrated $Co^{2+}$-zeolites [13,43,44]. This suggests that at least part of the spectrum of $Co_xMg_{1-x}O$ is due to trigonal $Co^{2+}$. Asmolov et al. [45] have suggested a five-coordinate surface $Co^{2+}$. Extension of the DRS spectra down to at least 5000 $cm^{-1}$ and ligand field calculations of the type presented by Klier [14] are necessary to discriminate between these possible geometries.

On the surface of silica, pseudotetrahedral $Co^{2+}$ is the dominant species after calcination [46], whereas on aluminas and oxides such as $Ga_2O_3$, ZnO, and $GeO_2$, surface spinels are formed and a $Co_3O_4$ phase [47-51]. The tetrahedral triplet band in the visible (16,000, 17,000, and 18,200 $cm^{-1}$) dominates the spinel spectrum, whereas $Co_3O_4$ can be identified by two broad bands around 13,300 and 22,200 $cm^{-1}$. Various factors such as the dispersion effect of $Na^+$ and B, as evidenced by the appearance of the triplet at the expense of the $Co_3O_4$ bands, and the effect of the loading and the preparation method can be studied, but up to now these DRS studies are all qualitative [47-51].

## D. $Cr^{x+}$ (x = 2, 3, 4)

The spectra of Cr on silica and alumina can be interpreted in terms of $Cr^{3+}$ and $Cr^{6+}$ surrounded by oxygen ligands. $Cr^{6+}$ ($3d^\circ$) in a tetrahedral ligand field is characterized by two CT bands at 27,000 $cm^{-1}$

(very broad) and 37,000 $cm^{-1}$. The two characteristic d-d transitions of $Cr^{3+}$ ($3d^3$) in a ligand field of oxide ions are located at 23,500 and at 17,100 $cm^{-1}$ [52,53]. Kazansky and colleagues [54] have reported somewhat lower frequencies: 21,200 and 15,900 $cm^{-1}$.

Impregnation of a silica with $CrO_3$ solution followed by calcination gives more or less isolated $Cr^{3+}$ ions in an octahedral ligand field of oxide ions. They sinter to $Cr_2O_3$ [52]. $Cr^{6+}$ is stable on alumina under calcination conditions [55]. Impregnation of alumina with $CrCl_3$ or coprecipitation of chromium and aluminum hydroxyde gels results in mixed ($Cr^{3+}$, $Cr^{6+}$) oxides upon calcination [53]. These mixed oxides have collective electrons and a characteristic broad absorption band between 14,000 and 4000 $cm^{-1}$ [52,53,56]. Kazansky has also studied the redox chemistry of chromium on silica [54]. Thus after calcination in $O_2$ of a chromic acid-impregnated silica, reduction with $H_2$ or CO at 773 K gives $Cr^{2+}$ in a tetrahedral-like environment. The characteristic d-d band is at 13,000 $cm^{-1}$, in good agreement with its position in dehydrated CrA zeolites [57]. The second d-d band at 17,000 $cm^{-1}$ was not seen in Kazansky's spectra, but this is probably due to poor resolution. In any case this $Cr^{2+}$ is converted to $Cr^{3+}$ in hydrothermal conditions or under the action of light.

$Cr^{4+}$ in a pseudotetrahedral environment of oxide ions in zeolites has three characteristic d-d bands: 13,000, 20,000, and 27,500 $cm^{-1}$ [57]. In the light of these data the interpretation of bands at 27,000 and 36,500 $cm^{-1}$ as d-d bands of $Cr^{4+}$ in $\alpha$-$Al_2O_3$ and $\beta$-$Al_2O_3$ seems to be incorrect [58]. They were obtained after heating in $O_2$ and are therefore more correctly assigned to the charge transfer bands of $Cr^{6+}$.

## E. 4d and 5d Transition Metal Ions

The catalytically very important 4d and 5d transition metals are immobilized on the carriers as complexes, mostly chloro or ammine complexes. These complexes are usually decomposed in a controlled manner to yield a well-dispersed metallic catalyst. DRS has been applied qualitatively on these systems to characterize the complexes on the surface, that is, as long as well-defined, isolated, mononuclear or polynuclear species are present. After destruction of the complexes in an oxidizing or reducing atmosphere, DRS has been of little or no help to characterize the metallic phase or the supported metal oxide.

The interpretation of the spectra of 4d and 5d transition metals is not straightforward. Charge transfer and d-d bands occur in the same frequency range. As a consequence, the latter are often masked by the more intense charge transfer bands. Usually, the spectra of catalysts are compared to solution spectra of known compounds in order to decide about the nature of the surface complexes.

The spectroscopy of Mo is a good example to illustrate these points. When $\eta$-$Al_2O_3$ is impregnated with $(NH_4)_2 Mo_7O_{24} \cdot 4H_2O$, the wet samples show a single band in the range 43,500 to 41,700 $cm^{-1}$ at 1 to 3 wt % Mo loading. This band is due to isolated tetrahedral $MoO_4^{2-}$ [59]. Upon drying, or at high loadings, a band at 35,700 to 34,500 $cm^{-1}$ develops at the expense of the $MoO_4^{2-}$ band. It is characteristic of the Mo-O-Mo bridge in polymeric species, but the exact geometry around $Mo^{6+}$ is unknown. All these bands are oxide → $Mo^{6+}$ charge transfer bands as $Mo^{6+}$ is a 4d° ion.

Literature reports [55,60,61] gave a band in the range 38,460 to 35,700 $cm^{-1}$ for tetrahedral $MoO_4^{2+}$ and in the range 33,300 to 30,000 $cm^{-1}$ for octahedral $Mo^{6+}$. The former is observed on silica, the latter on MgO, while both are found on alumina, their relative concentration depending on the loading and the method of immobilization or the precursor complex. Proposed characteristic bands for $Mo^{5+}$ ($4d^1$) in octahedral and tetrahedral symmetry are located respectively at 25,000 and 20,000 $cm^{-1}$ [61]. For octahedral $Mo^{4+}$ ($4d^2$) bands are reported at 28,600 and 20,400 $cm^{-1}$ [61]. At first sight all these bands are due to d-d transitons, but in the absence of intensity data this assignment is by no means sure. Polymeric Mo species especially may give rise to low-lying charge transfer bands.

When the carriers are impregnated with aqueous solutions of chloro complexes, the nature of the surface complexes not only depends on the type of support and the loading, but also on the excess $Cl^-$ present in solution. This is exemplified by the studies of Bozon-Verduraz et al. [62,63] on Ir and Pd. This is because the stability of complexes such as $IrCl_6^{2-}$ and $PdCl_4^{2-}$ strongly depends on the $Cl^-$ concentration and on the ionic strength. Both factors are affected by the surface because excess $Cl^-$ may form a partially chlorinated surface, especially on alumina. The Pd species found on various surfaces and their characteristic bands are shown in Table 7.

When $H_2IrCl_6$ is supported from HCl solution, the surface complex is predominantly $IrCl_6^{2-}$. Its thermal stability is proportional to the ease with which the support can accommodate $Cl^-$. In aqueous solutions at low loadings, partially chlorinated Ir(III) complexes are deposited and at higher loadings $IrCl_6^{2-}$ dominates the reflectance spectra. This is especially evident on MgO. It is highly probable that these impregnating solutions contain various species and so does the support. However, with DRS one detects the most abundant species only.

These problems are avoided by the use of stable ammine complexes such as $[Pd(NH_3)_4]^{2+}$ [63,64], $[Pt(NH_3)_4]^{2+}$, $[Ru(NH_3)_6]^{2+}$, and $[Rh(NH_3)_5Cl]^{2+}$. It is then possible to start from well-defined complexes on the surface. They decompose via routes well known in inorganic chemistry. For instance, $[Ru(NH_3)_6]^{3+}$ hydrolyzes on zeolites with formation of Ru-red as an intermediate and the rate of the reaction depends on the type of zeolite [65]. $[Rh(NH_3)_5Cl]^{2+}$ is stable at RT on zeolites but decomposes slowly on clays on standing in air with formation of $NH_4^+$ [66]. This illustrates the difference between the

TABLE 7 Reflectance Spectra of Pd Complexes on Oxidic Supports

| Support | Percent Pd | Band maxima ($cm^{-1}$) | Assignment |
|---|---|---|---|
| $\eta$-$Al_2O_3$ | 10 | 35,700, 29,850, 21,050 | $PdCl_4^{2-}$ |
| $\delta$-$Al_2O_3$ | Up to 10 | 35,700, 29,850, 21,050 | $PdCl_4^{2-}$ |
| $SiO_4$ | 1.5-12 | 27,000 | $Pd(H_2O)_4^{2+}$ |
| | | 20,000 | $PdCl_2$ |
| $TiO_4$ | 0.4-1.6 | 35,700 | $PdCl_4^{2-}$ |
| | 2-10 | 20,000 | $PdCl_2$ |

*Source*: Data from Ref. 63.

surface acidity of zeolites and those of clays. Similar differences between the surface properties of aluminas, silica, MgO, and $TiO_2$ will determine the decomposition of surface-immobilized complexes.

## F. Combination of Transition Metal Ions

In mixed transition metal oxides or sulfides, as such or supported, substitution of one metal into the lattice of the other may influence the geometry of the coordination sphere and its coordination bond characteristics. In cobalt chromium oxide the bands of tetrahedral $Co^{2+}$ and octahedral $Co^{3+}$ in the visible shift to higher wavenumber by ~700 $cm^{-1}$ with increasing $Cr^{3+}$ content. Kadenatsi et al. [67] suggested that this was evidence for increased ionicity of the Co-O bond. The effect is small, however, and the proposed interpretation vague. Upon substitution of Fe into $Co_6Mo_{12}O_x$, Isaev and Margolis [68] found a small effect of the Co spectrum, indicating that $Fe^{3+}$ substitutes $Co^{3+}$.

The most studied effect is, however, the promoter effect of Co and Ni on Mo in the hydrodesulfurization (HDS) catalysts. In its oxidic form the spectra are dominated by tetrahedral $Mo^{6+}$ and tetrahedral $Co^{2+}$. Only at high coverages is there evidence for octahedral $Mo^{6+}$ and octahedral $Co^{2+}$. The effect of $Co^{2+}$ is to reduce the tetrahedral $Mo^{6+}$ band and shift it to lower wavenumbers. Presumably, Co-O-Mo bonds are formed [69] together with octahedral $Mo^{6+}$, although the majority species remains tetrahedral $Mo^{6+}$. Tetrahedral $Co^{2+}$ is due to the formation of $CoAl_2O_4$ upon calcination especially

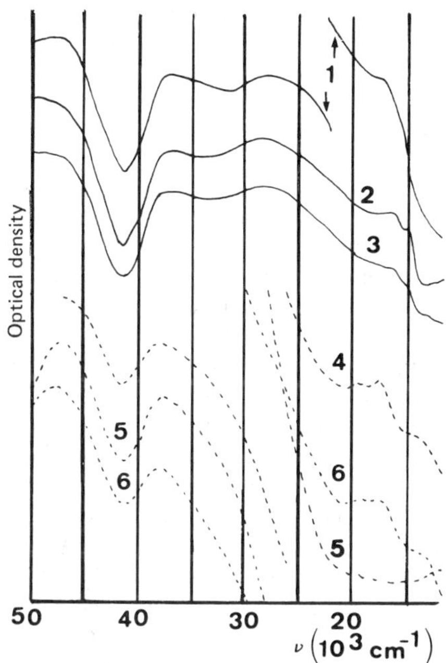


FIG. 12. Reflectance spectra of sulfided (--) and oxidic silica-supported hydrodesulfurization catalysts. (From Ref. 72.)

above 873 K [70]. This does not mean that octahedral $Co^{2+}$ is absent. Indeed, the d-d transition intensities of octahedral $Co^{2+}$ are at least 100 times weaker and can be completely masked by tetrahedral $Co^{2+}$ even when present in appreciable concentration. Some of the $Co^{2+}$ is certainly present as a surface species, probably in $C_{3v}$ symmetry. The d-d transitions in $C_{3v}$ and $T_d$ symmetries overlap to a large extent but small changes were observed upon adsorption of $H_2O$ on a calcined hds catalyst [71]. The changes were in the expected direction for a conversion of $C_{3v}$ to $T_d$ symmetry, but any quantitative estimate from DRS spectra was impossible.

The spectra of these HDS catalysts can be quite complicated, but by comparison with reference compounds, the different species of the oxidic form and sulfidic form can be readily distinguished [72]. Figure 12 gives an example. Some other examples of application of DRS to HDS catalysts in conjunction with other techniques can be found in the papers of Delmon and co-workers [73-75].

All these spectra were recorded after activation of the catalysts. After deposition of the complexes on the surface, the overall reflectance spectrum is usually the superposition of the spectra of the individual components. This was shown by Blanchard et al. [76] for deposition of $H_2PtCl_6$ and $H_2RuCl_6$ on silica and alumina. After reduction a bimetallic catalyst is formed.

## VI. ADSORBED ORGANIC MOLECULES

In earlier work organic molecules were adsorbed onto $SiO_2$, $Al_2O_3$, and $SiO_2$-$Al_2O_3$ to probe the acidity of their surfaces. Carbenium ions were formed and stabilized and could be detected by DRS [17]. An interesting new development in this area is the study of the luminescence and photochemical properties of surface-immobilized organic molecules. The preliminary results obtained so far indicate that the properties of the excited state of adsorbed molecules are strongly dependent on the surface properties of the support. Thus the method may yield valuable information on the properties of surfaces but also new photochemical and photocatalytic processes may be developed. For instance, trans-stilbene, chemisorbed on alumina, can be removed by irradiation at 31,950 $cm^{-1}$, its absorption band maximum being around 33,000 $cm^{-1}$. It returns in a dark reaction. The intermediate is believed to be stilbene chemisorbed on a surface Al through its ethylenic band [77]. Oelkrug et al. [78] have measured the luminescence characteristics of aromatics chemisorbed on $\gamma$-$Al_2O_3$. Both the population of the triplet states and the thermal quenching of the phosphorescence are affected by the activation temperature of the support. As the number of surface OH groups decreases with increasing pretreatment temperature, it is tempting to suggest that they are involved in the thermal phosphorescence quenching.

A special technique for DRS of excited states of adsorbed molecules has been developed by Kessler and Wilkinson [79]. It is expected that surface properties can be probed by a study of the excited-state properties of adsorbed molecules.

## VII. CONCLUSIONS

DRS is an easily applicable tecchnique with commercially available attachments to each spectrometer. Computer-assisted DRS allows almost unlimited data manipulation. The interpretation of the spectra is based on known and easily accessible theories.

On catalysts TMI in various coordination geometries have been identified. The type of support, the loading, and the pretreatment determine the behavior of the TMI. Quantitative studies have been scarce. It has been shown that they are possible. It is hoped that more quantitative studies will appear in the literature. An interesting new development is the study of surface properties of catalysts from a knowledge of the excited-state properties of adsorbed molecules.

## ACKNOWLEDGMENTS

The author acknowledges a permanent research position as Senior Research Associate of the National Fund of Scientific Research (Belgium). He has appreciated very much the stimulating interest of Professor J. B. Uytterhoeven in the course of this work. The author thanks Mrs. P. Van Brusselen for typing this manuscript.

## REFERENCES

1. A. Rosencwaig, *Photoacoustics and Photoacoustic Spectroscopy*, Wiley, New York, 1981.
2. R. Kellerman, in *Spectroscopy in Heterogeneous Catalysis* (W. N. Delgass, G. L. Haller, R. Kellerman, and J. H. Lunsford, eds.), Academic Press, New York, 1979, p. 86.
3. R. L. Schmidt, in *Advanced Chemical Methods for Soil and Clay Minerals Research* (J. W. Stucki and W. L. Banwart, eds.), NATO Advanced Study Institutes Series C: Mathemaical and Physical Sciences, D. Reidel, Dordrecht, Holland, 1980, p. 451.
4. G. Kortüm, *Reflectance Spectroscopy*, Springer-Verlag, Berlin, 1969.
5. K. Klier, in *Vibrational Spectroscopies for Adsorbed Species* (A. T. Bell and M. L. Hair, eds.), *ACS Symp. Ser., 137*: 141 (1980).
6. K. Klier, *J. Opt. Soc. Am., 62*: 882 (1972).
7. R. A. Schoonheydt, in *Advanced Methods in Clay Minerals Analysis* (J. J. Fripiat, ed.), Elsevier, Amsterdam, 1981, p. 169.
8. D. S. Schonland, *Molecular Symmetry*, D. Van Nostrand, London, 1965.
9. A. B. P. Lever, *Inorganic Electronic Spectroscopy*, Elsevier, Amsterdam, 1968, p. 241.
10. J. S. Griffith, *The Theory of Transition-Metal Ions*, Cambridge University Press, Cambridge, 1971, p. 437.
11. S. Sugano, Y. Tanabe, and H. Kamimura, *Multiplets of Transition-Metal Ions in Crystals*, Academic Press, New York, 1970.
12. T. M. Dunn, D. S. McClure, and R. G. Pearson, *Some Aspects of Crystal Field Theory*, Harper & Row, New York, 1965, p. 86.
13. J. A. Duffy, *Struct. Bonding, 31*: 147 (1975).
14. K. Klier, P. J. Hutta, and R. Kellerman, *ACS Symp. Ser., 40*: 108 (1977).
15. D. H. Strome and K. Klier, in *Molecular Sieves II* (J. Kotrer, ed.), *ACS Symp. Ser., 135*: 137 (1980).
16. C. N. R. Rao, *Ultra-violet and Visible Spectroscopy*, Butterworth, London, 1975.
17. Kh. Dimitrov, N. A. Zubareva, V. I. Lygin, and I. Topalova, *Kinet. Katal., 18*: 1501 (1977).

18. G. Herzberg, *Molecular Spectra and Molecular Structure* Vol. 2: *Infrared and Raman Spectra of Polyatomic Molecules*, D. Van Nostrand, Princeton, N.J., 1968, p. 201.
19. V. B. Kazanski, *Proc. 6th Int. Congr., Catal.*, Vol. 1 (G. C. Bond, P. B. Wells, and F. C. Tompkins, eds.), The Chemical Society, London, 1977, p. 50.
20. F. S. Stone, *J. Solid State Chem.*, *12*: 271 (1975).
21. R. G. Herman, K. Klier, G. W. Simmons, B. P. Finn, J. B. Bulko, and T. P. Kobylinski, *J. Catal.*, *56*: 407 (1979).
22. J. Ferguson, K. Knox, and D. L. Wood, *J. Chem. Phys.*, *35*: 2236 (1961).
23. R. Pappalardo, D. L. Wood, and R. C. Linares, Jr., *J. Chem. Phys.*, *35*: 2041 (1961).
24. F. S. Stone and A. Zecchina, *Proc. 6th Int. Congr. Catal.*, Vol. 1 (G. C. Bond, P. B. Wells, and F. C. Tomkins, eds.), The Chemical Society, London. 1977, p. 162.
25. S. Coluccia, M. Deane, and A. J. Tench, *Proc. 6th Int. Congr. Catal.*, Vol. 1 (G. C. Bond, P. B. Wells, and F. C. Tomkins, eds.), The Chemical Society, London. 1977, p. 171.
26. M. Breysse, B. Claudel, L. Faure, M. Guenin, R. J. J. Williams, and T. Solkenstein, *J. Catal.*, *45*: 137 (1976).
27. V. M. Aras, M. Breysse, B. Claudel, L. Faure, and M. Guenin, *J. Chem. Soc., Faraday Trans. 1*, *74*: 1039 (1978).
28. G. T. Pott and B. D. McNicol, *Discuss. Faraday. Soc.*, *52*: 121 (1971).
29. G. T. Pott and B. D. McNicol, *Chem. Phys. Lett.*, *12*: 62 (1971).
30. G. T. Pott, *Proc. 6th Int. Congr. Catal.*, Vol. 1 (G. C. Bond, P. B. Wells, and F. C. Tomkins, eds.), The Chemical Society London. 1977, p. 195.
31. G. T. Pott and B. D. McNicol, *J. Chem. Phys.*, *56*: 5246 (1972).
32. J. B. Bulko, R. G. Herman, K. Klier, and G. W. Simmons, *J. Phys. Chem.*, *83*: 3118 (1979).
33. D. A. Dowden, in *Proc. 4th Int. Cong. Catal.*, Akadémiai Kiadó, Budapest, 1971, p. 163.
34. G. K. Boreskov, *Proc. 6th Int. Congr. Catal.*, Vol. 1 (G. C. Bond, P. B. Wells, and F. C. Tomkins, eds.), The Chemical Society, London. 1967, p. 204.
35. J. J. Freeman and R. M. Friedman, *J. Chem. Soc., Faraday Trans. 1*, *74*: 758 (1978).
36. P. K. Sharpe, J. C. Vickerman, and M. H. Stacey, *Proc. 6th Int. Congr. Catal.*, Vol. 1 (G. C. Bond, P. B. Wells, and F. C. Tompkins, eds.), The Chemical Society, London, 1977, p. 225.
37. A. P. Hagan, M. G. Lofthouse, F. S. Stone, and M. A. Trevethan, in *Preparation of Catalysts II* (B. Delmon, P. Grange,

P. Jacobs, and G. Poncelet, eds.), Elsevier Scientific, New York, 1979, p. 417.
38. V. A. Kaverinskii, V. Yu. Borovkov, V. A. Shvets, and V. B. Kazanskii, *Kinet. Katal.*, *15*: 819 (1974).
39. K. Klier and M. Ralek, *J. Phys. Chem. Solids*, *29*: 451 (1968).
40. M. Houalla and B. Delmon, *J. Phys. Chem.*, *84*: 2194 (1980).
41. M. Houalla, F. Delannay, and B. Delmon, *J. Phys. Chem.*, *85*: 1704 (1981).
42. S. Engels, W. Mörke, M. Wilde, W. Roschke, B. Freitag, and H. Siegel, *Z. Anorg. Allg. Chem.*, *472*: 162 (1981).
43. P. J. Hutta and J. H. Lunsford, *J. Chem. Phys.*, *66*: 4716
44. R. A. Schoonheydt, D. Van Wouwe, and M. Van Hove, *J. Colloid Interface Sci.*, *83*: 279 (1981).
45. G. N. Asmolov, V. A. Matyshak, A. A. Kadushin, and O. V. Krylov, *Kinet. Katal.*, *18*: 1506 (1977).
46. O. I. Brotikovskii, V. A. Shvets, and V. B. Kazansky, *Kinet. Katal.*, *13*: 1342 (1972).
47. M. Lo Jacono and M. Schiavello, in *Preparation of Catalysts I* (B. Delmon, P. A. Jacobs, and G. Poncelet, eds.), Elsevier Scientific, New York, 1976, p. 473.
48. A. Lycourghiatis, C. Defosse, F. Delannay, J. Lemaitre, and B. Delmon, *J. Chem. Soc.*, *Faraday Trans. 1*, *76*: 1677 (1980).
49. A. Lycourghiotis, C. Defosse, and B. Delmon, *Bull Soc. Chim. Belg.*, *89*: 929 (1980).
50. M. Houalla and B. Delmon, *Appl. Catal.*, *1*: 285 (1981).
51. A. Lycourghiotis, *React. Kinet. Catal. Lett.*, *17*: 165 (1981).
52. A. Cimino, B. A. De Angelis, A. Luchetti, and G. Minelli, *J. Catal.*, *45*: 316 (1976).
53. A. Ellison and K. S. W. Sing, *J. Chem. Soc.*, *Faraday Trans. 1*, *74*: 2017 (1978).
54. L. K. Pezheval'skaya, V. A. Shvets, and V. B. Kazanski, *Kinet. Katal.*, *11*: 1310 (1970).
55. A. Iannibello, S. Marengo, F. Trifiro, and P. O. Villa, in *Preparation of Catalysts II* (B. Delmon, P. Grange, P. Jacobs, and G. Poncelet, eds.), Elsevier Scientific, New York, 1979, p. 65.
56. A. Ellison and K. S. W. Sing, *J. Chem. Soc.*, *Faraday Trans. 1*, *74*: 2807 (1978).
57. R. Kellerman and K. Klier, *ACS Symp. Ser.*, *40*: 120 (1977).
58. J. R. Akridge and J. H. Kennedy, *J. Solid State Chem.*, *26*: 147 (1978).
59. H. Jeziorowski and H. Knözinger, *J. Phys. Chem.*, *83*: 1166 (1979).
60. N. Giordano, J. C. J. Bart, A. Vaghi, A. Castellan, and G. Martinotti, *J. Catal.*, *36*: 81 (1975).
61. M. Che, F. Figueras, M. Forissier, J. McAteer, M. Perrin, J. L. Portefaix, and H. Praliaud, *Proc. 6th Int. Congr. Catal.*,

Vol. 1 (G. C. Bond, P. B. Wells, and F. C. Tompkins, eds.), The Chemical Society, London, 1977, p. 261.

62. F. Bozon-Verduraz, M. Tardy, G. Bugli, G. Pannetier, and C. Leclère, in *Preparation of Catalysts I* (B. Delmon, P. Jacobs, and G. Poncelet, eds.), Elsevier Scientific, New York, 1976, p. 265.
63. F. Bozon-Verduraz, A. Omar, J. Escard, and B. Pantiranne, *J. Catal.*, *53*: 126 (1978).
64. G. R. Tauszik, A. Marzi, and R. Covini, *React. Kinet. Catal. Lett.*, *7*: 7 (1977).
65. J. J. Verdonck, R. A. Schoonheydt, and P. A. Jacobs, *J. Phys. Chem.*, *85*: 2393 (1981).
66. R. A. Schoonheydt, V. Marien, and H. Van Brabant, *Proc. 7th Int. Clay Conf.* (H. E. Van Olphen and F. Veniale, eds.), *Dev. Sedimentol.*, *35*: 253 (1982).
67. B. M. Kadenatsi, K. N. Spiridonov, M. D. Shibanova, and M. Ya. Rushnerev, *Kinet. Katal.*, *19*: 1259 (1978).
68. O. V. Isaev and L. Ya. Margolis, in *Preparation of Catalysts I* (B. Delmon, P. A. Jacobs, and G. Poncelet, eds.), Elsevier Scientific, New York, 1976, p. 177.
69. A. Iannibello and P. C. H. Mitchell, in *Preparation of Catalysts II* (B. Delmon, P. Grange, P. Jacobs, and G. Poncelet, eds.), Elsevier Scientific, New York, 1979, p. 469.
70. R. Moné, in *Preparation of Catalysts I* (B. Delmon, P. A. Jacobs, and G. Poncelet, eds.), Elsevier Scientific, New York, 1976, p. 381.
71. P. Ratnasamy and H. Knözinger, *J. Catal.*, *54*: 155 (1978).
72. M. J. M. Van der Aalst and V. H. J. De Beer, *J. Catal.*, *49*: 247 (1977).
73. P. Gajardo, P. Grange, and B. Delmon, *J. Phys. Chem.*, *83*: 1771 (1979).
74. P. Gajardo, D. Pirotte, P. Grange, and B. Delmon, *J. Phys. Chem.*, *83*: 1780 (1979).
75. A. Lycourghiotis, C. Defossé, F. Delannay, and B. Delmon, *J. Chem. Soc., Faraday Trans.*, *1*, *76*: 2052 (1980).
76. G. Blanchard, H. Charcosset, M. T. Chenebaux, and H. Primet, in *Preparation of Catalysts II* (B. Delmon, P. Grange, P. A. Jacobs, and G. Poncelet, eds.), Elsevier Scientific, New York, 1979, p. 197.
77. H. G. Hecht and J. L. Jensen, *J. Photochem.*, *9*: 33 (1978).
78. D. Oelkrug, M. Plauschinat, and R. W. Kessler, *J. Lumin.*, *18/19*: 434 (1979).
79. R. W. Kessler and F. Wilkinson, *J. Chem. Soc.*, *Faraday Trans. 1*, *77*: 309 (1981).

# 5

# Electron Spin Resonance

JACQUES C. VEDRINE Centre National de la Recherche Scientifique (CNRS), Villeurbanne, France

## I. INTRODUCTION

Increasing interest has been devoted during the past decades in using different physical methods to better understand inorganic solids such as catalysts or organic complexes. It turns out that, in catalysis, the nature of the active sites remains rather unclear at the present time even if some new light has been thrown on it in the last few years. The major difficulties stem from the absence of in situ characterization of a catalyst and from the large heterogeneity within or at the surface of a given material on an atomic scale. A large part of the usual physical methods, frequently used, analyses the whole sample and great interest is now focused on techniques dealing with the very first surface layers of a solid (XPS, ISS, SIMS, or AES) and with high spatial resolution analysis rather than with an overall view. The latter techniques, such as microanalysis with a STEM at high resolution, obviously necessitate a large number of analyses to represent the material rather than some of its particularities. It then turns out to be obligatory to use several physical techniques in order to have a reasonable knowledge of the material. One of these techniques, which is only able to give part of the information, but a very powerful part, is the electron spin resonance (ESR) technique. Its main limitation—which is sometimes a great advantage—is that the technique applies only to paramagnetic species (i.e., compounds with unpaired spins).

## II. GENERAL PRESENTATION OF THE ESR TECHNIQUE

### A. Fundamental Principles

The fundamental principles of ESR have been covered in detail by many authors [1] and some specialized books on ESR spectroscopy are given in Ref. 2a. A somewhat briefer treatment follows to facilitate the reader's understanding.

Any spinning or rotating electric charge behaves like a magnet with its poles along the axis of rotation. An electron spinning about itself has a rotational angular momentum $\underline{S}$, called spin, and consequently a magnetic moment $\underline{\mu}_e$ which is proportional to and collinear with $\underline{S}$. The parameter $\gamma = \underline{\mu}_e/\underline{S}$ is designated the gyromagnetic ratio. Along a quantification axis, the spin vector $\underline{S}$ can take the value $\pm 1/2$ in unit multiples of $\hbar$. If a system containing unpaired electrons (i.e., spin $\neq 0$) is placed in an external magnetic field H, the energy of the system is given by the well-known equation

$$E = \underline{\mu}_e \cdot \underline{H} = -g_e \beta \underline{S} \cdot \underline{H} = \pm(1/2) g_e \beta H \tag{1}$$

which characterizes the interaction between the magnetic field and the spin $\underline{S}$ and which is designated as Zeeman interaction, and where $\cdot$ represents a scalar product or dot product, $g_e$ is a constant designated the g factor and will be described in Sec. II.B, and $\beta$ is the Bohr magneton for the electron. All the electronic spin axes are oriented by the magnetic field either in the same direction (+) (parallel) or in the opposite direction (−) (antiparallel) with respect to $\underline{H}$. In the absence of an applied magnetic field the electrons are oriented at random. Under an applied magnetic field, $\underline{H}$, there are then two populations of spins and a difference in energy, $\Delta E$, given by

$$\Delta E = g_e \beta H \tag{2}$$

At equilibrium, the ratio of populations of both states is given by the Maxwell-Boltzmann law,

$$\frac{n^+}{n^-} = \exp\left(-\frac{\Delta E}{kT}\right) \simeq 1 - \frac{\Delta E}{kT} \tag{3}$$

where k is the Boltzmann constant, and $n^+$ and $n^-$ are the populations of electrons with spin +1/2 and −1/2, respectively. It is worth noting at this stage that at 80 K, and for a microwave frequency of 9 GHz, $n^+$ and $n^-$ populations differ by less than 0.005, which is much less than in optical spectroscopy.

When such an electronic spin system is subjected to a magnetic field H and a photonicwave perpendicular to the magnetic field with a frequency of $\nu$, an electron spin flip from the antiparallel to parallel direction occurs when the photon energy, $h\nu$, is such that the condition $\Delta E = g_e \beta H = h\nu$ is obtained. This is the resonance condition and results in an energy absorption, as shown in Fig. 1. It also implies that the very first feature to remember is that ESR spectroscopy applies only to systems with at least one unpaired electron (i.e., to paramagnetic compounds). Note also that the whole material is concerned; that is, the technique is primarily a bulk *technique*, al-

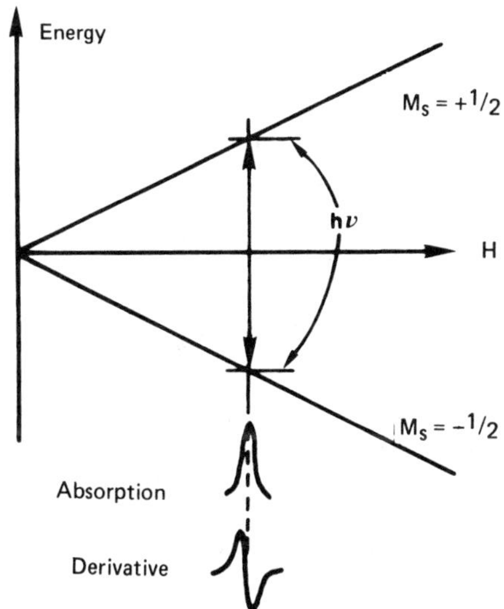


FIG. 1. Energy-level shift of the electron against an applied magnetic field, H.

though it could be applied to surface chemistry when studying adsorbed species.

The electrons return to their initial spin states according to Boltzmann equilibrium, releasing their energy, $h\nu$, which is dissipated into the structure. This is designated as spin-lattice relaxation and is characterized by a time constant $T_{1e}$ of the exponential decay in energy. Return to the initial state also occurs for the spin phase by energy exchange between spins without energy loss to the lattice, and is designated as spin-spin relaxation characterized by the time constant $T_{2e}$. When both spin-spin and spin-lattice relaxations contributes to the ESR line width ($\Delta H$), one can write

$$\Delta H \propto \frac{1}{T_{2e}} + \frac{1}{T_{1e}}$$

In general, $T_{2e} < T_{1e}$ and the line width depends mainly on spin-spin interaction. However, when $T_{1e}$ becomes very short ($<10^{-7}$ s), its effect on the lifetime of a species in a given energy level makes an important contribution to the line width. The lifetime is given by the uncertainty law,

$$\Delta E \Delta t \geqslant \hbar$$

For free radicals or ions in the S state ($L = \Sigma m_L = 0$, where $m_L$ is the magnetic quantum number), the coupling between the orbit and the spin is negligible, $T_{1e}$ is large, and the ESR line reasonably narrow. By contrast, $T_{1e}$ for transition metal or rare earth ions may be very small and broad lines are obtained, sometimes beyond detection. It has been shown that $T_{1e}$ is then inversely proportional to temperature ($T_{1e} \propto T^{-n}$), the value of n depending of the relaxation mechanism. In such cases, cooling down of the sample increases $T_{1e}$ and gives rise to detectable ESR lines. It is therefore necessary to record such spectra at liquid-nitrogen or even at liquid-helium temperature. Obviously, to do that it is also necessary to have the instrumental capability for a wide range of recording temperatures. Note also at this stage that ESR line intensities, which depend on paramagnetic susceptibility, are inversely proportional to the absolute temperature (Curie law), and the capability of recording spectra at low temperature could be very interesting and informative as to the magnetic properties of the sample.

The conclusion that can be drawn at the present time is that ESR spectroscopy can detect paramagnetic compounds, but if the relaxation mechanisms are too fast, ESR signals may not be seen. In other words, it is worth stressing that when an ESR signal is observed, a paramagnetic compound is necessarily involved, while the absence of an ESR signal *does not necessarily mean* that the paramagnetic compounds do not exist in a material.

Another point is also worth emphasizing. When a strong magnetic dipole-dipole interaction takes place between different magnetic species, there exists a very efficient relaxation path, provided that there is a slight overlap in the magnetic energy levels. Such a cross-relaxation process is important for surface studies because $O_2$ from the air is paramagnetic with two unpaired electrons and can absorb on a catalyst surface very readily. This results in a dipolar broadening that makes the signal of the paramagnetic species under study broad or undetectable. Therefore, one way to determine if a paramagnetic species is present in the outermost layer of a material ($d < 10$ Å) is to record its ESR spectrum in vacuum and in air or $O_2$. The presence of an ESR signal in both cases clearly indicates that the paramagnetic species is in the bulk. If there is a signal in vacuum which disappears reversibly in air or $O_2$, the paramagnetic species is in the surface layer. This clearly helps in locating such species in a solid catalyst.

The line intensity is an important characteristic of an ESR spectrum since ESR spectroscopy can be a very reliable method for *quantitative determination* of spin concentrations. This arises from the fact that the spin population directly determines susceptibility. The line intensity is proportional to the magnetic susceptibility, $\chi_0$. One usually integrates point by point the derivative curves and one measures the area of the integrated curves. Comparison is then performed with the standard samples such as strong Pitch Varian (C in KCL: $3 \times 10^{14}$ spins per centimeter length), or diphenylpicrylhydrazil (DPPH) free radical.

As shown above, spin flip will occur when the material is submitted to both a continuous magnetic field and a microwave field applied perpendicularly. Consequently, a spectrometer will be composed of a magnet, giving a continuous magnetic field whose intensity may be varied over a large range (typically 0 to 10,000 G), a resonance cavity where the sample is introduced, and a microwave source designated a klystron (typically 9,000 MHz). The microwave irradiates the sample by means of a waveguide (Fig. 2).

The experiment consists of sweeping the magnetic field until the resonance condition ($h\nu = g\beta H$) is fulfilled, resulting in an energy absorption. The detection is performed using magnetic T properties with a crystal detector located in one of the T arms. As in the case of a Wheatstone bridge, when disequilibrium is created by energy absorption due to resonance in one of the T arms where the sample is placed (resonance cavity), current variation occurs in the crystal detector giving an absorption curve. In practice, absorption curves are weak, but their intensity may be sharply increased by modulating the magnetic field at low frequency (100 kHz). The result is a derivative curve, as shown in Fig. 1.

A solid sample may be analyzed as a single crystal or as a powder. Single crystals may be attached to a sample holder within the resonance cavity and rotated in different directions. Powders ($p \simeq 30$ mg) are generally placed in silica tubes, typically 5 or 6 mm in outside diameter (o.d.). The vertical detection region in the cavity is roughly 2 cm long, with the sensitivity being the greatest at the center and decreasing uniformly (gaussian-type law) along the vertical axis. In some experiments, such as studying anisotropy of single crystals, the cavity and therefore the sample may be kept fixed while the magnet is rotated through 360°.

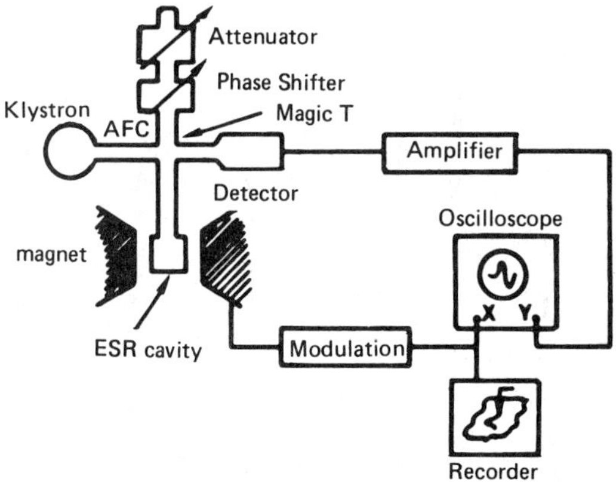


FIG. 2. Scheme of an ESR spectrometer.

When outgassing a material is necessary, for instance when dipolar broadening of the signals due to paramagnetic oxygen occurs, the silica tube may be evacuated in an ordinary vacuum line and sealed off under vacuum. This is important when surface properties of the material have to be studied.

When introducing a sample into the magnet, the resonance frequency of the cavity is altered slightly. It is therefore necessary to tune the klystron frequency in accordance with that of the cavity in order to obtain stationary waves. Recording may be easily performed in a wide range of temperatures, typically 77 to 600 K. Additional accessories may be used to expand the temperature range down to 4.2 K (even 2.2 by pumping) or up to 1300 K, but conducting the experiments is then rather difficult.

It is important to note at this stage that in situ studies may well be performed with such a spectrometer since the temperature may be regulated at a given value rather precisely (±2°). The only experimental difficulty is to design a small reactor able to enter the variable temperature device (i.e., with a 6 mm o.d. in pure silica). However, such a reactor has been built with an inlet and outlet for reactant and product circulation as shown in Fig. 3, and roughly 10 mg of catalyst may be used. A gas chromatograph is put at the output. The limitation in such a use mainly arises from two facts:

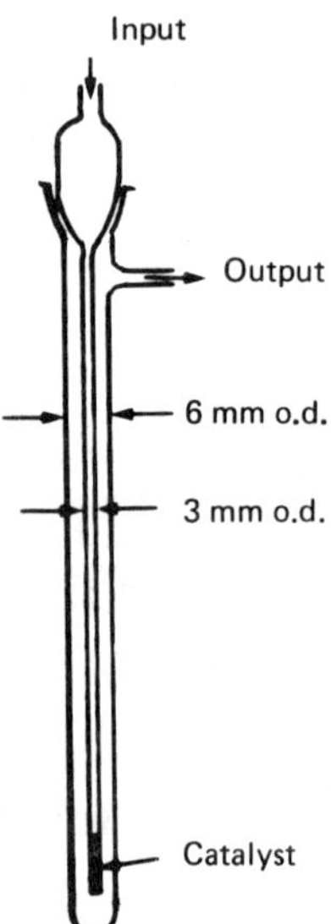


FIG. 3. In situ cell for ESR measurement in catalytic studies.

1. The line intensity follows the Curie law, decreasing when the temperature increases.
2. The line width is a function of the reciprocal $T_{1e}$ and $T_{2e}$ and it is known that the relaxation time $T_{1e}$ sharply decreases when the temperature increases. Thus the line may be broadened beyond detection at high temperature.

As mentioned above, the spectrometer usually works with a 9000-MHz klystron ($\lambda$ = 3 cm, X band). However, for some experiments, other frequencies, such as 23,000 MHz (K band) or 35,000 MHz (Q band, $\lambda$ = 8 mm) are used but require special microwave bridges and different waveguides and cavities.

It is worth noting that the energy involved in such spin-flip transitions is very small ($\simeq 10^{-4}$ eV) compared to molecular spectroscopies ($10^{-1}$ to $10^{2}$ eV, $\lambda = 10^{1}$ to $10^{-2}$ $\mu$m) or surface techniques ($<10^{3}$ eV, $\lambda < 10^{-3}$ $\mu$m).

This means that the ESR technique is not destructive and therefore *does not modify the catalysts during the analysis.*

## B. ESR Parameters [3-8]

The main information that may be gained from ESR experiments arises from three main parameters which are presented below. For a free electron alone, resonance occurs for a magnetic field intensity H according to the fundamental relationship

$$h\nu = g_e \beta H \tag{4}$$

where $g_e$ = 2.0023 and $\beta$ is the Bohr magneton ($\beta = 9.273 \times 10^{-21}$ erg/G). The small deviation of $g_e$ from 2.00 is due to relativistic correction. For such a free electron, a single resonance is always obtained at the same field position and the method would be of very limited interest. Fortunately, however, the spin magnetic moment may be influenced by various interactions with the electron environment when the electron is involved in a molecule or a compound. These interactions result in a shift of the ESR line with respect to the free-electron position and are thereby the principal factors responsible for the power of the technique. These interactions can be either electrical or magnetic.

The electron moves along a given orbit (molecular orbital, for instance), resulting in a magnetic orbital moment ($\underline{\mu}_L$) and a kinetic or angular momentum ($\underline{P}_L$), designated by the quantum number L. In the same way, a nucleus rotating about itself has a nuclear magnetic moment ($\underline{\mu}_N$) and a kinetic or angular momentum designated its nucleus spin, $\underline{I}$. The magnetic interactions correspond to interactions between $\underline{\mu}_e$ and $\underline{\mu}_N$ or even $\underline{\mu}_e$ of other electrons (dipolar coupling). Electrical interactions that tend to orientate a magnetic moment along the other involve interaction of the electron charge with neighboring charges (exchange interaction) or nuclei (quadrupolar interactions) or ions (crystal field influence). These different interactions are characterized by various parameters, which will be considered in detail below. Each interaction corresponds to a given energy, and the hamiltonian operator ($\mathcal{H}$) acting on the wavefunction ($\psi$) of the electron is usually used to characterize the interaction. From the general hamiltonian, only the part concerning the electron spin, designated the "spin hamiltonian," is kept. In general, the Hamiltonian operator acts on the orbital wavefunction, resulting in eigenvalues that represent the energies of the system submitted to different types of interactions. The hamiltonian is only *a mathematical tool* that is used for convenience in calculating eigenvalues (i.e., to represent the energies corresponding to the different interactions). One usually writes in quantum mechanics symbolism,

$$\mathcal{H}\,|\psi_k\rangle = E\,|\psi_k\rangle$$

The eigenstates of the hamiltonian applied to the wawefunction $\psi_k$ are given by

$$E_K = \langle k|\mathcal{H}\,|k\rangle$$

where $|k\rangle$ represents the wavefunction $|\psi_k\rangle$.

The spin hamiltonian for all interactions can be written

$$\mathcal{H}_S = \mathcal{H}_{LS} + \mathcal{H}_{SH} + \mathcal{H}_{LH} + \mathcal{H}_{SS} + \mathcal{H}_{SI} + \mathcal{H}_{IH} + \mathcal{H}_Q \qquad (5)$$

where

$\mathcal{H}_{LS}$ = spin-orbit coupling
$\mathcal{H}_{SH}$ = electron Zeeman effect
$\mathcal{H}_{LH}$ = orbital Zeeman effect
$\mathcal{H}_{SS}$ = electron spin-spin interaction
$\mathcal{H}_{SI}$ = electron spin-nuclear spin interaction
$\mathcal{H}_{IH}$ = nuclear Zeeman effect
$\mathcal{H}_Q$ = quadrupolar interaction

The relative energy domains of these interactions are given in Table 1.

The term $\mathcal{H}_{LS} + \mathcal{H}_{LH}$ allows us to account for the interaction of the spin with its orbit and plays a determining role in the calculation

TABLE 1 Energy Domains ($cm^{-1}$) of the Various Interactions Influencing the Spin Magnetic Moment of an Electron in a Matrix

| | | |
|---|---|---|
| | $\mathcal{H}_{SH} = 1$ | $\mathcal{H}_{SI} = 10^{-2}$ |
| | $\mathcal{H}_{LH} = 1$ | $\mathcal{H}_{IH} = 10^{-3}$ |
| $\mathcal{H}_{LS} = 10^{+2}$ | $\mathcal{H}_{SS} = 1$ | $\mathcal{H}_{Q} = 10^{-3}$ |

[a]1 eV corresponds to 8065.8 $cm^{-1}$.

of the g factor (see Sec. II.B.I). The $\mathcal{H}_{SI} + \mathcal{H}_{IH}$ term characterizes the interaction with the nuclei and will be considered below in our discussion of the "hyperfine structure" (Sec. II.B.2). The $\mathcal{H}_{SS} + \mathcal{H}_{Q}$ term characterizes the interaction and will be analyzed in our discussion of fine structure (Sec. II.B.3). These are the three ESR parameters of main interest.

1. g-Factor Parameter [1-3]

*a. General Presentation.* The definition of g has been given above in relation (4) for a free electron. It may be shown that for an electron in an atom, $g_e$ in (4) must be replaced by the Landé factor in optical spectroscopy, given by

$$g_L = 1 + \frac{J(J+1) + S(S+1) - L(L+1)}{2J(J+1)} \tag{6}$$

where $\underline{J}$ is the kinetic momentum equal to the vectorial sum of the orbital $\underline{p}_L$ and spin $\underline{S}$ momenta. $\underline{p}_L$, the orbital angular momentum, is defined by the vectorial product designated by the symbol ^:

$$\underline{p}_L = m\underline{v} \wedge \underline{r}$$

where m is the electron mass, $\underline{v}$ is its velocity, and $\underline{r}$ is the orbital radius. For a free electron or a S-state ion, L = 0 and subsequently $g_L = 2$. In fact, $g_L = 2.0023 = g_e$ because of relativistic correction. For the rare earth ions, g-factor values are given by Eq. (6). This is not observed to be true for transition ions. This "discrepancy" is explained by considering that the paramagnetic 3d levels of these transition ions may be influenced by a very intense electrical field due to ions or polar molecules attached to the central ion. There then exist 2L + 1 orbital sublevels and one can consider the orbital moment, $\underline{p}_L$, as blocked or "quenched" by the crystal field, or that it is nonorientable under the influence of a magnetic field. This acts to break (more or less completely) the coupling between $\underline{L}$ and $\underline{S}$, since $\underline{L}$ is quenched by electrical fields, whereas $\underline{S}$ is not.

For transition metal ions, the L-S coupling is only partly quenched and the spin-orbit coupling interaction is represented by the operator

$$\mathcal{H}_{LS} = \lambda \underline{p}_L \cdot \underline{S}$$

where $\lambda$ is called the spin-orbit coupling constant. The spin Hamiltonial can be written

$$\mathcal{H}_S = \beta \underline{H} \cdot \tilde{g} \cdot \underline{S} = \lambda \underline{p}_L \cdot \underline{S} + \beta \underline{H} \cdot (\underline{p}_L + g_e \cdot \underline{S}) \qquad (7)$$

where $\tilde{g}$ is a second-order tensor defined by the latter relationship. The $g_L$ (Landé) factor thus becomes meaningless. The $\tilde{g}$ tensor can be represented by the third-order matrix operator

$$\begin{bmatrix} g_{xx} & g_{xy} & g_{xz} \\ g_{yx} & g_{yy} & g_{yz} \\ g_{zx} & g_{zy} & g_{zz} \end{bmatrix}$$

When the x, y, and z axes are chosen to be those of the $\tilde{g}$ tensor, one has a diagonal tensor,

$$\begin{bmatrix} g_{xx} & 0 & 0 \\ 0 & g_{yy} & 0 \\ 0 & 0 & g_{zz} \end{bmatrix}$$

Note that for simplicity one usually uses the $g_x$ symbols rather than $g_{xx}$ when assuming a diagonal tensor, and so also for $g_y$ and $g_z$.

Equation (7) may also be represented by defining the "effective" magnetid field $\underline{H}_{eff}$ by

$$\underline{H}_{eff} = \tilde{g} \cdot \underline{H}_0 \qquad (8)$$

This effective field is in general not collinear with the actual field, $\underline{H}_0$, since g-factor values depend on the orientation. One can write

$$\underline{H}_{eff} = \underline{i} g_{xx} H_x + \underline{j} g_{yy} H_y + \underline{k} g_{zz} H_z$$

where $\underline{i}$, $\underline{j}$, and $\underline{k}$ are the unit vectors along the x, y, and z axes and thus

$$\frac{\underline{H}_{eff}}{H_0} = \underline{i}g_{xx}\frac{H_x}{H_0} + \underline{j}g_{yy}\frac{H_y}{H_0} + \underline{k}g_{zz}\frac{H_z}{H_0}$$

If $\underline{H}$ is expressed in polar coordinates, $\theta$ and $\phi$, with respect to the x, y, and z axes defined as the main axes of the g tensor and recalling that Eq. (4) states that

$$h\nu = g\beta H_0 = \beta \|\underline{H}_{eff}\|$$

where g = modulus of $\underline{H}_{eff}/H_0$, one can write further

$$g = \text{mod}\,(\underline{i}g_{xx} \sin\theta\cos\phi + \underline{j}g_{yy} \sin\theta\sin\phi + \underline{k}g_{zz}\cos\theta)$$

resulting in

$$g^2 = g_{xx}^2 \sin^2\theta\cos^2\phi + g_{yy}^2 \sin^2\theta\sin^2\phi + g_{zz}^2\cos^2\theta \qquad (9)$$

Note that the $H_{eff}$ vector extremity describes an ellipsoid with semiaxes $g_{xx}$, $g_{yy}$, and $g_{zz}$ since the components of the $\underline{H}_{eff}/H_0$ vector along the x, y, and z axes are $g_{xx}\eta_x$, $g_{yy}\eta_y$, and $g_{zz}\eta_z$, where $\eta_x$, $\eta_y$, and $\eta_z$ are the director cosines of $\underline{H}_0$ along the x, y, and z axes which fulfill the ellipsoid formula

$$\frac{g_{xx}^2\eta_x^2}{g_{xx}^2} + \frac{g_{yy}^2\eta_y^2}{g_{yy}^2} + \frac{g_{zz}^2\eta_z^2}{g_{zz}^2} = \eta_x^2 + \eta_y^2 + \eta_z^2 = 1$$

For clarity, a representation of the g factor is given in Fig. 4.

The important point to note at this stage is that Eq. (9) shows that the g-factor values depend on the orientation of g-factor coordinates relative to the magnetic field. Thus *anisotropy* could occur leading to complex ESR spectra.

Values for the g-factor tensor may be calculated theoretically, considering the Hamiltonian (Eq. 7) as a *perturbation* of the spin Hamiltonian and using *perturbation theory.* Considering the spin-orbit coupling interaction as a perturbation, it can be shown that

$$g_{ij} = g_e\delta_{ij} - 2\lambda \sum_{n\neq 0} \frac{\langle 0|L_i|n\rangle\langle n|L_j|0\rangle}{E_n - E_0} \qquad (10)$$

where i and j correspond to two axes of the coordinate system, $\delta_{ij}$ is the Kronecker symbol ($\delta_{ij} = 1$ for i = j and $\delta_{ij} = 0$ for i ≠ j). 0 rep-

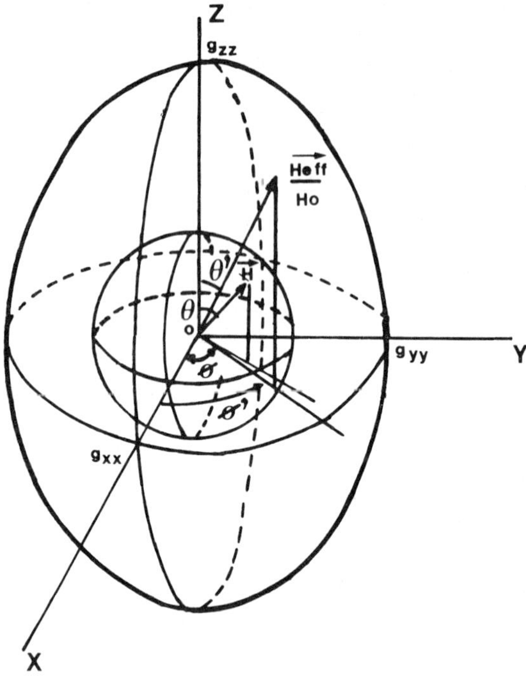


FIG. 4. Ellipsoidal representation of variations in the g-tensor value in the x, y, and z coordinates.

resents the ground state and n the different excited states. The operator L is defined by the relation

$$L_z = -i\left[x\frac{\delta}{\delta y} - y\frac{\delta}{\delta x}\right]$$

where i equals $\sqrt{-1}$ and $L_x$ and $L_y$ are defined by circular permutation. The operator L acts on a given orbital by a 90° rotation about the given axis. For instance, $L_z|s\rangle = 0$ and $L_z|p_z = 0$, while

$$L_z|p_x\rangle = i|p_y\rangle \quad \text{and} \quad L_z|p_y\rangle = -i|p_x\rangle$$

In other words, the operator L may act only on a given orbital if by a 90° rotation an existing orbital is obtained. Equation (10) thus means that the g-factor value will *only* couple by spin-orbit interaction the orbitals such that $L_i|n\rangle$ and $L_j|0\rangle$ results in orbital $|0\rangle$ and $|n\rangle$, respectively. It corresponds to a kind of "allowed" coupling between orbitals. An example of such a concept is given in

Appendix 1 for clarity. The $\Delta g = (g - g_e)$ shift will be either positive or negative depending on which orbitals of lower or higher energy could be coupled with the unpaired spin orbital. Thus the excited electron will have an opposite spin with respect to the unpaired electron when the excited state is formed by exciting an electron from an inner, filled orbital to the orbital occupied by the unpaired electron. Moreover, the order of magnitude of $\Delta g$ will be given by the ratio of the spin-orbit interaction constant, $\lambda$, to the excitation energy of the lowest excited states which can be admixed with the ground state by the L operator. We will see below that the amplitude of this energy depends greatly on the neighboring symmetry.

*b. Uses of g-Factor Parameter Values.* At least three kinds of information can be obtained once the g values are known. First, an idea as to the type of molecular motion can be deduced. This is possible because a rotation around a given axis averages out the g-factor components from the other two axes, resulting in one value for $g_\parallel$ and one for $g_\perp$ ($g_\parallel$ means parallel to the rotation axis and $g_\perp$ is the average of the other two perpendicular components, $(g_1 + g_2)/2$. For a complete rotation around all axes, or a random motion, the three g values are averaged to an isotropic g value, that is,

$$g_{ave} = \frac{g_1 + g_2 + g_3}{3}$$

Second, paramagnetic species can be identified. Once the g values have been extracted from an experimental spectrum the paramagnetic species may be immediately identified in many cases simply by comparing the observed g value with either theoretical or known values for paramagnetic species.

Two well-known examples illustrate these qualitative predictions. In NO (nitrous oxide) molecules, which are paramagnetic, there is one electron in the antibonding $\pi^*$ orbitals, while in $O_2^-$ (superoxide) there are three electrons. Upon adsorption of these paramagnetic species onto an oxide surface, the surface crystal field splits the $\pi^*$ electron energy level, thus removing its degeneracy to give two $\pi^*$ orbitals separated by an energy of $\Delta E$. So for NO the lone electron is excited from the lower half-filled $\pi^*$ orbital to the higher, empty $\pi^*$ orbital, whereas for $O_2^-$, one electron from the lower filled orbital is excited into the higher half-filled orbital. Consequently, the g values are less than $g_e$ (in the range 1.9 to 2.0) for NO and larger than $g_e$ for $O_2^-$ (2.038, 2.008, and 2.002 for instance for $O_2^-$ adsorbed on $Al_2O_3$), as expected.

Third, the symmetry of the ion environment can be characterized. Equation (10) clearly indicates that g values are dependent on the spin-orbit coupling between the ground state and the different excited

TABLE 2 Characteristics of the Ground-State Levels of Free Transition Metal Ions

| Number of d electrons | Quantum numbers S | L | J | Spectroscopic $^{(2S+1)}L_J$ | Orbital degeneracy |
|---|---|---|---|---|---|
| 1 | 1/2 | 2 | 3/2 | $^2D_{3/2}$ | 5 |
| 2 | 1 | 3 | 2 | $^3F_2$ | 7 |
| 3 | 3/2 | 3 | 3/2 | $^4F_{3/2}$ | 7 |
| 4 | 2 | 2 | 0 | $^5D_6$ | 5 |
| 5 | 5/2 | 0 | 5/2 | $^6S_{5/2}$ | 1 |
| 6 | 2 | 2 | 4 | $^5D_4$ | 5 |
| 7 | 3/2 | 3 | 9/2 | $^4F_{9/2}$ | 7 |
| 8 | 1 | 3 | 4 | $^3F_4$ | 7 |
| 9 | 1/2 | 2 | 5/2 | $^2D_{5/2}$ | 5 |

states. However, the crystal field to which the paramagnetic ion is submitted greatly influences the magnitude of separation in orbital levels. This results in a variation in g values, which may then be correlated to perturbation in crystal field symmetry.

c. *Case of Transition Metal Ions.* The properties of the ground-state level of free transition metal ions with $d^n$ electronic configurations (where n = 1 to 9) are reported in Table 2.

The orbital degeneracy of the free ion is 1, 5, or 7, but when placed in a crystal structure, or when the ion is coordinated to polar molecules, this orbital degeneracy is partially removed by the crystal field.

Two theorems play an important role in understanding the orbital energy levels of transition metal ions: (1) the *Jahn-Teller theorem* states that in any orbitally degenerate ground state there will be a distortion to remove the degeneracy, except in linear molecules and in systems having Kramer's doublets; and (2) *Kramer's theorem* states that any system containing an odd number of electrons will show at least twofold degeneracy in the absence of a magnetic field. It follows from theorem 2 that ions having an even number of electrons exhibit a complete splitting of energy levels (i.e., no ground-state degeneracy). In most cases the energy difference of this splitting is very large (1 $cm^{-1}$), so no ESR signal is expected. In ions with an odd number of electrons, levels with Kramer's degeneracy are present and an ESR signal is expected since the applied magnetic field splits this degeneracy.

Indeed the spin-orbit constant $\xi$, which measures the energy of the interaction between the spin and the orbital angular momentum of the electron, is a property of the electron configuration. It may be calculated from the expression

$$\xi = \frac{Z_{eff}e^2}{2m^2c^2 \langle r^3 \rangle}$$

where e, m, and c bear their usual significance. $\xi$ is thus a positive quantity but depends on the effective nuclear charge $Z_{eff}$ and on the average distance of the electron from the nucleus, $\langle r \rangle$. $\xi$ is also related to $\lambda$, the spin-orbit interaction constant, by the expression

$$\lambda = \pm \frac{\xi}{2S}$$

where S is the spin multiplicity.

In the literature, the intensity of *crystal fields* is often referred to as being *weak, medium, or strong*. The strong field is defined as one with sufficient strength to pair electrons such that they occupy lower levels. Medium and weak fields obviously correspond to lesser strengths usually not high enough to pair electrons.

According to Hund's law, the d electrons are distributed in the five d orbitals in such a way as to maximize S. The result, then, is that $d^1$ and $d^6$ configurations split in the same manner when exposed to a given crystal field. The same considerations prevail for $d^2$ and $d^7$, $d^3$ and $d^8$, and $d^4$ and $d^9$.

To illustrate these principles more clearly, examples of $d^1$ and $d^9$ ions are given below. More detailed analysis of $d^1$ to $d^9$ may be found in Ref. 3.

$d^1$ ions ($Mo^{5+}$, $Ti^{3+}$, $V^{4+}$, $W^{5+}$, $Cr^{5+}$). It is known that coordination compounds of these ions usually exhibit either octahedral ($O_h$) or tetrahedral ($T_d$) symmetry, which splits the fivefold degenerate state of the free ion into two states of different energy: $t_{2g}$ (triply degenerate) and $e_g$ (doubly degenerate).

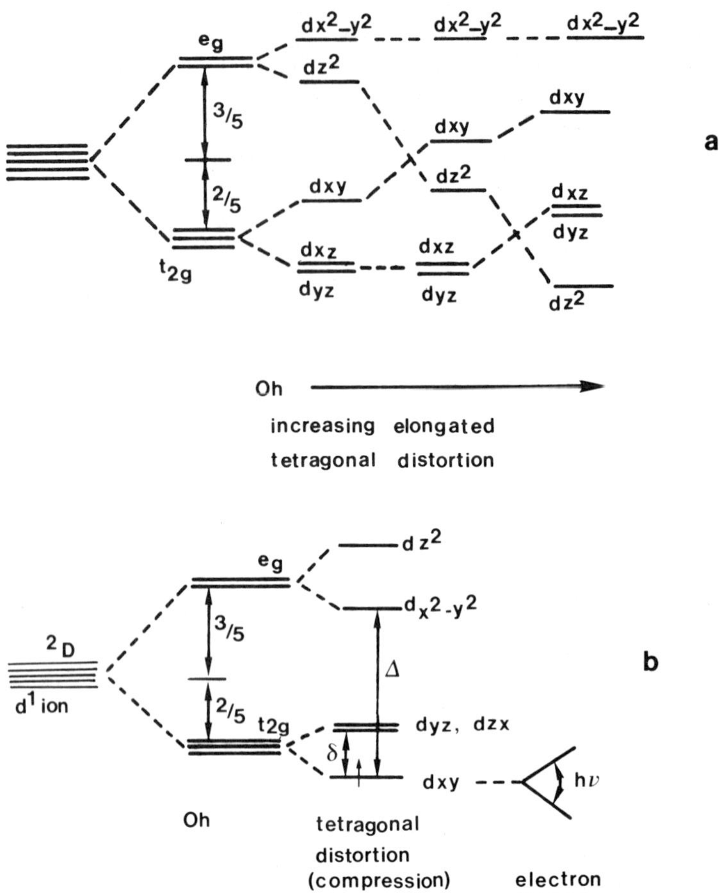


FIG. 5. Energy levels of a $d^1$ ion placed in an octahedral field with a tetragonal distortion: (a) tetragonal elongation and increasing crystal field intensity; (b) tetragonal compression.

Under the effect of Jahn-Teller distortion or through spin-orbit coupling the degeneracy of the ground state is finally removed. Furthermore, when a component with a crystal field of lower symmetry is superimposed on the $O_h$ or $T_d$ symmetry, further splitting of the $t_{2g}$ and $e_g$ states will occur. Consider first the effects of these distortions when the ion is in octahedral coordination. The splitting that removes fivefold degeneracy as the ion is placed in an octahedral crystal field is shown in Fig. 5. Note the effect of increasing distortion on relative energies of the different levels.

Two types of distortion can occur: (1) for elongated octahedral or square pyramidal complexes (Fig. 5a), the unpaired electron occupies the doubly degenerate level (which corresponds to the $d_{yz}$ and $d_{xz}$ orbitals), which is the lowest level, and no ESR spectrum would be observed since cross relaxation will occur, resulting in a very short spin-lattice relaxation time. For strong distortion the ground state is $d_z2$ (Fig. 5a) and an ESR spectrum could be observed. (2) for compressed octahedral or square-pyramidal complexes (Fig. 5b), the nondegenerate $t_{2g}$ ($d_{xy}$) level lies lowest. The g values are then given by the following equations, demonstrated in Appendix 2:

$$g_{xx} = g_{yy} = g_{\perp} = g_e - \frac{2\lambda}{\delta}$$
$$g_{zz} = g_{\parallel} = g_e - 8\,\frac{\lambda}{\Delta} \tag{11}$$

where $\delta$ and $\Delta$ are as defined in Fig. 5b.

An example of a $3d^1$ ion in a tetragonally distorted octahedral is given by the ESR spectrum of $Ti^{3+}$ in CaO with $g_{\parallel} = 1.9427$ and $g_{\perp} = 1.9380$. The experimental results of $g_{\perp} < g_{\parallel} < g_e$ corresponds to a $d_{xy}$ ground state (i.e., to a tetragonal compression of the octahedron. Equation (11) applies and then gives $\Delta \simeq 4.3\delta$.

For comparison, note that the $Ti^{3+}$ ion in anatase ($TiO_2$) has $g_{\perp} = 1.99$ and $g_{\parallel} = 1.959$, while in rutile $g_{\perp} = 1.975$ and $g_{\parallel} = 1.9360$, which is reverse with respect to $Ti^{3+}$ in CaO, as could be possible from Eq. (11) depending on $\delta$ and $\Delta$ values. $Ti^{3+}$ is indeed also in an Oh symmetry with elongated tetragonal distortion on rutile, while for anatase strong tetragonal distortion of the square plane is high and is additional to the elongation. It follows a greater degeneracy of energy levels in the latter case (i.e., g values closer to $g_e$ than in the case of rutile).

When the ion is in a purely tetrahedral crystal field the fivefold degeneracy is split into a twofold degenerate $e_g$ ground state and an upper threefold-degenerate $t_{2g}$ state. A tetragonal distortion may lift the ground-state degeneracy as shown in Fig. 6.

However, the ground state could be either the $d_{x^2-y^2}$ or the $d_{z^2}$ orbital, depending on the distortion (elongation or compression). For instance, for a compressed tetrahedron the $d_z2$ level lies lower and one can show that g values are given by

$$g_{zz} = g_{\parallel} = g_e$$
$$g_{xx} = g_{yy} = g_{\perp} = g_e - 6\,\frac{\lambda}{\Delta} \tag{12}$$

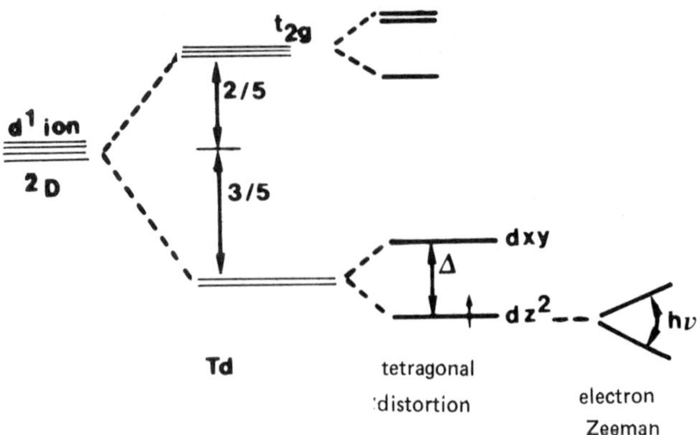


FIG. 6. Energy levels of a $d^1$ ion placed in tetrahedral symmetry with a tetragonal distortion (compression).

where $\Delta$ is defined in Fig. 6. This is the case found for $Cr^{5+}$ in $CrO_4^{3-}$ with $g_\parallel = 1.9936$ and $g_\perp = 1.9498$.

For an elongated tetrahedron the $d_{x^2-y^2}$ level lies lower and the theoretical values of the g factor would be

$$g_{zz} = g_\parallel = g_e - 8\frac{\lambda}{\Delta}$$

$$g_{xx} = g_{yy} = g_e - 2\frac{\lambda}{E} = g_\perp \tag{13}$$

where $\Delta$ is given in Fig. 6 and E is the energy difference between the $t_{2g}$ and $e_g$ states.

In summary, from equations above it is clear that $d^1$ ions in a tetrahedral site compressed along a fourfold axis result in $g_\parallel > g_\perp$, while if the tetrahedron is elongated along the same axis the result is $g_\parallel < g_\perp$. Furthermore, in both cases g values would be less than $g_e$. It is worth noting also that the splitting of the $e_g$ ground state by tetragonal distortion is generally small. This could therefore result in short relaxation times and ESR spectra could by observable only at liquid-nitrogen temperatures or below. Finally, these considerations indicate that ESR spectra are very sensitive to the symmetry of the environment surrounding the $d^1$ ion. This sensitivity, in turn, makes ESR an important tool for obtaining information about this symmetry. However, if one considers the relationships given above, one can see that symmetry considerations will not distinguish a tetragonally distorted octahedral site from a tetragonally distorted tetrahedral site. One therefore often uses the $1/\alpha$ quotient as a quantitative, empirically derived measure of the degree of distortion of the site, where [6]

$$\frac{1}{\alpha} = \frac{g_e - g_\perp}{g_e - g_\parallel} = \frac{1}{4}\frac{\Delta}{\delta}$$

$d^9$ ions ($Cu^{2+}$, $Ni^+$, $Co^0$, $Rh^0$, $Ag^+$, etc). Usually, this configuration can be considered as having one hole in the orbital levels, and may be treated as a $d^1$ configuration, except that g values are larger than $g_e$ rather than smaller, as is true for $d^1$ ions. In $O_h$ complexes g values are the same as for the $d^1$ ions with the signs changed, and for tetrahedral complexes g values are the same as for $d^1$ ions except that $\delta$ and $\Delta$ are now negative [1,3,6].

The crystal field splitting is described in Figs. 5 and 6. As can be seen in these figures, the ground state is $e_g$ in $O_h$ symmetry. Jahn-Teller distortion is possible since spin-orbit coupling produces a fourfold degeneracy and is often very large. In lower symmetries the ground state is a Kramer's doublet and spectra are readily observed, even at room temperature.

In summary, g-factor values are of great interest when informations about the symmetry neighboring a paramagnetic species are required. This is mainly true for transition metal ions. The high sensitivity of g-factor parameter to environmental symmetry makes the ESR technique very powerful. The difficulty is often in the interpretation of the g-value shift. The data above are supposed to give some ideas to the readers how to handle such a parameter.

## 2. Hyperfine Interaction

As indicated above, hyperfine interaction corresponds to the interaction between electrons and nuclei. One can write

$$\mathcal{H}_{SI} = \sum_{i=1}^{n} \underline{S} \cdot \tilde{A}_i \cdot \underline{I}_i \tag{14}$$

where $\tilde{A}_i$ is the hyperfine tensor and i corresponds to the different nuclei involved. The nuclear Zeeman interaction is given by

$$\mathcal{H}_{IH} = \sum_{i=1}^{n} \gamma_{N_i} \underline{I}_i \cdot \underline{H}$$

where $\gamma_{N_i}$ is the nuclear gyromagnetic ratio of nucleus i. This term is generally rather small and can be neglected in first-order approximations.

As in the case of the g-factor tensor, the hyperfine tensor characterizes the anisotropy of the interaction of nuclei with p or d orbital electrons. The tensor $\tilde{A}$ is usually decomposed into isotropic (a) and anisotropic (b) parts, and is then written as

$$\tilde{A} = a\tilde{u} + \tilde{b}$$

where $\tilde{u}$ is the unity tensor.

*a. Isotropic Hyperfine Interaction.* Let us first consider the interaction with a single nucleus of nonzero nuclear spin, I. The spin hamiltonian may then be written

$$\mathcal{H}_S = g_0 \beta \underline{S} \cdot \underline{H} + ha\underline{S} \cdot \underline{I} - g_N \beta_N \underline{I} \cdot \underline{H} \tag{14a}$$

where a is the isotropic hyperfine coupling, expressed in frequency units (hertz). Note that because of isotropic interaction, the g factor and hyperfine tensor have been replaced by scalar values $g_0$ and a.

The term a was introduced by Fermi, who demonstrated that its magnitude is related to the spin density, $|\psi(0)|^2$, of the unpaired electron at the nucleus and is given by the relation

$$a = \frac{-8\pi}{3} g_e g_N \beta \beta_N |\psi(0)|^2 \tag{15}$$

It follows that an isotropic hyperfine interaction requires a nonzero spin density at the nucleus, which theoretically precludes all p or d orbitals since their wavefunctions exhibit nodes ($|\psi(0)|^2 = 0$) at the nucleus. In the absence of a magnetic field, $\underline{I}$ and $\underline{S}$ are coupled, resulting in a momentum $\underline{F}$. For S = 1/2, the electronic level is split into two levels with a separation equal to

$$\Delta E = \frac{1}{2} ha(2I + 1)$$

When the material is submitted to a sufficiently strong external magnetic field, $\underline{H}$, the $\underline{I}$-$\underline{S}$ coupling is broken and $\underline{I}$ and $\underline{S}$ orient independently along the direction of the field. This is known as the *Back-Goudsmit effect.*

When the microwave and magnetic fields are applied perpendicularly, as is usually done in ESR as described above, the selection rules correspond to $\Delta M_S = \pm 1$ and $\Delta M_I = 0$, where $M_S$ and $M_I$ are the magnetic quantum numbers of electron and nucleus, respectively, along $\underline{H}$. (These rules are reversed for NMR transitions.) It follows as shown in Fig. 7 that (2I + 1) transitions may occur, resulting in (2I + 1) "hyperfine" lines of equal intensity.

As the microwave energy is kept constant and the magnetic field is swept, the hyperfine lines are obtained as in the case of Fig. 7 with I = 1 for magnetic field values such as

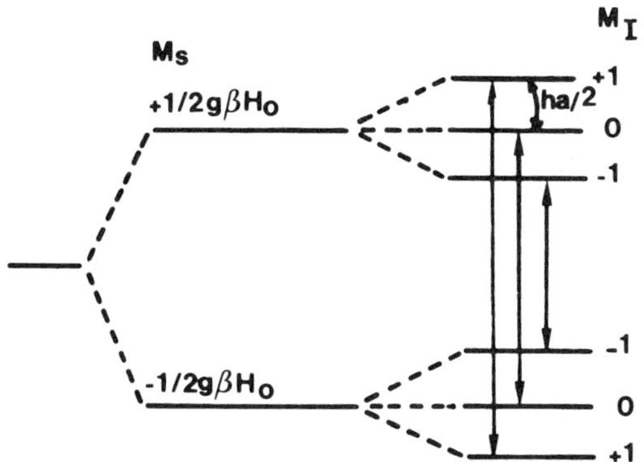


FIG. 7. ESR transition corresponding to an isotropic hyperfine interaction of one electron with one nucleus of spin I = 1.

$$\Delta E = g_0\beta H_1 + ha = h\nu$$

$$\Delta E = g_0\beta H_2$$

$$\Delta E = g_0\beta H_3 - ha$$

that is, if $H_0$ is the magnetic field for the central line (no hyperfine coupling), the lines are obtained for $H_0 - ha/g_0\beta$, $H_0$, and $H_0 + ha/g_0\beta$. It follows that the splitting between two successive lines equals $ha/g_0\beta$. Such a splitting makes possible the experimental determination of the hyperfine coupling constant, a.

When the unpaired spin interacts with several nonzero nuclear spins, the hyperfine structure is more complex. In the strong field approximation each electronic level is split by nucleus i into $(2I_i + 1)$ levels. Each is then split again by nucleus j into $(2I_j + 1)$ levels, and so on. It follows that the number of hyperfine lines will increase drastically with the number of nuclei present, and follows a multiplicity rule of $(2I_i + 1)(2I_j + 1) \cdots (2I_k + 1)$. However, if the hyperfine coupling with identical nuclei is of the same strength, one observes an overlapping of levels as shown in Fig. 8.

If n nuclei of nuclear spin I are equally involved, it can thus be easily shown that the number of hyperfine lines is equal to $(2nI + 1)$. Their relative intensities are then given by the coefficients of the binomial expansion of $(1 + x)^n$.

If there are two more groups of nuclei with different hyperfine splittings, the overall pattern is more complex than before but can be constructed by extending the energy-level diagram shown in Fig. 8. Two main conclusions can then be deduced: (1) when hyperfine lines are observed with equal intensity, one can identify the nuclei with

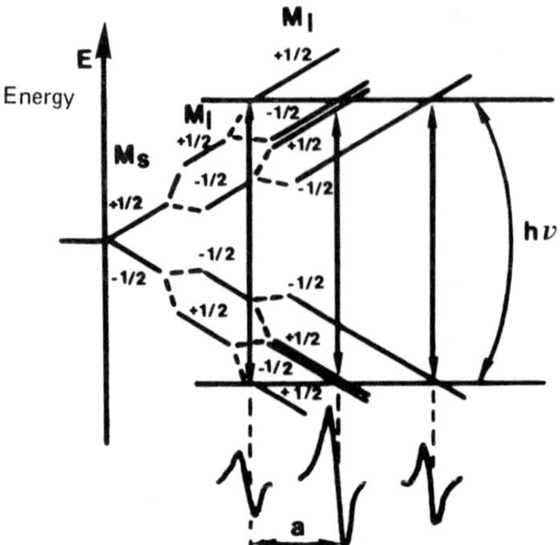


FIG. 8. Hyperfine spitting of each electronic level by equal coupling with two nuclei of nuclear spin 1.

unequal coupling since the number of lines is given by $(2I_i + 1)(2I_j + 1) \cdots (2I_k + 1)$; when hyperfine lines are observed with unequal intensity, from their relative intensities and their number, one may deduce the number and the nature of nuclei concerned by applying the above principles. (2) From the hyperfine coupling constant, one can obtain the unpaired spin density at each nucleus of a molecule, that is, *a kind of map of unpaired spin density* along a molecule, using the relation

$$a = A_0 C_{ns}^2 \tag{15a}$$

where $A_0$ is the hyperfine splitting if the electron spends all its time on the nucleus (the values of $A_0$ are known for each nucleus) and $C_{ns}^2$ is the spin density on orbital ns.

*b. Anisotropic Hyperfine Interaction.* Dipolar interaction between electrons or between the electron and a nucleus may be expressed by the general dipolar hamiltonian

$$\mathcal{H}_{dip} = -\gamma_1\gamma_2\hbar^2\left[\frac{\underline{\mu}_1\cdot\underline{\mu}_2}{r^3} - 3\,\frac{(\underline{\mu}_1\cdot\underline{r})(\underline{\mu}_2\cdot\underline{r})}{r^5}\right] \tag{16}$$

The hyperfine hamiltonian may then be written

$$\mathcal{H}_{IS} = -g_e g_N \beta \beta_N \left[ \frac{\underline{I} \cdot \underline{S}}{r^3} - 3 \frac{(\underline{I} \cdot \underline{r})(\underline{S} \cdot \underline{r})}{r^5} \right] \tag{16a}$$

If one designates by $\phi$ the angle between the vector $\underline{r}$ connecting a nucleus and the electron in displacement with its orbital and by $\theta$ the angle between the main axis of symmetry of this orbital and the applied magnetic field, relation (16a) may be written

$$\mathcal{H}_{IS} = \frac{-g_e g_N \beta \beta_N}{r^3} (1 - 3 \cos^2 \theta) \frac{1}{2} (1 - 3 \cos^2 \phi) \underline{I} \cdot \underline{S}$$

Because of the motion of the electron along its orbital, the $(1 - 3 \cos^2 \phi)/r^3$ term may be replaced by a mean value calculated along the orbital, that is, $\langle(1 - 3 \cos^2 \phi)/r^3\rangle$. If the unpaired electron spends all of its time on this orbital, the anisotropic hyperfine constant, $B_0$, is defined as (in frequency units)

$$B_0 = \frac{1}{2} \frac{g_e g_N \beta \beta_N}{h} \left[ \frac{1 - 3 \cos^2 \phi}{r^3} \right] \tag{17}$$

and the spin hamiltonian can be written

$$\mathcal{H}_S = g \beta \underline{S} \cdot \underline{H} + hb \underline{I} \cdot \underline{S} - g_N \beta_N \underline{I} \cdot \underline{H} \tag{14b}$$

where

$$b = B_0(1 - 3 \cos^2 \theta) \tag{18}$$

which in strong-field approximation results in the energy relation

$$E\,|M_S, M_I\rangle = g \beta M_S H + hbM_I M_S - g_N \beta_N M_I H \tag{16b}$$

For an isotropic g-factor tensor, the hyperfine spectra obtained for the usual selection rules ($\Delta M_I = 0$, $\Delta M_S = \pm 1$) contain $2I + 1$ lines at magnetic field positions of

$$H_{M_I} = H_0 \pm \frac{M_I bh}{g_0 \beta} \tag{19}$$

The hyperfine pattern is symmetrically distributed about the position $H_0 = h\nu/g_0\beta$ with a central line at that position if I is odd-numbered and no central line for even numbers of I.

It is worthwhile to note that $B_0$ values can be calculated from the relation (17). For instance, for a 2p orbital, one can show that $\langle \cos^2 \phi \rangle = 3/5$, leading to

$$B_0 = \frac{2}{5} \frac{g_e g_N \beta \beta_N}{h} \langle r^{-3} \rangle$$

in frequency units. When H is oriented parallel to the p orbital axis, the term $(1 - 3\cos^2\theta) = -2$; therefore, from Eq. (18), $b_\parallel = -2B_0$. If H is oriented perpendicularly, $1 - 3\cos^2\theta = 1$; therefore, $b_\perp = B_0$. It follows from this fact and from Eq. (19) that hyperfine lines for each $M_I$ value will vary in field position when the orientation of H changes. This is the reason for the term "anisotropic." As for isotropic coupling, one can show that the hyperfine constant, $b = b_\perp = -b_\parallel/2$, is given by $b = B_0 C_{np}^2$ (i.e., is proportional to the unpaired spin density on the p, d, and f orbitals involved). Obviously, $\Sigma C_x^2 = 1$ (x referring to all orbitals s, p, d, f, etc.).

c. *Total Hyperfine Interaction.* Now consider the general case where both isotropic and anisotropic interactions occur. The total hyperfine tensor is written

$$\tilde{A} = a\tilde{u} + \tilde{b} = \begin{vmatrix} A_{xx} & A_{xy} & A_{xz} \\ A_{yx} & A_{yy} & A_{yz} \\ A_{zx} & A_{zy} & A_{zz} \end{vmatrix} = a\tilde{u} + \begin{vmatrix} b_{xx} & b_{xy} & b_{xz} \\ b_{yx} & b_{yy} & b_{yz} \\ b_{zx} & b_{zy} & b_{zz} \end{vmatrix} \qquad (20)$$

and the spin hamiltonian is

$$\mathcal{H}_S = \beta \underline{H} \cdot \tilde{g} \cdot \underline{S} + h \underline{I} \cdot \tilde{A} \cdot \underline{S} - g_N \beta_N \underline{I} \cdot \underline{H} \qquad (14c)$$

For simplicity one usually uses the diagonal tensors by a choice of the axis and then one uses $A_x$ . . . , $b_x$ . . . rather than $A_{xx}$ . . . , $b_{xx}$ . . . as in the case of the g tensor (see above).

Determination of the *unpaired spin density* within a molecule or a transition metal ion complex is one of *the most striking features* of ESR spectroscopy since it allows one to draw a kind of spin density map all along a compound. Determination of the s and/or p character of a given orbital bearing the unpaired electron is also of great interest. Consider the paramagnetic $NO_2$ radical as an example. The unpaired electron is located in the sp orbital of the N atom. The hyperfine parameters are

$$\frac{a}{h} = 146.5 \text{ MHz/s}$$

$$\frac{b}{h} = 19.2 \text{ MHz/s}$$

These parameters are obtained from the experimental values of $A_{\parallel} = a + b_{\parallel}$, $A_{\perp} = a - b_{\parallel}/2$, and $b_{\parallel} = -2b$. From $b = B_0 C_{np}^2$ and $a = A_0 C_{ns}^2$, one then gets

$$C_{2s}^2 = 0.095$$
$$C_{2p}^2 = 0.405 \qquad \text{leading to } C_{2s}^2 + C_{2p}^2 = 0.50$$

This means that the unpaired electron spends half of its time in the sp orbital of N and the other half on the oxygen atoms. Moreover, the unpaired electron orbital is roughly 20% s character and 80% p character. It can be shown that this hybridization, due to the bending of the $\widehat{ONO}$ bond, is related to the bond angle $\alpha$ by

$$\alpha = 2 \cos^{-1}(\lambda^2 + 2)^{1/2}$$

in $C_2$ symmetry, where $\lambda^2 = (C_{2p}/C_{2s})^2$. Using this expression for $\lambda^2$ and the values given above for $C_{2p}^2$ and $C_{2s}^2$, one can easily calculate the value of $\alpha$, which is 132.8 Å. The actual value is 134°. The agreement is quite good and illustrates the usefulness of ESR parameters.

If the g factor is isotropic, or its main axes are coincident with those of the hyperfine tensor, the overall pattern should arise as the sum of all the g and hyperfine factors. For a given orientation, the number and relative intensities of the hyperfine lines allow, as shown above, identification of the nuclei involved in the interactions with the unpaired electron. The g-factor values are determined from the *center* of the hyperfine pattern corresponding to $h\nu = g\beta H_0$. Often, the magnetic field $H_0$ and the frequency $\nu$ are known only approximately. One then uses a double resonance cavity which allows simultaneous recording of a standard with the sample (common standards are DPPH, g = 2.0036; Varian Pitch, g = 2.0028). In such cases one has

$$h\nu = g\beta H_0 = g_{ref}\beta H_{ref}$$
$$g = \frac{g_{ref} H_{ref}}{H_0} \qquad (21)$$

3. Hyperfine and Superhyperfine Interactions

The superhyperfine interaction corresponds to the interaction of nuclei other than the nucleus directly involved with the unpaired electron. It obviously arises from the overlap of the molecular orbital with the ligand atoms, and corresponds to a splitting of each first hyperfine line.

An example of superhyperfine interaction is found when W or $M_0$ [7] ions are introduced into a rutile-type $SnO_2$ material by impregnating $SnO_2$ with an ammonia solution of $WO_3$ or $MoO_3$, and then calcining the sample at high temperature (1000°C) in air. $W^{5+}$ or $Mo^{5+}$ ($d^1$ ions) ions are thus incorporated into the $SnO_2$ matrix. In the $SnO_2$ rutile structure there are two equivalent sites into which Sn has been substituted. These are obtained by a rotation of 90° about the crystallographic y axis |(00 1) direction|, and each Sn is surrounded by an elongated octahedron of oxygen ions. In addition, Sn is located into four other interstitial sites that are equivalent. Each of these Sn ions is surrounded by a flattened oxygen octahedron (Fig. 9). The ESR spectrum is obtained at either liquid-nitrogen or room temperature, and gives for $W^{5+}$ the parameters [7a] $g_{xx} = 1.671$, $g_{yy} = 1.500$, and $g_{zz} = 1.732$, $A_{xx} = 62$, $A_{yy} = 80$, and $A_{zz} = 120$ G for the $^{183}W$ hyperfine structure (I = 1/2), $^1A_{xx} = 430$, $^1A_{yy} = 520$, and $A_{zz} = 450$ G for the superhyperfine structure of the two equivalent Sn nuclei designated 1 with I = 1/2 16% natural abundance, and $^2A_{xx} = 78$, $^2A_{yy} = 80$, and $^2A_{zz} = 64$ G for the superhyperfine structure of the four equivalent Sn nuclei designated 2 and lying in the diagonal plane of the unit cell (Figs. 9 and 10).

The ESR spectrum presented in Fig. 10 is very complex and a detailed interpretation is given in Ref. 7a. About 16% of the Sn nuclei have a nuclear spin I = 1/2 ($^{117}Sn$, 7.7% with $\beta_N = 0.99$ nuclear magneton, and $^{119}Sn$, 8.7% with $\beta_N = 1.04$) and about 14.3% of the W have a nuclear spin I = 1/2 ($^{183}W$). As the nonzero nuclear spin isotopes are in low abundance, the spectrum is mainly composed of a strong central spectrum due to the even isotopes (I = 0) flanked on both sides by satellites lines (8% intensities) due to hyperfine ($^{103}W$) and superhyperfine couplings ($^{117}Sn$, $^{119}Sn$).

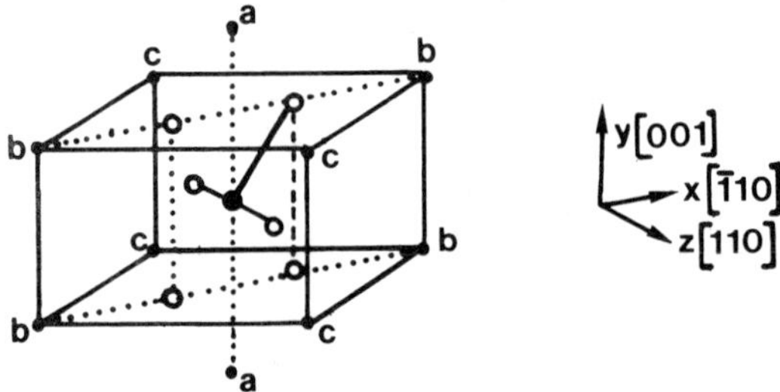


FIG. 9. Schematic representation of $SnO_2$ structure around a central W ion. Closed circles, $Sn^{4+}$; open circles $O^{2-}$ ions.

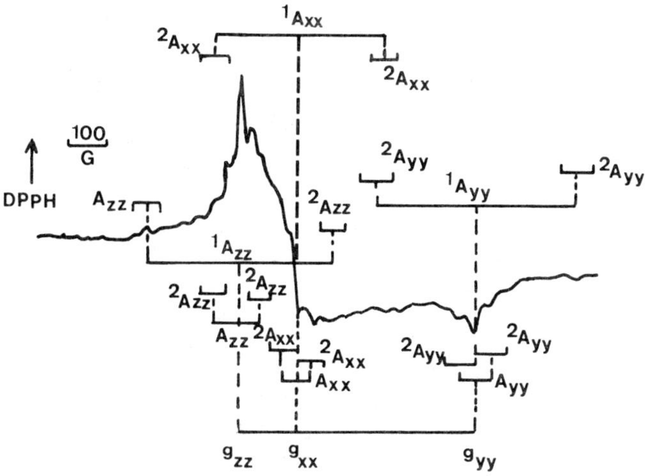


FIG. 10. ESR spectrum at 77 K of W in natural isotopic abundance of doped $SnO_2$. (From Ref. 7a.)

For the $Sn^{4+}$ cation superhyperfine coupling, the intensities of the ESR lines can be predicted from a calculation of the probability of finding one or two or more $^{117}Sn$ or $^{119}Sn$ nuclei surrounding the $W^{5+}$ substitutional site. The probability is given by

$$P_n^{(m)} = \binom{n}{m} p^{n-m} q^m \quad \text{with} \binom{n}{m} = \frac{n!}{m!(n-m)!}$$

where n refers to the number of nearest-neighbor Sn cations, m is the number of these cations occupied by $^{117}Sn$ or $^{119}Sn$, and p is the natural abundance of the Sn with I = 0 and q with I = 1/2. The resolution as presented in Fig. 10 considers that only one $I \neq 0$ neighbor atom is concerned (i.e., only doublets for each line), since the probability of having more than one $I \neq 0$ neighbor atom is very small. $W^{5+}$ occupies a substantial site and the next-nearest neighbors can be divided into three groups; a, b, and c, along the y (2Sn), x (4Sn), and z (4Sn) axes, respectively. The W-Sn distance for group (a) is 3.2 Å, which is smaller than the 3.7 Å distance for group (b). One can then expect the superhyperfine splitting due to the two nuclei of group (a) to be much larger than that of the four in group (b). Interaction with group (c) is too weak to be detected since the unpaired electron is in a $d_{x^2-y^2}-\lambda d_{z^2}$ orbital which will not "see" the Sn atoms of this group. Similar information was obtained for $Mo^{5+}$ [7b].

This example demonstrates how ESR may be used to locate paramagnetic ions in a matrix, and to identify the molecular orbital bearing the unpaired electron. Further, interactions of the unpaired electron with nuclei of nearest neighbors may be characterized, and thereby the location of the electron within the lattice can be identified.

### 4. Fine Structure

The discussion in preceding sections has focused on systems with only one unpaired electron, where the electron spin is 1/2. The majority of systems studied by ESR falls within this category. However, for biradicals and transition metal ions, the number of unpaired electrons may be more than 1, resulting in $S > 1/2$. In such cases it can be shown by following the same general approach as in preceding sections that the magnetic field splits the electron levels into $2S + 1$ magnetic sublevels, characterized by their $M_S$ value. The section rule $\Delta M_S = \pm 1$ is still valid and gives 2S transitions. For high environmental symmetry, the 2S transitions occur at the same magnetic field value, resulting in a single resonance line (Fig. 11a).

If the crystal field contains a component in a given direction, and in the absence of any magnetic field the fundamental energy level is split into as many sublevels as there are $M_S$ values (Fig. 11b), this splitting is designated the decomposition at zero field and arises from the dipolar hamiltonian:

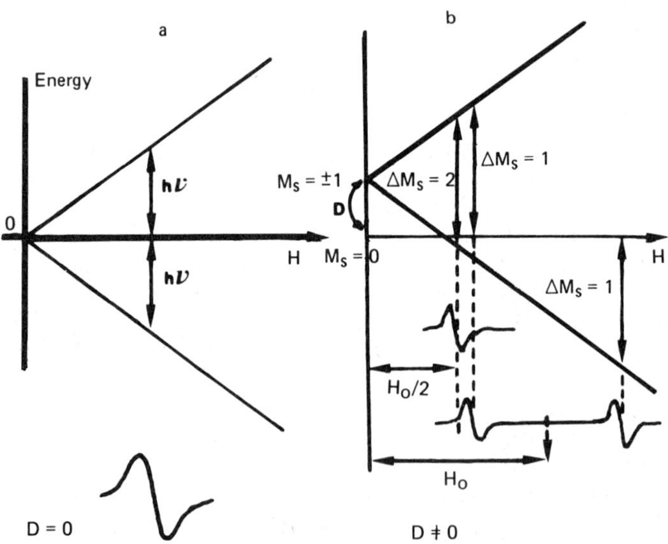


FIG. 11. Electron energy levels for $S = 1$ and a crystal field environment with (a) high symmetry and (b) an axial component.

$$\mathcal{H}_d = \underline{S}\cdot\tilde{D}\underline{S} \tag{22}$$

where $\tilde{D}$ is a second-order tensor as $\tilde{g}$ and $\tilde{A}$.

The $\tilde{D}$ tensor is particularly important for transition metal ions since it corresponds to an indirect coupling of electron spins via spin-orbit coupling, and arises from a second-order perturbation calculation. One can write either

$$\mathcal{H}_d = D_{xx}S_x^2 + D_{yy}S_y^2 + D_{zz}S_z^2 \tag{22a}$$

or

$$\mathcal{H}_d = D\left[S_z^2 - \frac{S(S+1)}{3}\right] + E(S_x^2 - S_y^2) \tag{22b}$$

where $D = D_{zz} - (D_{xx} + D_{yy})/2$ and $E = (D_{xx} - D_{yy})/2$.

$\tilde{D}$ is a dipolar tensor having a null trace in its axis system (i.e., $D_{xx} + D_{yy} + D_{zz} = 0$). The D and E constants are called fine-structure parameters at magnetic field equal to zero. E represents deviations from axial symmetry.

*a. The Case of Axial Symmetry.* For axial symmetry, the value of E is zero in Eq. (22b) and one can write

$$\mathcal{H}_S = g_\parallel \beta H S_z + D\left[S_z^2 - \frac{S(S+1)}{3}\right] \tag{22c}$$

For S = 1, the $\Delta M_S = \pm 1$ transitions are separated by 2D (energy units) or $2D/g_\parallel \beta$ (magnetic field units). This allows determination of the value of D and also of $g_\parallel$, which corresponds to the center of the fine structure. A $\Delta M_S = \pm 2$ transition is also observed at a magnetic field value which is half that for $\Delta M_S = \pm 1$. This is called the *half-field line* (Fig. 11b).

When H is perpendicular to the z axis, the energies of the allowed transitions ($\Delta M_S = \pm 1$) are either

$$h\nu = g_\perp \beta H_\perp \pm \frac{D}{2}$$

or

$$H_\perp = \frac{h\nu}{g_\perp} \pm \frac{D}{2g_\perp \beta}$$

This means that the resonance lines are separated by D when using energy units, and by $D/g_\perp \beta$ when using magnetic field units.

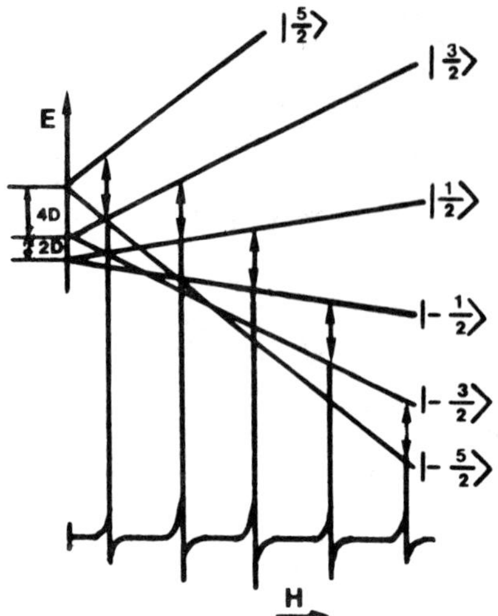


FIG. 12. Energy-level diagram for S = 5/2, H parallel to the z axis, and axial symmetry.

The center of the pattern corresponds to $g_{\perp}$ (Fig. 11). The zero-field splittings deduced from Eq. (22c) are therefore D, for levels 0 and ±1 for S = 1 (Fig. 11) and 2D and 4D between levels ±1/2, ±3/2, and ±3/2, ±5/2, respectively, for S = 5/2 (Fig. 12).

*b. The Case of Orthorhombic Symmetry (Lower Than the "Axial" Symmetry).* The value of E in the dipolar hamiltonian (Eq. 22b) is

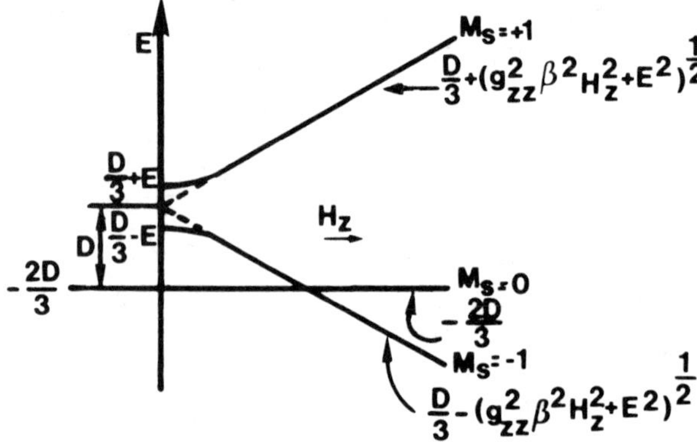


FIG. 13. Energy-level diagram for S = 1, H parallel to the z axis, and orthorhombic symmetry.

no longer zero. One may show that for S = 1 and H parallel to the z axis, three energy levels are obtained: $(\pm g_{zz}^2 \beta^2 H^2 + E^2)^{1/2} + (1/3)D$ for $S_z = \pm 1$, and $-(2/3)D$ for $S_z = 0$, as shown in Fig. 13. The separation between lines equals 2D (energy units). For H perpendicular to the z axis, the transitions are separated by D + 3E and D − 3E.

## C. Powder Spectra [2]

In heterogeneous catalysis one is usually dealing with powders that could be amorphous or crystalline. We have seen above that some parameters are isotropic, that is, their values do not depend on the orientation of the paramagnetic species with respect to the magnetic field, but that other parameters do depend on this orientation. For amorphous or polycrystalline materials the ESR spectra will then appear as the summation of all randomly distributed orientations. This gives rise to "powder" spectra.

If we assume that the crystallites are randomly distributed, the probability of finding a crystallite at an angle $\theta$ with respect to the magnetic field is proportional to the area of an angular ring of width $d\theta$ and circumference $2\pi r \cos \theta$. This will cause the number of crystallites dN to vary as

$$dN = \frac{N_0}{2} \sin \theta d\theta \tag{23}$$

where $N_0$ is the total number of crystallites and $0 < \theta < \pi/2$. The absorption line intensity can be written

$$\frac{dN}{dH} = \frac{dN}{d\theta} \frac{d\theta}{dH} \tag{24}$$

### 1. g Factor

For axial symmetry, and assuming no hyperfine coupling, one has from Eqs. (4) and (9),

$$h\nu_0 = (g_\parallel^2 \cos^2 \theta + g_\perp^2 \sin^2 \theta)^{1/2} \beta H \tag{25}$$

The ESR line shape should then be given by

$$S(H_0) = \frac{dN}{N_0} \frac{1}{dH} = H_\perp^2 H_\parallel (H_\perp^2 - H_\parallel^2)^{-1/2} H_0^{-2} (H_\perp^2 - H_0^2)^{-1/2}$$

with $\int_0^\infty S(H)\, dH = 1$, and where $H_\perp$ and $H_\parallel$ are the values of $H_0$ for $\theta = \pi/2$ and 0, respectively. The calculated line shapes are shown in Fig. 14, which assumes a Dirac-type delta function for individual lines

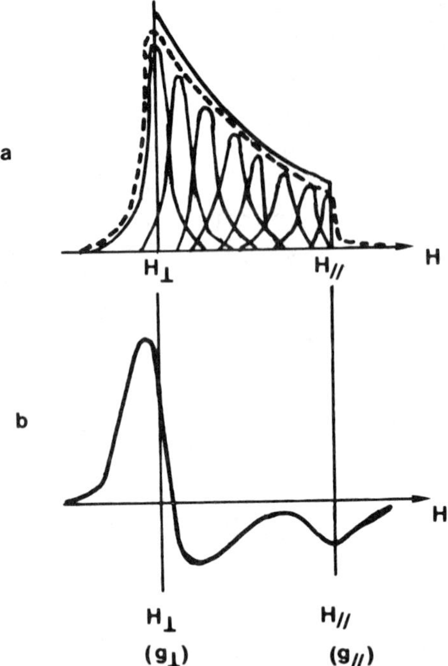


FIG. 14. Typical ESR (a) absorption and (b) derivative spectra for powder samples. Solid line assumes a $\delta$ function for line width in (a); solid and dashed lines assume lorentzian or gaussian line shapes for individual lines in (b) and in (a), respectively.

since the spectrum turns out to be due to an overlap of all lines corresponding to the whole angular range. Individual lines, indeed, are of insufficient width to be treated independently, but may be represented by either a lorentzian or a gaussian law $F(H - H_0)$. Thus the overall ESR spectrum is represented by

$$S(H) = \int_{H_\perp}^{H_\parallel} F(H - H_0)S(H_0)\, dH_0$$

where $F(H - H_0)$ represents either the gaussian or lorentzian function.

This integral has been calculated according to the following hypotheses: (1) crystallites are independent and randomly distributed; (2) no thermal motion occurs; (3) environmental symmetry is of axial type; (4) widths for individual lines, $(\Delta H_i)$ are $\theta$-independent; and (5) anisotropy is small (i.e., $\Delta H_{an} = |H_\parallel - H_\perp| \ll H$).

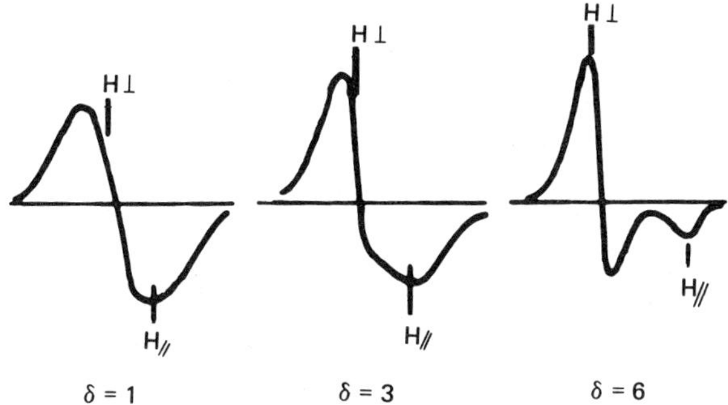


FIG. 15. Changes in line shapes for powder spectra as a function of the ratio of anisotropy to individual line width ($\delta = \Delta H_{an}/\Delta H_i$).

The different types of line shapes as a function of the anisotropy parameter $\delta = \Delta H_{an}/\Delta H_i$ are given in Fig. 15. The corresponding g values are also shown and are determined approximately from the inflection points. Accurate determination necessitates computer simulation of the spectrum to the best fit with the experimental spectrum.

In the case of "orthorhombic" symmetry in ESR, the symmetry is lower than axial symmetry and consequently the calculation of the line shape is somewhat more difficult. The resulting spectra are similar to those shown in Fig. 16.

The three g values corresponding to the eigenvalues of the g-factor tensor are given by the inflection points as shown in Fig. 16. Resolution of the spectrum depends on the degree of anisotropy ($g_1 - g_2$ or $g_2 - g_3$) relative to the individual line width. For poorly resolved spectra, computer simulation of the ESR spectrum is absolutely necessary if accurate values of the g factor are expected. For unresolved spectra, computer simulation is not useful as it is meaningless. For well-resolved spectra simulation allows one to obtain accurate values, which is not of great interest in the majority of cases in the catalysis field and can therefore be avoided.

2. Hyperfine Interaction and the g Factor

In the presence of hyperfine splitting, assumed to be axially symmetric, the hyperfine lines are easily shown to resonate at magnetic field values given by (from Eqs. 4 and 19)

$$H = \frac{g_0 H_0}{g} - \frac{hM_I K}{\beta g} \tag{19a}$$

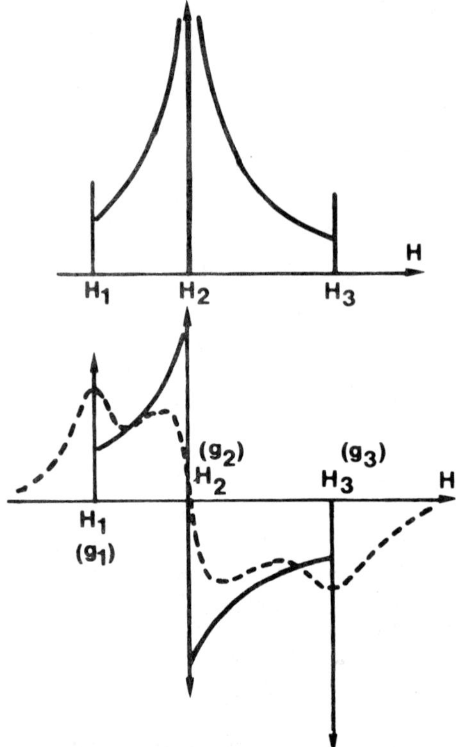


FIG. 16. Calculated absorption (upper curve) and derivative (lower curve) line shapes for orthorhombic-type symmetry assuming a $\delta$ function (solid line) and gaussian or lorentzian (dashed line) individual line shapes.

where K is defined in frequency units by

$$K = (g_\parallel^2 A_\parallel^2 \cos^2 \theta + g_\perp^2 A_\perp^2 \sin^2 \theta)^{1/2} g^{-1} \tag{26}$$

and

$$g = (g_\parallel^2 \cos^2 \theta + g_\perp \sin^2 \theta)^{1/2} \tag{27}$$

The line shape is then given by the relation

$$\frac{dN}{dH} = \frac{1}{2} N_0 \left\{ \frac{2 \cos \theta}{g^2} \left[ \frac{(g_{\parallel}^2 - g_{\perp}^2) g_0 H_0}{2g} + \frac{hM_I}{\beta} \left( \frac{g_{\parallel}^2 A_{\parallel}^2 - g_{\perp}^2 A_{\perp}^2}{2Kg^2} - \frac{K(g_{\parallel}^2 - g_{\perp}^2)}{g^2} \right) \right] \right\}^{-1}$$

Extreme hyperfine lines described by the relations

$$H_{\parallel} = \frac{g_0 H_0}{g_{\parallel}} - \frac{hM_I A_{\parallel}}{\beta g_{\parallel}} \qquad H_{\perp} = \frac{g_0 H_0}{g_{\perp}} - \frac{hM_I A_{\perp}}{\beta g_{\perp}} \tag{19b}$$

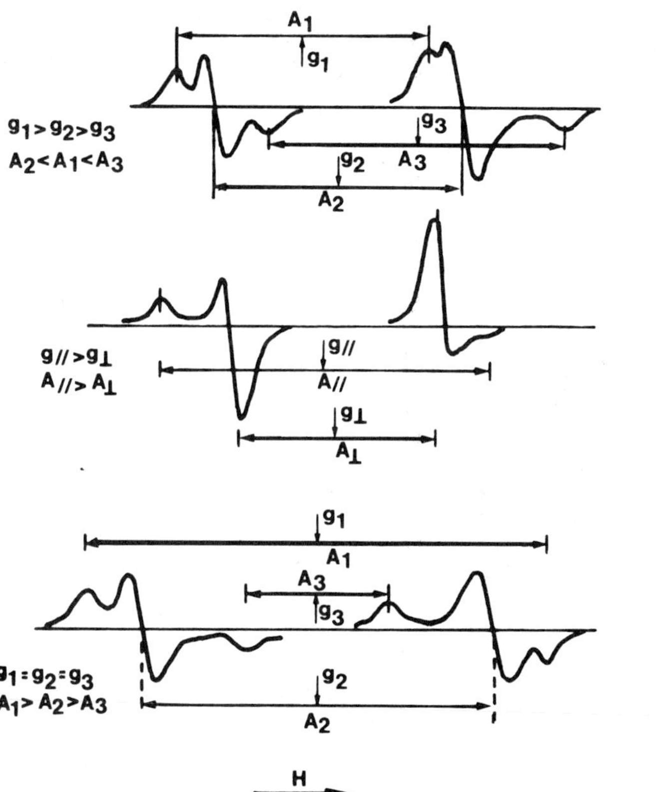


FIG. 17. Typical ESR powder spectra for different g-factor values (g) and hyperfine tensor eigenvalues (A).

are obtained for $\theta = 0$ and $\theta = \pi/2$, respectively. Typical spectra of powder samples, including g-factor and hyperfine anisotropies, are given in Fig. 17.

*Note*: Values for the hyperfine coupling, A, should be expressed in units of frequency, MHz, rather than units of magnetic field. The conversion factor that is sometimes to use in the relationships above is

$$2.8H_G = H_{MHz}$$

which stems from Eq. (4) and assumes that $g = g_e$. Any change in the value of g will alter the value of the conversion factor. Hence it turns out that when expressed in magnetic field units (G), the hyperfine coupling may differ from the experimental hyperfine splitting depending on the magnitude to which g deviates from $g_e$. The frequency unit is thus more correct since it corresponds to an energy. But since in the majority of cases $g = g_e$, authors habitually express the experimental splitting in magnetic field units (G) as measured directly from the experimental spectra. This could be confusing to one unaware of the inherent assumption.

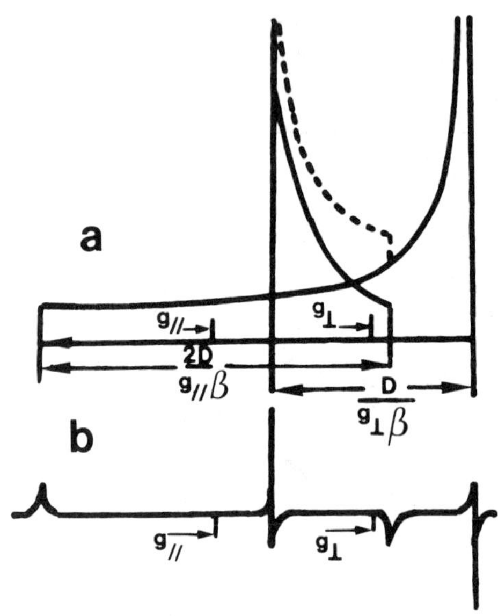


FIG. 18. Theoretical (a) absorption and (b) derivative spectra for S = 1 and axial symmetry.

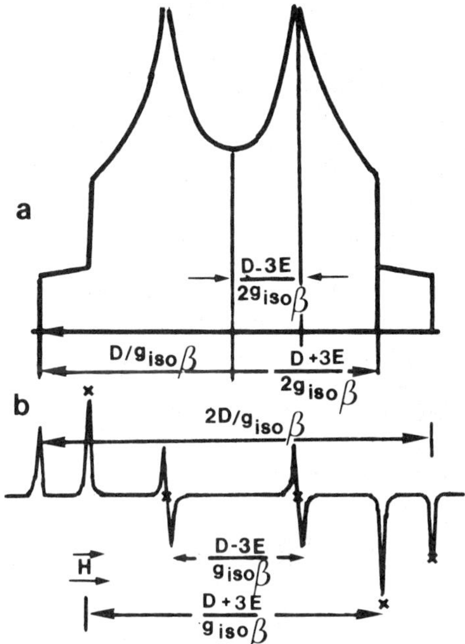


FIG. 19. Theoretical (a) absorption and (b) derivative spectra for S = 1, orthorhombic symmetry, and isotropic g factor.

### 3. Fine Structure of Powder Samples

This is the most striking and complex case and only a few examples have been clearly analyzed. The approach for calculating line shapes is similar to that given for g-factor and hyperfine tensors. For clarity, Figs. 18 and 19 show the cases for axial and orthorhombic symmetries, respectively, where S = 1. When S > 1 and the g factor is anisotropic, the spectrum generally turns out to be rather complex and difficult to analyze. One practical example will be given in the next section in the case of $Cu^{2+}$ pairs in a zeolite matrix.

## III. APPLICATIONS OF ESR TECHNIQUE TO HETEROGENEOUS CATALYSTS

Several fields of applications of ESR technique in heterogeneous catalysis have been developed in the past 20 years. They correspond to the characterization of:

1. Adsorbed paramagnetic species.
2. Paramagnetic species introduced in a catalyst in order to "probe" the material via the ESR parameter responses (tracers).
3. Surface properties giving rise to paramagnetic species (radical ion). This is due to the electron donor or electron acceptor capacities of a surface, which acts on a more or less readily ionizable compound to give a charge transfer complex. For instance, compounds such as perylene, anthracene (for the radical cation), tetracyano ethylene, or trinitrobenzene (for the radical anions) are often used.
4. Bulk properties as evidenced by ionization of bulk atomic arrangements to make them paramagnetic. The ionization is usually performed using UV light from a mercury lamp or $\gamma$ rays from a $^{60}Co$ source.
5. Transition metal ions within or at the surface of a material.

This book is devoted to the characterization of solid catalysts and thus we will focus our interest on points 2, 4, and 5. An exhaustive presentation of the literature is not given. We prefer to present a few examples simply to make clear to the reader the main fields of application in heterogeneous catalysis.

### A. Uses of Paramagnetic Probes [9]

This technique is used to characterize catalyst properties somewhat by "feel." It consists of introducing a paramagnetic probe into the material in place of an element or available free space or cavities within the solid and then, from the ESR parameters, obtaining useful information about the material itself. Such a technique has been applied successfully in biochemistry by attaching compounds such as nitroxide to some organic chains. The ESR parameters used were either g values probing the environmental symmetries or hyperfine coupling anisotropy as described above. For these parameters, motion of the paramagnetic species with respect to the host lattice was analyzed as a function of temperature. One expects an averaging effect when the motion around a given axis is high enough. For instance, high motion around the z axis results in $g_{ave} = (g_x + g_y)/2$. High rotation rates average out the anisotropic hyperfine splitting and the following $A_0$ and $g_0$ values are observed:

$$g_0 = g_{ave} = \frac{g_x + g_y + g_z}{3} \quad \text{and} \quad A_0 = \frac{1}{3}(A_x + A_y + A_z)$$

The most commonly used spin "probes" or "labels" contain the nitroxide free radical rendered unusually stable and inert by a steric protective effect, as for instance in ditertiobutyl nitroxide:

$$(CH_3)_3C-\dot{N}(O)-C(CH_3)_3$$

The unpaired electron is largely localized on the $2p\pi$ nitrogen orbital. In liquid solvents the molecular rotation is rapid enough to average the dipolar interaction to zero, leaving only the isotropic hyperfine interaction to produce the three-line hyperfine splitting. For low levels of motion, incompletely averaged anisotropic terms of the magnetic Hamiltonian produce measurable line broadening (Fig. 20).

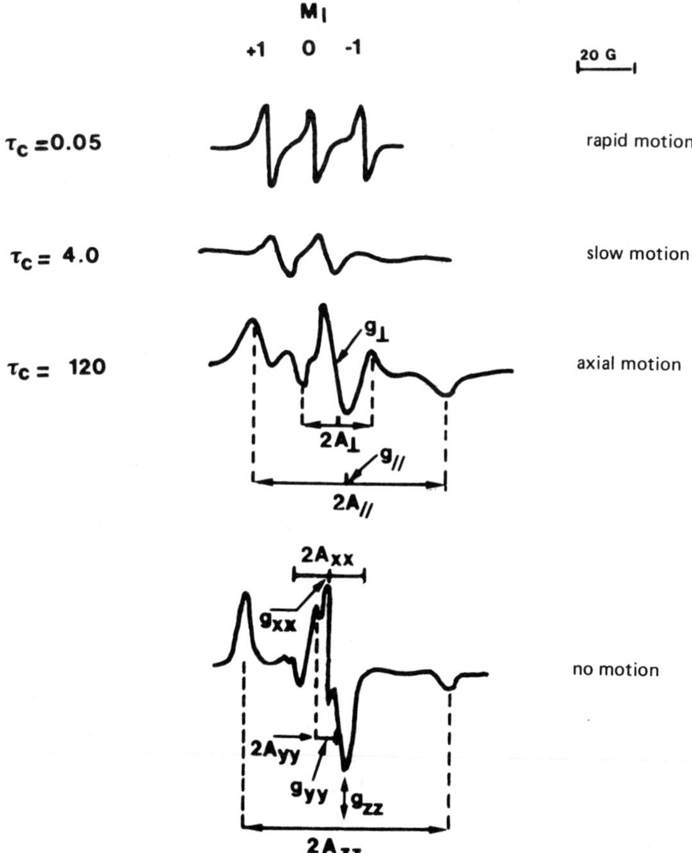


FIG. 20. Effect of motion on the ESR spectra of nitroxide radicals. $\tau_c = 4\pi\eta\, r^3/3kT$ in solution of varying viscosity $\eta$.

The motion of magnetic probes is obviously related to the chemical interaction between a probe and the catalytic material. The orientation depends on electrostatic and hydrophobic attractive forces and on the free space available. For instance, in the case of layered materials such as nickel antigorite or clays, the magnetic probe may obviously be orientated between the layers and the main axis of the spin Hamiltonian, and therefore the ESR spectrum parameter will obviously be related to (1) the layers arrangement and (2) the presence of water molecules in the material surrounding the magnetic probe. One can therefore follow the removal of water and even the collapsing of the interlayers by determining the variations of $A_{zz}$ and $A_{xx}$ values (zz being along the N $2p\pi$ orbital and xx along the N—O bond). Finally, such a study may give information about the mobility of a probe within cavities of the material, which is obviously related to the free void volume available (i.e., to the cavity size and to the presence of other species in the cavity). Unfortunately, such a technique has been used only rarely for heterogeneous catalysts. An example of $Mn^{2+}$ in a zeolite matrix is given in Sec. III.B.

## B. Transition Metal Ions

Transition metal ions correspond to the widest and the most fruitful field of applications of ESR spectroscopy in heterogeneous catalysis. Some ions have been particularly well studied:

$d^1$ ions: $Mo^{5+}$, $V^{4+}$, $Ti^{3+}$, $Cr^{5+}$, $W^{5+}$
$d^5$ ions: $Fe^{3+}$, $Mn^{2+}$
$d^9$ ions: $Cu^{2+}$, $Ni^+$, $Ag^+$

Such ions may be either incorporated within an host lattice at interstitial or substitutional positions or deposited at the surface of a catalyst or at cationic positions of a zeolite matrix. ESR spectroscopy was then used to obtain information about the location of the ion, its motion under chemisorption or heat treatment, and its chemical reactivity.

A striking example corresponds to the use of $Mn^{2+}$ in a zeolite matrix. Usually, the ESR spectra of these ions show only the $\pm 1/2$ transition [10]. Mn(II) ions exist in various states within the zeolite structure. In hydrated samples the ESR spectrum is identical to that observed for $Mn^{2+}$ aqueous solutions [i.e., in the form of hexa aquo complexes in the supercages (a = 96 G)]. Dehydration of the samples at 150°C results in a decrease in the hyperfine splitting down to 87 G and a fine constant D = 240 G. More dehydration (200 to 300°C) gives a hyperfine splitting of 89 G with smaller line width (12 G instead of 50 G) and D < 100. Completely dehydrated samples give an ESR spectrum with a 95-G hyperfine splitting (D < 100 G, $\Delta H_{pp} \simeq 13$ G) and assigned to $Mn^{2+}$ in an octahedral ligand ligand field. The center of the hexagonal prism of Y-type zeolite corresponds to such a symmetry. It was therefore concluded that dehydration of the samples results in a migration of $Mn^{2+}$ from the supercages toward the sodalite cages (partial dehydration) and further to hexagonal prisms (total dehydration). Rehydration results in a backward migration toward the supercage sites. These results show the dynamic behavior of ions in a zeolite matrix as a function of the surrounding atmosphere. This is obviously important under catalytic properties, since as a function of the effect of the reactants—which obviously depend on their nature—such ions may or may not migrate toward accessible sites. The presence of other ions either more hydrophilic, such as $La^{3+}$, $Zn^{2+}$, $Mg^{2+}$, or less hydrophilic, such as $Ca^{2+}$, $Cd^{2+}$, and $Mn^{2+}$, modifies the migration.

1. Doped or Supported Catalysts

The aim of preparing such materials was to introduce an ion, known to be active in catalysis, within the host lattice of a given symmetry or at the surface of a high-surface-area material. The ion is usually introduced at a very small extent (<1% atom) and its ESR parameters are expected to depend on the symmetry of the host lattice. Such studies are of interest in basic research since one could expect to be dealing with a model catalyst.

Let us look at an example. Mo or V ion may be introduced into a $TiO_2$ matrix by impregnation with a Mo or V salt (usually molybdate or vanadate) and then calcinating in air at 500°C (anatase) or 800°C (rutile) [11]. The ESR spectra obtained are then typical of $Mo^{5+}$ or $V^{4+}$ ions at a substitutional position [12] or at a distorted tetrahedral position with $g_1 = 1.911$, $g_2 = 1.919$, and $g_3 = 1.952$ [13]. This clearly shows that the ions have been incorporated into the host lattice (Fig. 21) (see also Ref. 14). One may note that the ESR spectrum of $Mo^{5+}$ is much better resolved than for anatase, which shows that the lattice is much better defined in the former case (i.e., that ion-lattice atom distances are unique and not randomly distributed) [15]. In other words, the crystalline order is higher for 800°C heated samples, as could be expected. ESR spectra for ions incorporated in $TiO_2$ are given in Ref. 11, and ESR parameters of V ions are given in Table 3.

Molybdena-silica or molybdena-alumina materials are chemically interesting models for several industrially significant catalysts and thus have received considerable attention. The main question that arises is whether Mo ions react with alumina to give Mo aluminate and/or are reduced to Mo (V) under catalytic reaction conditions. It has been observed that Mo ions supported on $SiO_2$ or $Al_2O_3$ give an ESR spectrum typical of Mo(V) ions after reducing the solid under hydrogen [16,17]. Hyperfine splitting may be observable since about 25.4% Mo

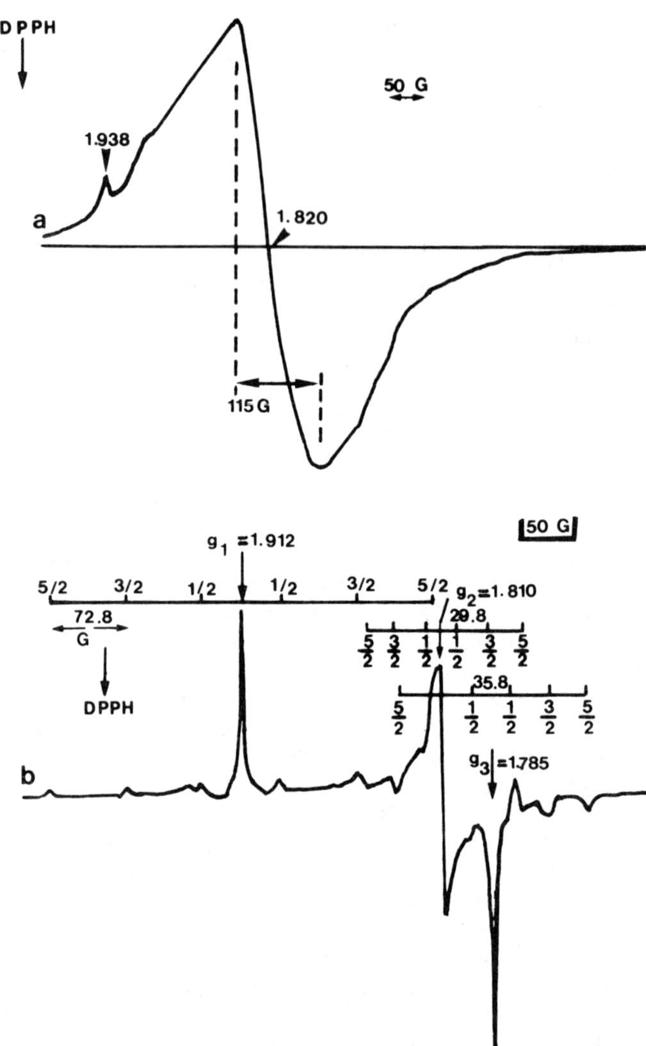


FIG. 21. ESR spectra for 0.51% Mo in $TiO_2$ sample heat-treated in air: (a) at 500°C, anatase; (b) at 800°C, rutile. (From Ref. 11.)

is present with I = 5/2 in natural abundance (15.8% $^{95}Mo$ and 9.6% $^{97}Mo$ with $\beta_N$ = −0.927 and −0.948 nuclear magneton, respectively). A better resolution of the spectra is observed for $^{95}Mo$-enriched catalyst [18], as shown in Fig. 22. From the anisotropy of the ESR parameters (g factor and hyperfine splitting) information about the

TABLE 3 ESR Parameters of $V^{4+}$ and $VO^{2+}$ in $TiO_2$ Matrices

| Ion | Position | Matrix | $g_3$ | $g_2$ | $g_1$ | $A_3$[a] | $A_2$[a] | $A_1$[a] |
|---|---|---|---|---|---|---|---|---|
| $V^{4+}$ | Substitutional | Rutile | 1.913 | 1.913 | 1.955 | 31 | 44 | 142 |
| $V^{4+}$ | Interstitial | Rutile | 1.993 | 1.986 | 1.940 | 60 | 45 | 111 |
| $VO^{2+}$ | – | Anatase | 1.973 | 1.973 | 1.905 | 72 | 64 | 186 |
| $VO^{2+}$ | – | Rutile | 1.967 | 1.967 | 1.906 | 75 | 75 | 192 |

[a]In frequency units, $10^{-4}$ $cm^{-1}$.
*Source*: Ref. 14.

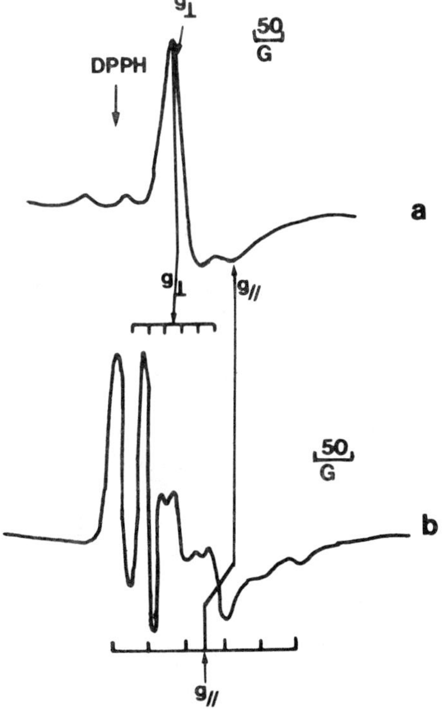


FIG. 22. ESR spectra (X band, 25°C) of a $Mo/SiO_2$ catalyst reduced at 500°C by hydrogen: (a) normal Mo; (b) enriched in $^{95}Mo$. (From Ref. 18.)

coordination chemistry of the paramagnetic ions is obtained. For instance, one can get $g_\perp > g_\parallel$ inversed to $g_\perp < g_\parallel$ by changing only the coordination of molybdenyl complexes [18,19]. The $Mo^{5+}$ on $SiO_2$ was then shown [18] to be surrounded by O ions with one Mo=O bond and to be related to silicomolybdic acid with $g_\perp = 1.94$, $g_\parallel = 1.882$, $A_\perp = 44$ G, and $A_\parallel = 98$ G. The latter point may mean that under reducing conditions, Mo and $SiO_2$ may combine into a definite compound rather than leading to Mo ions in Mo oxide simply deposited on a $SiO_2$ support.

In the case of Mo-$Al_2O_3$ materials, ESR spectroscopy has been used to try to characterize the effect of the support and of the reduction treatment conditions on Mo(V) ions formation and neighboring symmetry. The results clearly show that alumina support and reduction conditions play a determining role, since ESR parameters change significantly. However, the difficulty in correlating the ESR parameters with the catalytic properties of the materials makes the results rather useless. The use of other techniques is therefore necessary since the main conclusion that could be drawn from ESR results is that the material is very complex and heterogeneous, so that efforts toward a detailed description of the catalyst could be vain!

It has often been observed that the amount of Mo(V) ions as quantitatively determined by ESR technique is very small and represents only a few percent of the number of Mo ions in the material [11, 20], although in some cases magnetic susceptibility measurements indicate that many more Mo ions have been reduced [20]. Several explanations may be given: (1) quantitative determination of metal ions concentration is meaningless in the ESR technique, or (2) part of the Mo(V) ions cannot be detected because of too-short relaxation times, resulting in too-broad ESR spectra. The second explanation seems more valid and could be explained if part of the Mo(V) ions are within given phases, such as $MoO_3$ or Mo aluminate crystallites. Indeed, when Mo(V) ion concentration increases, electronic interaction between ions increases and therefore the relaxation time can sharply decrease and/or dipolar broadening may occur.

In other words, the low number of Mo(V) ions detected by ESR may indicate that only a few Mo(V) ions are incorporated and reduced in $Al_2O_3$ matrix but also that either small $MoO_3$ clusters or Mo aluminate phase clusters are formed. Mo(V) ions in such phases cannot be detected by the ESR technique. One may then suggest that Mo ions may be clustered (as $MoO_3$ or Mo aluminate phases) when Mo(V) ions concentration decreases under a given treatment or under a catalytic reaction. The changes in Mo(V) ions concentration detected by ESR and in their ESR parameters under treatment conditions or with regard to support effects may well result from a change in the nature of the combination of Mo with the support [18].

2. Aggregates of Transition Metal Ions

Transition metal ions may well be analyzed by ESR spectroscopy when they are paramagnetic and dispersed enough not to interact too strongly with each other, as seen in the preceding section. When the metal ion concentration increases, the ESR signal line width broadens and may even disappear. As indicated above, this is very probably due to the clustering of paramagnetic ions. This has been observed, for instance, for Cr on $Al_2O_3$ [21] or $SiO_2$ [16], and for Cu on $Al_2O_3$ [22], $SiO_2$ [23], or $SiO_2/Al_2O_3$ [24]. The change in shape of the spectra is a good criterion to follow regarding the formation of aggregates of metal ions.

The case of $Cu^{2+}$ ($d^9$ ion) has been studied extensively since such an ion gives rise to nice ESR spectra with resolved hyperfine structure and g factor, even for powders. For Cu in zeolite [25] it has been observed that $Cu^{2+}$ clusters are formed at high Cu concentration and after evacuation above 150°C to eliminate water molecules. Two asymmetric peaks are obtained with $g_\perp = 2.048$, $g_\parallel = 2.333$ and $g_\perp = 2.084$, $g_\parallel = 2.386$, and a symmetric one at $g = 2.17$. The latter signal is similar to the one observed in the hydrated form and increases in intensity with the Cu concentration. The asymmetrical and sharper lines are due to isolated $Cu^{2+}$ in two different environments and predominate at low $Cu^{2+}$ ion concentration (<5%).

One even more (Fig. 23) striking feature has been observed in such systems since pairs of Cu ions [26] have been identified in CuCaY [26a] and CuCeY [26b] zeolites outgassed at 500°C. The fine structure (S = 1) is presented in Fig. 23 and is interpreted according

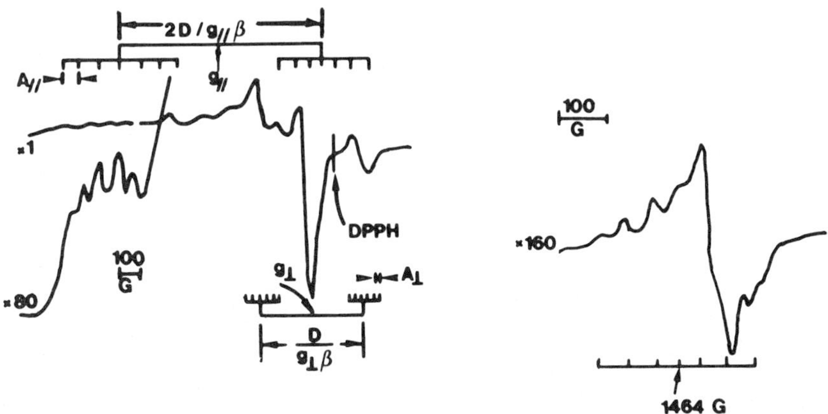


FIG. 23. 77 K ESR spectra of $\Delta M_S = \pm 1$ and $\Delta M_S = \pm 2$ (left- and right-hand sides, respectively) of identical $Cu^{2+}$ pairs in a CuCaY zeolite outgassed at 500°C. (From Ref. 26a.)

TABLE 4 Spin Hamiltonian Parameters of Cu Centers in Y-Type Zeolites

| Paramagnetic species | Samples | g-Factor values | | Zero field splitting[a] | | Hyperfine splitting[a] | |
|---|---|---|---|---|---|---|---|
| | | $\Delta M_S = \pm 1$ | $\Delta M_S = \pm 2$ | D | E | $A_\parallel$ | $A_\perp$ |
| Isolated $Cu^{2+}$ | CuCay outgassed at 200°C | $2.320_\parallel$, $2.066_\perp$ | — | — | — | 176 | 24 |
| | | $2.383_\parallel$, $2.066_\perp$ | | | | 133 | 24 |
| Identical $Cu^{2+}$ pair | CuCay outgassed at 500°C | $2.345_\parallel$, $2.066_\perp$ | 4.13 ($\alpha = 90°$), 4.428 ($\alpha = 30°$) | 476 | 0 | 150 | unresolved[b] |
| Nonlinear $Cu^{2+}$ pair | CuY 74% exchanged | 2.170 ($\Delta H_{pp} = 88$ G) | 4.19 | — | — | — | — |

[a]Expressed in $10^{-4}$ $cm^{-1}$.
[b]Half-field value $A = 134 \times 10^{-4}$ $cm^{-1}$ ($\alpha = 30°$).
*Source*: Ref. 26a.

to the theoretical procedure given in Fig. 18. The experimental data are given in Table 4. The zero-field splitting equals $D = 0.0476\ cm^{-1}$, while the hyperfine pattern corresponds to two equally coupled $Cu^{2+}$ [$2 \times 2 \times (3/2) + 1 = 7$ hyperfine lines]. The spectrum is characterized by two parts: (1) the $\Delta M_S = \pm 1$ transition part and (2) the "half-field" line ($\Delta M_S = \pm 2$). Such pairs of ions may give rise to an ESR spectrum if the ions are coupled by exchange interaction. The quadruplet then splits into a triplet state with electron spins parallel (S = 1) and a singlet state with electron spins antiparallel (S = 0). Only the triplet state is paramagnetic and may give an ESR spectrum.

Two types of Cu ion pairs may be identified. One exchange-coupled pair is characterized by identical spin hamiltonian parameters and principal axes for both ions; this is the identical pair. In the other pair the symmetry axis of the two ions forms an angle; hence they are termed the nonlinear pair. The former type gives an ESR spectrum consisting of two parts: the $\Delta M_S = \pm 1$ and $\Delta M_S = \pm 2$ transitions, as seen above with $g_{1\|} = g_{2\|} = g_{\|}$ and so on.

The static magnetic field is taken to be along the z direction. The "identical pair" obviously has axial symmetry which makes an angle $\alpha$ with respect to the z (or H) direction. If $\alpha = 0$, two ESR transitions are allowed, with a separation equal to $2D/g_{\|}\beta$. If $\alpha = 90°$, three transitions are allowed. Two are centered at

$$H_{\perp} = \frac{[(h\nu)^2 - D^2/4]^{1/2}}{g_{\perp}\beta}$$

with a separation of $D/g_{\perp}\beta$. The third line is at

$$H_{\perp} = \frac{[(h\nu)^2 - D^2]^{1/2}}{2g_{\perp}\beta}$$

which is slightly lower than the field of the other two lines.

The low-field set of lines is resolved in Fig. 23 with a splitting equal to $0.0075\ cm^{-1}$, about half that of the $A_{\|}$ component for a single $Cu^{2+}$ ion and with the expected seven hyperfine lines. The hyperfine line splitting is $0.0134\ cm^{-1}$ and is greater than for $\Delta M_S = \pm 1$ transition. From Eqs. (26) and (27) one gets

$$A(\alpha) = \frac{(g_{\|}^2 A_{\|}^2 \cos^2\alpha + g_{\perp}^2 A_{\perp}^2 \sin^2\alpha)^{1/2}}{g}$$

$$g = (g_{\|}^2 \cos^2\alpha + g_{\perp}^2 \sin^2\alpha)^{1/2} \qquad \alpha = 30°$$

In an isotropic system one has $g_{11} = g_{22} = g_{33}$ and one can deduce from the experimental isotropic g value the angle between the symmetry axes of the two Cu ions. Using eulerian angles $\theta$, $\Phi$, and $\psi$ for rotational transformation matrices R, one obtains $\theta = 55°$, $\psi = 45°$, and $g = 2.17$, as observed for the other ESR signal. It follows that symmetry axes of the two Cu ions form an angle of $2\alpha = 110°$, in agreement with X-ray data.

Assuming that the isotropic exchange interaction is small, the observed zero-field splitting is due to dipolar interaction and one has $D = \beta^2(2g_{\parallel}^2 + g_{\perp}^2)/2r^3$ and $E = 0$. Thus the observed zero-field splitting can be used to calculate the separation between two ions in a pair. One then gets 4.2 Å. Considering the ion location in Y-type zeolite as determined from X-ray diffraction analysis [27], it is reasonable to conclude that the ion pairs are formed by Cu(II) ions located at site I' in the *same* sodalite cavity and are responsible for the isotropic ESR line.

This example shows two main aspects of ESR technique:

1. The possibility of locating ions in a matrix even for low ion concentration, but knowledge about the crystallography of the material and the possible locations of the ions is necessary to be really confident in the interpretation.
2. The location of ions and their more or less intimate relationship (isolated ions, pairs, aggregates, etc.) may greatly change with the type of treatment of the material (desorption, adsorption of reactants, etc.).

In other words, the heterogeneity of the distribution and arrangements of ions is often very large. This obviously makes determination of the nature of the catalytically active site very difficult, since ions may move under experimental conditions such as heat treatment and/or adsorption or desorption of reactants.

### 3. Dispersion of Transition Metal Ions Ensembles

Another interesting application of ESR spectroscopy is the characterization of the enhancement of the dispersion state of transition metal ions. For instance, when alumina is impregnated by an oxalic solution of $Cr^{3+}$ (oxalic acid is known to form a very stable 3:1 complex ion with $Cr^{3+}$) rather than by a Cr nitrate or sulfate, the Cr(III) ion is observed and gives a much better resolved ESR spectrum. This clearly shows that the Cr(III) ions are much better dispersed in the former case and that the formation of an $\alpha$ phase of clusters of $Cr^{3+}$ is prevented [28].

4. Diffusion of Ions Between the Surface and the Bulk, and Vice Versa

This is obviously a very important point since catalytic sites may then be largely modified in nature, location, and accessibility. $Mn^{2+}$ ion in MgO is an interesting example [29]. $Mn^{2+}$ is a $d^5$ ion of high spin [i.e., corresponds to a S state with a spherical symmetry (S = 5/2)]. In general, only the Kramer doublet is observed ($+1/2 \rightarrow -1/2$) at $g \simeq g_e$, with a six-line hyperfine structure (I = 5/2). For most of the MnO/MgO samples (Mn in the range 50 to 2000 atomic ppm) the ESR spectrum for $Mn^{2+}$ consists of two overlapping spectra. The sharp signal is resolved into six hyperfine lines of the same intensity and is attributed to substitutional $Mn^{2+}$ diluted in the matrix. The second signal is broad and unresolved and corresponds to $Mn^{2+}$ clusters, as discussed above. The progressive change from the second to the first signal was observed to occur as a function of activation temperature. This is interpreted as a progressive diffusion of $Mn^{2+}$ between the surface (cluster) and the bulk (dispersion) under heat treatment, which is the opposite case of that of the examples in Sec. III.B.1, p. 201. This is clearly true when an unresolved spectrum is transformed into a resolved one, that is, when broadening by bipolar interaction (recall the $r^{-3}$ function law) or strong narrowing due to strong electron-electron coupling interactions occurs.

A more complex phenomenon occurs in the case of V or Mo ions in $TiO_2$. We have seen previously (Sec. III.B.1, p. 201) that heating the doped oxide up to 500°C in air favors the incorporation of V or Mo into the $TiO_2$ matrix, as for Mn ion in MgO. However, if heating is performed at a higher temperature (e.g., 800°C) the crystallization state of $TiO_2$ is better and the rutile phase is obtained. In the meantime, part of the V or Mo ions were shown by XPS [11] to diffuse from the bulk toward the surface, whereas the ESR technique shows that the remaining V or Mo ions are at a substitutional position, as seen in Sec. III.B.1, p. 201. One then gets a material composed of small clusters of crystallites, very probably $V_2O_5$ or $MoO_3$ in nature, lying on the doped oxide. A detailed ESR study carried out by reducing the material under varying conditions [11] shows that the material is even more complex, since $Mo^{3+}$, pairs of $Mo^{3+}$, and so on, could also be detected. Such a "heterogeneity" in doped oxide surfaces is very important for an understanding of catalytically active sites.

We have shown recently by XPS [30,31] that the enhancement of the catalytic selectivity of SbSnO catalysts for the reaction of mild oxidation of propene into acrolein is related to the migration of Sb from the bulk of the solid solution $Sb/SnO_2$ toward the surface under activation in air at temperatures higher than 600°C. The highly selective material is then composed of $Sb_2O_4$ particles, as evidenced by infrared and X-ray diffraction techniques, lying on a Sb surface-enriched $Sb/SnO_2$ solid solution. At this stage it is important to emphasize (1) the absolute necessity of using different physical techniques, including surface techniques, to better characterize the heterogeneous catalysts, and (2) the great importance of the preparation conditions for making reproducible and "homogeneous" catalysts. This is a very important feature if one desires to improve catalysis as a science.

### 5. Location, Complexes, and Unusual Oxidation States of Metal Ions in Zeolites

We have already seen some examples for which ESR spectroscopy could help to determine where transition metal ions are located (Secs. II.B.3 and III.B). Let us consider other examples with some ions in a rather unusual oxidation state.

*a. Palladium Ion in Zeolite.* All known stable square-planar complexes of Pd(II) are diamagnetic with low-spin $d^8$ configuration. However, the Pd(I) $4d^9$ and Pd(III)$4d^7$ ions may be observable by ESR. For instance, Pd(II) ions have been introduced into a NaY zeolite sample by the classical ion exchange method ($Pd^{2+} \leftrightarrow Na^+$) [32,33]. When the material is heated at 500°C under oxygen, a symmetrical ESR signal is observed with $g_{iso} = 2.223$ and $\Delta H_{pp} = 16$ G.

If the material is then heated in vacuo at 500°C, an asymmetrical spectrum is observed with $g_\perp = 2.10$ and $g_\parallel = 2.33$. The former signal is assigned to $Pd^{3+}$ and the latter one to $Pd^+$. As in the case of Cu ion, the Pd ions are in a tetragonal field with $g_\parallel = g_e + 8\lambda/\delta$ and $g_\perp = g_e + 2\lambda/\Delta$ from relation (13). If one compares the g-factor values for $Pd^+$ and $Cu^{2+}$ ions ($g_\parallel = 2.32$, $g_\perp = 2.06$) in the same dehydrated Y zeolite with $\lambda = 1412\ cm^{-1}$ for Pd(I) and $828\ cm^{-1}$ for Cu(II), one can deduce that the crystal field splitting of the d levels is larger for Pd than for Cu. This indicates that Pd ions must be *more covalently bonded* to the lattice oxygens than are Cu ions. The isotropic ESR signal for $Pd^{3+}$ ($4d^7$) may be interpreted by a dynamic Jahn-Teller distortion since tetragonal distortion should result in an axially symmetric g tensor ($g_\parallel \simeq g_e, g_\perp = g_e + 6\lambda/\Delta$ [3]. In dynamic distortion the three equivalent static distortions may resonate around one axis, resulting in an isotropic spectrum.

*b. Cobalt Ion.* $Co^{2+}$ is also a $d^7$ ion which can be of either low or high spin, depending on the ligand field strength (Fig. 5a). In symmetry Oh and a high crystal field, one obtains the configuration $t_{2g}^6 e_g^1$ (S = 1/2), whereas in a weak field, one has $t_{2g}^5 e_g^2$ (S = 3/2). In the second case, as for $Co(NH)_3^{2+}$ in zeolite, the level shift is small and therefore the relaxation time too short to lead to an ESR signal, even at −196°C. If strong ligands such as methyl isocyanate are added, an ESR spectrum with 11 hyperfine lines is observed [34] with $g_\parallel = 2.008$, $g_\perp = 2.087$, $A_\parallel^{Co} = 68$ G, $A_\perp^{Co} = 75$ G, and $I_{Co} = 7/2$. The $e_g$ level is then occupied by the unpaired electron and the static

Jahn-Teller effect stabilizes the $d_{z^2}$ orbital by elongating the octahedron along one axis. As we saw in relation (12) of Sec. II, one has $g_{\parallel} \simeq g_e$ and $g_{\perp} = g_e + 6\lambda/\Delta$. The $d^9$ complexes of Co° could be detected by reacting $Co^{2+}$ with NO, and identified by ESR, UV, and IR techniques. In the case of a zeolite matrix, one gets a spectrum with a hyperfine pattern characteristic of Co. Interpretation is then very difficult, as several possibilities exist. The most probable consists of a Co° dinitrosyl in a $C_{2h}$ distorted octahedral complex with a $d_{x^2-y^2}$ ground state [35].

*c. Nickel Ion.* $Ni^+$ is a $d^9$ ion in an unusual oxidation state. It can be obtained, for instance, by reducing NiCa-Y zeolite by hydrogen at 200°C [36]. It was shown to react easily with CO molecules, giving rise to different $Ni(CO)_x^+$ (x = 1, 2, . . . ) species identified by the number of hyperfine lines due to $^{13}CO$ (I = 1/2).

*d. Chromium Ion.* $Cr^{5+}$ ($d^1$ ion) has been observed in many matrices, particularly in $Cr/SiO_2$ polymerization catalysts. One interesting example is obtained when NaA zeolite containing Cr sample is oxidized [37]. A six-line hyperfine structure is observed on the perpendicular and parallel features of a $Cr^{5+}$ ESR signal, which is interpreted as an interaction with $^{27}Al$ nuclei (I = 5/2). It is possible that Cr ions are bonded to Al ion in a species that would appear as follows:

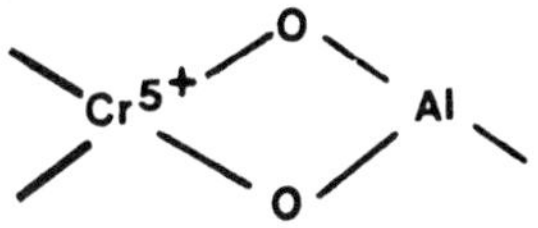

This result shows that in favorable cases ESR technique may give useful information about the bonding of the ions and the lattice nuclei.

*e. Migration of Ions.* The migration of cations within a zeolitic lattice upon dehydration has often been demonstrated by X-ray diffraction [38]. Such a phenomenon, already mentioned for $Mn^{2+}$ in zeolite (Sec. III.B), has been followed by ESR in the case of $W(CO)_6$ adsorbed in the supercage of H-Y and Na-Y zeolites [39]. In HY zeolite, decomposition of the carbonyl is accompanied by oxidation of W into the +5 oxidation state. Decomposition proceeds in a similar manner for $Mo(CO)_6$. The complex is initially located in the supercages and migrates to hidden sides (sodalite unit and hexagonal prisms) upon high-temperature activation in vacuo [39]. Three ESR signals have been detected with $g_{\parallel} < g_{\perp}$ consistent with both distorted Td coordination of $W^{5+}$ (see p. 177 and Refs. 6, 7, and 39). Examination of known cationic sites within the zeolite reveals that only site I in the hexagonal prism offers the possibility of distorted $O_h$ coordination to oxide ions from the framework. Sites I' and II' in sodalite cavities and site II in the supercage may present distorted Td symmetry. Moreover, only sites in the supercage are accessible to molecular oxygen. These various points suggest the following reasonable assignments:

One signal with $g_\parallel = 1.59$, $g_\perp = 1.82$, $A_\parallel = 160 \times 10^{-4}\ cm^{-1}$, and $A_\perp = 75 \times 10^{-4}\ cm^{-1}$ ($I = 1/2$ for $^{183}W$), assigned to $W^{5+}$ in site II.

One signal with $g_\parallel = 1.64$, $g_\perp = 1.86$, $A_\parallel = 170 \times 10^{-4}\ cm^{-1}$, and $A_\perp = 75 \times 10^{-4}\ cm^{-1}$, corresponding to a hidden site (I, I', or II').

One signal with $g_\parallel = 1.71$, $g_\perp = 1.84$, $A_\perp = 75 \times 10^{-4}\ cm^{-1}$, and $A_\parallel$ unresolved, with an eleven-line superfine structure, due to the interaction of $W^{5+}$ with two equivalent Al nuclei, indicating coupling between W and two Al.

These assignments clearly indicate that migration of ions under given conditions may well be followed by ESR, although a good knowledge of the possible ion location is necessary.

*f. Organic Complexes.* For metal ion complexes formed by reacting some reactants with metal ions, the ESR technique may permit the characterization of such complexes (as indicated on pp. 185–188). The relative intensities and the number of hyperfine lines permit determination of the nature and number of the ligands when superhyperfine structure is detected. For $Cu^{2+}$ in Y-type zolite it has been possible to determine from the hyperfine pattern not only that four $NH_3$ ligands are attached to the Cu ion, but also the ion-ligand stretching vibration frequency [40]. The variation of the hyperfine splitting and g-factor values as a function of the recording temperature has indeed been studied. The law

$$A_\parallel(T) = A_\parallel(O) - L_\parallel \cos \frac{\hbar\omega}{2kT}$$

allows us to calculate $\omega$. The good agreement observed with far-infrared data for more concentrated Cu samples shows that applications of the ESR technique may be extended to vibrational studies. This holds particularly for low and even very low ion concentrations, when techniques such as infrared or X-ray diffraction are not sufficiently sensitive to produce meaningful results.

### 6. Desulfurization and Demetallization Catalysts

Catalytic desulfurization and demetallization are performed for treating many crude oil feeds, but rapid catalyst deactivation precludes the application of such treatments to heavier residue. One reason is the deposit of metals, particularly Ni and V, present in the oil. Vanadium has been shown above to be readily detectable by ESR when in its +4 oxidation state [41]. It was therefore interesting to follow, using such a technique, the chemistry of V deposition of a hydrodesulfurization catalyst such as Co-Mo/$\gamma$-$Al_2O_3$ during the HDS process. Three forms of vanadium ESR spectra have been detected, due to different vanadyl complexes. One form dominates at low V contents. Its ESR parameters are different from those in crude oil, as shown in Table 5.

In crude oil a narrow, well-resolved 16-component spectrum is observed, as in porphyrin. On HDS catalyst, line broadening is obtained but this broadening does not depend on vanadium loading or on the presence of Co and Mo on the catalyst. It is important to note that the ESR parameters for spent catalyst are different from those on starting materials but are nearly identical to those obtained when a calcined catalyst is subsequently sulfided (see the last line of Table 5). This close proximity suggests that S is a component of the $VO^{2+}$ complex encountered on the catalyst surface. Moreover, Fig. 24 shows that a strong correlation exists between the anisotropy of the ESR parameters and the coordination chemistry of V ions.

Such a study has been extended to the characterization and the understanding of the role of Ni and Co promoters on HDS catalysts, such as sulfided tungsten and sulfided molybdenum [45], since $Mo^{5+}$ and $W^{5+}$ are known to give ESR signals. The major difficulty is that several overlapping signals are often observed and the interpretation of all of them is very difficult since changes in environmental symmetry, coordination ligands, the covalency character of the ligand-to-ion bond, and oxidation state ($Mo^{3+}$, $W^{3+}$) may have occurred, which may have modified the ESR parameters. It was observed that promoters Ni or Co both give about the same effect and give rise to a new signal ($g = 2.06$, $\Delta H_{pp} = 220$ G for Ni-Mo; $g = 2.08$, $\Delta H_{pp} =$

TABLE 5 ESR Parameters of Different Vanadyl Complexes ($I = 7/2$)

| Matrix | $g_{\parallel}$ | $g_{\perp}$ | $A^{a}_{\parallel}$ | $A^{a}_{\perp}$ | Reference |
|---|---|---|---|---|---|
| Porphyrin in THF | 1.964 | 1.989 | 170.5 | 58.1 | 42 |
| $\gamma$-$Al_2O_3$ calcined | 1.916 | 1.989 | 181.2 | 70.8 | 16 |
| $SiO_2$ calcined | 1.922 | 1.982 | 195.1 | 77.2 | 16 |
| HDS catalyst | 1.926 | 1.972 | 193.9 | 64.2 | 43 |
| Spent HDS catalyst | 1.920 | 1.972 | 197.2 | 66.5 | 43 |
| $VOSO_4$ on $Al_2O_3$ | 1.920 | 1.966 | 193.4 | 64.3 | 43 |

[a]Expressed in gauss.

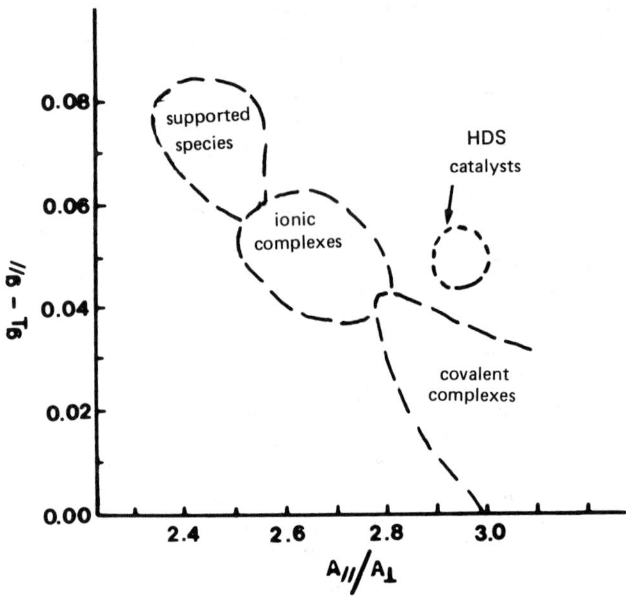


FIG. 24. Correlation between anisotropies in g-factor and hyperfine coupling constants for $VO^{2+}$ in a series of vanadyl complexes. (From Ref. 43.)

220 G for Ni-W; and $\Delta H_{pp}$ = 320 G for Co promotor). This signal has been assigned to electrons located on Mo or W ions, with a very pronounced influence of the Ni or Co which causes a change in values between d orbitals. The other five signals observed on unpromoted [45a] and promoted [45b] catalysts have been interpreted in terms of oxo-$Mo^{5+}$ or oxo-$W^{5+}$, paramagnetic surface species, and surface $M^{3+}$ or $M^{5+}$ ions with different sulfur ligand symmetries. Their intensities have been followed as a function of $H_2S/H_2$ treatment and of the addition of promoters and have been compared to thiophene HDS activity or butene hydrogenation activity. Unfortunately, no clear correlations have been observed, which may indicate that the corresponding paramagnetic species are not related directly to catalytic properties. These unsatisfactory results also show the great difficulty in using a unique physical technique for the understanding of a catalyst. Some aspects of the catalyst properties are determined, but their role in catalysis is somewhat difficult to establish clearly even if modifications of the material obviously influence both ESR response and catalytic properties.

## C. Paramagnetic Defects in Heterogeneous Catalysts

The presence of defects or vacancies in solid catalysts has often been suggested as playing a role in catalysis. If such species are paramagnetic, they can be studied by ESR (V-type or F-type centers, for instance). When they are diamagnetic, they can be made paramagnetic by ionization by UV light or $\gamma$ rays from a $^{60}Co$ source since such photons induce electron displacement by the Compton effect and stabilization at low temperature (e.g., $-196°C$).

### 1. Case of MgO

Paramagnetic V-type centers in MgO have been observed and have been related to its catalytic activity for the $H_2$-$D_2$ exchange reaction [46]. These V centers [47] consist of a surface $B_3$ site identical to that found on MgO (111) surface planes and presenting three $O^-$ ions replacing three $O^{2-}$ anions with a nearby hydroxyl. Such V-type centers have been observed after activation of MgO and depend on the water vapor adsorbed.

### 2. Case of Zeolite and Silica-Alumina

Y-type zeolites, in their acidic or rare earth exchanged form, have been used in numerous industrial applications in the last decade, especially in petroleum refining plants. It has been observed that the thermal and mechanical stability of such catalysts was considerably improved by steam treatment at high temperature. The resulting material is usually designated as being "ultrastable." If such a material is $\gamma$-irradiated at liquid-nitrogen temperature, a V-type-center ESR signal is obtained. On the starting material this signal has a six-line hyperfine structure and was assigned to $Si{-}\overset{\circ}{O}{-}Al$ [48]. For ultrastabilized zeolite one has an eleven-line hyperfine structure pattern which was assigned to $Al{-}\overset{\circ}{O}{-}Al$ [49]. It was concluded that steam treatment eliminated Al atoms from the zeolite lattice, yielding a hydroxyaluminic acid compound which fills the zeolitic cavity and may be eliminated by dissolution by NaOH, N/10 [49,50].

In a similar manner silicoaluminate entities giving rise to a V-type center with a six-line ESR spectrum upon $\gamma$ irradiation have been found to follow the catalytic properties of a silica-alumina catalyst in an acid-type reaction (cracking of cumene) [51]. It was then concluded that in silica-alumina there exists an association of Si and Al in tetrahedral coordination (as in zeolites). This results in Brönsted acidity which compensates for the minus charge borne by the tetracoordinated Al and is responsible for catalytic activity.

In Mg- and Ca-exchanged Y zeolites, $Mg^{2+}$ and $Ca^{2+}$ are known to occupy well-defined cationic sites, as seen above. However when the material was heated at high temperature, ESR signals typical of the F centers in MgO and CaO, respectively, were detected after $\gamma$ irradiation [52]. This clearly shows that upon heat treatment, diamagnetic Mg or Ca ions may agglomerate to form tiny clusters of the corresponding oxide. The number of MO entities in the clusters could not be determined precisely by ESR but were tentatively estimated from the void volume in zeolite cavities to be within the range 2 to 10. These tiny clusters were not detectable by other techniques, such as X-ray diffraction, either because they are in too low concentration or because these entities are too small, resulting in line broadening.

These different examples show that the ESR technique may shed some unique light on peculiar features of a material. This allows us to determine more exactly the intimate organization of a solid. This is unfortunately very often of little interest, since heterogeneity is then clearly demonstrated. The difficulty is thus to determine if such peculiar species for the catalytic properties of the material are important or if one is concerned only with inactive impurity-type entities!

## D. State of a Promoter in a Catalyst

Investigation of the state of a promoter in a catalyst has been an important and striking feature of research in catalysis since its origin. It has long been known that small amounts of a supplementary element may sharply enhance the catalytic properties of a solid [53]. It can be either an electronic or a structural effect. Such effects have been widely used for famous multicomponent mixed oxides (mainly Mo- and Bi-based) in mild oxidation reactions, for Fischer-Tropsch and $NH_3$ synthesis reactions on iron catalysts, and so on. Surface techniques such as AES, XPS, ISS, and SIMS have recently been used to determine if the promoter is really incorporated within the material or if it is only deposited at the surface of the solid. However, the effect of the additive to the active component itself has not yet been clarified and remains rather obscure. When the promoter is paramagnetic, it may be used as a tracer to demonstrate its effect on the active element.

Let us look at an example. The $Rh/SiO_2$ catalyst is used for the selective conversion of synthetic gas. Mn ion may be used as a promoter and we have seen that it is also detectable by ESR p. 200. Kinetic studies have shown that the overall kinetics of CO hydrogenation for $Rh/SiO_2$ and $Rh\text{-}Mn/SiO_2$ catalysts is similar [54]. Therefore, the changes in catalytic performance observed may only be related to changes in the population of active surface species. It has been observed that coverage of the surface of Rh particles decreases on the catalyst surface as a result of Mn addition. This might be due to chemical effects (valence state, ligand nature) or geometrical effects of Mn on Rh particles. The increased catalytic activity (the turnover number increased by 10 with 0.2% Mn for 2.5% Rh) with respect to the $Rh/SiO_2$ catalyst was therefore attributed to the stabilization of an oxidized and active form of Rh on the metal surface.

Moreover, the $Mn/SiO_2$ catalyst showed an unresolved $Mn^{2+}$ ESR spectrum, whereas the $Rh\text{-}Mn/SiO_2$ catalyst showed only a weak signal when reduced under $H_2$ at 500°C and evacuated [54]. The addition of water (synthetic gas reaction involves the presence of $H_2O$) at room temperature resulted in the appearance of a resolved $Mn^{2+}$ for both solids. However, treatment of the $Rh\text{-}Mn/SiO_2$ catalyst with a CO + $H_2O$ mixture led to a threefold increase in intensity of resolved $Mn^{2+}$ signal, whereas no effect was observed on $Mn/SiO_2$. This was interpreted as being due to the formation of a mixed Rh/Mn oxide (i.e., as due to the stabilization of Rh ion by Mn at the Rh metal surface). Even if such a conclusion is speculative since Rh ions were not identified by ESR or other techniques, these results show clearly that Mn additive was modified by the presence of Rh, which is obviously related to modification of the material and presumably to improvement in catalytic performance.

## IV. CONCLUSIONS

We have tried in this chapter to present the reader with some basic data for an understanding of the ESR technique and its fields of application. It can easily be concluded that the use of ESR may yield very useful information, often of unique value, for a wide range of heterogeneous catalysts. The great sensitivity of the technique to the environment of paramagnetic species, as evidenced by the ESR parameters, is a very important factor and allows one to obtain important data about this environment (symmetry, number and nature of the ligands, etc.). The technique also possesses the great advantage (which may be a disadvantage) of being very sensitive to low concentrations in paramagnetic species but of being very poor for high concentrations. It is then complementary to techniques such as X-ray diffraction and infrared and UV spectroscopies. However, the technique is limited to paramagnetic species, that is, to a very restricted domain, even if the domain may be artificially extended by the use of tracers or by ionization by UV or $\gamma$ photons.

We have also emphasized the importance of using several physical techniques to understand the catalyst better. The ESR technique is one of these techniques. It has its limitations but also allows one to answer a number of questions related to the existence, nature, and location of paramagnetic species. It can be of unique value in acquiring particular information and is therefore an obvious tool for use in research laboratories when paramagnetic species or free radical or radical ions are under investigation.

## ACKNOWLEDGMENT

The author gratefully acknowledges the permission of D. Reidel Publishing Company, Dordrecht, Holland, to use a large part of a previous article (Ref. 1) in Secs. I and II.

## APPENDIX 1: EXAMPLE OF A $NO_2$ PARAMAGNETIC MOLECULE

This example of a $NO_2$ paramagnetic molecule is given to illustrate the physical concepts of g-factor parameter. The paramagnetic $NO_2$ molecule is known to be bent 134° in the ground state, with the unpaired electron occupying a nitrogen hybrid orbital directed along the external bisector of the $\widehat{ONO}$ angle. When the magnetic field is perpendicular to the $NO_2$ plane, two excited states may be involved. Excited state 1 is produced by exciting an electron from one of the NO bonding orbitals into the nonbonding ground-state orbital. Because of the Pauli exclusion principle, the spins must be opposite, resulting in a positive value for $\Delta g_1$. The second excited state is just the reverse—the unpaired electron is excited into an NO $\sigma$ antibonding orbital. This gives a negative value for $\Delta g_2$. Although a detailed calculation of energy levels and wavefunction are required for a definite answer, the antibonding orbital is known to be further above than the NO $\sigma$ orbital and is below the nonbonding ground-state orbital. Therefore, the first excited state must be dominant and $\Delta g_2$ is expected to be positive, and thus $g_2$ can be assigned a value of 2.0062.

If the direction of the magnetic field is changed so that $\underline{H}$ lies along the third axis of the $NO_2$ molecule (i.e., in the plane perpendicular to the bisector axis), $\underline{L}$ can excite the unpaired electron from its sp orbital into a nitrogen orbital along the second axis, which lies perpendicular to the plane. This is believed to be a low-lying excited state because it differs in energy from the ground state only by virtue of the bending of the $NO_2$ molecule. The g shift is then expected to be negative since the nitrogen orbital is empty. This prediction is consistent with the observed value of 1.9910 ($\Delta g_3 = -0.0113$). The experimental values may then be assigned as follows: $g_1 = 2.0012$, $g_2 = 2.0062$, and $g_3 = 1.9910$.

## APPENDIX 2: EXAMPLE OF A THEORETICAL CALCULATION OF g-FACTOR VALUES

Let us take an example of a theoretical calculation of g-factor values for a $d^1$ ion in a tetragonally distorted $O_h$ symmetry, as described in Fig. 5. The d orbitals may be characterized by the corresponding $m_L$ values: $|2\rangle$, $|1\rangle$, $|-1\rangle$, and $|-2\rangle$. One can write

$$e_g \begin{cases} d_{z^2} = 0 \\ d_{x^2-y^2} = \frac{1}{2}(|2\rangle + |-2\rangle) \end{cases}$$

and

$$t_{2g} \begin{cases} d_{xy} = -\frac{1}{i\sqrt{2}}(|2\rangle - |-2\rangle) \\ d_{yz} = -\frac{1}{i\sqrt{2}}(|1\rangle + |-1\rangle) \\ d_{xy} = -\frac{1}{i\sqrt{2}}(|1\rangle - |-1\rangle) \end{cases}$$

The ground-state function is $d_{xy}$ and relation (10) can be rewritten

$$g_{ij} = g_e\delta_{ij} - 2\lambda \sum_{n \neq xy} \frac{\langle xy|L_i|n\rangle\langle n|L_j|xy\rangle}{E_n - E_{xy}}$$

### A. $g_{xx}$ and $g_{yy}$ Calculation

One uses the shift operators $L^+ = L_x + iL_y$ and $L^- = L_x - iL_y$. Since $L^{\pm}Y_l^m = [l(l+1) - m(m \pm 1)]^{1/2} Y_l^{m\pm 1}, 1$

$$L_x|xy\rangle = \frac{L^+ + L^-}{2}|xy\rangle$$

and since $|xy\rangle = (1/i\sqrt{2})(|2\rangle - |-2\rangle)$, we have

$$L_x|xy\rangle = \frac{1}{2}\left\{\frac{1}{i\sqrt{2}}[L^+|2\rangle - L^+|-2\rangle + L^-|2\rangle - L^-|-2\rangle]\right\}$$

$$= -\frac{1}{\sqrt{2}}(|Y_2^1\rangle - |Y_2^{-1}\rangle) = +1\,\frac{|1\rangle - |-1\rangle}{\sqrt{2}} = i|xz\rangle$$

In the same way, $L_y|xy\rangle = i|yz$ and we then get

$$g_{xx} = g_e - \frac{2\lambda}{E_{xz} - E_{xy}}$$

$$g_{yy} = g_e - \frac{2\lambda}{E_{yz} - E_{xy}}$$

## B. $g_{zz}$ Calculation

Let us calculate the matrix element $\langle n|L_i|0\rangle$ from the relation $|xy\rangle = (1/i\sqrt{2})(|2\rangle - |-2\rangle)$. We can write $L_z|xy\rangle = (1/i\sqrt{2})(L_z|2\rangle - L_z|-2\rangle)$, but $L_z|Y_l^m\rangle = m\hbar|Y_l^m\rangle$, resulting in

$$L_z|2\rangle = L_z|Y_2^2\rangle = 2|Y_2^2\rangle$$

$$L_z|-2\rangle = L_z|Y_2^{-2}\rangle = 2|Y_2^{-2}\rangle$$

or

$$L_z|xy\rangle = -2i|x^2 - y^2\rangle$$

The element $\langle x^2 - y^2|L_z|xy\rangle$ equals $\langle x^2 - y^2|-2i|x^2 - y^2\rangle = -2i$, where $L_z$ is a hermitian operator. It then follows that

$$\langle x^2 - y^2|L_z|xy\rangle^* = \langle xy|L_z|x^2 - y^2\rangle = 2i$$

and therefore

$$g_{zz} = g_e - 2\lambda \frac{-4i^2}{E_{x^2-y^2} - E_{xy}} = g_e - \frac{8\lambda}{E_{x^2-y^2} - E_{xy}} \tag{11}$$

The summation on $n \neq xy$ gives only one term, since other excited states, $|z^2\rangle$, $|yz\rangle$, and $|zx\rangle$, lead to $\langle n|L_z|xy\rangle$ elements equal to zero because of the orthogonality of the wavefunctions.

## REFERENCES


1. J. C. Védrine, in *Advanced Methods of Soil and Clay Minerals Research* (J. W. Stucki and W. L. Banwart, eds.), Reidel Publ. Co., Dordrecht, Holland, 1980, pp. 331-389.
2. (a) R. Freymann and M. Soutiff, *La spectroscopie hertzienne appliquée à la chimie*, Dunod, Pairs, 1960; P. B. Ayscough, *ESR in Chemistry*, Methuen, London, 1967; A. Carrington and A. D. Mc Lachlan, *Introduction to Magnetic Resonance*, Harper & Row, New York, 1967; I. Ursu, *La résonance paramagnétique électronique*, Dunod, Paris, 1968; J. E. Wertz and J. R. Bolton, *ESR Elementary Theory and Practical Applications*, McGraw-Hill, New York, 1972. (b) F. J. Adrian, *J. Coll. Interface Sci.*, *26*: 317 (1968); M. Che, J. Védrine, and C. Naccache,

*J. Chim. Phys.*, *66*: 579 (1969); P. Mériaudeau and Y. Ben Taarit, in *Magnetic Resonance in Colloid and Interface Science* (J. P. Fraissard and H. A. Resing, ed.), D. Reidel, Dordrecht, Holland, 1980, p. 29.

3. B. A. Goodman and J. B. Raynor, *Adv. Inorg. Chem. Radiochem.*, *13*: 135 (1979).
4. R. D. Dowsing and J. F. Gibson, *J. Chem. Phys.*, *50*: 294 (1969); D. Olivier, J. C. Védrine, and H. Pézerat, *Bull. Groupe Fr. Argiles*, *27*: 153 (1975); R. Aasa, *J. Phys. Chem.*, *32*:3919 (1970).
5. M. Che, J. Fraissard, and J. C. Védrine, *Bull. Groupe Fr. Argiles*, *26*: 1 (1974).
6. M. Dufaux, M. Che, and C. Naccache, *J. Chim. Phys.*, *67*: 527 (1970); C. Naccache, J. Bandiera, and M. Dufaux, *J. Catal.*, *25*: 334 (1972); K. S. Seshadri and L. Petraskis, *J. Catal.*, *30*: 195 (1973); P. Mériaudeau, M. Che, P. C. Gravelle, and S. J. Teichner, *Bull. Soc. Chim. Fr.*, 13 (1971).
7. (a) P. Mériaudeau, Y. Boudeville, P. de Montgolfier, and M. Che, *Phys. Rev. B*, *16*: 30 (1977). (b) P. de Montgolfier, P. Mériaudeau, Y. Boudeville, and M. Che, *Phys. Rev. B*, *14*: 1788 (1976).
8. R. Neiman and D. Kivelson, *J. Chem. Phys.*, *35*: 156 (1961); Y. S. Lebedev, *Zh. Strukt. Khim.*, *4*: 19 (1963); P. Kottis and R. Lefebvre, *J. Chem. Phys.*, *41*: 379 (1964); J. Maruani, *Cahiers Phys.*, *202*: 1 (1967).
9. J. H. Freed, in *Spin Labeling: Theory and Applications* (L. J. Berliner, ed.), Academic Press, New York, 1976, p. 53; M. B. McBride, in *Advanced Chemical Methods for Soil and Clays Minerals Research* (J. W. Stucki and W. L. Banwart, eds.), D. Reidel Publ. Co., Dordrecht, Holland, 1980, p. 423.
10. I. Ursu and A. Nicula, *Rev. Roum. Phys.*, *9*: 343 (1964); J. J. Barry and L. A. Gray, *J. Phys. Chem.*, *29*: 1395 (1968); N. N. Tikhomirova, I. V. Nikolaeva, V. V. Demkin, E. N. Rosolovskaya, and K. V. Topchieva, *J. Catal.*, *29*: 105, 500 (1973).
11. P. Mériaudeau and J. C. Védrine, *Nouv. J. Chim.*, *2*: 133 (1978); J. C. Védrine, H. Praliaud, P. Mériaudeau, and M. Che, *Surf. Sci.*, *80*: 101 (1979).
12. M. Che, G. Fichelle, and P. Mériaudeau, *Chem. Phys. Lett.*, *17*: 66 (1972).
13. B. N. Shelimov, A. N. Pershin, and V. B. Kazanskii, *J. Catal.*, *64*: 426 (1980).
14. J. L. Marill and D. Cornet, *J. Chim. Phys.*, *70*: 336 (1973); F. Kubec and F. Sroubek, *J. Chem. Phys.*, *57*:1660 (1972).
15. B. Fubini and F. S. Stone, *J. Mater. Sci.*, *16*: 2439 (1981).
16. L. L. Van Reijen and P. Cossee, *Discuss. Faraday*, *41*: 277 (1966).

17. M. Che, F. Figueras, M. Forissier, J. M. McAteer, M. Perrin, J. L. Portefaix, and H. Praliaud, *Proc. 6th Int. Congr. Catal.*, Vol. 1 (G. C. Bond, P. B. Wells, and F. C. Tompkins, eds.), The Chemical Society, London, 1977, p. 261, L. Petrakis, P. L. Meyer, and T. P. Debies, *J. Phys. Chem.*, *84*: 1020 (1980).
18. M. Che, J. M. McAteer, and A. J. Tench, *J. Chem. Soc., Faraday Trans. 1*, *74*: 2378 (1978).
19. M. Che, M. Fournier, and J. P. Launay, *J. Chem. Phys.*, *71*: 1954 (1979).
20. S. Abdo, R. B. Clarkson, and W. K. Hall, *J. Phys. Chem.*, *80*: 2431 (1976).
21. D. E. O'Reilly, *Adv. Catal.*, *12*:31 (1960); D. E. O'Reilly, F. D. Santiago, and R. G. Squires, *J. Phys. Chem.*, *73*: 3172 (1969).
22. P. A. Berger and J. F. Roth, *J. Phys. Chem.*, *71*: 4307 (1967).
23. H. Tominaga, Y. Ono, and T. Keii, *J. Catal.*, *40*: 197 (1975); H. Lumbeck and J. Voitlander, *J. Catal.*, *13*: 117 (1969).
24. K. C. Khulbe, A. Manoogian, R. S. Mann, and P. D. Grover, *J. Catal.*, *56*: 290 (1979).
25. A. Nicula, D. Stamires, and J. Soria, *J. Chem. Phys.*, *42*: 3634 (1965); J. Turkevich, Y. Ono, and J. Soria, *J. Catal.*, *25*: 44 (1972).
26. (a) C. C. Chao and J. H. Lunsford, *J. Chem. Phys.*, *57*: 2890 (1972); (b) J. C. Conesa and J. Soria, *J. Phys. Chem.*, *82*: 1575 (1978).
27. C. Naccache and Y. Ben Taarit, *Chem. Phys. Lett.*, *11*: 11 (1971); C. Naccache, M. Che, and Y. Ben Taarit, *Chem. Phys. Lett.*, *13*: 109 (1972).
28. D. E. O'Reilly, J. E. Salamony, and R. G. Squires, *J. Chem. Phys.*, *55*: 4147 (1971).
29. D. Cordischi and M. Lo Jacono, *Z. Phys. Chem.*, *74*: 93 (1971).
30. Y. Boudeville, F. Figueras, M. Forissier, J. L. Portefaix, and J. C. Védrine, *J. Catal.*, *58*: 52 (1979).
31. J. C. Védrine, *Analusis*, *9*: 199 (1981).
32. C. Naccache, J. F. Dutel, and M. Che, *J. Catal.*, *29*: 179 (1973).
33. C. Naccache, M. Primet, and M. V. Mathieu, in *Molecular Sieves, ACS Adv. Chem. Ser.*, *121*: 990 (1976).
34. J. H. Lunsford and E. F. Vansant, *J. Chem. Soc., Faraday Trans. 2*, *69*: 1028 (1973).
35. H. Praliaud, G. F. Coudurier, and Y. Ben Taarit, *J. Chem. Soc., Faraday Trans. 1*, *74*: 3000 (1978).
36. E. D. Garbowski and J. C. Védrine, *Chem. Phys. Lett.*, *48*: 550 (1977); J. A. Rabo, C. L. Angell, P. H. Kasai, and V. Schoemaker, *Discuss. Faraday*, *41*: 326 (1966).

37. J. Hemidy and D. Cornet, *J. Chim. Phys., 71*: 739 (1974); J. Hemidy, J. Goupil, and D. Cornet, *J. Chim. Phys., 74*: 74 (1977); J. M. Goupil, J. F. Hemidy, and D. Cornet, *Zeolite, 2*: 47 (1982).
38. P. Gallezot, *Catal. Rev., 20*: 121 (1979); A. Chambellan, T. Chevreau, and D. Cornet, *J. Chim. Phys., 75*: 511 (1978).
39. S. Abdo, J. Gosbee, and R. F. Howe, *J. Chim. Phys., 78*: 885 (1981).
40. J. C. Védrine, E. G. Derouane, and Y. Ben Taarit, *J. Phys. Chem., 78*: 531 (1974).
41. A. Bielanski, K. Dyrek, and E. Serwicka, *J. Catal., 66*: 316 (1980).
42. D. Kivelson and S. K. Lee, *J. Chem. Phys., 41*: 1896 (1964).
43. B. G. Silbernagel, *J. Catal., 56*: 315 (1979).
44. S. B. Nikishenko, E. S. Brodskii, Yu. K. Varl, E. I. Bobkovskii, and U. V. Manshilin, *Int. Chem. Eng., 16*: 320 (1976).
45. (a) A. J. A. Konings, A. M. Van Dooren, D. C. Koninesberger, V. H. J. de Beer, A. L. Farragher, and G. C. A. Schuit, *J. Catal., 54*: 1 (1978). (b) A. J. A. Konings, W. L. J. Brentjens, D. C. Koningsberger, and V. H. J. de Beer, *J. Catal., 67*: 145 (1981).
46. J. H. Lunsford, *J. Phys. Chem., 68*: 2312 (1964); D. D. Eley and M. A. Zammitt, *J. Catal., 21*: 377 (1971).
47. M. Boudart, A. J. Delbouille, E. G. Derouane, V. Indovina, and A. B. Walters, *J. Am. Chem. Soc., 94*: 6622 (1972).
48. A. Abou Kais, J. C. Védrine, and J. Massardier, *J. Chem. Soc., Faraday Trans. 1, 71*: 1697 (1975).
49. J. C. Védrine, A. Abou Kais, J. Massardier, and G. Dalmai-Imelik, *J. Catal., 29*: 120 (1973).
50. G. T. Kerr, *J. Phys. Chem., 71*: 4155 (1967); *72*: 2594 (1968); *J. Catal., 15*: 200 (1969).
51. J. C. Védrine, D. Barthomeuf, G. Dalmai-Imelik, Y. Trambouze, B. Imelik, and M. Prettre, *C. R. Acad. Sci. Paris, Ser. C, 267*: 118 (1968).
52. A. Abou Kais, C. Mirodatos, J. Massardier, D. Barthomeuf, and J. C. Védrine, *J. Phys. Chem., 81*: 397 (1977).
53. T. Halachev and E. Ruckenstein, *J. Catal., 73*: 171 (1982).
54. T. P. Wilson, P. H. Kasai, and P. C. Ellgen, *J. Catal., 69*: 193 (1981).

# 6
# X-Ray Photoelectron Spectroscopy

CAMILLE DEFOSSE Laboratoire Dowell-Schlumberger, Saint-Etienne, France

## I. INTRODUCTION

Photoelectron spectroscopy came into existence only in the late 1960s [1], but developed rapidly to emerge as a well-established technique that encompasses several fields of physics and virtually all those of chemistry. In photoelectron spectroscopy, electrons are expelled from their original orbitals by a photoelectric effect; depending on the type of primary radiation used to eject the electrons, a distinction is made between XPS (X-ray photoelectron spectroscopy) and UPS (UV photoelectron spectroscopy). This distinction also rests on significant differences in the information provided. XPS is also often referred to by the acronym ESCA (electron spectroscopy for chemical analysis), introduced by Siegbahn and co-workers [1].

The usefulness of photoelectron spectroscopy in the field of catalysis was quickly recognized [2] and the technique is currently one of the physical tools commonly employed in catalytic research, especially in heterogeneous catalysis. This chapter by no means pretends to be exhaustive, even in the latter limited field of application, as this would be beyond the scope of this book. Therefore, this chapter will not consider "ideal" systems (e.g., clean metal surfaces) or the adsorption of simple molecules; those topics are reviewed extensively elsewhere [3,4]. Rather, it will focus on practical or nearly practical systems, outlining particularly interesting and broadly applicable uses of XPS in heterogeneous catalysis.

After a substantial summary of the theoretical background, instrumentation is briefly reviewed as well as some experimental considerations. Next, examples of applications in recurrent themes of catalysis are given. The last section is devoted to Auger electron spectroscopy (AES), a related technique that has found numerous applications in heterogeneous catalysis.

# II. THEORY

## A. General Considerations

### 1. Overview

Photoelectron spectroscopy is based on the photoelectric effect. Photons from a suitable source (an X-ray anode in the case of XPS, an ultraviolet lamp for UPS) impinge on the sample (Fig. 1). Photoionization occurs according to

$$A + h\nu \rightarrow A^{+} + e^{-} \tag{1}$$

where the electron $e^-$ is expelled from the sample with a certain amount of kinetic energy $E'_K$.

Depending on the energy of the incoming photon $h\nu$, emission of photoelectrons will take place from the valence band only (UPS) or from both the valence and core levels (XPS) (Fig. 2). Any electronic level of any atom present in the portion of sample probed by the technique will thus contribute to the flux of photoelectrons expelled, pro-

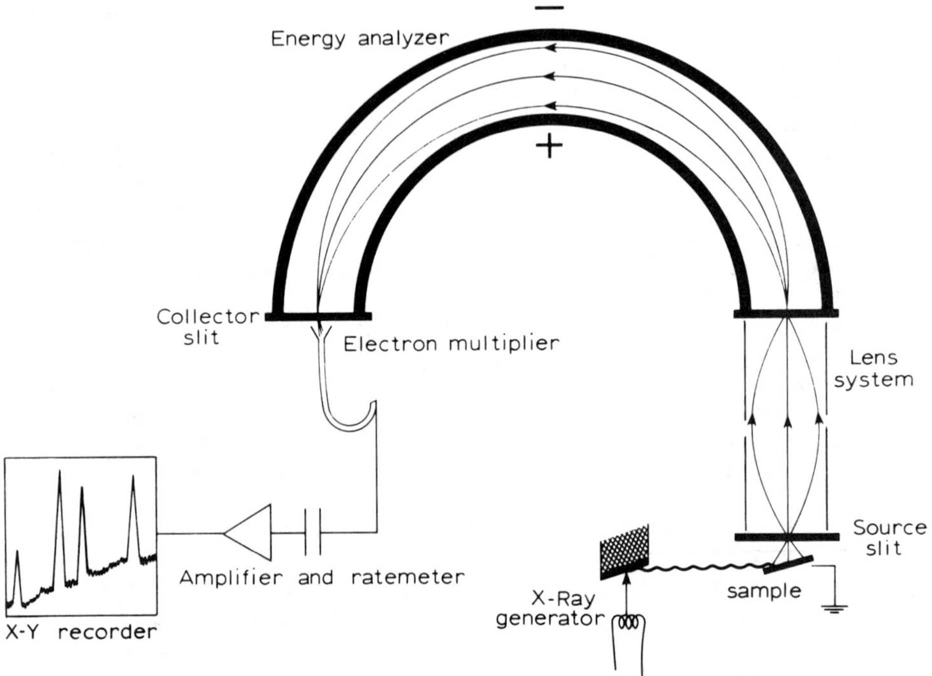


FIG. 1. Schematic representation of an X-ray spectrometer. (From Ref. 32.)

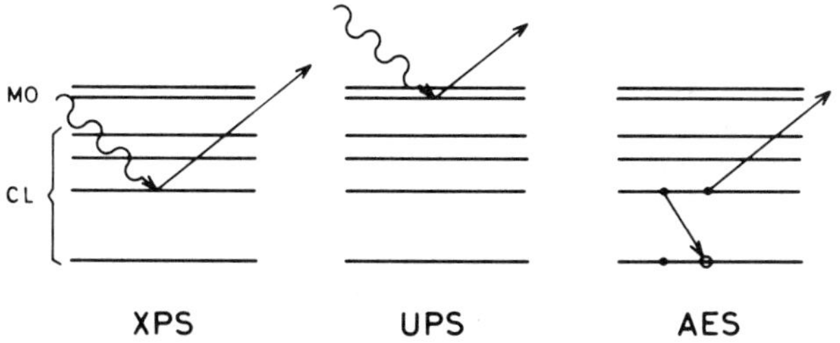


FIG. 2. Schematic sketch of the main three electron spectroscopies. CL and MO stand for core-level and molecular orbitals, respectively. Closed circles, electrons; open circles, vacancy.

vided that (1) the photon energy $h\nu$ is sufficient to eject the electron from the level considered, and (2) the atom "owns" electrons. The first condition will be dealt with below when we consider the basic equation of photoelectron spectroscopy; the second one implies that any element, except hydrogen and helium, is detectable by means of its core levels (XPS) and that any valence band is visible both by XPS and UPS. This universal character of photoelectron spectroscopy is in sharp contrast with many other types of spectroscopy, such as EPR, NMR, or Mössbauer spectroscopy, where specific conditions for detectability limit their use to a restricted number of elements.

Auger electron spectroscopy (AES) is named after the deexcitation mechanism known as the Auger effect. When a vacancy is created in a core level (e.g., K or 1s) of an atom by X-ray or electron bombardment, one possible mechanism of deexcitation for the ion created consists of emitting an Auger electron from an upper orbital, say L. The energy required for this ejection comes from the quasisimultaneous decay of a third electron from another upper level, say L, into the K vacancy (Fig. 2). In this particular example the Auger electron will be denoted KLL.

AES will be dealt with at the end of the chapter. Although Auger peaks can also be visible in a XPS spectrum, the acronym AES refers specifically to the emission of Auger electrons using an electron gun, thus excluding X-ray sources.

As will be detailed in Sec. III, the ejected photoelectrons are further analyzed for their kinetic energy (Fig. 1) by means of an energy analyzer and finally counted by an electron multiplier. The intensity of the output signal from the multiplier is plotted against kinetic energy to give the photoelectron spectrum.

### 2. Basic Equation of Photoelectron Spectroscopy

In the process described above, energy conservation requires that

$$E'_K = h\nu - E'_b \qquad (2)$$

where $h\nu$ is the incident photon energy and $E'_b$ the binding energy of the electronic level considered.

The binding energy is the energy necessary to bring the electron from its original level to a state of rest outside the atom (the zero binding energy), characterized by a zero attraction (Fig. 3). Strictly speaking, it is thus equal to the difference in energy of the system after ($E_f$) and before ($E_i$) photoionization, that is, the final state $A^+$ and the initial state A of Eq. (1), respectively; therefore,

$$E'_b = E_f - E_i \qquad (3)$$

Although the relations above may seem rather obvious, they imply the definition of the zero binding energy level. This is rather straightforward for gaseous systems, where the only possibility of being formally at zero attraction and zero kinetic energy is outside the molecule (i.e., in the vacuum). In this case, Eq. (2) holds, neglecting the recoil energy of the atom, and $E'_b$ is the binding energy with respect to the vacuum level.

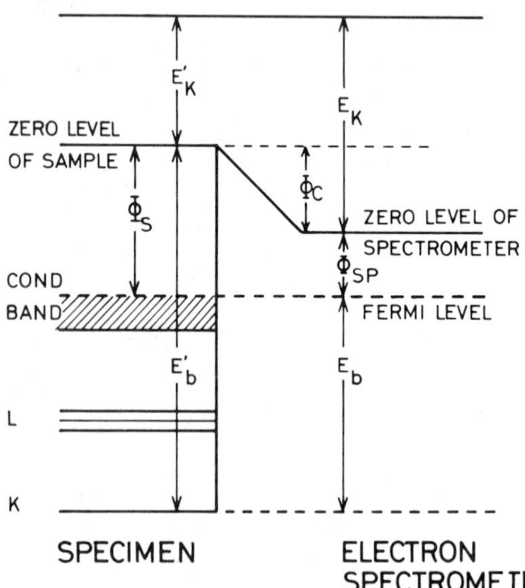


FIG. 3. Schematic representation of the energy levels of a conducting solid in electrical contact with the spectrometer. $\Phi_S$ is the work function of the sample.

For both solids and liquids, the situation is more complex. Let us take the simple case of a conducting sample in electrical contact with the spectrometer. The kinetic energy $E'_k$ with respect to the zero-binding-energy level of the sample is not measured but, instead, $E_K$, which is its counterpart with respect to the zero level of the spectrometer. This is due to the contact potential $\Phi_C$ existing between the conducting sample and the spectrometer itself (Fig. 3). Thus

$$E_b = h\nu - E_K - \Phi_{SP} \tag{4}$$

where $\Phi_{SP}$ is the work function of the spectrometer, that is, the energy required to bring an electron from the Fermi level of the spectrometer to its zero level, and $E_b$ is the binding energy with respect to the Fermi level of the spectrometer. Since the sample and the spectrometer are in electrical contact, their Fermi levels coincide (Fig. 3), and $E_b$ is the binding energy with respect to the Fermi level of the sample as well.

The advantage of this way of referencing is that $E_K$ (as opposed to $E'_K$) is the quantity actually measured; in addition, $\Phi_{SP}$ is constant and depends only on the spectrometer, as opposed to $\Phi_S$, the work function of the sample, which is not always easily measured and varies from one sample to another. The drawback is that the reference level is not the actual zero level of the sample; hence comparisons of $E_b$ between two samples should take into account the difference in their respective work functions $\Phi_S$.

If the sample is an insulator, as in the case with heterogeneous catalysts, it is assumed that their Fermi levels still coincide. In addition, however, a positive charge develops on the sample because of its nonconducting nature. This charge stabilizes almost immediately to a value of a few volts and

$$E_b = h\nu - E_K - \Phi_{SP} - E_C \tag{5}$$

where $E_C$ is the positive charge that exists on the sample surface and acts as an additional retarding potential. The value of $E_C$ depends on the sample itself and is influenced, among other things, by the level and quality of the vacuum, the geometry of the analyzer chamber, and the presence of a contamination overlayer on the sample. The exact value of $E_C$ must be determined if $E_b$ is to be known; however, it can only be measured indirectly. This will be described in Sec. III.

Tables of binding energies for all the electronic levels of all the elements are readily available in the literature [1,5,6]. They have been obtained by theoretical calculations on single atoms or, in some cases, determined experimentally from X-ray spectroscopy data.

3. General Features of Photoelectron Spectra

According to Eq. (5), the photoelectron spectrum can be plotted versus the kinetic energy $E_K$ or, more conveniently, as a function of binding energy $E_b$ expressed in electron volts. Figure 4 is an illustration of an XPS spectrum for an alumina-supported molybdenum oxide doped with sodium; it was obtained using an aluminum anode.

The valence band is readily observable close to the zero in binding energy, as well as the core levels of all the elements present in the sample, as long as their binding energy is less than hν.

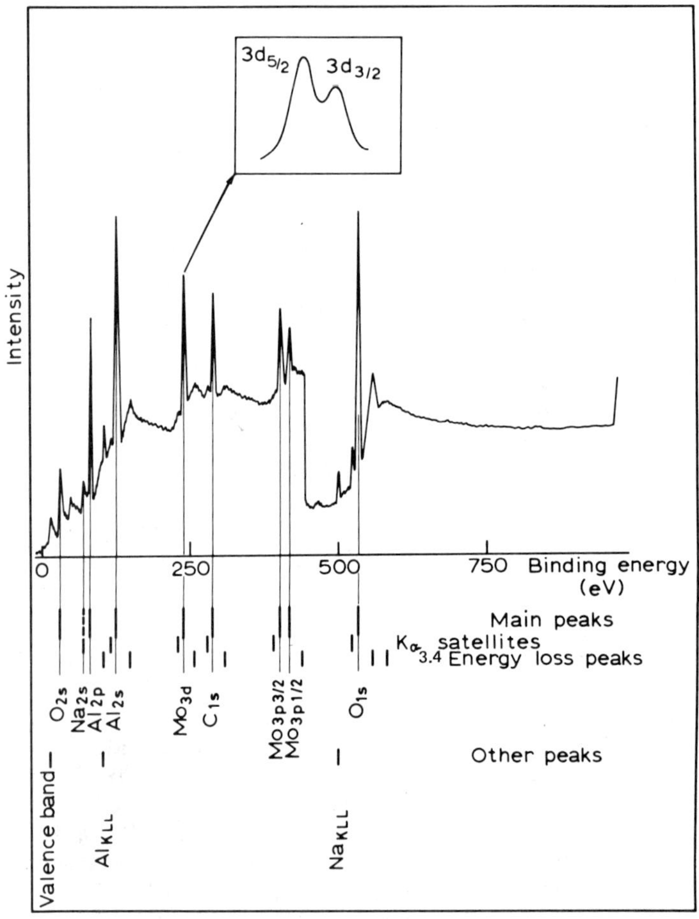


FIG. 4. Typical XPS spectrum obtained for an alumina-supported molybdenum oxide doped with sodium. Peak assignments are given in the lower part of the figure. The intensity scale of the left-hand part was expanded by a factor 3.5. (From Ref. 32.)

Peak assignment is easily done with the help of a binding energy table. Indeed, the chemical process of valence orbital formation manifests itself only as a first-order perturbation on the binding energy of the core levels. This perturbation is the chemical shift, which is usually small (<10 eV) compared to the value of $E_b$ for the neutral isolated atom (50 to 1000 eV), yet sufficiently large to yield valuable information on the chemical state of the atom in the sample considered. Immediate qualitative elemental analysis is therefore rather straightforward with XPS; cases of peak overlapping are relatively rare and easily overcome because they rarely affect more than one core level of an element at a time. Common sense in the examination of XPS spectra for the presence or absence of the other core levels of the suspected element with their proper intensity ratios helps solve virtually any potential ambiguity.

Thus the $Na_{2s}$ (62 eV) and $O_{2s}$ (24 eV), $Al_{2p}$ (74 eV) and $Al_{2s}$ (118 eV), $Mo_{3d}$ (227 and 230 eV), $Mo_{3p}$ (393 and 410 eV), and $O_{1s}$ (532 eV) levels are observed. $Na_{1s}$ (1072 eV) would be visible if the display extended as far as the end of the $E_b$ range (~1480 eV). On the other hand, the $Al_{1s}$ line is not observed for obvious reasons; its $E_b$ (1560 eV) is greater than the photon energy of the $Al_{K\alpha}$ line (1486.6 eV) used as the excitation source. Similarly, all the 1s, 2s, and 2p levels of molybdenum are not visible because their binding energy is far larger than $h\nu$.

Several other features require some explanations. First, it is found, as expected, that each line is more or less intense according to the concentration of the element to which it corresponds. Peak intensities, however, also depend on the probability of photoemission, that is, the cross section.

The probability of a particular transition taking place may be so low that the corresponding line will be hardly visible in the spectrum; this is the case in Fig. 4 for $Na_{2p}$, $Mo_{3s}$, and $Mo_{4s}$ (respectively 31, 505, and 62 eV), also taking the concentrations into account. The $Na_{2s}$ line is, furthermore, partially superimposed on the $Mo_{4s}$ line. The $C_{1s}$ line does not originate from the presence of any structural carbon in the sample but is due to a contamination overlayer on the specimen surface; this will be discussed later in relation to experimental problems.

Second, some electronic levels do not give a single line but rather a doublet that can be completely ($Mo_{3p}$) or partially ($Mo_{3d}$) resolved or totally unresolved ($Al_{2p}$) (Fig. 4). This will be the case with any orbital that does not possess spheric symmetry (i.e., for any orbital quantum number $\ell$ different from 0). Indeed, in that case, coupling between $\ell$ and the spin magnetic moment s equal to +1/2 or −1/2 lifts the degeneracy. Any subshell with $\ell \neq 0$ therefore splits into two levels characterized by the quantum number j equal to $\ell \pm |s|$, where $|s| = 1/2$—hence the presence of the $Mo_{3d5/2}$ and $Mo_{3d3/2}$ lines. The $Mo_{3p3/2;1/2}$ doublet is explained similarly. The magnitude of the spin-orbit splitting depends on the element itself and on the subshell [6]; this explains the various degrees of resolution observed, with the $Al_{2p3/2;1/2}$ being an extreme case where the resolution of the doublet is much smaller than the resolving power of the instrument.

Third, it should be stressed that the observable peaks in an XPS spectrum are due to only a small fraction of the electrons initially photoemitted from within the sample. Indeed, electrons photoejected from atoms below the top molecular layer at the solid-vacuum interface have a certain probability of undergoing inelastic collisions before leaving the solid. The larger the distance to be traveled inside the solid (escape depth), the lower the probability of escaping into the vacuum without undergoing an inelastic collision. The amount of kinetic energy lost in such a process is random and any photoelectron undergoing collision will conbribute to the general background. This explains the background increase observed on the high $E_b$ side of each no-loss peak. An important consequence is that the sample thickness explored by XPS is restricted to the upper layers below the interface, from which the no-loss peaks originate. The strong implication is that photoelectron spectroscopy is selective toward the 3 to 6 outermost nanometers below the surface (see Sec. II.C).

Finally, it will be noticed that other lines appear in the spectrum as well (Fig. 4). Some of them, the $K_{\alpha 3,4}$ satellites, are associated with the source and will be discussed later, as will the Auger peaks. Energy loss peaks, also called plasmons, result from discrete energy losses associated with a collective excitation or oscillation of free electrons inside the solid; they are present on the low-$E_K$ side of every peak.

Corresponding to another type of discrete energy loss, the shake-up peaks are characteristic of certain elements, contrary to the plasmons. They are typically observed for the 2p levels of transition metals with unpaired d electrons (paramagnetic species). For example, for a fraction of 2p electrons ejected from $Cu^{2+}$, photoemission will be accompanied by the simultaneous promotion of a 3d electron to an upper level. The energy required for this process is taken from the kinetic energy of the outgoing 2p photoelectron and an additional peak will appear on the low-kinetic-energy side of the parent 2p peak. This peculiar type of satellite peak has practical applications; it is indeed very useful as a fingerprint of the oxidation and/or spin state of those elements susceptible to giving it. Figure 5 illustrates this discrimination between diamagnetic (low spin) and paramagnetic (high spin) complexes of Co [7]; the former shows few or no shake-up satellites at about 793 eV (all 3d electron paired, d10 configuration), whereas the latter does (one 3d electron unpaired, d9 configuration). Similarly, distinctions between low-spin diamagnetic and high-spin paramagnetic complexes of Cu [8] and Ni [9] have been reported. Shake-up peaks have been studied extensively [10].

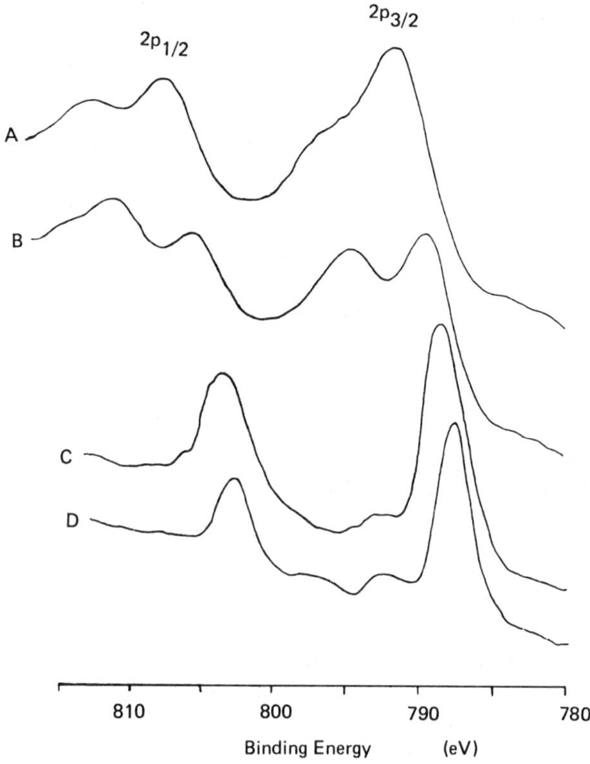


FIG. 5. XPS spectrum of the $Co_{2p}$ region, illustrating the fingerprint nature of the shake-up peaks. A, $CoF_2$; B, $CoCl_2$; C, $K_3Co(CN)_6$; D, $Co(en)_3Cl_3$. (From Ref. 163.)

## B. Peak Position

### 1. General

According to Eq. (3), the difference $\Delta E_b$ in binding energy between an atom C chemically bound in a molecule or a solid and its neutral isolated counterpart A is given by

$$\Delta E_b = [E_f(C) - E_i(C)] - [E_f(A) - E_i(A)]$$

or (6)

$$\Delta E_b = [E_i(A) - E_i(C)] - [E_f(A) - E_f(C)] = \Delta E_i - \Delta E_f$$

Thus a shift of peak position in a photoelectron spectrum can be due to both initial-state ($\Delta E_i$) and final-state ($\Delta E_f$) effects. The chemist will, of course, be especially interested in the initial-state effects, that is, those related to the oxidation or valence state of the atom (i.e., the chemical shift). Although not correct, the expression "chemical shift" is sometimes used to denote the global peak displacement $\Delta E_b$, which also includes final-state effects, discussed later.

Peak displacement shifts $\Delta E_b$ can be interpreted according to different approaches. If absolute quantitative comparisons are to be established between theory and experiment, extensive theoretical calculations must be carried out. Ab initio calculations yield values of $E_f$ and $E_i$ with no approximation and therefore of $\Delta E_b$. This process is usually long and costly even for small molecules and prohibitive or impossible for solids. Approximate methods such as $X\alpha$ scattering [11], EHMO [12], or CNDO [13] can be used to alleviate the problem.

The second approach, although more pragmatic, tends to be more approximate and subject to criticisms. It consists, if only relative comparisons are sought, of running various standards to which the position of the element of interest in the sample is compared. This approach is very simple but should be used with a very critical mind, as it can be dangerously misleading. Indeed, similar $\Delta E$'s are not definite proof of chemical identity, as will be evident in the next sections.

An intermediate possibility is to correlate the experimentally determined binding energy shift with the charge on the atom. The charge can be calculated according to very simple models based on electronegativity [1,6] or by approximate quantum methods. Another approach based on thermodynamic concepts has been developed by Jolly [14] but has found limited application so far.

Practical catalytic systems are impossible to deal with following the rigorous approach based on final- and initial-state calculations. Most of the time, the researcher will resort to the second pragmatic approach, with all its limitations, and run as standards more or less related compounds.

### 2. Initial-State Effects

The most common chemical shifts are those associated with changes in the oxidation state of the atom, but a change in the charge carried by the atom can also be induced by ligand association or, in a more general way, by a change in the surroundings of the atom. As stated earlier, valence orbital formation affects the core levels only as a perturbation that can be theoretically predicted by calculations. It can also be explained using simple concepts.

If electrons are removed from an atom because of chemical bonding (e.g., carbon being oxidized to $C^{4+}$ as in $CF_4$), the attraction from the nucleus experienced by the remaining electrons, for instance, those of the $C_{1s}$ level, has not changed, but the repulsive forces inside the electron cloud have decreased. Hence the net effect will be a lowering of all the electronic levels in the energy-well diagram (Fig. 3). In other words, the binding energy of the core levels, and of the $C_{1s}$ level in our example, will increase; a positive shift will thus reflect oxidation to $C^{4+}$. The opposite is also true, when carbon is reduced formally to $C^{4-}$ (as in $CH_4$), and a negative shift will be observed. Thus peak shifts will provide extremely valuable information on the valence state, as long as they are due only to chemical (i.e., initial state) effects, that is, if

$$\Delta E_b \simeq \Delta E_i \tag{7}$$

or

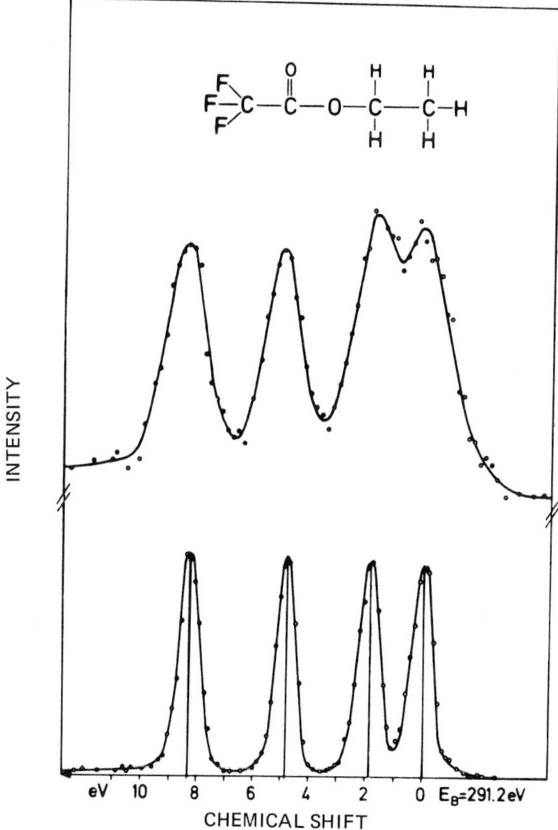


FIG. 6. X-ray photoelectron spectrum of the $C_{1s}$ level of ethyl trifluoroacetate obtained with a low (upper trace) and high (lower trace) resolution spectrometer. (From Ref. 15.)

$$\Delta E_f \simeq 0 \tag{8}$$

A now classic and very illustrative example is that of the four $C_{1s}$ peaks observed in the photoelectron spectrum of ethyl trifluoroacetate (Fig. 6). The charge on the carbon atom increases positively from the $CH_3$ to the $CF_3$ group because of the increasing inductive effect of the atoms bound to the four successive carbons. It also happens that the sequence of the four $C_{1s}$ peaks in the spectrum is the same as that of the carbon atoms in the molecule. Note also the 1:1 intensity ratio observed for the four peaks.

This dependence of the chemical shift on the charge of the atom can be described by more or less elaborate models. The simplest is the electrostatic sphere model [1,16], which approximates atom A of Eq. (1) to a conducting sphere of radius r. Increasing the oxidation state of A by one unit to give species C is equivalent to removing one electron from the sphere to rest at infinity. This requires an energy equal to

$$\frac{-e^2}{r} \tag{9}$$

which is also the change in potential energy for the interior of the sphere, that is, the chemical shift experienced by all the atomic levels of species A upon oxidation to C.

Thus this model implies that all the core levels of the element considered will display the same chemical shift, a somewhat unexpected conclusion which is approximately verified (Table 1) by theoretical

TABLE 1 Binding Energies ($E_b$) and Binding Energy Changes ($\Delta E_b$) in eV[a]

| Shell | $E_b$ | $\Delta E_b$ |
|---|---|---|
| 1s | 15,828 | 15.3 |
| 2s | 2,160 | 15.3 |
| 2p | 1,956 | 15.1 |
| 3s | 357 | 14.9 |
| 3p | 282 | 14.9 |
| 3d | 145 | 15.0 |
| 4s | 49 | 14.3 |
| 4p | 28 | 14.3 |

[a]Calculated according to Eq. (6) for the oxidation of Sr to $Sr^{2+}$. Note that, according to Eq. (9), $\Delta E_b = -2e^2/r = 14.6$ eV.
*Source*: Ref. 6.

calculations on initial- and final-state energy differences. Its magnitude, as predicted by the sphere model, is, however, much too large and of the order of 15 eV for a one-unit oxidation change. Part of the discrepancy arises from the fact that we reasoned on formal oxidation states instead of the actual change of charge $e_f$. In addition, in a real system such as a gas molecule or a solid, the electron removed is not transferred to infinity but rather to a neighboring atom B. Finally, we must take into account the potential V generated by all other ions in the solid or the molecule at the positions of species A and B, as well as its change ($\Delta V$) upon oxidation of A. This can be approximated by regarding the other ions as effective point charges and carrying out a Madelung-like summation on all the lattice positions in the case of a solid [17]. Thus for a unit change in oxidation state, we have

$$\Delta E_i = \frac{e_f^2}{r} - \Delta V \tag{10}$$

This will reduce the magnitude of the shift actually observed and explains why the experimental chemical shifts depend on the solid itself through $\Delta V$, even if the net charge transferred $e_f$ and the distance of transfer r are equal; this potential limitation must be kept in mind when comparing the binding energy of a core level of an element present in a catalyst with that of other compounds containing the same element in more or less well-defined oxidation states. A striking illustration of a peak shift due solely to changes in crystal potential is the 1.2 eV displacement observed for the $Si_{2p}$, $Al_{2p}$, and $O_{1s}$ lines of the framework of zeolite X when sodium is exchanged for calcium [18].

Although $\Delta V$ can obscure the contribution of the charge transfer term in Eq. (10), surprisingly good correlations have been observed between experimental chemical shifts and the charge on the atom calculated using quantum chemistry methods [19,20] or even simple electronegativity calculations [1,6,21]. An example of the latter is given in Fig. 7, where an excellent correlation is obtained for the 2p level of sulfur.

### 3. Final-State Effects

The excellent agreement between experimental shifts and calculated initial-state effects is all the more surprising as we have as yet completely neglected $\Delta E_f$ in Eq. (6). This requires some explanation concerning the final state of the atom after photoionization.

When a photoelectron is ejected from an atom, the latter readjusts its orbitals almost immediately to the new ionized situation in order to "screen" the vacancy (hole). It is, however, very convenient to assume that the atom does not relax but, rather, remains frozen, so that the photoejection process should be rewritten

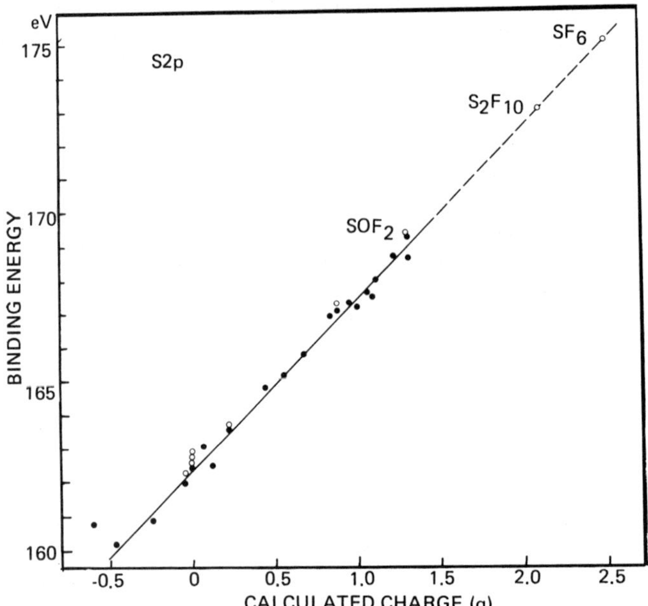


FIG. 7. Binding energy for the sulfur 2p level versus charge on the S atom calculated according to electronegativity. (From Ref. 15.)

$$A + h\nu \rightarrow A+^{*} + e^{-} \tag{11}$$

where $A^{+*}$ is the frozen ion. This is the so-called "sudden approximation," which has an important consequence known as Koopman's theorem. It states that if the ion did not relax, the binding energy of level j, $E_b^j$ would be equal to $-\varepsilon_j$, the eigenvalue of the j orbital wavefunction of atom A taken positively. The difference between $-\varepsilon_j$ and $E_b^j$ is the relaxation energy $E_R^j$ carried off by the outgoing photoelectron and corresponding to the relaxation process

$$A^{+*} \rightarrow A^{+} \tag{12}$$

Thus

$$E_b^j = -\varepsilon_j + E_R^j \tag{13}$$

and recalling Eq. (6), the peak shift between valence states C and A can be rewritten as

$$\Delta E_b^j = -\Delta \varepsilon_j + \Delta E_R^j \tag{14}$$

$$= -[\varepsilon_j(C) - \varepsilon_j(A)] + [E_R^j(C) - E_R^j(A)] \tag{15}$$

where $-\Delta \varepsilon_j$ is the contribution of the chemical shift or initial-state effect discussed previously and $\Delta E_R^j$ the difference in relaxation energy between the reference state A (e.g., a single neutral atom) and the particular valence state C considered (molecule or solid).

Relaxation energies $E_R^j$ are usually quite large (10 to 20 eV) with respect to the peak shift $\Delta E_b^j$ and the fact that correlations between calculated chemical shifts $-\Delta \varepsilon_j$ and peak shifts are usually good simply points out that assumptions (7) and (8) (i.e., $\Delta E_R^j \simeq 0$) are valid in most cases. In other words, relaxation energies do not vary significantly from one valence state to another, provided that the environment of the atom does not change very much. Indeed, it has been shown that relaxation not only takes place within the atom (intraatomic relaxation) but depends on its surroundings (extraatomic relaxation) [22]. A few cases have been reported in the literature where changes in relaxation energy inverse the observed peak shift with respect to the expected chemical shift [23].

Other features in a photoelectron spectrum can be treated as final-state effects. This is the case for the shake-up satellites mentioned previously and for multiplet splitting [6], which we will not consider here as it is only of limited practical interest for catalytic systems.

## 4. Conclusions and Guidelines

If we neglect extraatomic relaxation and further assume, as verified in first approximation, that intraatomic relaxation does not depend on the valence state, we reach the conclusion that the chemical shift is a characteristic of the element itself. We also assume that the variation in crystal potential $\Delta V$ in Eq. (10) is close to zero or can be accounted for. This conclusion was predicted by the potential sphere model, despite its imperfection, and is readily apparent from Eq. (9), where the dependence on the element arises from the $1/r$ term (i.e., from the valence radius). Accordingly, the sensitivity toward chemical shift, namely the magnitude of the chemical shift for the same variation in oxidation state, will increase from left to right in the periodic table and decrease with Z [6]. An example of this is given in Table 2 for the halogens, as one goes from Cl to I.

This trend may not always be as clear, primarily because the assumptions regarding final-state effects and $\Delta V$ are not fulfilled. Striking examples are the $Co_{2p}$ levels, which do not display a measurable shift between CoO and $Co_2O_3$ [26], and the 4f lines of Pb,

TABLE 2 Trend in Binding Energies with Z in Group VII Elements

| Compound | Formal oxidation state of the halogen | Shift with respect to the −1 state | Reference |
|---|---|---|---|
| NaCl | −1 | 0 | 24 |
| $NaClO_3$ | +5 | 6.5 | 1 |
| $NaClO_4$ | +7 | 9.6 | 1 |
| KBr | −1 | 0 | 25 |
| $KBrO_3$ | +5 | 5.9 | 25 |
| $KBrO_4$ | +7 | 7.6 | 25 |
| KI | −1 | 0 | 24 |
| $KIO_3$ | +5 | 4.6 | 16 |
| $KIO_4$ | +7 | 6.1 | 16 |

*Source*: Data from Ref. 6.

where the binding energy actually decreases by 1.8 eV when going from PbO to $PbO_2$ [27].

In general, the span of chemical shift between the lowest and highest oxidation states of an element lies between 1 and 6 eV; a general overview can be obtained using the periodic table compiled by Fernelius [28], where the maximum peak shift observed and the number of compounds studied are given for each element. More detailed and exhaustive data can be found in the literature [6,29,30], where the compounds studied and the binding energy of, usually, the most intense line are compiled for each element.

As will be shown in Sec. IV, peak shifts can yield valuable insight into catalyst architecture, and very often their relation to chemical shifts is quite obvious. In general, however, other external evidence should be used to support the interpretation.

## C. Peak Intensities

### 1. Explored Depth

*a. Theoretical Aspects.* As mentioned in Sec. II.A.3, not all the photoelectrons generated at a given depth x below the solid-vacuum interface will leave the solid unperturbed. Instead, a certain fraction contribute to the background because they have lost nondiscrete amounts of kinetic energy in inelastic collisions as they travel inside the solid toward the surface. The probability Q of escape without inelastic scattering decreases with increasing escape depth x; it is further determined by $\lambda$, the inelastic mean free path of the electron (IMFP). The IMFP is the average distance traveled between two successive collisions; it is of the order of 1 to 3 nm in XPS. Thus

$$Q = \exp\left(\frac{-x}{\lambda \sin \theta}\right) \tag{16}$$

where $\theta$ is the angle between the surface plane of the sample—supposedly flat—and the direction of electron collection, the emission angle. In other words, Q is the damping ratio of the intensity originating from thickness dx at depth x.

Hence the total intensity $I_{Xy}$ for peak y of element X is obtained by multiplying the number of atoms X in the volume element S dx/sin $\theta$ situated at depth x by the corresponding probability and integrating over x from zero (surface of the sample) to infinity (i.e., over practically the entire sample thickness). Therefore,

$$I_{Xy} = SK_{Xy} \frac{1}{\sin \theta} \int_0^\infty C_X \, \sigma_{Xy} \exp\left(\frac{-x}{\lambda_{Xy} \sin \theta}\right) dx \tag{17}$$

where $K_{Xy}$ is a factor related to theoretical and experimental aspects that will be discussed later. S is the area of the sample irradiated by X-rays; $C_X$ is the volume concentration of element X inside the solid and is supposedly uniform [$C_X \neq f(x)$]. Finally, the photoelectric cross section $\sigma_{Xy}$ is the probability of photoelectric effect from level y when atom X is hit by a photon. It should be noted that relation (17) further assumes that the attenuation of X-rays over the depth explored by XPS is negligible, which is indeed the case.

Integration of (17) for successive layers of thickness $\lambda$ yields their respective contributions to the total XPS intensity and illustrates in a striking way the sensitivity of XPS toward the surface or, more precisely, toward the first few layers below the solid-vacuum interface (Fig. 8). For $\theta = 90°$, 95% of the intensity originates from the upper layer, $3\lambda$ thick (3 to 9 nm). The right part of the same figure is a plot of the integrand in (17) versus depth x (solid line) and further illustrates the concept of equivalent thickness [32], which is very useful in situations where the integration cannot be performed or even approximated.

*b. Electron Mean Free Path.* Even today, accurate knowledge of electron inelastic mean free paths is probably one of the most limiting factors to a more thorough use of XPS intensities. In a first approx-

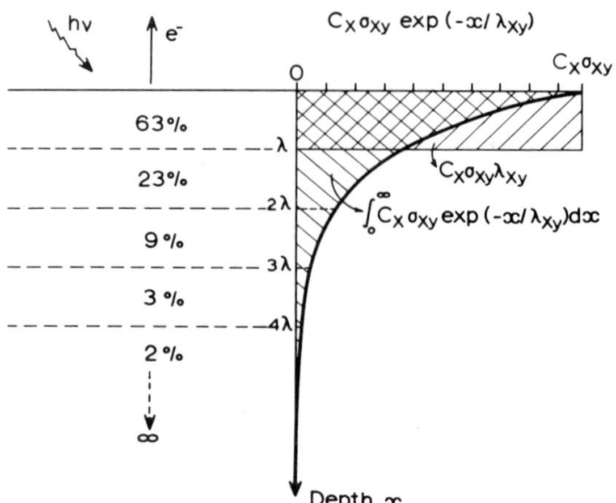


FIG. 8. Left: Contribution of successive layers of thickness λ to the total XPS intensity for θ = 90°. (From Ref. 31.) Right: Attenuation of photoelectron intensity with depth of escape. The rectangular shaded area illustrates the concept of equivalent thickness. (From Ref. 32.)

imation, λ depends on the kinetic energy $E_K$ of the photoelectron and, as a consequence of (5), on the binding energy of the level and the element considered. This is expressed in (17) by the subscripts X and y. The dependence versus $E_K$ is illustrated in Fig. 9, which shows that IMFPs in XPS vary roughly from 0.5 to 3 nm.

Curves such as that of Fig. 9 are based on compilations of λ for various materials and, although the scattering of the points is severe, support the existence of a universal $\lambda = f(E_K)$ relationship [33-35]. More accurate analytical expressions have been proposed, such as $k\,E_K^{1/2}$ [35-37], $kE_K^p$ with p varying between 0.68 and 0.82 [38-40], and $E_K/[(\ln E_K) - b]$ [41,42], where k, a, and b are constants. Seah and Dench [43], in an updated and extensive compilation of over 350 data, have reviewed the subject and shown that the scatter about the universal curve is reduced when IMFPs are expressed in monolayers. In this case, the most accurate relation for inorganic compounds is given by

$$\lambda = k_1 E_K^{-2} + k_2 (aE_K)^{1/2} \tag{18}$$

where $k_1$ and $k_2$ are equal to 2170 and 0.72, respectively, and a is the monolayer thickness, given by

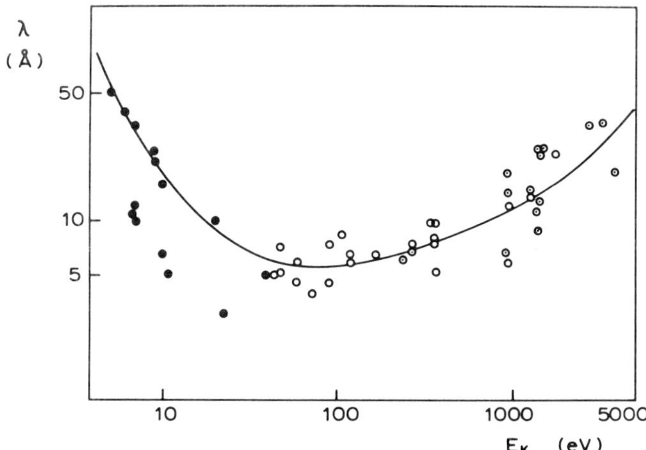


FIG. 9. Compilation of inelastic mean free paths versus the photoelectron kinetic energy obtained for various solids. (From Ref. 33.)

$$a^3 = \frac{M_w}{\rho n N} \times 10^{24} \tag{19}$$

where $M_W$ is the atomic or molecular weight, $\rho$ the bulk density, n the number of atoms in the molecule, and N is Avogadro's number.

The universal relationship holds especially well inside a given class of solids (e.g., oxides or metals) characterized by a certain value of $k_1$ and $k_2$. However, marked discrepancies have been reported in the literature; they show that little-understood matrix effects can sometimes be predominant on the $E_K$ dependence [44]. Electron channeling due to anisotropy or diffraction effects observed for crystals [45,46] are unlikely for catalysts, especially in powder form.

*c. Implications of Selectivity Toward the Surface.* The implications of surface selectivity are numerous; some of them will be treated more specifically later as examples of applications to the field of catalysis. We will now consider more general consequences.

Surface segregation. The most obvious consequence of the surface selectivity of XPS is that any element segregated on the surface or in the surface layers will be readily detected even if its overall bulk concentration as determined by standard analytical methods is at trace levels. Thus surface segregation of tin and indium in their corresponding alloys with lead can be evidenced by plotting the Sn/Pb (In/Pb) surface concentration ratio determined by XPS versus its bulk counterpart; a roughly 10-fold enhancement of their concentration ratio in the surface layers is shown with respect to the bulk [47].

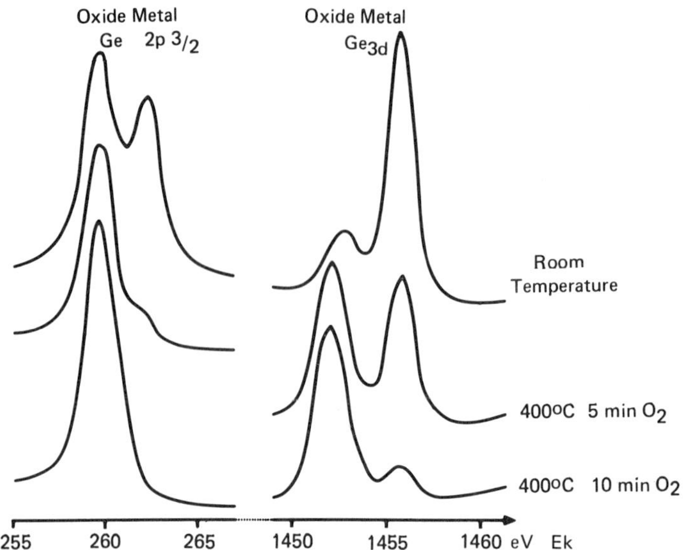


FIG. 10. Ge 3d and 2p levels of metallic germanium sample coated with an oxide overlayer. Note the reversed oxide/metal intensity ratios due to the different sampling depths. (From Ref. 48.)

Similarly, most metals, when taken from the shelf, appear in XPS as covered by an oxide layer. According to the metal and the history of the sample, the thickness of this overlayer can be of the order of magnitude of the IMFP or much larger. Provided that the peak shift between oxide and metal is large enough, any core level will yield two peaks, that of the metal substrate and that of the oxide overlayer, if the thickness of the latter is not substantially larger than the inelastic mean free path [48,49]. This is illustrated in Fig. 10.

Quantitative analysis of trace quantities. Enhancement of the intensity by surface segregation can be taken advantage of to analyze traces quantitatively. This procedure always involves the deposition of the element on the surface of a support which provides, at the same time, the reference intensity needed. Calibration curves on known compositions have to be established. Selective deposition can be achieved by stripping voltammetry in the case of metals in solution [50]. Alternatively, they can be complexed by chelating groups grafted onto a glass slide [51]. Ion exchange by polymer surfaces [52] or adsorption by a $MnO_2$ overlayer deposited on an Al substrate have also been reported [53]. In every case, simultaneous multi-element quantitative analysis is possible and the detection limit is of the order of a few tens of ppb.

Enhancement of surface sensitivity. Surface segregation can also be evidenced by enhancing the surface character of XPS either by collecting the electrons at a more grazing emission angle (lower value of $\theta$) or by selecting a line with a lower kinetic energy and hence a shorter IMFP. This is a direct consequence of integrating Eq. (17) from 0 to the overlayer thickness.

The first approach has been addressed extensively by several authors [54-56]. For a perfectly flat sample, the overlayer/substrate intensity ratio can be enhanced by one order of magnitude by decreasing the emission angle $\theta$ from 80° to 15° [56]. Microroughness, such as in optics gratings, alters the angular dependence of the overlayer/substrate intensity ratio [57]. However, it can still be adequately described. Macroroughness, as in powders, considerably decreases the surface-sensitivity enhancement at grazing angles [58,59]; the emission angle therefore has a negligible influence on the intensity ratio [60,61], especially if the IMFPs for the photoelectron lines involved are not too different [62]. This conclusion is of prime importance for quantitative interpretation of intensities for heterogeneous catalysts in powder form.

The second approach, selecting a second line with a shorter IMFP, has been well illustrated by Holm [48] (Fig. 10). For metallic germanium taken from the shelf and thus covered with an oxide overlayer, the greater sampling depth of the $Ge_{3d}$ line ($E_K \sim 1360$ eV, $\lambda \sim 2.5$ nm) leads to a metal/oxide intensity ratio greater than 1, whereas for the $Ge_{2p}$ level ($E_K \sim 250$ eV, $\lambda \sim 0.7$ nm) it is less than unity. Mathematical treatment of such a system may yield surface composition and depth profiles [63-65], but is usually limited by the difficulty in having two lines of widely different kinetic energies for the element the repartition of which is investigated.

Effect of surface contamination. Another implication of the surface sensitivity of XPS concerns the influence of a contamination overlayer on intensities and intensity ratios. Unless treated in situ by annealing, reduction, oxidation, or ion etching, any surface, as seen by XPS, is more or less contaminated by a carbonaceous deposit that is responsible for the systematic presence of a $C_{1s}$ line. According to (16), this overlayer will dampen intensities from the underlying sample by the factor

$$\exp\left(\frac{-\tau}{\lambda'_{Xy}\sin\theta}\right) \tag{20}$$

where $\tau$ is the thickness of the contamination overlayer and $\lambda'_{Xy}$ the IMFP of photoelectrons from the sample in the contaminant.

Consequently, if the contamination increases with time, the line intensities from the sample will decrease accordingly, as has been nicely illustrated by Swingle [66]. The signal-to-noise ratio will decrease, giving poor-quality spectra, and any quantitative interpretation of intensities will be impossible. Insulators, and hence most heterogeneous catalysts, are especially prone to contamination buildup [67]; the rate of increase depends on the quality of the vacuum. Remedies include shortening of the analysis duration, improvement of the vacuum, and the use of intensity ratios rather than absolute intensities, as will be discussed later.

2. Peak Intensities

*a. Basic Equation of Intensity Ratio.* For a perfectly flat sample, the contribution to the total intensity of peak y of element X from the layer dx located at depth x is given by [56]

$$dI_{Xy} = F\left(\frac{\delta\,\sigma_{Xy}}{\delta\,\Omega}\right)\Omega C_X\left(\frac{S}{\sin\,\theta}\right)dx\,\exp\left(\frac{-x}{\lambda_{Xy}\,\sin\,\theta}\right)L_{Xy}\,\exp\left(\frac{-\tau}{\lambda'_{Xy}\,\sin\,\theta}\right) \tag{21}$$

where F is the photon flux supposedly uniform at the sample surface. We further assume that the attenuation of the X-rays over the depth probed is negligible. $\Omega$ is the solid angle for photoelectron collection and $L_{Xy}$ is the analyzer luminosity (i.e., the fraction of electrons transmitted by the analyzer). The first exponential factor is the escape probability Q; the second is the damping factor due to the contamination overlayer.

The photon flux and the damping factors, especially the contaminant thickness $\tau$, are difficult, if not impossible, to determine accurately. Therefore, one is reduced to using intensity ratios $R_X$ defined by

$$R_X = \frac{I_{Xy}}{I_{Rz}} \tag{22}$$

where $I_{Rz}$ is the intensity of peak z from reference element R. For practical purposes, $(\delta\,\sigma_{Xy}/\delta\,\Omega)\,\Omega$ can be replaced by

$$\frac{\sigma_{Xy}}{4\pi}[1 + 0.5\beta_{Xy}(1.5\,\sin^2\alpha - 1)] \tag{23}$$

where $\alpha$ is the angle between the X-ray beam and the direction of electron emission and $\beta$ is the asymmetry parameter. Substitution of (23) and (21) into (22) and integration leads to

$$R_X = R'_A R'_L \left(\frac{\sigma_{Xy}}{\sigma_{Rz}}\right) \frac{\int_0^\infty C_X \exp[-x/(\lambda_{Xy} \sin\theta)]\, dx}{\int_0^\infty C_R \exp[-x'/(\lambda_{Rz} \sin\theta)]\, dx'} R'_C \tag{24}$$

where

$$R'_C = \exp\left[\frac{-\tau(1/\lambda'_{Xy} - 1/\lambda'_{Rz})}{\sin\theta}\right] \tag{25}$$

$$R'_L = \frac{L_{Xy}}{L_{Rz}} \tag{26}$$

$$R'_A = \frac{1 + 0.5\beta_{Xy}(1.5\sin^2\alpha - 1)}{1 + 0.5\beta_{Rz}(1.5\sin^2\alpha - 1)} \tag{27}$$

Relation (24) as such is useless and does not allow any access to $C_X$ and $C_R$. Modeling of the solid (i.e., of the concentration profile) is therefore necessary in order to perform both integrations. The equation obtained in this way will then allow either verification of the model by comparing experimental and theoretical intensity ratios or access to the concentrations $C_X$ and $C_R$. For example, if the concentrations are uniform over the depth probed and X and R belong to the same phase, integration can be performed algebraically to give

$$R_X = R'_A R'_L \frac{\sigma_{Xy}}{\sigma_{Rz}} \frac{C_X}{C_Z} R'_\lambda R'_C \tag{28}$$

where

$$R'_\lambda = \frac{\lambda_{Xy}}{\lambda_{Rz}} \tag{29}$$

More qualitative interpretation of the intensity ratios involves the study of their trend versus a given parameter, such as temperature of treatment, yet with the implicit support of concentration models.

Whatever the model or strategy used, quantitative interpretation will be limited by the accuracy that can be achieved on the various factors R. We will now consider this important point more specifically.

b. *Problems Associated with the Accuracy of the Various Parameters*

Asymmetry parameter. Only a few publications deal with asymmetry parameters [68-70], and there is only one extensive source [69]. Therefore, evaluation of the imprecision involved is difficult unless $\alpha = 54°44'$, in which case $R'_A = 1$ (Eq. 27). According to theory, $\beta$ should vary from 2 for s subshells to an extreme of 0.5 for others. Therefore, if $\alpha = 90°$, as for most commercial instruments, the imprecision on $R'_A$ can be at most ~20%, even if both $\beta$ values are known to not better than 50%.

Analyzer luminosity. Analyzer luminosity depends essentially on the kinetic energy of the photoelectron. Theoretical calculations according to Helmer and Weichert [71] and Wannberg et al. [72] give $E_K^{-1}$ and $E_K^{-1/2}$ dependences, respectively. Analyzer luminosity also depends on the analyzer mode; most spectrometers work in the constant-pass-energy mode ($E_A$ constant), some in the constant-retarding-ratio mode ($E_A/E_K$ constant). Seah [73] in an extensive review shows that, for the constant-pass-energy mode, the $E_K^{-1}$ dependence is valid at high kinetic energy and the $E_K^{-1/2}$ dependence is more acceptable at low $E_K$ values. Slit width and pass (or analyzing) energy $E_A$ may shift the transition region. Most commercial instruments are reviewed and their luminosity given as a function of energy mode, slit width, and kinetic energy [73]. The Vacuum Generators ESCA 3 [74,75] and Hewlett-Packard 5950B [76] have been dealt with more specifically elsewhere. In any case, the imprecision on the $R'_L$ factor is rather limited and can be further reduced to a negligible level by taking two lines, X and R, with kinetic energies as close to each other as possible.

Photoionization cross sections. A wealth of $\sigma$ data has been published in the literature since the pioneering work of Wagner [77] on relative intensities; they are either calculated theoretically or determined experimentally.

Scofield [78] has calculated Hartree-Slater subshell photoionization cross sections for all the elements. For each element, absolute $\sigma$ values have been calculated for all subshells and for the most widely used X-ray radiations, $Al_{K\alpha}$ ($h\nu = 1486.6$ eV) and $Mg_{K\alpha}$ ($h\nu = 1253.6$ eV).

Experimentally derived data are invariably obtained by determining $R_X$ for homogeneous solid standards, assuming that the surface composition is identical to its bulk counterpart. If this condition is fulfilled, the $C_X/C_R$ concentration ratio in (28) is readily calculated from the stoichiometry of the compound; the R' factors are then determined with variable degrees of approximation and with levels of inaccuracy discussed in this section, and eventually the cross-section ratios $\sigma_{Xy}/\sigma_{Rz}$ can be obtained. Thus the values obtained are essentially relative; the figures are usually converted by normalization with respect to $\sigma_{F\ 1s}$ [36,77,79,84-87] or $\sigma_{Na\ 1s}$ [80-83]. Normalization can also take place [88] with respect to the theoretical value of $\sigma_{Na\ 1s}$ ($6.025 \times 10^{-24}$ m$^2$) given by Scofield.

Thus relative subshell photoionization cross sections for $Al_{K\alpha}$ have been given by Wagner [77,84,85], Carter et al. [89], Janghorbani et al. [90], Vulli and Starke [91], Nefedov et al. [80-82], Kemeny et al. [83,92], and Berthou and Jørgensen [86,87], for more or less wide fractions of the periodic table. The most extensive tables for $Al_{K\alpha}$ are given by Szajman et al. [88]. Similarly, data for $Mg_{K\alpha}$ excitation have been reported by Adams et al. [93], Cadman et al. [94], Brillson and Caesar [95], Calabrese and Hayes [96], Berthou and Jørgensen [86], Wagner [84], and Evans et al. [36,79]. The most extensive are those of Evans et al. [79] and Berthou and Jørgensen [86,87]; the latter, however, are based on heights rather than surface areas, as is the case for all others, and should therefore be less accurate. Castel and West [97] have also published a set of relative subshell photoionization cross sections for the $Si_{K\alpha}$ radiation.

It is generally agreed that experimental values, when available, should be preferred to data calculated theoretically [79,88]. However, Scofield's cross sections agree rather well with experimental values [73], especially for 1s, 2p, and 3d subshells [88]; they are also the most extensive.

Contamination overlayer. Treatment in situ to remove the contamination layer is not always acceptable, for various reasons; for example, it can alter the concentration in the surface layers or change the valence state of some elements. Therefore, $R'_C$ in relations (24) and (28) may be less than unity.

There are basically two ways of handling the problem. The first one consists, when feasible, of choosing lines X and R with kinetic energies as close to each other as possible, so as to minimize their difference in IMFP $\lambda'_X$ and $\lambda'_R$. Consequently, the exponential term in (25) is close to zero and $R'_C \simeq 1$ [89,98]. In addition, and as stated earlier, $R'_L$ is also approximately equal to 1. Such lines, however, are not always available, in which case serious distortion of the true intensity ratio may result, especially in the case of coke deposition on catalysts [99].

The alternative is to evaluate $R'_C$, either by monitoring the intensity ratio of two lines from the same element but with widely different $E_K$ [64,84] or by a least-squares statistical approach on a large number of data [36,84,92]. Yet another possibility for determining $R'_C$ arises when the sample itself contains carbon (e.g., as carbonate) displaying a sufficiently large chemical shift with respect to the carbonaceous surface deposit [100].

Finally, the determination of the reduced thickness $\tau/\lambda'_{Xy}$ in (20) can also be accomplished by varying the emission angle $\theta$. This approach has been extensively investigated by Ebel [60,61], especially in relation with surface roughness. Although this method is particularly general and reliable, it can also be time consuming.

c. *General Considerations.* Provided that all the R' factors in (24) are taken into account, a reliability of ~10% can be expected for the quantitative analysis of XPS intensity ratios [79]. More approximate evaluation of these factors leads to an average accuracy of about 20% [88].

If relative intensities from other users' sets are employed, their transfer from one instrument to another should be carried out with caution; this problem has been considered extensively by Seah [73]. Even so, the XPS user must be aware that comparison of intensities between different laboratories and/or instruments can be subject to errors up to 100%, as illustrated in a round robin on high-purity samples of copper and gold [101]. Wagner et al. [85] have challenged this conclusion; they conclude that the reproducibility between different instruments should be far better than that of the round-robin study, provided that the instruments are properly maintained. The reader is also referred to Wagner and co-workers [84,85] for the discussion of some factors affecting quantitative determination by XPS.

## III. INSTRUMENTATION AND EXPERIMENTAL CONSIDERATIONS

### A. Description of Instrument

A thorough review of instrumentation would require a chapter in itself, so only the most important features will be recalled here, together with some details that may be of special interest in the field of catalysis.

#### 1. Vacuum Requirement

Above $10^{-6}$ torr, residual molecules provoke excessive inelastic scattering of the photoelectrons inside the analyzer; hence $10^{-6}$ torr is a minimum requirement for the analyzer-detector part of the system if satisfactory no-loss peak intensities are to be obtained. Somewhat paradoxically, a so-called "high pressure" spectrometer has been built recently, where the dynamic pressure around the specimen is of the order of 1 torr. This is accomplished by the intercalation of differential pumping stages between the photoelectron chamber and the analyzer [4,102]. This design is evidently aimed at monitoring dynamic effects related to adsorption in situ [103] and could be extended to the study of "catalytic work" in situ at low pressures. Another design for high-pressure photoelectron spectroscopy has been proposed by Powell [104], where the gas around the solid is used as a signal converter.

These designs, however, are exceptions, and all the commercial instruments operate well below $10^{-6}$ torr. In fact, if surface cleanliness is an absolute requirement, such as in the characterization of metal valence bands, the ultimate vacuum should be of the order of $10^{-10}$ to $10^{-11}$ torr. This ensures that the initial perfectly cleaned surface is not significantly recontaminated within the time necessary for data collection. For practical catalytic systems, however, such vacuum levels will seldom be reached; furthermore, the ultimate vacuum does not seem critical as long as a vacuum of $10^{-8}$ to $10^{-9}$ torr can be achieved.

More important than the vacuum level reached is its quality, that is, the nature of the residual gas molecules. Carbon-bearing molecules, such as those originating from the diffusion pump oil, tend to decompose when impinging on the surface irradiated by X-rays. This process is responsible for the buildup of the contamination overlayer discussed previously [66]. In addition, this carbonaceous residue can act as a reducing agent, noticeably for transition metals such as $Cr^{6+}$ in chromia-silica catalysts [105] or nickel- or copper-exchanged zeolites [99].

This problem can be tackled by placing on top of the diffusion pump a liquid-nitrogen trap fitted with baffles. It has also been shown that cooling the X-ray source window, even simply with running water, can substantially reduce the contamination buildup [106].

2. X-Ray Source

The X-ray tube is separated from the photoelectron chamber by a thin aluminum foil that absorbs the electrons emitted by the anode. The most widely used anode materials are aluminum and magnesium, but yttrium [107] and other anodes with photons of higher energy than $Al_{K\alpha}$ [97,108] have been reported. A particularly appealing and useful improvement is the twin anode setup, which allows taking spectra on the same sample successively with the $Mg_{K\alpha}$ and the $Al_{K\alpha}$ lines simply by switching. This is particularly useful for the identification of Auger lines, as will be discussed in Sec. IV.H.

Associated with the source is the problem of satellite emission lines and monochromation. In addition to bremsstrahlung radiation and to the $K\alpha_{1,2}$ line, the X-ray source also generates other less intense lines, especially the $K\alpha_{3,4}$, which is roughly one order of magnitude less intense than the $K\alpha_{1,2}$. The $K\alpha_{3,4}$ will generate its own photoelectron lines, as shown in Fig. 4, which can be very troublesome, not only in line assignment but also in the case of superimposition with other "true" photoelectron lines generated by the $K\alpha_{1,2}$. X-ray satellite energies and intensities for Mg and Al anodes can be found elsewhere [30].

Complete removal of the satellite lines and of the bremsstrahlung radiation from the emission spectrum of the anode can be achieved by a monochromator placed between the source and the sample. This is done at the expense of the intensity, even though the loss in X-ray intensity is partially compensated by a simultaneous increase in the signal-to-noise ratio. For catalysts, the benefit of monochromation may not be evident because of line broadening due to various factors such as sample charging, the band width of the spectrometer, and so on. Even now, many commercial instruments do not have monochromation or provide it only as an option.

### 3. Electron Analyzer

The role of the analyzer is to separate electrons according to their kinetic energy so that the detector can count them separately. There are several types of analyzer: magnetic, hemispherical electrostatic, and double-pass cylindrical mirror electrostatic. The last two types are the most widely used; details on their principles and operation can be found elsewhere [72]. In most cases, one prefers to apply a retarding voltage with a grid before the photoelectrons enter the analyzer. In this case, the kinetic energy of the electron passing through the analyzer is fixed—this is called the analyzing or pass energy—and the spectrum is obtained by scanning the retarding voltage. This mode of operation is called the constant-pass-energy mode; the luminosity of the analyzer varies then roughly as $E_K^{-1}$ (see Sec. II.2.B) and the resolution is constant over the whole kinetic energy range. If no retarding voltage is applied, scanning takes place on the pass energy itself; this is the constant-retarding-ratio mode. In the latter case, the resolution varies throughout the kinetic energy range and the luminosity follows roughly an $E_K$ dependence.

### 4. Detector

The detector is an electron multiplier, usually of the channeltron type; see Ref. 109 for details of operation. When a monochromator is used, a position-sensitive detector is very often used to compensate for the loss in intensity.

### 5. Data Collection and Handling

A signal averager is a minimum requirement for data collection. By repetitively scanning the same $E_K$ range, it improves the signal-to-noise ratio and is thus especially useful when monitoring weak peaks such as those arising from impurities or of supported species in heterogeneous catalysts.

A minimum requirement for data handling is a provision for peak integration; this should yield the surface area of peaks after linear subtraction of the background under the peak itself [110]. Almost any system configuration is possible between the minimum requirement reported here and the situation where a dedicated computer system monitors both data acquisition and handling. As for other spectroscopies, decomposition of overlapping lines by least-squares fitting is often needed, but the computer-optimized solution should be examined critically. Decomposition methods have been reviewed by Carley and Joyner [111]; removal of X-ray—especially $K\alpha_{3,4}$ satellites [112]—and spectrum smoothing [113] have also been considered in the literature.

The precision of intensity measurements depends primarily on the signal-to-noise ratio, but other factors play a role as well, such as the neglect of energy loss and satellite peaks as well as background evaluation.

As to the first of the above-mentioned approximations, correct measurement of the intensity should include the integration of its associated energy loss and satellite (shake-up) peaks. Although this is possible for shake-ups, it can prove very difficult or impossible for energy loss peaks which are very broad and ill defined. Neglecting them amounts to assuming that they always represent a nonvarying fraction of the total intensity.

As concerns the evaluation of the background, its shape under the peak envelope is very often assumed to be linear; sometimes, polynomial fitting of the background before and after the peak is used to interpolate the shape of the background under the peak envelope. Another more attractive alternative is to assume that the background under the peak behaves like the sigmoid-shaped integral of the peak itself. This has some physical meaning, as it amounts to assuming that each increment of photoelectrons belonging to the peak generates its own contribution to the background on its low-kinetic-energy side. This approach was first proposed by Barrie and Street [114]. A comparative study of the linear and sigmoid-shaped backgrounds has recently been published and shows that the latter results in better fittings [115].

### 6. Miscellaneous Accessories

After prolonged periods of work, especially on heavily outgassing samples, the internal walls of the spectrometer may be seriously contaminated and the ultimate vacuum can no longer be obtained. Hence provision for system bakeout is very useful and almost essential. The operation consists of heating up to 100 to 150°C for several hours all of the machine that is in contact with the high vacuum.

It is desirable to be able to rotate the sample holder in order to modify the emission angle $\theta$, even if the angular dependence of intensities will reveal only qualitative trends for most catalytic systems. It is also a minimum requirement that the probe can be heated up to 600 °C for in situ sample heating.

All machines now have a preparation chamber that can be isolated from the photoelectron chamber by a gate valve and where catalyst pretreatment can be carried out. In this respect it should be possible to connect the preparation chamber to a gas manifold that allows the admission of various gases. The preparation chamber should also include an evaporation stage, which makes it possible to evaporate metals onto the sample surface, such as gold for calibration (see Sec. III.B), and an argon gun, which, by its etching action, makes it possible to clean superficial contamination from the surface of the specimen. The gun can be placed on the photoelectron chamber to monitor a particular peak or sequentially a set of peaks while the sample surface is being eroded. Concentration profiles may be obtained in this way; care should be taken to avoid craterizing the sample by, for instance, rastering the ion beam continuously across the specimen.

Presently, there is a general trend toward combining several related techniques within a single instrument. This stems from a common need for the same basic vacuum equipment. Often associated with XPS are UPS, AES (Auger electron spectroscopy), and SIMS (secondary ion mass spectroscopy). Each of them has its own merits and limitations [116]. These should be considered critically, keeping in mind the information sought. For practical heterogeneous catalysts, AES seems the most useful.

## B. Experimental Considerations

Useful considerations and simple hints can be found in the Perkin-Elmer handbook on sample preparation, spectrum recording, peak assignments, and measurement of line position, line widths, and intensity [30]. We will now consider a few other interesting points related especially to the experimental conditions.

### 1. Sample Preparation

There is presently no technique of sample preparation free of drawbacks if the sample is in powder form, as is the case for heterogeneous catalysts. The powder, ground or not, can be sprinkled on double-sided adhesive tape, which is itself stuck onto the sample introduction device (the "probe"), or pressed onto a mesh, a soft indium foil [117], or in a small trough. It can also be pressed into a self-supporting wafer that is attached to the probe using small clips.

The adhesive tape approach is very simple and quick. In addition, the tape does not usually yield any line of its own except the $C_{1s}$ and $O_{1s}$ peaks that would be present anyway because of surface contamination. Finally, it requires only minute amounts of sample. Its ease of application explains its widespread use; however, one must be aware of certain limitations and drawbacks. First, the tape has a tendency to deteriorate under the X-ray beam because of heating, and consequently it gives off gases that degrade the vacuum and can react with the sample. Second, it completely precludes any heating of the specimen and impairs the efficiency of argon etching. Finally, sample charging is unavoidable and indeed sometimes enhanced; as the latter is not identical at each point of the irradiated surface (because of heterogeneities), peaks will be broadened (i.e., the resolution will be impaired).

On the other hand, the mesh or indium foil backings reduce the charging effect by achieving better electrical contact than with the tape between the sample surface and the probe, which is at ground potential. However, the rate of coverage of the backing is far from complete and the loss in intensity can be appreciable. Furthermore, powder losses in the photoelectron chamber are likely. The main disadvantage, however, is that the lines from the backing will almost always appear in the spectrum, although the opposite has been claimed [117]. They can mask or obscure those from the sample itself. A graphite sample holder proposed recently circumvents the latter drawback [118].

The wafer and trough solutions provide the highest intensities and allow the heating and pretreatment of catalysts in situ. The compaction associated with the wafer approach sometimes leads to surface vitrification, which casts some doubts on the results. If the trough is well designed, with slightly receding lateral walls, only very slight pressures are needed to obtain a shock-proof sample. The author has successfully used a polyacetal piston to press the powder; after each preparation, a new surface of polymer is exposed by machining the piston. This and the unreactivity of the polyacetal ensures that the sample surface is not contaminated. It is quick and convenient and deformation of the trough by excessive pressure application is virtually impossible. The only drawback is the unavoidable sample charging. Ways of reducing it are discussed next and it is the author's experience that charging is certainly no more severe with the trough than with the adhesive tape.

Finally, it is also highly desirable that the probe accommodate several samples simultaneously, so that the time-consuming operations of pumping down and pretreatment can be performed only once.

### 2. Sample Introduction in a Controlled Atmosphere

The most elegant and safest way to pretreat a sample is to do it in situ, (i.e., in the sample preparation chamber of the spectrometer). However, this is very often a lengthy operation, during which the machine is not available for recording spectra. Some of the latest commercial versions permit treatment of one sample in the preparation chamber while analyzing another. An alternative solution is to have two preparation chambers connected to the same analyzer. Nevertheless, these solutions may prove too expensive and alternative solutions have been developed, all consisting of having the sample treated outside the machine and subsequently transferred to the spectrometer without reexposure to atmosphere. A very elegant solution has been designed by Hercules [119], consisting of a retractable probe whose surrounding atmosphere can be sealed off by means of a sliding cylindrical envelope. Another more common solution is to seal the pretreated catalyst in a vial under vacuum or inert atmosphere and to transfer it into a glove box hermetically connected to the preparation chamber [120]. For many systems, the purity of the inert atmosphere achieved in a simple home-built glove box is sufficient to prevent surface modification; however, pressing the powder into a trough is virtually impossible, due to the space restrictions.

3. Recording Strategy

An excellent outline has been described by Wagner et al. [30]. For best results, the reference peaks, whether for position or intensity, should be run both before and after the line of interest [121]. This almost doubles the analysis time but yields much more reliable data, especially when some drift in peak position or intensity takes place during analysis. Alternatively, if the spectrometer can be driven by computer, a repetitive scanning of the series of peaks investigated will overcome problems associated with drift and contamination [122].

4. Handling the Charging Effect

Determination of the superficial charge $E_C$ on the sample (relation 5) is still one of the major problems in XPS, essentially for two reasons. First, as stated earlier, charging is detrimental to resolution. The higher the $E_C$ value, the worse the peak broadening [123]. Thus charging must be minimized as much as possible. Second, $E_C$ must be determined precisely, ideally to ±0.1 eV, in order to determine $E_b$ and to measure the chemical shift with some confidence. This can be achieved only indirectly, by means of a reference. Several articles deal most specifically with the fundamental understanding of the mechanisms involved in sample charging and their respective contribution [124-128].

*a. Reduction of the Charging Effect.* This can be attempted by preparing thin samples in good electrical contact with the support (mesh or indium backings) or alternatively by placing the sample in a shallow cavity [129]. It has also been shown that charging is reduced when the backing around the specimen is irradiated [126]; this is probably the reason $E_C$ is rather small when the powder is compacted in a trough. The contamination overlayer also tends to reduce $E_C$ [130]. Finally, the use of a low-energy electron gun, called a flood gun, pointed at the sample surface can also help [131]. Its use is delicate; peak distortion or splitting as well as inconsistency [101] have been reported. An excellent fundamental study of its use has been made [132], and a good, criticism-minded example of its use in catalytic systems is given by Barr [18].

*b. Determination of the Charging Effect.* This always involves determining precisely the kinetic energy $E_K$ of a line whose binding energy is known with accuracy, provided that the phase giving the reference line is in good electrical contact with the sample. For example, a conducting element or phase such as graphite [133] or $MoO_3$

[134,135] can be purposely mixed with the sample; however, differential charging may arise because of differences in particle size. This method is therefore uncertain.

The element can also be deposited on the sample surface as an overlayer thin enough to avoid excessive damping of the intensities originating from the sample itself. Along this line, gold evaporated from a tungsten filament has been widely used [136,137]. Its 4f binding energy is usually reported to be between 83.8 and 84.0 eV. Its use has also been widely criticized because gold tends to form islands [39]. As a consequence, differential charging may develop with a magnitude depending on the amount of gold deposited [138-140].

Furthermore, it is highly advisable to run the sample twice (i.e., both before and after gold deposition), as evaporation itself can alter the specimen surface [99].

The $C_{1s}$ line from the contamination overlayer is also very frequently used. Although it can safely be assumed to be in good electrical contact, its adventitious nature casts some doubt on its reliability and reproducibility [141]. Nevertheless, several authors showed it to be sufficiently reliable (±0.1 to 0.2 eV) [101,134,142] provided that the sample is not heated or argon-etched [143]. Its binding energy is usually reported as between 284.6 and 285.0 eV when referred to the $Au_{4f}$ doublet [144].

Finally, a line from an element belonging to the sample itself can be chosen. This is typically the case for a line from the support when dealing with heterogeneous catalysts. For example, $Si_{2p}$ has been used in zeolites Y [98]. Usually, the line is itself calibrated once with respect to gold, or even more simply, its $E_b$ is arbitrarily fixed to a given value. For supported catalysts, this appears to be a rather reliable reference. Indeed, the chemical modification brough about by pretreatment, catalytic work, or deactivation will usually only marginally affect, if at all, a small fraction of the surface atoms of the support; thus the binding energy of the reference can be assumed to be unperturbed. Ogilvie and Wolberg [145] have shown that the standard deviation for the $Al_{2p}$ binding energy in a series of alumina catalysts is reduced from 0.49 to 0.14 eV when $O_{1s}$ from the support is chosen as the reference instead of the more widely used $C_{1s}$.

Comparative studies of the various methods for charge correction have been conducted [101,146] and a round-robin study of binding energy determination on copper and gold standards involving 38 instruments has been reported [101]. It shows that, even with well-defined procedures of preparation, reproducibility is poor from one laboratory to another. Similarly, a large spread in line positions and intensity ratios was observed earlier in a survey of catalyst supports involving 12 laboratories [147]. These observations clearly stress the need for good maintenance practices, for improved calibration methods, and for the necessity to run one's own standards.

## IV. APPLICATION TO HETEROGENEOUS CATALYSTS

The usefulness of XPS in the field of catalysis was pointed out early by both academians [2] and those in industry [148,149]. A review of surface techniques and their application to catalytic systems can be found elsewhere [150]. An up-to-date review of the application of photoelectron spectroscopy to catalysis is largely beyond the scope of this book: a literature search of *Chemical Abstracts* between 1975 and 1981 yields some 250 articles, to which should be added related or relevant articles. In an effort to synthetize all this information, we have deliberately chosen to illustrate the application of XPS to heterogeneous catalysts by gathering together the most interesting and exemplary articles under certain headings which reflect the major recurrent problems faced by researchers in the field of catalysis. These topics can be somewhat arbitrarily divided as follows:

1. Characterization in general or following pretreatment
2. Characterization by the joint use of several techniques, including XPS
3. Support effects
4. Dispersion
5. Distribution of the active species within the support
6. Correlation between XPS data and activity
7. Deactivation

Finally, the application of Auger electron spectroscopy to the field of catalysis will be briefly reviewed.

### A. General Characterization

This section is devoted to the characterization of catalysts in the very broad sense of the term; it usually involves a study of the catalyst that is not related to specific topics such as dispersion or deactivation but is performed after either catalyst preparation or a particular treatment.

Probably the most heavily studied class of supported catalysts is that used for the hydrodesulfurization (HDS) of petroleum feedstocks. The active species, usually molybdenum, sometimes tungsten, is initially deposited on the support, most often alumina, by impregnation, subsequent calcination giving the oxide. However, the catalyst, when active, is in a sulfided state, resulting from contact with the feedstock when the reactor is started. Most, if not all, HDS catalysts contain a "promoter" that enhances the catalytic performances. The promoter is often cobalt or nickel, which is deposited on the support either at the same time as or after the deposition of molybdenum. The exact nature of the active species, as well as the role of the promoter and its fate, are still highly controversial and will not be debated here. Grange [151] has reviewed the subject.

Unpromoted catalysts have been studied by Cimino and de Angelis [152]. After impregnation of the support with sodium heptamolybdate, heating 1 h under $O_2$ at 250°C is sufficient to start forming the Mo(VI) oxide, as shown by the binding energy (BE) values of the $Mo_{3d}$ doublet.

Whereas the superficial layers of unsupported pure $MoO_3$ reduce easily to metal by heating in $H_2$ at 400°C, the reduction of its supported counterpart is limited to Mo(IV). It is further noted that Mo reduces more easily when supported on $SiO_2$ than on $Al_2O_3$, an observation that points to a stronger interaction of the supported species with alumina. More special methods of preparation of supported Mo have been monitored by XPS; they include interaction between various supports and $Mo(CO_6)$ [153], Mo carboxylates [154], and $Mo(\pi\text{-}C_2H_5)_4$ [155].

The behavior of pure $WO_3$, $WO_3/\gamma\text{-}Al_2O_3$, and $WO_3/SiO_2$ toward reduction was studied by Biloen and Pott [156]. It leads to conclusions quite similar to those given above for Mo. However, in this case, no BE shift of the $W_{4f}$ doublet, and hence no reduction, is observed when the alumina-supported $WO_3$ is treated at 550°C in flowing hydrogen.

Promoted catalysts have been studied extensively. On the basis of $Mo_{3d}$ binding energies, there is a general consensus that molybdenum oxide is sulfided to $MoS_2$ by pretreatment in $H_2S$ (or thiophene + $H_2$) at 400°C [119,157]. Decomposition of the $Mo_{3d}$ envelope has further allowed Patterson et al. [119] to measure the respective amounts of Mo(VI), Mo(V), and Mo(IV) at increasing times of reduction. Figure 11 shows that whereas Mo(V) is an intermediate in the reduction of Mo(VI) to Mo(IV) ~ 35% of Mo remains present as Mo(V) at equilibrium, a surface proportion five times higher than that of its bulk counterpart determined by EPR. The fate of cobalt is more complex: part of it is present as cobalt aluminate that remains unaffected by any of the sulfiding and reducing treatments [157,158]. The rest is $CoO_3$ which is sulfided to $Co_9S_8$ by treatment in $H_2S$ + $H_2$ [158], but not in $H_2$ + thiophene [119]. When present alone on the alumina support, $CoO_3$ is instead reduced to $Co^0$ by $H_2S$ + $H_2$ [159]. This is in contradiction with the findings of Brinen and Armstrong [160], who report that even for $CoMo/Al_2O_3$ catalysts, treatment by $H_2S$ + $H_2$ reduces deposited cobalt to the metallic state. The latter discrepancy illustrates that BE values, in this case that of $Co_{2p}$, cannot be taken as unequivocal clues to the chemical state, as discussed in Sec. II.B. Cobalt oxide supported on other supports has also been characterized by XPS [161].

Unsupported cobalt-molybdenum binary oxides catalysts have been investigated after calcination, reduction, and sulfidation. The surface composition of the oxidic form as monitored by the XPS inten-

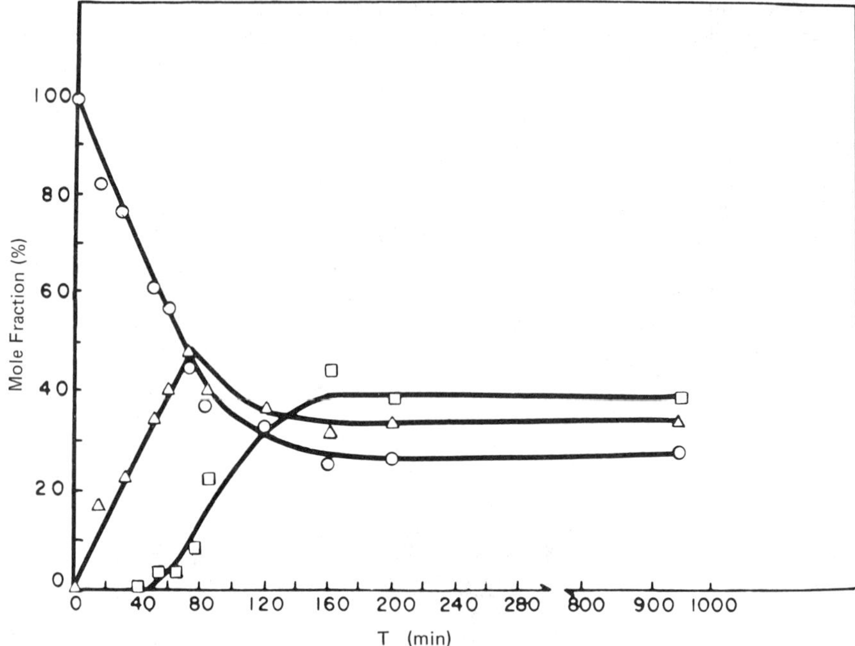


FIG. 11. Respective amounts (in percent) of Mo(VI) (open circles), Mo(V) (open triangles), and Mo(IV) (open squares) present in the surface region of a CoMo/$Al_2O_3$ HDS catalyst as a function of reduction time at 500°C in $H_2$. (From Ref. 119.)

sities is shown to be dependent on the precursors and the method of preparation used; drastic segregation of Co in the surface layers, most probably as $Co_9S_8$, is brought about by sulfidation, whereas reduction in $H_2$ favors surface enrichment in Mo [162]. At this point it should also be noted that a distinction between $Co^{2+}$ and $Co^{3+}$ is a particular favorable case, because $Co^{2+}$ displays intense shake-up satellites on the low-kinetic-energy side of the 2p lines, whereas $Co^{3+}$ does not (see Fig. 5). In addition, the spin-orbit splitting between the 2p 3/2 and 2p 1/2 peaks is 16 eV for $Co^{2+}$ and 15 eV for $Co^{+3}$ [161,163]. Finally, the study of NiW/$Al_2O_3$ HDS catalysts offers a rare example where it is taken advantage of sample charging: its decrease as a function of sulfidation time indicates that, after 1 to 2 h, a conductive network is formed on the sample surface due to the increasing concentration in conductive $WS_2$ crystallites [164].

Zeolites, as a class of heterogeneous catalysts, have also been extensively studied by XPS. Ni-exchanged Y zeolites have been characterized by Minachev et al. [165]. Reduction of $Ni^{2+}$ by $H_2$ was followed by monitoring the $Ni_{2p}$ region. In addition to a shift of ~2 eV for the $Ni_{2p\ 3/2}$ line when going from $Ni^{2+}$ to $Ni^0$, the distinction is made straightforward by the presence of very intense shake-up satellites for the paramagnetic $Ni^{2+}$ species. The ease of reduction by $H_2$ increases in the order Ag > Cu > Pd > Pt ~ Ni > Co > Fe for faujasites [166].

Rhodium zeolites carboxylation catalysts obtained by interaction of a 13X molecular sieve with $RhCl_3$ have been investigated by XPS at different steps of their preparation and after various treatments of reduction, oxidation, or carbonylation [167]; similarly, Mo-containing zeolites for epoxidation reactions were studied by Dai and Lunsford [168]. In each case the catalysts were thoroughly characterized by the binding energies and intensity ratios of their constituting elements. Zeolites exchanged with Cu, Co, and Fe have been considered by Knecht and Stork [169-171].

There is general agreement that the superficial layers of most types of zeolites are enriched in silicon; that is, their surface is dealuminated due to uncontrolled hydrolysis reactions similar to those leading to ultrastable zeolites. Such a conclusion is obtained by comparing the experimental $Al_{2p}/Si_{2p}$ intensity ratio with its theoretical value calculated according to (28). This has been reported to varying degrees for types A [169-172], X [167,172], Y [172-174], and Z [172]. Another conspicuous observation, possible only by XPS, is the reduction of silicon in the superficial layers of HY zeolites when pyridine is adsorbed at 150°C [175]. It is readily noticeable by the presence of a second $Si_{2p}$ line at ~99 eV, a binding energy typical of Si(0) and some 4 eV lower than that of the $Si_{2p}$ from the zeolitic network. Ethylene adsorption under the same conditions produces the same effect.

Other catalysts studied by photoelectron spectroscopy include carbon-supported rhodium catalysts [176]. The $Rh_{3d}/C_{1s}$ intensity ratio was shown to vary linearly with rhodium loading as expected from Eq. (28), but the slope is strongly dependent on the porosity (average pore radius) of the support. Platinum-supported catalysts prepared by impregnation with an hexachloroplatinic acid solution display three plateaus in their TGA thermogram, at 250, 380, and 520°C, when the impregnated support is heated. By monitoring the Cl/Pt intensity ratio, Escard et al. [177,178] assigned them to decomposition steps leading to the species $PtCl_4$, $PtCl_2$, and Pt, respectively. The respective amounts of $Cr^{3+}$ and $Cr^{6+}$ were estimated in copper chromite dehydrogenation catalysts [179]. This was realized by decomposition of the $Cr_{2p\ 3/2}$ profile by means of the 2.2-eV shift between the two oxidation states. The speciation between $Cr^{3+}$ and $Cr^{6+}$ was shown to be dependent on the time and temperature of calcination. When barium oxide is added as a promoter, the +6 state is favored.

## B. Joint Use of XPS with Other Techniques for Catalyst Characterization

It may appear trivial that a catalytic system, especially when it is complex, should be characterized by several techniques. These can be chosen according to the type of information sought (dispersion, distribution, deactivation, etc.), and ideally, should be as complementary to each other as possible. Although this book itself is devoted to such a multidisciplinary approach, we feel that this particular point should be stressed.

As XPS is surface sensitive, the joint use of techniques yielding information on the bulk of the catalysts is sound and justified. Thus Raman spectroscopy has been used in conjunction with XPS to characterize $Mo/Al_2O_3$ catalysts [180] and $MoCo/Al_2O_3$ catalysts prepared in both orders of impregnation [181]. Similarly, IR can be helpful, especially when the catalyst precursors or the final system itself include organic species with well-defined IR bands. Thus decarbonylation of $Rh(CO)_6$ in a zeolite support has been jointly followed by IR and XPS [167].

DRS (diffuse reflectance spectroscopy) has rather limited applications because of the very broad bands usually observed; nonetheless, it can prove very useful when information is needed regarding the symmetry and environment of atomic species in the bulk phases constitutive to a catalyst. Thus the surface concentration and oxidation state of Mo in $Mo/TiO_2$ systems used for selective oxidation of olefins was monitored using XPS. In parallel the coordination geometry of the incorporated Mo ions was followed by UV as a function of preparation and heat-treatment conditions [182]. The influence on the nature of the cobalt phase of support dopes such as Na [183,184] and B [185] has been studied jointly by DRS and XPS as a function of dope content and treatment conditions.

Another bulk technique of choice is EPR, whenever information is sought on oxidation state and environment symmetries. Thus the $Mo/TiO_2$ oxidation catalysts were further characterized for the presence, concentration, and coordination of $Mo^{+5}$ [182]. Electron transfer between Pt or Pd metallic aggregates and Y zeolite was monitored and quantified by following with EPR the concentration of charge transfer complexes formed upon adsorption of radical-generating molecules such as TCNE, TNB, or perylene and anthracene [186]. Electron transfer was shown to occur from the Pt aggregates to the zeolite framework, thus enhancing the reducing power of the latter, and was further supported by the positive chemical shifts (±0.7 eV) observed for the $Pt_{4f}$ lines. No such effects were detected for Pd. On the other hand, atomically dispersed $Pt^0$ and $Pd^0$ display a 1.3-eV shift that has been correctly attributed by the use of EPR to a change in relaxation energy (see Sec. II.B.3) rather than to electron transfer. This strongly illustrates once again how superficial and

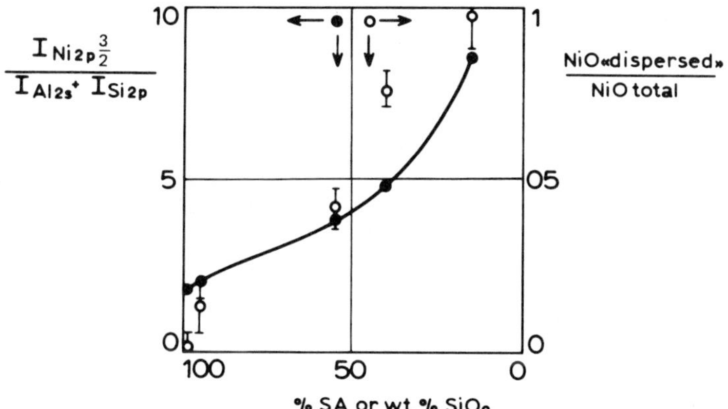


FIG. 12. Variation as a function of silica content of the XPS intensity ratio of nickel (closed circles) and the fraction of nickel finely dispersed on the carrier (open circles), as determined by EPMA (see Chap. 3). The loading in Ni is constant at 10 wt % NiO. (From Ref. 189.)

unsupported interpretation of peak shifts can be misleading because of the contribution to peak shift of final-state effects and changes in crystal potential.

Another particularly powerful association is with analytical electron microscopy, which is treated in Chap. 3. This combination is particularly useful for interpreting XPS line intensities and has been illustrated extensively elsewhere [187,188].

A particularly illustrative example is given by the study of Ni supported on silica-aluminas [189]. The loading in Ni was constant and equal to 10 wt %, but the $SiO_2$ content of the carrier was varied between 0 and 100%. On the basis of the XPS results presented in Fig. 12, it can be concluded that nickel dispersion as measured by the Ni/(Al + Si) intensity ratio increases with alumina content. AEM brings a remarkable refinement by showing that dispersion enhancement is brought about by two effects: (1) a reduction in the average size of the NiO particles, as shown by TEM, and (2) the appearance of a finely dispersed phase for contents higher than 5% in $Al_2O_3$, as evidenced by EMPA (see Chap. 3).

The fraction of Ni contained in the dispersed phase increases with alumina content as shown in Fig. 12. Such a detailed picture would be impossible to obtain solely on the basis of XPS data, as only one of the two contributions can be a sufficient explanation for the increase in Ni intensity ratio. In this case, AEM yields essential information on the biphasic nature of the supported species. Other examples of the joint use of AEM and XPS involve $CoMo/Al_2O_3$ catalysts in their sulfided state [190], Ni supported on silica [191], and boron-modified silica [192]. Another excellent example is given in the study of Pt-Rh gauzes used for catalytic oxidation of ammonia [193].

The advantage of AEM is that, by virtue of its spatial resolution, it allows us to comprehend the heterogeneity of the system and to measure selectively the amount of supported phase present as crystalline aggregates and as a finely dispersed phase on the carrier. XPS, on the other hand, is especially helpful when size changes occur in the range 0.5 to 5 nm. In addition, it can provide information on the chemical state (shifts) and selectively probes the surface, a region of prime importance in catalysis. As such, these two techniques are thus highly complementary.

## C. Support Effects

Evidence of support effects is usually obtained either by monitoring by XPS the change in reactivity of the active species between its unsupported and supported states or by interpreting the shift or change of shape of its line between both states.

As to the first approach, the samples are, for instance, submitted to reduction, usually by $H_2$, at a given temperature, and the degree of reduction is followed by means of the BE of a line of the active species. Obviously, the degree of reduction can be determined much more simply by measuring the amount of hydrogen consumed. This can be done either in a dynamic way by TPR (see Chap. 2) or in static conditions by reduction isotherms using a McBain balance (see, e.g., Ref. 194). The advantage of the more cumbersome XPS approach lies in the possibility of speciating the active species after reduction versus the various oxidation states present as well as the possibility of monitoring sintering and/or migration of the reduced crystallites (see Sec. IV.E). Furthermore, no other alternative is possible when reduction takes place only in the surface layer of the particles of active species, in which case only minute amounts of hydrogen are consumed. Examples of the first approach include the previously cited article by Cimino and De Angelis on $MoO_3$ supported on $SiO_2$ and $Al_2O_3$ [152] as well as that of Biloen and Pott [156] on $WO_3$ supported on silica or alumina. In the first example, XPS enables monitoring the complete reduction to $Mo^0$ of the surface of unsupported $MoO_3$ at 400°C, whereas reduction of the supported species at the same temperature does not go beyond Mo(IV). Reduction of nickel by CO at 550°C in polycationic form of Y zeolites was shown by XPS to be increasingly incomplete, in the order Cr < Co < Ni < Cu [195]. Similarly, interaction between cobalt oxide and its carrier increases in the order $SiO_2$ < $\gamma$-$Al_2O_3$ < $La_2O_3$, based on the difficulty in reducing it at 400°C under $H_2$ [161]. Furthermore, the fraction of cobalt present in the +3 state is monitored by the 2p 3/2-2p 1/2 spin-orbit splitting and shown to increase with loading. This indicates, quite expectedly, that an increasing fraction is present as bulklike $Co_3O_4$ unperturbed by the support. The hard-to-reduce fraction predominantly present at low loading corresponds in fact to $CoAl_2O_4$ and $LaCoO_3$, as shown by XRD. For alumina-supported CuO, formation of $CuAl_2O_4$ is shown by XPS to be favored by an increase in both the temperature of calcination and the support surface area [196].

Other examples include the work by Cimino et al. [197] on silica-supported chromium oxide catalysts. In this case, sintering at 350 to 450°C of the supported species is monitored by the decrease in intensity of the $Cr_{2p\ 3/2}$ line (see Sec. IV.E). It is shown that the temperature at which this occurs decreases with increasing Cr loading within the range 350 to 450°C, thus pointing out the stabilizing effect of the support at low concentrations in chromium. For hydrazine decomposition catalysts [198], both $Ir^0$ and $Ir^{+3}$ are present if the content in Ir does not exceed 3.6%. The more acid the support, the higher the concentration of $Ir^{+3}$, which was interpreted in relation to the ability of the support to accept electrons [199].

Peak broadening of the active species arising from support interaction [200] is now a trivial observation explained by the heterogeneous nature of the surface sites of the carrier. In addition, interpreting the peak shift in terms of support effect should be viewed with extreme caution, as peaks shifts can arise not only from chemical shifts but also from changes in crystal potential or final-state effects (see Sec. II.B.3).

An illustration of crystal potential effects has been given by Lindsay et al. [201] in an XPS study of various types of aluminates. This study is relevant to catalyst supports either as such or modified with dopes or promoters. It shows that, for a given coordination of aluminum, the $Al_{2p}$ binding energy depends on the number and nature of charge compensating cations. Another example of crystal field effects has been discussed previously [18].

Changes in extra atomic relaxation, on the other hand, may arise from variations in environment (change of support) of the active species or from changes of its particle size. This was shown by evaporating gold on a silica substrate and monitoring its $Au_{4f}$ binding energy after erosion by argon etching [202]. As the thickness was reduced from a calculated value of 43 Å to a submonolayer coverage of 0.2 Å, the $Au_{4f}$ BE increased by 1.1 eV from an original value equal to that of bulk Au metal. This was shown to be due to the lower extra-atomic relaxation provided by $SiO_2$ at small Au particle sizes compared with the large electron flooding that exists inside the thick Au coating. The 1.5-eV positive shift observed for highly dispersed $Pt/SiO_2$ with respect to pure platinum probably has the same explanation [203].

This has obvious implications in catalysis, and other examples of positive peak shifts attributed to an increase in dispersion of the active species have been given for Pd and Pt zeolites [186] as well as nickel oxide supported on silica-aluminas ranging from 0 to 100% $Al_2O_3$ [204].

Support effects in their wide sense also include the effect of a second species deposited simultaneously on the carrier. Bowman and Biloen have shown that Pt + $Ge/Al_2O_3$ catalysts reduced at 650°C by $H_2$ display a −0.8-eV shift of the $Pt_{4d}$ line with respect to the monometallic $Pt/Al_2O_3$ system similarly reduced. They interpreted this as the result of alloying between Pt and Ge [205]. Deposition of Mo, W, or Re on silica gel prior to interaction with Pt organic complexes and subsequent reduction by $H_2$ results in a $Pt_{4f\ 7/2}$ binding energy 0.5 eV higher than for $Pt/SiO_2$ [206]. Based on extensive XPS results, it has been proposed that cobalt in HDS catalysts stabilizes the molybdenum phase [207], whereas interaction of Mo with $SiO_2$ in the same catalysts has been shown to be weaker than with $Al_2O_3$ [208].

Finally, catalysts obtained by impregnation of $SiO_2$, $TiO_2$, and $Al_2O_3$ with $PdCl_2$ solutions have been investigated by photoelectron spectroscopy; $SiO_2$ and $TiO_2$ have been shown to act as inert carriers, whereas the BE shift of Pd supported on alumina was related directly to the concentration of $Cl^-$ [209].

## D. Determination of the Dispersion

Access to dispersion by XPS can be achieved by interpretation of intensity ratios $R_X$, equal according to (22) to $I_{Xy}/I_{Rz}$, where X is the supported species and R an element from the carrier. Obviously, the model used for integrating Eq. (24) will have to express the influence of the dispersion of the supported species. Ideally, it should also take into account the influence of the support surface area and porosity, if any. Finally, we assume that intensity ratios are not obscured by distribution effects; that is, the loading in supported species in the surface region probed by XPS is representative of that of the bulk of the carrier grain, thus no surface enrichment or depletion exists. This problem will be addressed specifically in the next section.

Qualitatively speaking, and all other conditions being identical, an increase in dispersion will yield an increase in the intensity ratio $R_X$, and vice versa. This was reported for the first time by Sharpen [210], who showed that, for a given method of catalyst preparation (impregnation or ion exchange) and constant loading, the $Pt_{4f}/Si_{2p}$ intensity ratio of $Pt/Si_2O$ catalysts is proportional to the platinum dispersion, as measured by hydrogen chemisorption. Similar observations were made by Angevine et al. [211] for the same system.

Intuitively, this can be understood by noticing that, for an identical loading in supported species, the higher the dispersion (i.e., the smaller the average particle size), the larger the area it will offer to the X-ray beam and hence the higher the intensity ratio will be with respect to the support. Ever since, similar observations have been made by numerous researchers: for instance, sintering of silica-supported palladium [178] and carbon-supported rhodium catalysts [212] has been monitored by XPS and the interpretations confirmed by X-ray diffraction or electron microscopy.

Development of models for the quantitative interpretation of the intensity ratio has been given by Fung [213], to which the reader is referred for the complex analytical expressions. In an extensive study, this author derives a relationship between $R_X$ and the size of the active-species particles. This relationship is shown to depend, to a minor extent, on the shape assumed for the particles (spherical, hemispherical, or cubic). Figure 13 shows that the agreement observed for the average particle size $\delta_X$ between XPS and TEM is excellent for a silica-supported platinum film sintered under hydrogen. Provided that $\delta_X$ is larger than $3\lambda_{Xy}$ and $6\lambda_{Xy}$ for the cubic and spherical shapes, respectively, it is shown that

$$R_X = k' \frac{W}{S_A} \frac{1}{\rho_X} R'_\lambda R'_A R'_L R'_\sigma \frac{1}{\delta_X} \tag{30}$$

where k' is an empirical constant describing the distribution of the

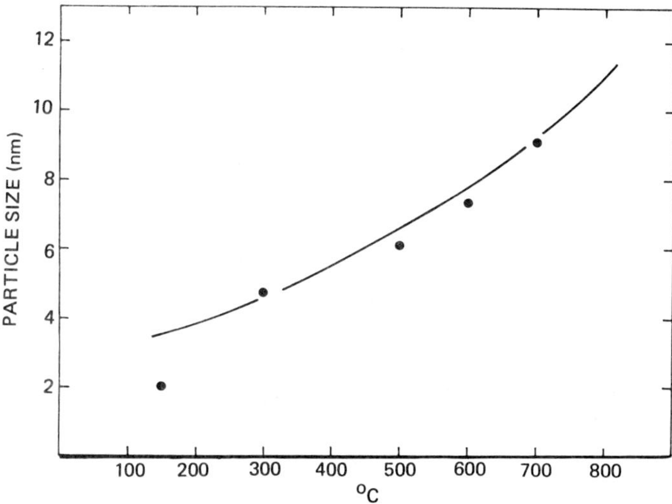


FIG. 13. Sintering of a monatomic Pt film supported on silica as a function of the temperature of reduction in $H_2$. Solid lines, from electron micrograph; solid circles, from observed XPS intensity ratio. (From Ref. 213.)

active species, W the loading in dispersed phase in (grams per gram of catalyst), $S_A$ the surface area of the carrier, and $\rho_X$ the density of the active phase. Equation (30) shows that, all else being constant, the intensity ratio is proportional to the loading in active species.

Another interesting observation is that $R_X$ is inversely proportional to the surface area of the support $S_A$. This rather simple dependence had been proposed by Delgass and co-workers [211] in their study of sodium monatomically dispersed on $\gamma$-aluminas by impregnation, and used successfully by Kerkhof et al. [214] in their study of fluorinated aluminas. Another model that takes the surface area of the carrier into account was proposed by Defossé et al. [215] in their study of the adsorption of pyridine on silica-aluminas. This model simulates the porosity of the support by a stacking of elementary nonporous fictitious particles (cubes, spheres, or sheets). Their characteristic dimension t (edge, radius, or thickness) is such that the surface/mass ratio of the particle is equal to the carrier surface area.

The monatomically deposited species is further assumed to be adsorbed on the surface of these elementary particles. The intensity ratio $R_X$ can then be calculated theoretically, giving

$$R_X = \alpha d_X q \tag{31}$$

where q depends on the model chosen and, for the sheet model, is equal to

$$1 + 2\left[\frac{\exp(-t/\lambda_{Rz})}{1 - \exp(-t/\lambda_{Rz})}\right] \tag{32}$$

In (31), $\alpha$ is a constant equal to

$$\frac{R'_A R'_L R'_\sigma}{C_R \lambda_{Rz}} \tag{33}$$

where $C_R$ is the volume concentration of reference element R in the carrier. Finally, $d_X$ is the surface density of the supported species given by

$$\frac{n_X}{S_A} \tag{34}$$

where $n_X$ is the number of supported-species atoms per gram of catalyst. Interestingly, for low surface areas, q tends to unity and $R_X$

becomes equal to

$$\alpha d_X \tag{35}$$

which is the expression proposed by Delgass and co-workers [211] and implicitly contained in expression (30), given by Fung [213]. On the other hand, for high surface areas, it can be shown [216,217] that relation (31) reduces to that given in (28), for a homogeneous solid solution.

This is the model implicitly applied to high-surface-area catalysts by Shalvoy and Reucroft [218]. The physical meaning behind the stacking model is given elsewhere [216,217], especially in relation to its limit cases, for high and low surface areas. Its validity has been proved by investigating a series of $Mo/Al_2O_3$ catalysts having approximately the same loading in Mo but with surface areas ranging from 10 to 320 $m^2/g$ [217]. Figure 14 shows that the theoretical intensity ratio calculated according to the sheet variant of the stacking model matches satisfactorily the experimental values over the whole range of intensity ratios (surface areas), whereas the solid-solution and Delgass's models are valid only at respectively high and low surface areas. Kerkhof and Moulijn [219] have amalgamated the stacker model and the effect of dispersion, assuming a cubic shape for the supported-species particles. This is the most complete treatment of dispersion measurements by XPS to date.

In the absence of effects due to changes in distribution, dispersion measurements by XPS are a chosen method because XPS is not restricted to metals as is the case with chemisorption. Dispersion of supported oxides or sulfides can also be studied and the method is especially useful below the limit of ~3 nm, where particles are no longer visible in TEM, and for amorphous materials, for which XRD is inapplicable. The only other factor that could possibly play a role is the porosity (distribution of pore sizes) of the support. It is felt, however, that the effect of porosity on the intensity ratios reported for Rh/C catalysts [176] and discussed previously (Sec. IV.A) is probably due to concomitant changes in distribution. A similar explanation can be put forward for the difference observed between impregnated and ion-exchanged catalysts in the studies previously cited [210,211]. We will now give an illustrative example of a dispersion study by XPS.

The difference between ion-exchanged (e) and impregnated (i) catalysts mentioned previously has been investigated in detail by Houalla et al. [191,220] in their study of silica-supported nickel catalysts. The nickel content was varied between 2 and 10 wt % both for the e and i series and the $I_{Ni_{2p}}/I_{Si_{2p}}$ ratio monitored. Figure 15

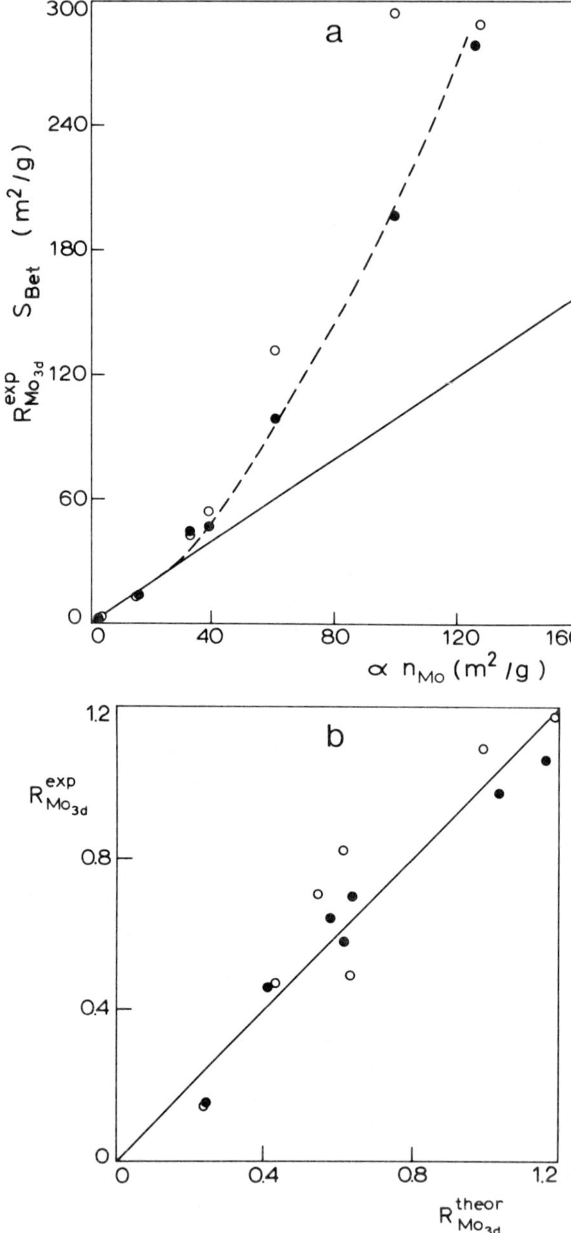


FIG. 14. Plot of the experimental $R_{Mo_{3d}}$ data ($R^{exp}_{Mo_{3d}}$) as a function of $R^{theor}_{Mo_{3d}}$ calculated theoretically according to (a) Delgass's model,

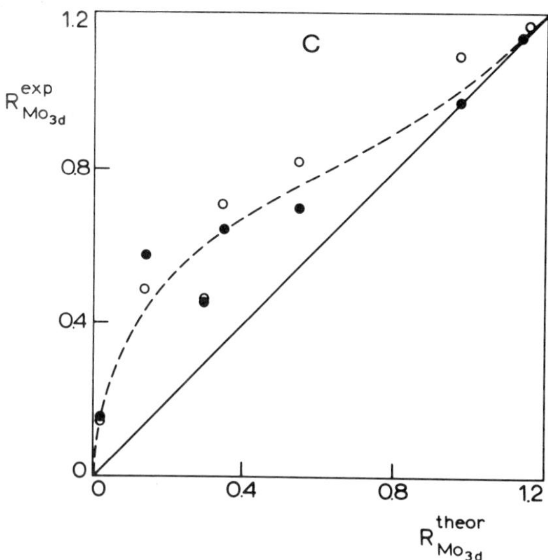


FIG. 14. (Continued) (b) the sheet variant of the stacking model, and (c) the solid solution model. Ordinate and abcissa of (a) were rearranged according to Eq. (35). Closed circles, 400 to 200; open circles, 71 to 36 granulometric fractions. (From Ref. 217.)

shows the intensity ratio as a function of Ni loading. For the impregnated samples, the initial slope is low and the curve starts to level off almost immediately. In the other case, the ion-exchange samples display a very high slope and a remarkable linearity. According to what has been outlined above, these results are indicative of a very high dispersion of Ni for the e series (high value of the slope), with no "crystallite" size variation as a function of Ni loading (constancy of the slope). The i series, on the other hand, displays a poor dispersion and a steady increase in particle size with Ni content (leveling off). These conclusions are further supported by TEM and reduction studies [191]. The value of the slope for the e series also indicates that ion-exchanged nickel is probably atomically dispersed, although discrepancies in the literature on $\lambda_{Si_{2p}}$ values prevents a fully quantitative analysis of intensities [220]. Dispersion of NiO supported on boron-modified silica was also monitored by XPS and TEM as a func-

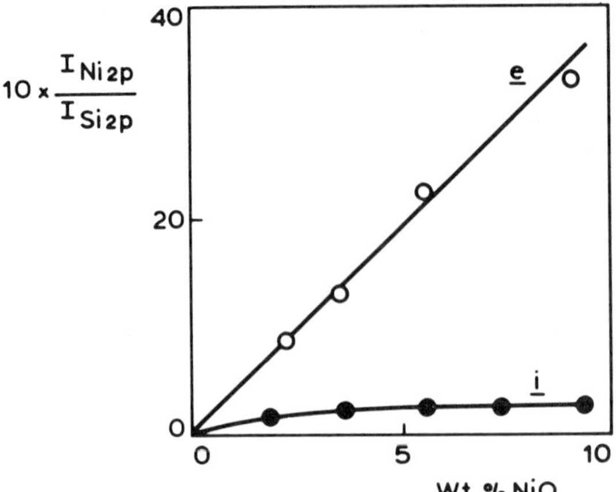


FIG. 15. Variation of the $R_{Ni_{2p}}$ intensity ratio as function of Ni content. Open circles, ion-exchanged samples; closed circles, impregnated samples. (From Ref. 191.)

tion of boron content [192]. Variations of dispersion measured by both techniques were in excellent agreement.

Dispersion can also vary because of a change in the nature of the supported phase. This was the case for the studies on NiO/SiO-$Al_2O_3$ systems previously cited [189,204], where the fractions of Ni supported phase present as NiO crystallites and "dispersed" phase, respectively, vary with the alumina content of the carrier. Changes in dispersion with increasing content in supported species also occur typically when, above a certain threshold, the carrier can no longer accommodate the deposited species in the same phase. This is, for instance, the case for the $Mo/Al_2O_3$ system, where molybdenum at low loadings is present as a monolayer in register with the underlying alumina surface [221-223]. If, for $Mo/Al_2O_3$ catalysts calcined at 550°C, the $I_{Mo_{3d}}/I_{Al_{2p}}$ intensity ratio is plotted versus the Mo surface density $d_{Mo}$, a linear relation is observed up to four atoms per square nanometer [224]. Above this threshold, the curve levels off, indicating that molybdenum is increasingly present as "free" $MoO_3$ on top of the epitaxial Mo monolayer. Similar observations have been made for nickel [225], molybdenum [226], and cobalt [227,228] oxides supported on γ-alumina modified with sodium, when the Na content reaches a critical level of about four atoms per square nanometer. It has also been shown by XPS and IR [216] that this superficial density in Na corresponds to the upper limit for monatomic dispersion of the deposited sodium and to a complete neutralization of strong acid sites by Na. Full interpretation of the catalytic transition metal oxide systems is given in the corresponding references.

Finally, an intensity model for binary oxides systems has been conceptually developed [32] for cases where the metals X and R are present in two different phases, on the one hand, and where metal X is present in only one phase whereas metal R is present in both phases, on the other hand. Intensity ratios are then a function of weight concentrations and specific surface areas of both phases. For the particular case where X and R are present in two different phases, Garbassi et al. [229] have independently developed the same concept and proposed thorough analytical expressions. They have used them in a study of coprecipitated $RuO_2$-$Al_2O_3$ catalysts to estimate the respective average particle radii of both $Al_2O_3$ and $RuO_2$ grains.

## E. Determination of the Distribution of Supported Species

Since XPS is selective to the first 6 nm below the surface, any changes in concentration of the active species within that region will be readily observed, whether it is enrichment by migration to the external surface or impoverishment by embedment in the bulk of the particle. Qualitative monitoring is thus rather straightforward. Determination of concentration profiles, however, proves to be substantially more difficult. In any case, reasonable caution must be exercised, because, as seen in the preceding section, changes in dispersion also affect the XPS intensities. Hence the respective contribution of concomitant distribution and dispersion changes can be very difficult to assess even qualitatively. For example, an intensity rise due to the migration of a monatomically dispersed active species from within the porosity of the carrier to the external surface of the grain can be accidentally compensated by simultaneous sintering. This might be an alternative explanation for the conflicting TEM and XPS results obtained for PtCa Y zeolites when submitted to reduction in $H_2$ at 400°C [230]. Indeed, no increase in the $Pt_{4f}/Si_{2p}$ ratio is observed by XPS, whereas TEM shows the presence of 2- to 15-nm Pt particles that cannot be accommodated in the supercages.

A review of surface enrichment effects in catalysts has been published in *Catalysis Review* [231]. Finster et al. [232] have also covered the subject with special emphasis on the quantitative interpretation of XPS intensity data and a model is proposed to derive concentrations gradients. A three-layer modeling of methanol adsorbed on ZnO has been given by Dreiling [233].

Quantification of concentration gradients (or profiles) can be tentatively achieved by three different approaches: either by varying the emission angle, by recording intensities of two lines from the same element but with very different mean free paths, or finally by progressive erosion of the surface by argon etching while monitoring the intensity of the supported species.

1. Variation of Takeoff Angle

The theoretical background has been outlined in Sec. II.C. To the author's knowledge no quantitative application of this approach has been attempted for heterogeneous catalysts. This stems partly from the quasi-impossibility of accurately quantifying the effects of surface roughness on the variation of XPS intensities with emission angle $\theta$. The principal reason, however, is that enhancement of the surface selectivity of XPS at grazing angles is drastically dampened, if not totally suppressed, for the majority of heterogeneous catalytic powders, since they usually possess surface roughness well in excess of 1 $\mu$m [62]. This is because the photoemission angle as seen by the entrance slit is an average obtained by integration over the directions unshaded by adjacent particles. This average, for particles coarser than 1 $\mu$m, does not vary significantly over a wide range of nominal angle $\theta$. Thus no $Mo_{3d}/Al_{2p}$ intensity increase was observed for the 71- to 36-$\mu$m fraction of a series of $Mo/Al_2O_3$ catalysts when $\theta$ was allowed to vary between 70 and 10°, even though Mo surface segregation did exist [217]. A positive example for catalysis-related systems has been given by Baird et al. [59].

2. Lines with Widely Different IMFPs

The mathematical expressions have been given in Sec. II.C. Although this approach in principle suffers from the same limitations as concerns powder roughness, it has been applied more often. It is, however, limited to supported species having two XPS photoemission lines of widely different kinetic energies.

Bouwman and Biloen have modeled the concentration profiles of Sn in PtSn and $Pt_3Sn$ alloys in this way [63]. In general, however, almost any type of analytical expression can fit the data, so that the real physical meaning of the shape of the profile is highly questionable. Since the precision of IMFPs, in addition, is rather limited, only qualitative trends can be obtained. In a study of a 150-$m^2$/g $\gamma$-$Al_2O_3$ doped with sodium, the $I_{Na_{1s}}/I_{Na_{KLL}}$ was taken as a clue to the location of Na within the modified alumina, both after drying at 110°C and calcination at 600°C [216]. The kinetic energies of $Na_{1s}$ and $Na_{KLL}$ lines are ~400 and ~1000 eV, respectively; hence the IMFP for $Na_{1s}$ is shorter. Therefore, the more "embedded" the sodium in the alumina host lattice, the lower the intensity ratio, because according to (16), dampening will be more important for $Na_{1s}$ than for the more energetic $Na_{KLL}$ line. After drying at 100°C, ratios were independent of sodium loading and no more than 15% higher than the 1.71 value observed for $Na_2Al_2O_4$. After calcination, they were substantially higher (3.0 on the average), showing the preferential surface location of sodium. Similar reasoning was used by Okamoto et al. [234] to assess qualitatively the location of Ni in Raney and Urushibara catalysts by using the $Ni_{3p}/Ni_{2p}$ intensity ratio.

### 3. Argon Etching

Argon etching provides the most direct access to concentration profiles. A recent review of depth profiling using XPS has been published [235]. The main limitations are preferential sputtering and chemical effects. Even if the argon beam is rastered, preferential sputtering of an element can occur [236], leading to erroneous depth profiles. Although argon etching is particularly attractive for removing the superficial contamination overlayer, it can also induce chemical changes, particularly the reduction of some transition metal oxides [237,238].

Depth profiles of tin antimony mixed-oxide selective oxidation catalysts have been determined by coupling XPS and argon etching [239]. Figure 16 shows that the surface region of $Sn_{0.8}Sb_{0.2}O_2$ calcined at 900°C is enriched in antimony over a depth of about 5 nm; the initial decrease of the $C_{1s}$ contaminant line is also noticeable. Differential sputtering was ruled out by check experiments on mechanical mixtures, and Sb segregation was shown to depend on the composition (Fig. 17) and the temperature of calcination. A multilayer model has been proposed for Bi-Mo-Fe selective oxidation catalysts, based on depth profiling [240], but it has subsequently been questioned [241, 242]. It should also be noted that depth profiling over extended periods of time becomes progressively meaningless, even in the absence of differential sputtering and other perturbing effects, because the etching front becomes less and less edgy as it progresses [243,244].

Qualitative clues to the distribution of an element can also be obtained by monitoring the changes in XPS intensities as a function of pretreatment or versus another parameter, such as loading in supported species. For instance, when NaAg Y and NaPd Y zeolites are outgassed in vacuum at 380°C, the metal ions originally distributed in the cavities are reduced and migrate onto the external surface of the zeolite grains. This is revealed by an important increase in the $Ag_{3d}$ and $Pd_{4f}$ intensity ratios [245]. Similarly, formation of $RuO_2$ particles outside the zeolite porosity have been reported for RuNa Y by Pedersen and Lunsford [246] when they are treated in $O_2$. If, however, $O_2$ is

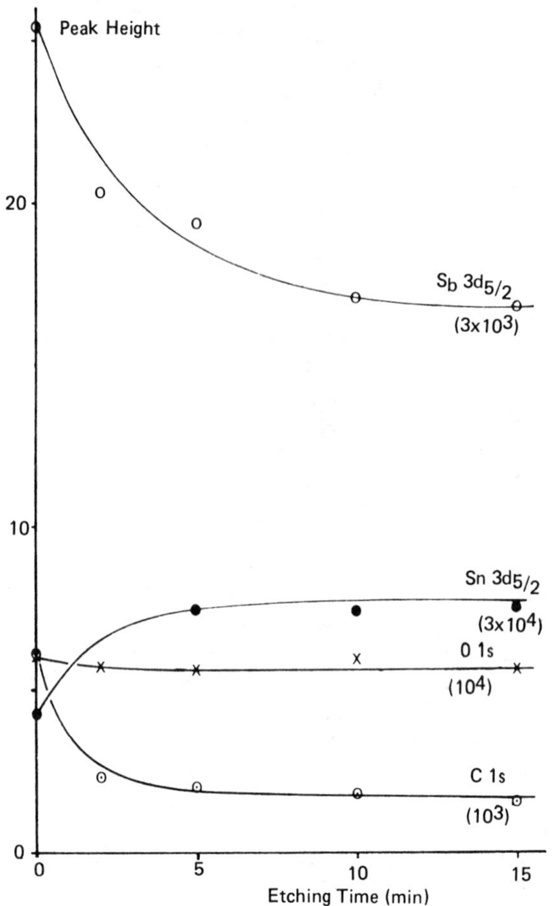


FIG. 16. Argon etching profile for a $Sn_{0.8}$-$Sb_{0.2}O_2$ catalyst calcined at 900°C. Etching rate is ~4 Å/min. (From Ref. 239.)

excluded at any time, metallic Ru remains inside the cavities following reduction by $H_2$, as evidenced by the almost constant $Ru_{3d}/Si_{2p}$ ratio. Shifts in the $Ru_{3d}$ lines have also been critically discussed in relation to crystal potential and extraatomic relaxation effects. When the oxidic precursors of HDS catalysts are calcined above 600°C, the $Co_{2p}/Al_{2p}$ intensity ratio decreases, indicating that $Co^{2+}$ diffuses into the alumina lattice, probably forming a spinel $CoAl_2O_4$ phase [247]. On the other hand, sulfur impurities diffuse and segregate on the surface of palladium upon annealing, as evidenced by AES, UPS, and XPS [248].

Changes in distribution in the surface layers versus catalyst composition are numerous. The relative surface compositions of Bi-

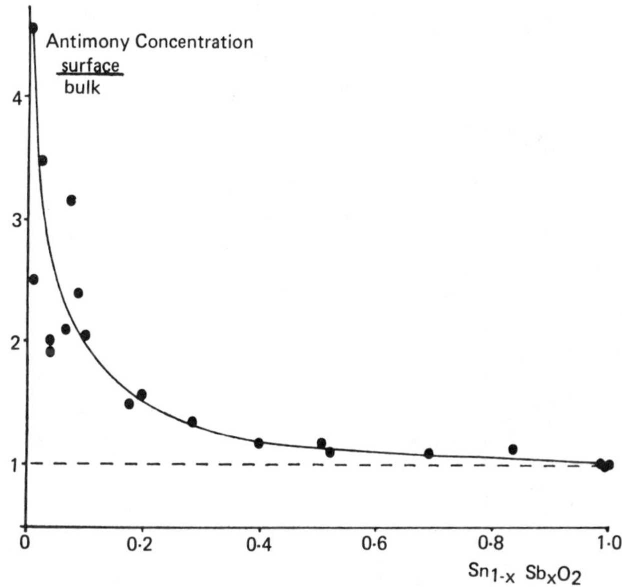


FIG. 17. Variation of the surface enrichment in antimony as a function of overall (bulk) composition for mixed Sn-Sb oxide catalysts calcined at 600°C. (From Ref. 239.)

molybdate [249], $SnO_2$-$MoO_3$ [250], and $SnO_2$-$ZrO_2$ [251] catalysts have been investigated as a function of bulk composition by monitoring the corresponding XPS intensity ratios. The $Mo_{3d}/Si_{2p}$ intensity ratio of $Mo/SiO_2$ catalysts displays a steep increase for $MoO_3$ concentrations higher than 12 wt % [208]. This was interpreted as a saturation of the adsorption sites inside the porosity of the silica carrier, leading to deposition of $MoO_3$ at the outer surface of the support particles. This interpretation was confirmed by AEM and TEM micrographs [252]. Similar behavior was observed for $Ni/Al_2O_3$ catalysts studied by XPS and ISS for Ni contents higher than 18 wt % and attributed to the appearance of a new nickel species on top of the saturated monolayer [253].

The method of preparation also plays a crucial role in the distribution of the active species and we have previously indicated that some of the discrepancies observed between impregnated and ion-exchanged catalysts [211] could well be explained in terms of a difference in distribution of the platinum on the silica carrier. Schreifels et al. [254] have shown that nickel boride hydrogenation catalysts are coated with a boron oxide overlayer. The oxide/boride ratio depends on the methods of preparation and is maximum when the reduction step is carried out in 95% ethanol, where the oxide cannot dissolve. In a study of systems relevant to catalytic preparations, Hirokawa and Oku [255] show that postprecipitation leading to coating formation or coprecipitation can be readily distinguished in binary systems such as $PbSO_4$-$BaSO_4$ and CuS-ZnS respectively, by monitoring the XPS intensity ratio (Pb/Ba or Cu/Zn) as a function of aging time of the precipitate.

Finally, such a simple experimental methodology as recording the XPS spectrum before and after grinding the sample can yield a wealth of information [149]. The distribution of molybdenum in $MoO_3$/$Al_2O_3$ extrudates was followed after drying and calcination in this way [256]. Pellets of bitumen processing catalysts were analyzed by XPS for the molybdenum content of their external surface and interior. Good agreement was observed between these two regions of the pellets and the bulk chemical composition [257]. High-temperature firing in air of hydrotreating catalysts induced changes in the distribution of Co, Mo, Si, and Ca that were followed by recording the XPS spectra of the outer and fractured surfaces of the catalyst pellets [258]. The surface composition of $V_2O_5$-$TiO_2$ [259] and $V_2O_5$-$SnO_2$ [260] catalysts used for the vapor-phase oxidation of alkylpyridines has also been studied by XPS. The mechanical mixtures of oxides used as standards for the calibration curves show very different surface concentrations before and after sintering. This is due to liquefaction and embedment, as revealed by grinding the sintered samples. The pore volume (so-called "dry") impregnation of alumina supports by sodium heptamolybdate solutions is a diffusion-controlled process. Two series of catalysts were prepared from two different grain sizes of the alumina carrier, 400 to 200 and 71 to 36 μm, respectively, and the $Mo_{3d}/Al_{2p}$ intensity ratio was monitored both before and after grinding. The larger-grained fraction was shown to be more depleted in molybdenum than its fine-grained counterpart [217].

## F. Correlation of Catalytic Activity and XPS Data

This section deals more particularly with publications where a more or less direct correlation has been specifically established between catalytic activity or selectivity and the presence (concentration) of an element, oxidation state, or stoichiometry within the surface region.

One of the first such correlations was described by Brinen and Melera [261] in their study of Rh/C catalysts for hydrogenation. Catalysts reduced by $H_2$ and reexposed to air displayed two oxidation states, one of them corresponding to the metal and the other having a BE volume similar to that of $Rh_2O_3$. The catalytic activity was shown to correlate with the presence of the oxidized species. Similarly, Okamoto et al. [262] claimed to distinguish two valence states, $Rh^+$ and $Rh^\circ$, for Rh-exchanged Y zeolites following reduction. $Rh^+$ was claimed to be active for hydrogenation and dimerization of ethylene and the metal for hydrogenation of acetylene and ethylene.

Alkaline earth metal oxides used as catalysts for ethylene hydrogenation were characterized by XPS for their $O_{1s}$, $Mg_{2p}$, $Ca_{2p}$, and $Ba_{4d}$ binding energies [263]. The $O_{1s}$ peak at 532.0 eV observed for CaO upon evacuation at 1053 K was ascribed to the formation of an $O^-$ species, which was proposed as being the site of activity. Another type of hydrogenation catalysts was prepared by reduction of nickel in solution or nickel hydroxyde in suspension to give nickel boride and nickel phosphide catalysts, respectively [264]. Specific activities were found to increase with surface content in boron and to decrease with surface concentration in phosphorus. These trends were attributed to the electron donation and withdrawal effects of boron and phosphorus, respectively.

The activity of HDS catalysts was shown to depend, at constant Mo loading, on the amount of cobalt convertible to $Co_9O_8$ [158]. The maximum activity was found at a Co/Mo surface ratio of ~0.2 to 0.3, this result being independent of the method of preparation. For unpromoted $Mo/Al_2O_3$ catalysts, the intrinsic activity peaked for a sulfidation degree of molybdenum equal to unity [224].

Figure 18 illustrates a correlation between XPS results and catalytic activity. It concerns the paper by Schreifels et al. cited previously [254] and shows that the activity for conversion of acrylonitrile to 3-ethoxypropionitrile is strongly correlated with the surface concentration in boron oxide present as an overlayer on the nickel boride catalysts. Correlation between XPS results and the catalytic behavior of MgO in dehydrogenation and dehydration reac-

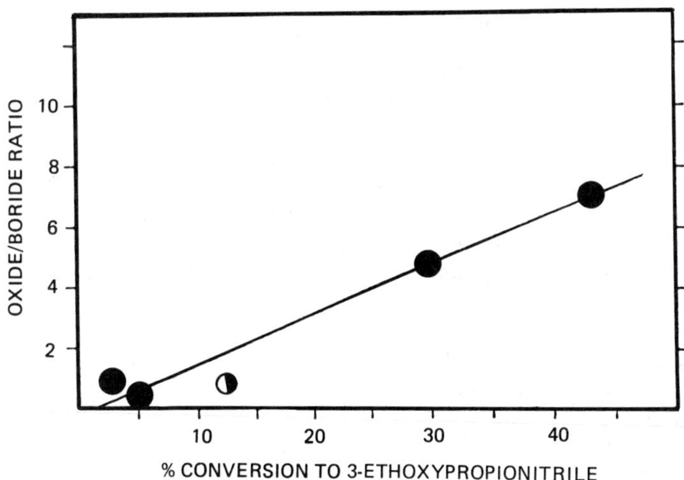


FIG. 18. Catalytic activity for the conversion of acrylonitrile to 3-ethoxipropionitrile as a function of boron oxide/boride XPS intensity ratio in nickel boride catalysts. (From Ref. 254.)

tions has been reported by Vinek et al. [265], whereas conversion of 2-butanol to butenes and ketone by $SnO_2$-$MoO_2$ catalysts has been shown to proceed at maximum rate when the surface layers contain equal amounts of Mo and Sn [250]. Activity and selectivity of a silver catalyst for ethylene oxide formation was correlated with the presence of Ca, in one of the first correlations between XPS and catalytic data [266]. The higher activity of nickel intermetallic compounds such as $ThNi_5$ for methanation has been related to their higher surface concentration in nickel, compared to conventional wet-impregnated $NiThO_2$ catalysts [267]. Finally, Boudeville et al. [268] have shown that the selectivity of Sb-Sn-O catalysts for oxidation of propylene to acrolein increases with surface content in Sb.

## G. Deactivation

Brinen [269] has demonstrated the ability of XPS in tracking down the causes of catalyst deactivation. For instance, a spent exhaust catalyst displayed the presence of phosphorus, lead, zinc, and sodium in addition to the lines observed for the unused catalyst, suggesting surface contamination as a possible cause for its deactivation. In the same paper, the 100-fold drop in activity of Rh/C catalysts heated at 700°C in $H_2$ was ascribed to sintering of the Rh particles [269].

Superficial contamination by impurities contained in the feed or in the lines of the reactor can be a major cause for catalyst deactivation and can be readily spotted using a surface-sensitive technique such as XPS. Another example has been given by Hoste et al. [270]. In a study of $NiAl_2O_4$ steam-reforming catalysts, they show that deactivation was due to surface poisoning by Pb and Si carried by the feed from the line.

Deactivation of Pt-Rh gauzes has also been investigated by XPS and AEM, by studying the catalysts both before and after its use in catalytic oxidation of $NH_3$ [193]. Reforming $Pt/Al_2O_3$ catalysts regenerated by coke burning have to be replenished in chlorine for optimum performance. This can be done in a continuous way by minute addition of $CCl_4$ to the feed. Careful investigation of such catalysts [271] has shown that the attenuation of the $Pt_{4d}/Al_{2p}$ ratio upon $CCl_4$ treatment can be accounted for only by a selective lay-down of coke on the Pt crystallites. This also explains the decrease in $H_2$ chemisorption capacity and hydrogenolysis activity observed following chloriding. At the same time, AEM shows that the clusters of Pt crystallites are redispersed but that individual Pt crystallites have grown in size, an observation also supported by XPS.

Finally, the activity and selectivity decline observed for Bi-molybdate multicomponent catalysts in propene ammoxidation has been attributed to the equalization of surface and bulk concentrations in Bi, Mo, and Fe observed by XPS and argon etching [272].

### H. Auger Spectroscopy

Auger electron spectroscopy (AES) was considered very briefly at the beginning of this chapter (see Sec. II.A.1 and Fig. 2). Its relation to and differences from X-ray fluorescence are further illustrated in Fig. 19. Deexcitation of sodium following photoemission of a 1s electron can take place by fluorescence or by Auger effect. In the latter case the atom is left in a two-hole state as a result of the emission of the Auger electron. In a first approximation, we can neglect the interactions between holes and those between the remaining electrons and the holes so that we can write

$$E_K \simeq E_b^1 - (E_b^2 + E_b^3) \tag{36}$$

where $E_K$ is the kinetic energy of the outgoing Auger electron. $E_b^1$, $E_b^2$, and $E_b^3$ are the binding energies of the electronic levels 1, 2, and 3 involved in the process, in the case of $Na_{KLL}$, the levels 1s, 2p 1/2, and 2p 3/2.

Several important consequences arise from this relation. First, it can be seen that the kinetic energy $E_K$ of the Auger electron does not depend on the energy hν of the excitation source needed to create the original photo-hole in level 1. An important consequence is that the position (i.e., the kinetic energy) of Auger peaks appearing in an XPS spectrum will not change when switching from the Mg to the Al anode on twin-anode instruments. This offers a particularly reliable and direct way to distinguish Auger peaks from genuine photoelectron

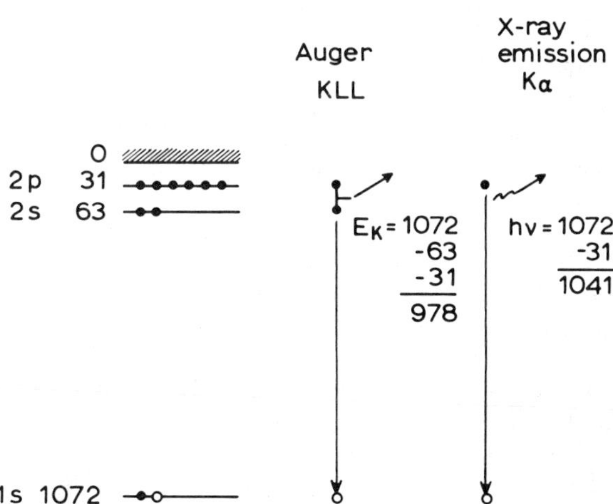


FIG. 19. Schematic representation of Auger and X-ray emission deexcitation process for sodium. (From Ref. 32.)

peaks in a XPS spectrum. It is thus very helpful for peak identification in complex XPS spectra.

Second, as the process involves one and two holes in the initial and final states, respectively, the exact value of $E_K$ (i.e., the line shift) will be determined predominantly by relaxation effects, as well as by the valence state, especially if the final state involves a hole in the valence band.

Auger and photoelectron spectrometers are built using the same basic equipment, except that an electron gun is used as the excitation source in AES. Consequently, the current, and hence the intensity, will be much higher (by a factor of $10^4$ to $10^6$) in Auger; thus the intensity and ability to detect traces will be enhanced. Another consequence is that spectra have to be recorded in a derivative mode because of the very high background arising from electrons originating from the unshielded source. Finally, moderate to high spatial resolution (a few micrometers) is possible because the electron beam can be finely focused, unlike its X-ray counterpart (irradiated area, ~1/2 $cm^2$). This is taken advantage of in the scanning Auger microprobe [273]. Due to the high electron flux impinging on the sample, AES is considerably more destructive than XPS, which can be considered as a nondestructive technique. This makes AES much less suitable for studies of adsorption and damage-sensitive samples.

AES and XPS have approximately the same selectivity toward the surface, because the kinetic energies, and thus the IMFPs, are of the same order of magnitude. Quantitative analysis is feasible by Auger electron spectroscopy, but its use has been less frequent than XPS, mostly because of the larger width of Auger lines and also due to a lack of data concerning the sensitivity factors. In principle, however, its accuracy is as good as that of EMPA, provided that standards of known composition are run for calibration. Wagner et al. [30] present the various methods used for calibration and give the most complete single source of sensitivity factors; experimental aspects are also discussed. An intensity model has been given by Chang [274] and the effect of surface roughness on quantitative AES analysis has also been investigated by Holloway [275].

As illustrated earlier, Auger peaks can be seen in an XPS spectrum (Fig. 4). One must be especially aware that the bremsstrahlung radiation can induce Auger lines such that the binding energy $E_b^1$ of the initially ejected photoelectron is larger than the photon energy $h\nu$ of the main X-ray excitation line (see, e.g., the $Al_{KLL}$ line in spectrum of Fig. 4, obtained with an $Al_{K\alpha}$ line). This can be utilized to advantage and several authors [276,277] have discussed the use of bremsstrahlung-induced Auger lines in XPS spectra.

---

FIG. 20. Two-dimensional chemical state plot: Auger kinetic energy versus the binding energy $E_b$ of the $Co_{2p\ 3/2}$ line. (From Ref. 283.)

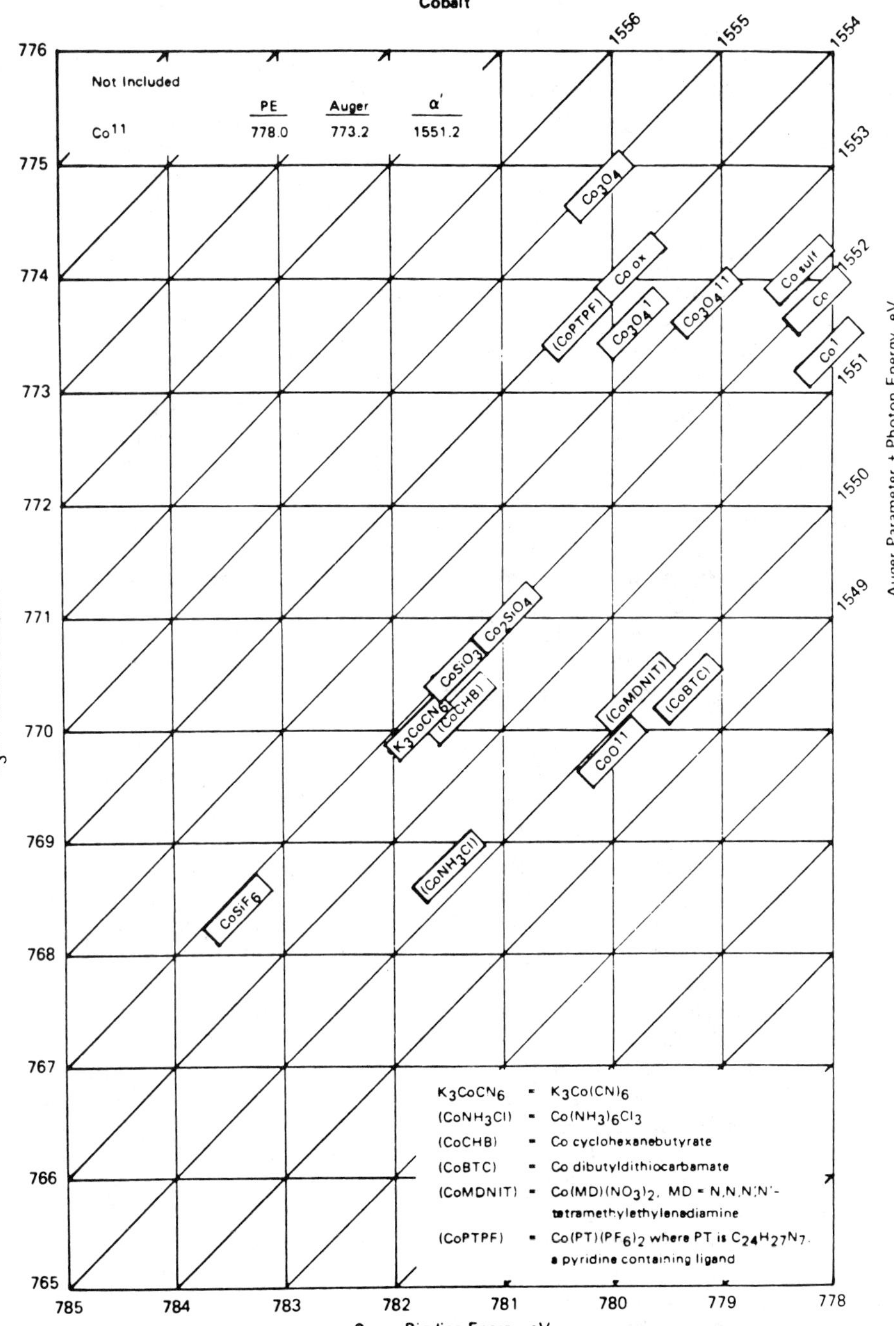
Cobalt
Not Included
PE
Auger
α′
Co11
778.0
773.2
1551.2
Co3O4
Co ox
(CoPTPF)
Co3O4 1
Co3O4 11
Co sulf
Co
Co1
Co2SiO4
CoSiO3
(CoCHB)
K3CoCN6
(CoMDNIT)
(CoBTC)
CoO11
(CoNH3Cl)
CoSiF6
K3CoCN6 = K3Co(CN)6
(CoNH3Cl) = Co(NH3)6Cl3
(CoCHB) = Co cyclohexanebutyrate
(CoBTC) = Co dibutyldithiocarbamate
(CoMDNIT) = Co(MD)(NO3)2, MD = N,N,N',N'-tetramethylethylenediamine
(CoPTPF) = Co(PT)(PF6)2 where PT is C24H27N7, a pyridine containing ligand
L3VV Kinetic Energy, eV
2p3/2 Binding Energy, eV
Auger Parameter + Photon Energy, eV
776
775
774
773
772
771
770
769
768
767
766
765
785
784
783
782
781
780
779
778
1556
1555
1554
1553
1552
1551
1550
1549

Auger shifts are less straightforward to analyze than their XPS counterparts because of relaxation effects, as mentioned previously, and also because three electronic levels are involved in the process. Wagner and Biloen [278] have discussed abnormal Auger chemical shifts and have shown that they can be, in a first approximation, four times as large as in XPS. The relationship between Auger shifts and extraatomic relaxation effects is treated extensively by several authors [279-281].

Wagner has defined the Auger parameter $\alpha$ as the difference between the kinetic energy $E_K$ of the Auger line and that of the photoelectron ejected from the core level 1 [281-283]. It is independent of the charging effect $E_C$ and can be plotted as a function of the corresponding binding energy $E_b^1$ to give a two-dimensional chemical state plot (Fig. 20). This plot is very helpful in identifying chemical compounds, especially since different chemical states can yield the same, usually small XPS shifts. Hence this approach can be of considerable value in the study of heterogeneous catalysts, although its applications to this field have been limited so far.

Applications of AES in general to the characterization of catalysts are much scarcer than those of XPS and oriented mostly toward the investigation of deactivation and poisoning. Thus sulfur poisoning by $H_2S$, COS, and thiophene of a methanol synthesis catalyst of proprietary composition has been studied by AES [284]. It is suggested that at low levels of $H_2S$ in the feed (<1 ppm) sulfur is deposited as a multilayer, while at high levels (>40 ppm) strong depletion in Zn, together with a marked enrichment in Cu, suggests that sulfur drives copper to the surface to form a copper sulfide species. Carbon and sulfur poisoning have been investigated for alumina-supported nickel, cobalt, iron, and ruthenium methanation catalysts [285]. On nickel and ruthenium, carbon deactivation is reversible, whereas for Fe and Co, bulk carburization and graphitic growth occur, leading to an irreversible deactivation. Figure 21 is a typical example of Auger spectra obtained on fresh and spent methanation catalysts.

The exact nature of carbonaceous deposits on Fe(110) has been investigated using AES and XPS after CO hydrogenation at ≃1 bar [287]. The fingerprint nature of the $C_{KLL}$ peak permits the classification of a carbonaceous layer in the first phase of the reaction as a heavily hydrogenated species.

As for XPS, monitoring the catalyst surface before and after high-pressure catalytic tests has prompted researchers to design special cells for AES studies "in situ." Dwyer and Somorjai have described an isolation cell that is placed inside the ultrahigh-vacuum system. It can be pressurized up to 20 bars and evacuated for subsequent AES analysis [288].

The reasons for a sudden loss of activity of a Pd/$\gamma$-$Al_2O_3$ catalyst for selective hydrogenation of diolefins to monoolefins has been investigated by Bhasin [289]. AES shows it to arise from complete

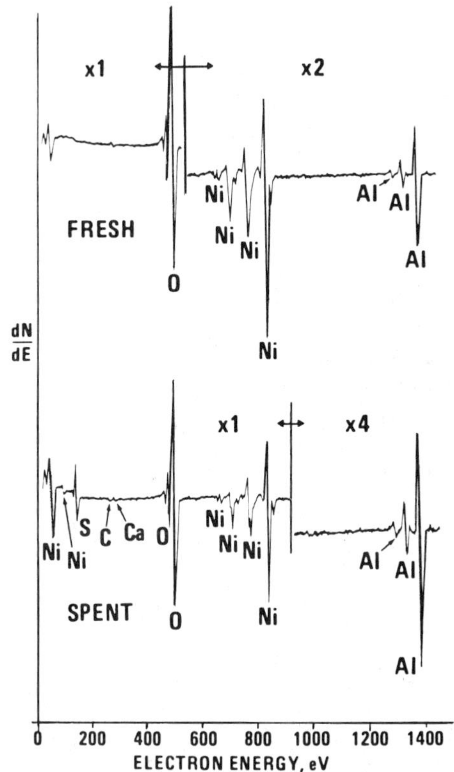


FIG. 21. Auger spectra of fresh and spent Ni-Al methanation catalysts. Note the presence of S, C, and Ca on the spent catalysts. (From Ref. 286.)

coverage of the external surface by Fe impurities present in the feed. Cation migration and surface composition of natural and synthetic zeolites were studied by AES [290,291]; contrary to the XPS studies reported previously, no noticeable difference in composition was observed between the surface and the bulk.

On the other hand, surface segregation of copper in a Cu-MgO catalyst was established [292] and poisoning of a copper catalyst has been shown to be caused by lead segregation on the surface [293].

Finally, AES is extensively used in combination with argon etching for depth profiling, especially in the field of alloys and metallurgy. This technique has been reviewed by Holloway [294] in 1975 and factors affecting the measurements discussed by Hooker and Grant [295].

## ACKNOWLEDGMENTS

I wish to express here my most sincere gratitude to Dr. R. Lemanczyk and Mr. J. Stockdale for reviewing the manuscript. I am also grateful to Dowell-Schlumberger for giving me access to their library and computer facilities.

## REFERENCES

1. K. Siegbahn, C. Nordling, A. Fahlman, R. Nordberg, K. Hamrin, J. Hedman, G. Johansson, T. Bergmark, S. E. Karlsson, I. Lindgren, and B. Lindberg, in *ESCA: Atomic, Molecular and Solid State Structure Studied by Means of Electron Spectroscopy*, Nova Acta Regiae Soc. Sci. Uppsaliensis, Ser. IV, Vol. 20.
2. W. N. Delgass, T. R. Hughes, and C. S. Fadley, *Catal. Rev.*, *4*: 179 (1970).
3. S. N. K. Chandhari and K. L. Cheng, *Appl. Spectrosc. Rev.*, *16*: 187 (1980).
4. M. W. Roberts, *Adv. Catal.*, *29*: 55 (1980).
5. J. A. Bearden and A. F. Burr, *Rev. Mod. Phys.*, *39*: 125 (1967).
6. T. A. Carlson, *Photoelectron and Auger Spectroscopy*, Plenum Press, New York, 1975.
7. D. C. Frost, C. A. McDowell, and I. S. Woolsey, *Mol. Phys.*, *27*: 1473 (1974).
8. D. C. Frost, A. Ishitani, and C. A. McDowell, *Mol. Phys.*, *24*: 861 (1972).
9. L. J. Matienzo, Lo. I. Yin, S. O. Grim, and W. E. Swartz, Jr., *Inorg. Chem.*, *12*: 2762 (1973).
10. M. A. Brisk and A. D. Baker, *J. Electron Spectrosc. Relat. Phenom.*, *7*: 197 (1975).
11. J. W. D. Connolly, H. Siegbahn, U. Gelius, and C. Nordling, *J. Chem. Phys.*, *58*: 4265 (1973).
12. F. Brogli and E. Heilbronner, *Theor. Chim. Acta*, *26*: 289 (1972).
13. R. M. Friedman, *J. Electron Spectrosc. Relat. Phenom.*, *5*: 501 (1974).
14. W. L. Jolly, in *Electron Spectroscopy* (D. A. Shirley, ed.), North-Holland, Amsterdam, 1972, p. 769.
15. K. Siegbahn, *J. Electron Spectrosc. Relat. Phenom.*, *5*: 3 (1974).
16. C. S. Fadley, S. B. M. Hagstrom, M. P. Klein, and D. A. Shirley, *J. Chem. Phys.*, *48*: 3779 (1968).
17. J. Q. Broughton and P. S. Bagus, *J. Electron Spectrosc. Relat. Phenom.*, *20*: 261 (1980).

18. T. L. Barr, ACS Meeting, Anaheim, March 12-17, Prepr., Div. Pet. Chem., Am. Chem. Soc., *23*(1): 82 (1978).
19. U. Gelius, P. F. Heden, J. Hedman, B. J. Lindberg, R. Manne, R. Nordberg, C. Nordling, and K. Siegbahn, *Phys. Scr.*, *2*: 70 (1970).
20. D. W. Davis and D. A. Shirley, *J. Electron Spectrosc. Relat. Phenom.*, *3*: 137 (1974).
21. J. Bus and S. De Jong, *Recl. Trav. Chim.*, *91*: 251 (1972).
22. D. W. Davis and D. A. Shirley, *Chem. Phys. Lett.*, *15*: 185 (1972).
23. D. A. Shirley, *J. Electron Spectrosc. Relat. Phenom.*, *5*: 135 (1974).
24. G. E. McGuire, Thesis, University of Tennessee, *Oak Ridge National Laboratory Report ORNL-TM-3820*, 1972.
25. L. D. Hulett and T. A. Carlson, *Appl. Spectrosc.*, *25*: 33 (1971).
26. N. S. McIntyre and M. G. Cook, *Anal. Chem.*, *47*: 2210 (1975).
27. C. K. Jørgensen, *Theor. Chim. Acta (Berl.)*, *24*: 241 (1972).
28. T. A. Carlson, in *Electron Spectroscopy* (D. A. Shirley, ed.), North-Holland, Amsterdam, 1972, p. 53.
29. C. K. Jørgensen and H. Berthou, *Det. K. Dan. Vidensk. Selsk, Mat.-Fys. Medd.*, *38*: 1 (1972).
30. C. D. Wagner, W. N. Riggs, L. E. Davis, J. F. Moulder, and G. E. Muilenberg, eds., *Handbook of X-ray Photoelectron Spectrometry*, Perkin-Elmer Corporation, Physical Electronics Division, Eden Prairie, Minn., 1979.
31. R. M. Friedman, *Silicates Ind.*, *39*, 247 (1973).
32. C. Defossé and P. Rouxhet, in *Advanced Chemical Methods for Soil and Clay Minerals Research* (J. W. Stucki and W. L. Banwart, eds.), D. Reidel, Dordrecht, Holland, 1980, p. 169.
33. C. R. Brundle, *J. Vac. Sci. Technol.*, *11*: 212 (1974).
34. I. Lindau and W. E. Spicer, *J. Electron Spectrosc. Relat. Phenom.*, *3*: 409 (1974).
35. C. J. Powell, *Surf. Sci.*, *44*: 29 (1974).
36. S. Evans, R. G. Pritchard, and J. M. Thomas, *J. Phys. C. Solid State Phys.*, *10*: 2483 (1977).
37. M. Klasson, J. Hedman, A. Berndtsson, R. Nilsson, C. Nordling, and P. Melnik, *Phys. Scr.*, 5: 93 (1972).
38. C. D. Wagner, in *Quantitative Surface Analysis of Materials* (N. S. McIntyre, ed.), American Society for Testing and Materials, ASTM-STP 643, American Technical Publisher, Philadelphia, 1978, p. 31.
39. J. Brunner and H. Zogg, *J. Electron Spectrosc. Relat. Phenom.*, 5: 911 (1975).
40. J. Szajman, J. Liesegang, J. G. Jenkin, and R. C. G. Leckey, *J. Electron Spectrosc. Relat. Phenom.*, *23*: 97 (1981).

41. P. C. Kemeny, A. D. McLachlan, F. L. Battye, R. T. Poole, R. C. G. Leckey, J. Liesegang, and J. G. Jenkin, *Rev. Sci. Instrum.*, *44*: 1197 (1973).
42. D. R. Penn, *J. Electron Spectrosc. Relat. Phenom.* *9*: 29 (1976).
43. M. P. Seah and W. A. Dench, *Surf. Interface Anal.*, *1*: 2 (1979).
44. D. M. Wyatt, J. C. Carver, and D. M. Hercules, *Anal. Chem.*, *47*: 1297 (1975).
45. D. T. Clark, A. Dilks, D. Schuttleworth, and H. R. Thomas, *J. Electron Spectrosc. Relat. Phenom.* *14*: 247 (1978).
46. J. M. Adams, S. Evans, and J. M. Thomas, *J. Am. Chem. Soc.*, *100*: 3260 (1980).
47. R. J. Bird, *Met. Sci. J.*, *7*: 109 (1973).
48. R. Holm, *Actualités Chim.*, *13* (January 1978).
49. R. O. Ansell, T. Dickinson, A. F. Powey, and P. M. A. Sherwood, *J. Electron Spectrosc. Relat. Phenom.*, *11*: 301 (1977).
50. J. S. Brinen and J. E. McLure, *J. Electron Spectrosc. Relat. Phenom.*, *4*: 243 (1974).
51. D. M. Hercules, L. E. Cox, S. Onisick, G. D. Nichols, and J. C. Carver, *Anal. Chem.*, *45*: 1973 (1973).
52. M. Czuha, Jr. and W. M. Riggs, *Anal. Chem.*, *47*: 1836 (1975).
53. D. G. Brulé, J. R. Brown, G. M. Bancroft, and W. S. Fyfe, *Chem. Geol.*, *28*: 311 (1980).
54. C. S. Fadley, R. J. Baird, W. Siekhaus, T. Novakov, and S. Å. L. Bergstrom, *J. Electron Spectrosc. Relat. Phenom.*, *4*: 93 (1974).
55. C. S. Fadley, *J. Electron Spectrosc. Relat. Phenom.*, *5*: 725 (1974).
56. W. A. Fraser, J. V. Florio, W. N. Delgass, and W. D. Robertson, *Surf. Sci.*, *36*: 661 (1973).
57. R. J. Baird, C. S. Fadley, S. Kawamoto, and M. Mehta, *Chem. Phys. Lett.*, *34*: 49 (1975).
58. D. Briggs and V. A. Gibson, *Chem. Phys. Lett.*, *25*: 493 (1974).
59. R. J. Baird, C. S. Fadley, S. K. Kawamoto, M. Mehta, R. Alvarez, and J. A. Silva, *Anal. Chem.*, *48*: 843 (1976).
60. M. F. Ebel, *J. Electron Spectrosc. Relat. Phenom.*, *22*: 157 (1981).
61. M. F. Ebel, *J. Electron Spectrosc. Relat. Phenom.*, *22*: 333 (1981).
62. H. Ebel, M. F. Ebel, and E. Hillebrand, *J. Electron Spectrosc. Relat. Phenom.*, *22*: 277 (1975).
63. R. Bouwman and P. Biloen, *Surf. Sci.*, *41*: 348 (1974).
64. M. F. Ebel, *Surf. Interface Anal.*, *2*: 173 (1980).

65. V. I. Nefedov, *Surf. Interface Anal.*, *3*: 72 (1981).
66. R. S. Swingle, *Anal. Chem.*, *47*: 21 (1975).
67. E. S. Brandt, D. F. Untereken, C. N. Reilley, and R. W. Murray, *J. Electron Spectrosc. Relat. Phenom.*, *14*: 113 (1978).
68. S. T. Manson, *J. Electron Spectrosc. Relat. Phenom.*, *1*: 413 (1972/73).
69. R. F. Reilman, A. Msezane, and S. T. Manson, *J. Electron Spectrosc. Relat. Phenom.*, *8*: 389 (1976).
70. M. Vulli, *Surf. Interface Anal.*, *3*: 67 (1981).
71. J. C. Helmer and N. H. Weichert, *Appl. Phys. Lett.*, *13*: 266 (1968).
72. B. Wannberg, U. Gelius, and K. Siegbahn, *J. Phys. E*, *7*: 149 (1974).
73. M. P. Seah, *Surf. Interface Anal.*, *2*: 222 (1980).
74. M. Vulli and K. Starke, *J. Phys. E*, *10*: 158 (1977).
75. M. Vulli, *J. Microsc. Spectrosc. Electron*, *5*: 337 (1980).
76. S. M. Hall, J. D. Andrade, S. M. Ma, and R. W. King, *J. Electron Spectrosc. Relat. Phenom.*, *17*: 181 (1979).
77. C. D. Wagner, *Anal. Chem.*, *44*: 1050 (1972).
78. J. H. Scofield, *J. Electron Spectrosc. Relat. Phenom.*, *8*: 129 (1976).
79. S. Evans, R. G. Pritchard, and J. M. Thomas, *J. Electron Spectrosc. Relat. Phenom.*, *14*: 341 (1978).
80. V. I. Nefedov, N. P. Sergushin, I. M. Band, and M. B. Trzhaskovskaya, *J. Electron Spectrosc. Relat. Phenom.*, *2*: 383 (1974).
81. V. I. Nefedov, N. P. Sergushin, Y. V. Salyn, I. M. Band, and M. B. Trzhaskovskaya, *J. Electron Spectrosc. Relat. Phenom.*, *7*: 175 (1975).
82. V. I. Nefedov and V. G. Yarzhemsky, *J. Electron Spectrosc Relat. Phenom.*, *11*: 1 (1977).
83. P. C. Kemeny, J. Liesegang, R. C. G. Leckey, and J. G. Jenkin, *Phys. Lett.*, *49A*: 171 (1974).
84. C. D. Wagner, *Anal. Chem.*, *49*: 1282 (1977).
85. C. D. Wagner, L. E. Davis, M. V. Zeller, and J. A. Taylor, R. H. Raymond and L. H. Gale, *Surf. Interface Anal.*, *3*: 211 (1981).
86. H. Berthou and C. K. Jørgensen, *Anal. Chem.*, *47*: 482 (1975).
87. C. K. Jørgensen and H. Berthou, *Discuss. Faraday Soc.*, *54*: 269 (1973).
88. J. Szajman, J. G. Jenkin, R. C. G. Leckey, and J. Liesegang, *J. Electron Spectrosc. Relat. Phenom.*, *19*: 393 (1980).
89. W. J. Carter, G. K. Schweitzer, and T. A. Carlson, *J. Electron Spectrosc. Relat. Phenom.*, *5*: 827 (1974).
90. M. Janghorbani, M. Vulli, and K. Starke, *Anal. Chem.*, *47*: 2200 (1975).

91. M. Vulli and K. Starke, *J. Microsc. Spectrosc. Electron.*, *3*: 57 (1978).
92. P. C. Kemeny, J. G. Jenkin, J. Liesegang, and R. C. G. Leckey, *Phys. Rev. B*, *9*: 5307 (1974).
93. J. M. Adams, S. Evans, P. I. Reid, J. M. Thomas, and M. J. Walters, *Anal. Chem.*, *49*: 2001 (1977).
94. P. Cadman, S. Evans, J. D. Scott, and J. M. Thomas, *J. Chem. Soc., Faraday Trans. 1*, *71*: 1777 (1975).
95. L. J. Brillson and G. P. Caesar, *Surf. Sci.*, *58*: 457 (1976).
96. A. Calabrese and R. G. Hayes, *Chem. Phys. Lett.*, *27*: 376 (1974).
97. J. E. Castle and R. H. West, *J. Electron Spectrosc. Relat. Phenom.*, *19*: 409 (1980).
98. C. Defossé and P. Canesson, *J. Chem. Soc., Faraday Trans. 1*, *72*: 2565 (1976).
99. C. Defossé, R. M. Friedman, and J. J. Fripiat, *Bull. Soc. Chim. Fr.*, *7-8*: 1513 (1975).
100. G. M. Bancroft, J. R. Brown, and W. S. Fyfe, *Anal. Chem.*, *49*: 1044 (1977).
101. C. J. Powell, N. E. Erickson, and T. E. Madey, *J. Electron Spectrosc. Relat. Phenom.*, *17*: 361 (1979).
102. R. W. Joyner, M. W. Roberts, and K. Yates, *Surf. Sci.*, *87*: 501 (1979).
103. R. W. Joyner and M. W. Roberts, *Chem. Phys. Lett.*, *60*: 459 (1979).
104. C. J. Powell, *J. Vac. Sci. Technol.*, *15*: 549 (1978).
105. A. Cimino, B. A. De Angelis, A. Luchetti, and G. Minelli, *J. Catal.*, *45*: 316 (1976).
106. D. T. Clarck, H. R. Thomas, A. Dilks, and D. Shuttleworth, *J. Electron Spectrosc. Relat. Phenom.*, *10*: 455 (1977).
107. M. S. Banna and D. A. Shirley, *Chem. Phys. Lett.*, *33*: 441 (1975).
108. C. D. Wagner, *J. Vac. Sci. Technol.*, *15*: 518 (1978).
109. C. D. Moak, S. Datz, F. G. Santibanez, and T. A. Carlson, *J. Electron Spectrosc. Relat. Phenom.*, *6*: 151 (1975).
110. C. J. Powell and P. E. Larson, *Appl. Surf. Sci.*, *1*: 186 (1978).
111. A. F. Carley and R. W. Joyner, *J. Electron Spectrosc. Relat. Phenom.*, *16*: 1 (1979).
112. P. M. Th. M. Van Attekem and J. M. Trooster, *J. Electron Spectrosc. Relat. Phenom.*, *11*: 363 (1977).
113. G. K. Wertheim, *J. Electron Spectrosc. Relat. Phenom.*, *6*: 239 (1975).
114. A. Barrie and F. J. Street, *J. Electron Spectrosc. Relat. Phenom.*, *7*: 1 (1975).
115. A. Proctor and P. M. A. Sherwood, *Anal. Chem.*, *54*: 13 (1982).

116. W. Katz, in *Microbeam Analysis* (R. H. Geiss, ed.), San Francisco Press, San Francisco, 1981, p. 287.
117. G. E. Theriault, T. L. Barry, and M. J. B. Thomas, *Anal. Chem.*, *47*: 1492 (1975).
118. D. M. Aylmer, H. Razzani, and J. C. Carver, *Anal. Chem.*, *51*: 581 (1979).
119. T. A. Patterson, J. C. Carver, D. E. Leyden, and H. M. Hercules, *J. Phys. Chem.*, *80*: 1700 (1976).
120. R. I. Declerck-Grimee, P. Canesson, R. M. Friedman, and J. J. Fripiat, *J. Phys. Chem.*, *82*: 885 (1976).
121. C. Defossé and P. Canesson, *React. Kinet. Catal. Lett.*, *3*: 161 (1975).
122. W. N. Delgass, G. L. Haller, R. Kellerman, and J. H. Lunsford, *Spectroscopy in Heterogeneous Catalysis*, Academic Press, New York, 1979.
123. T. Dickinson, A. F. Powey, and P. M. A. Sherwood, *J. Electron Spectrosc. Relat. Phenom.*, *2*: 441 (1973).
124. H. J. Freund, H. Gonska, H. Lohneis, and G. Hohlneischer, *J. Electron Spectrosc. Relat. Phenom.*, *12*: 425 (1977).
125. A. Jaegle, A. Kalt, G. Nanse, and J. C. Peruchetti, *J. Electron Spectrosc. Relat. Phenom.*, *13*: 175 (1978).
126. H. Gonska, H. J. Freund, and G. Hohlneischer, *J. Electron Spectrosc. Relat. Phenom.*, *12*: 435 (1977).
127. M. F. Ebel and M. Ebel, *J. Electron Spectrosc. Relat. Phenom.*, *3*: 169 (1974).
128. C. D. Wagner, *J. Electron Spectrosc. Relat. Phenom.*, *18*: 345 (1980).
129. R. Caillat, L. Fere, R. Fontaine, and F. Menes, *J. Microsc. Spectrosc. Electron.*, *4*: 73 (1979).
130. M. F. Ebel, *Vak. Tech.*, *23*: 33 (1974).
131. D. A. Huchital and R. T. McKeon, *Appl. Phys. Lett.*, *20*: 158 (1972).
132. R. T. Lewis and M. A. Kelly, *J. Electron Spectrosc. Relat. Phenom.*, *20*: 105 (1980).
133. M. K. Koppelman, in *Advanced Chemical Methods for Soil and Clay Minerals Research* (J. W. Stucki and W. C. Banwart, eds.), D. Reidel, Dordrecht, Holland, 1980, p. 205.
134. W. P. Dianis and J. E. Lester, *Anal. Chem.*, *45*: 1416 (1973).
135. W. E. Swartz, P. E. Watts, J. C. Watts, J. W. Brasch, and E. R. Lippincott, *Anal. Chem.*, *44*: 2001 (1972).
136. G. Johansson, J. Hedman, A. Berndtsson, M. Klasson, and R. Wilsson, *J. Electron Spectrosc. Relat. Phenom.*, *2*: 295 (1973).
137. D. J. Hnatowich, J. Hindis, M. L. Perlman, and R. C. Ragaini, *J. Appl. Phys.*, *42*: 4883 (1971).
138. C. R. Grignard and W. M. Riggs, *Anal. Chem.*, *46*: 1306 (1974).

139. D. Betteridge, J. C. Carver, and D. M. Hercules, *J. Electron Spectrosc. Relat. Phenom.*, *2*: 327 (1973).
140. Y. Uwamino, T. Ishizuka, and H. Hamatua, *J. Electron Spectrosc. Relat. Phenom.*, *23*: 55 (1981).
141. C. R. Brundle, *App. Spectrosc.*, *25*: 8 (1971).
142. J. P. Contour and G. Mouvier, *J. Electron Spectrosc. Relat. Phenom.*, *7*: 85 (1975).
143. A. Jaeghe, A. Kalt, G. Nanse, and J. C. Peruchetti, *Analusis*, *9*: 252 (1981).
144. R. J. Bird and P. Swift, *J. Electron Spectrosc. Relat. Phenom.*, *21*: 227 (1980).
145. J. L. Ogilvie and A. Wolberg, *Appl. Spectrosc.*, *26*: 401 (1972).
146. V. I. Nefedov, Ya. V. Salyn, G. Leonhardt, and R. Scheile, *J. Electron Spectrosc. Relat. Phenom.*, *10*: 121 (1977).
147. T. E. Madey, C. D. Wagner, and A. Joshi, *J. Electron Spectrosc. Relat. Phenom.*, *10*: 359 (1977).
148. J. S. Brinen, *J. Electron Spectrosc. Relat. Phenom.*, *5*: 377 (1974).
149. J. S. Brinen, *Acc. Chem. Res.*, *9*: 86 (1976).
150. I. Yasumori and Y. Inoue, *Petroteh (Tokyo)*, *3*: 317 (1980).
151. P. Grange, *Catal. Rev.*, *21*: 135 (1980).
152. A. Cimino and B. A. De Angelis, *J. Catal.*, *36*: 11 (1975).
153. D. A. Whan, M. Barber, and P. Swift, *J. Chem. Soc., Chem. Commun.*, 198 (1972).
154. S. A. Best, R. G. Squires, and R. A. Walton, *J. Catal.*, *60*: 171 (1979).
155. Yu. I. Yermakov, *Catal. Rev.*, *13*: 77 (1976).
156. P. Biloen and G. T. Pott, *J. Catal.*, *30*: 169 (1973).
157. R. M. Friedman, R. I. Declerck-Grimee, and J. J. Fripiat, *J. Electron Spectrosc. Relat. Phenom.*, *5*: 437 (1974).
158. R. I. Declerck-Griméee, P. Canesson, R. M. Friedman, and J. J. Fripiat, *J. Phys. Chem.*, *82*: 889 (1978).
159. R. I. Declerck-Grimée, P. Canesson, R. M. Friedman, and J. J. Fripiat, *J. Phys.*, *82*: 885 (1978).
160. J. S. Brinen and W. D. Armstrong, *J. Catal.*, *54*: 57 (1978).
161. Y. Okamoto, H. Nakano, T. Imanaka, and S. Teranishi, *Bull. Chem. Soc. Jpn.*, *48*: 1163 (1975).
162. Y. Okamoto, T. Shimokawa, T. Imanaka, and S. Teranishi, *J. Catal.*, *57*: 153 (1979).
163. D. C. Frost, C. A. McDowell, and I. S. Woosley, *Mol. Phys.*, *27*: 1473 (1974).
164. K. T. Ng and D. M. Hercules, *J. Phys. Chem.*, *80*: 2094 (1976).
165. Kh. Minachev, G. V. Antoshin, E. S. Shpiro, and Ya. I. Isakov, *Izv. Akad. Nauk SSSR, Ser. Khim.*, 2131 (1973).

166. Kh. M. Minachev, G. V. Antoshin, and E. S. Shapiro, *Izv. Akad. Nauk SSSR, Ser. Khim.*, 1012 (1974).
167. S. Lars, S. L. T. Anderson, and M. S. Scurrel, *J. Catal.*, *59*: 340 (1979).
168. P. S. E. Dai and J. Lunsford, *J. Catal.*, *64*: 173 (1980).
169. J. Knecht and G. Stork, *Z. Anal. Chem.*, *283*: 105 (1977).
170. J. Knecht and G. Stork, *Z. Anal. Chem.*, *286*: 44 (1977).
171. J. Knecht and G. Stork, *Z. Anal. Chem.*, *286*: 47 (1977).
172. J. F. Tempère, D. Delafosse, and J. P. Contour, *Chem. Phys. Lett.*, *33*: 95 (1975).
173. C. Defossé, P. Canesson, and B. Delmon, in *Molecular Sieves II* (J. R. Katzer, ed.), ACS Symposium Series 40, American Chemical Society, Washington, D.C., 1977, p. 86.
174. L. A. Perdersen and J. Lunsford, *J. Catal.*, *61*: 39 (1980).
175. C. Defossé, P. Canesson, and B. Delmon, *J. Phys. Chem.*, *80*: 1028 (1976).
176. J. S. Brinen and J. L. Schmitt, *J. Catal.*, *45*: 274 (1976).
177. J. Escard, B. Pontvianne, M. T. Chenebaux, and J. Cosyns, *Bull. Soc. Chim. Fr.*, *11-12*: 2399 (1975).
178. J. Escard, B. Pontvianne, M. T. Chenebaux, and J. Cosyns, *Bull. Soc. Chim. Fr.*, *3-4*: 349 (1976).
179. J. A. Schreifels, A. Roders, and W. E. Swartz, Jr., *Appl. Spectrosc.*, *33*: 380 (1979).
180. D. S. Zingg, L. E. Makosky, R. E. Tischer, R. F. Brown, and D. M. Hercules, *J. Phys. Chem.*, *84*: 2898 (1980).
181. E. Payen, J. Barbillot, J. Grimblot, and J. P. Bonnelle, *Inorg. Chim. Acta*, *34*: 29 (1979).
182. J. C. Védrine, H. Praliaud, P. Mériaudeau, and M. Che, *Surf. Sci.*, *80*: 101 (1979).
183. A. Lycourghiotis, C. Defossé, and B. Delmon, *Rev. Chim. Miner.*, *16*: 473 (1979).
184. A. Lycourghiotis, C. Defossé, and B. Delmon, *Bull. Soc. Chim. Belg.*, *89*: 929 (1980).
185. M. Houalla and B. Delmon, *Appl. Catal.*, *1*: 285 (1981).
186. J. C. Védrine, M. Dufaux, C. Naccache, and B. Imelik, *J. Chem. Soc., Faraday Trans. 1*, *74*: 440 (1978).
187. M. Houalla, F. Delannay, P. Gajardo, and C. Defossé, *Proc. Chin. Symp. Catal.*, Modern Engineering and Technology Seminar, Vol. 3, Chinese Petroleum Corporation, Taipei, Taiwan, 1980, p. 29.
188. C. Defossé, M. Houalla, A. Lycourghiotis, and F. Delannay, *Proc. Chin. Symp. Catal.*, Modern Engineering and Technology Seminar, Vol. 3, Chinese Petroleum Corporation, Taipei, Taiwan, 1980, p. 47.
189. M. Houalla, F. Delannay, and B. Delmon, *J. Chem. Soc., Faraday Trans. 1*, *76*: 1766 (1980).

190. F. Delannay, P. Gajardo, P. Grange, and B. Delmon, *J. Chem. Soc., Trans. 1, 76*: 988 (1980).
191. M. Houalla, F. Delannay, I. Matsuura, and B. Delmon, *J. Chem. Soc., Faraday Trans. 1, 76*: 2128 (1980).
192. M. Houalla, F. Delannay, and B. Delmon, *J. Electron Spectrosc. Relat. Phenom., 25*: 59 (1981).
193. J. P. Contour, G. Mouvier, M. Hoogewijs, and C. Leclerc, *J. Catal., 48*: 217 (1977).
194. M. Houalla and B. Delmon, *J. Phys. Chem., 84*: 2194 (1980).
195. Kh. Minachev, G. V. Antoshin, Yu. A. Yusifov, and E. S. Shpiro, *React. Kinetic. Catal. Lett., 4*: 137 (1976).
196. A. Wollberg, J. L. Ogilvie, and J. F. Roth, *J. Catal., 19*: 86 (1970).
197. A. Cimino, B. A. De Angelis, A. Luchetti, and G. Minelli, *J. Catal., 45*: 316 (1976).
198. J. Escard, C. Leclerc, and J. P. Contour, *J. Catal., 29*: 311 (1973).
199. J. Escard, B. Pontivianne, and J. P. Contour, *J. Electron Spectrosc. Relat. Phenom., 6*: 17 (1975).
200. A. W. Miller, W. Atkinson, M. Barber, and P. Swift, *J. Catal., 22*: 140 (1971).
201. J. R. Lindsay, H. J. Rose, W. E. Swartz, P. H. Watts, and J. A. Rayburn, *Appl. Spectrosc., 27*: 1 (1973).
202. K. S. Kim and N. Winograd, *Chem. Phys. Lett., 30*: 91 (1975).
203. P. N. Ross, K. Kinoshita, and P. Stonehart, *J. Catal., 32*: 163 (1974).
204. M. Houalla and B. Delmon, *J. Phys. Chem., 84*: 2194 (1980).
205. R. Bouwman and P. Biloen, *J. Catal., 48*: 209 (1977).
206. M. S. Ioffe, Yu. M. Shulga, Yu. Ryndin, B. N. Kuznetsov, A. N. Startsev, Yu. G. Borodko, and Yu. I. Yermakov, *React. Kinet. Catal. Lett., 4*: 2 (1976).
207. Y. Okamoto, H. Nakano, T. Shimokawa, T. Imanaka, and S. Teranishi, *J. Catal., 50*: 447 (1977).
208. P. Gajardo, D. Pirotte, C. Defossé, P. Grange, and B. Delmon, *J. Electron Spectrosc. Relat. Phenom., 17*: 121 (1979).
209. F. Bozon-Verduraz, A. Omar, J. Escard, and B. Pontvianne, *J. Catal., 53*: 126 (1978).
210. L. H. Sharpen, *J. Electron Spectrosc. Relat. Phenom., 5*: 369 (1974).
211. P. J. Angevine, J. C. Vartuli, and W. N. Delgass, *Proc. 6th Int. Congr. Catal.*, Vol. 2 (G. C. Bond, P. B. Wells, and F. C. Tompkins, eds.), The Chemical Society, London, 1977, p. 611.
212. J. S. Brinen, J. L. Schmitt, W. R. Doughman, P. J. Achorn, L. A. Siegel, and W. N. Delgass, *J. Catal., 40*: 295 (1975).

213. S. C. Fung, *J. Catal.*, *58*: 454 (1979).
214. F. P. J. M. Kerkhof, J. A. Moulijn, R. Thomas, and J. C. Oudejans, in *Preparation of Catalysts II* (B. Delmon, P. Grange, P. Jacobs, and G. Poncelet, eds.), Elsevier Scientific, New York, 1979, p. 77.
215. C. Defossé, P. Canesson, P. G. Rouxhet, and B. Delmon, *J. Catal.*, *51*: 269 (1978).
216. P. O. Scokart, A. Amin, C. Defossé, and P. G. Rouxhet, *J. Phys. Chem.*, *85*: 1406 (1981).
217. C. Defossé, *J. Electron Spectrosc. Relat. Phenom.*, *23*: 157 (1981).
218. R. B. Shalvoy and P. J. Reucroft, *J. Electron Spectrosc. Relat. Phenom.*, *12*: 351 (1977).
219. F. P. J. M. Kerkhof and J. A. Moulijn, *J. Phys. Chem.*, *83*: 1612 (1979).
220. M. Houalla and B. Delmon, *Surf. Interface Anal.*, *3*: 103 (1981).
221. J. M. J. G. Lipsch and G. C. A. Schuit, *J. Catal.*, *15*: 174 (1969).
222. J. Sonnemans and P. Mars, *J. Catal.*, *31*: 209 (1973).
223. N. Giordanno, J. C. J. Bart, A. Vaghi, A. Castellan, and G. Martinotti, *J. Catal.*, *36*: 81 (1975).
224. Y. Okamoto, H. Tomioka, Y. Katoh, T. Imanaka, and S. Teranishi, *J. Phys. Chem.*, *84*: 1833 (1980).
225. M. Houalla, F. Delannay, and B. Delmon, *J. Phys. Chem.*, *85*: 1704 (1981).
226. A. Lycourghiotis, C. Defossé, F. Delannay, and B. Delmon, *J. Chem. Soc., Faraday Trans. 1*, *76*: 2052 (1980).
227. A. Lycourghiotis, C. Defossé, F. Delannay, J. Lemaitre, and B. Delmon, *J. Chem. Soc., Faraday Trans. 1*, *76*: 1677 (1980).
228. C. Defossé, F. Delannay, A. Lycourghiotis, and M. Houalla, in *New Horizons in Catalysis* (Proc. 7th Int. Congr. Catal., Tokyo, June 30-July 4, 1980) (T. Seiyama and K. Tanabe, eds.), Elsevier, New York, 1981, p. 108.
229. F. Garbassi, A. Bossi, and G. Petrini, *J. Mater. Sci.*, *15*: 2559 (1980).
230. J. H. Lunsford and D. S. Treybig, *J. Catal.*, *68*: 192 (1981).
231. P. G. Menon and T. S. R. Prasada Rao, *Catal. Rev.*, *20*: 97 (1979).
232. J. Finster, P. Lorenz, and A. Meisch, *Surf. Interface Anal.*, *1*: 179 (1979).
233. M. J. Dreiling, *Surf. Sci.*, *71*: 231 (1978).
234. Y. Okamoto, Y. Nitta, T. Imanaka, and S. Teranishi, *J. Chem. Soc., Faraday Trans. 1*, *76*: 998 (1980).
235. S. Hoffmann, *Analusis*, *9*: 181 (1981).
236. J. E. Greene, R. E. Klinger, T. L. Barr, and L. B. Welsh, *Chem. Phys. Lett.*, *62*: 46 (1974).

237. K. S. Kim and N. Winograd, *Surf. Sci.*, *43*: 625 (1974).
238. S. Storp and R. Holm, *J. Electron Spectrosc. Relat. Phenom.*, *16*: 183 (1979).
239. Y. M. Cross and D. R. Pyke, *J. Catal.*, *58*: 61 (1979).
240. I. Matsuura and M. W. J. Wolfs, *J. Catal.*, *37*: 174 (1975).
241. D. Briggs, in *Electron Spectroscopy: Theory, Techniques, and Applications*, Vol. 3 (C. R. Brundle and A. D. Baker, eds.), Academic Press, New York, 1979, p. 305.
242. T. Noterman, G. W. Keulks, A. Skliarov, Y. Maximov, L. Y. Margalis, and O. V. Krylov, *J. Catal.*, *39*: 286 (1975).
243. A. Benninghoven, *Z. Phys.*, *230*: 403 (1970).
244. F. Delannay and C. Defossé, *Symp. Chem. Phys. Catal.*, Am. Chem. Soc. Meet., Atlanta, 1981, p. 385.
245. Kh. Minachev, G. V. Antoshin, E. S. Shpiro, and T. A. Navruzov, *Izv. Akad. Nauk SSSR, Ser. Khim.*, 2134 (1973).
246. L. E. Pedersen and J. H. Lunsford, *J. Catal.*, *61*: 39 (1980).
247. P. Dufresne, J. Grimblot, and J. P. Bonnelle, *Bull. Soc. Chim. Fr.*, *3-4*: I-89 (1980).
248. Y. Matsumoto, M. Soma, T. Onishi, and K. Tamaru, *J. Chem. Soc., Faraday Trans. 1*, *76*: 1122 (1980).
249. I. Matsuura, R. Schuit, and K. Hirakawa, *J. Catal.*, *63*: 152 (1980).
250. Y. Okamoto, T. Hashimoto, T. Imanaka, and S. Teranishi, *Chem. Lett.*, 1035 (1978).
251. T. Imanaka, T. Hashimoto, K. Sakurai, Y. Okamoto, and S. Teranishi, *Bull. Chem. Soc. Jap.*, *53*: 1206 (1980).
252. F. Delannay, M. Houalla, D. Pirotte, and B. Delmon, *Surf. Interface Anal.*, *1*: 172 (1979).
253. M. Wu and D. M. Hercules, *J. Phys. Chem.*, *83*: 2003 (1979).
254. J. A. Schreifels, P. C. Maybury, and W. E. Swartz, Jr., *J. Catal.*, *65*: 195 (1980).
255. K. Hirokawa and M. Oku, *Talanta*, *27*: 741 (1980).
256. T. Edmonds and P. C. H. Mitchell, *J. Catal.*, *64*: 491 (1980).
257. G. M. Bancroft, R. P. Gupta, A. H. Hardin, and M. Ternan, *Anal. Chem.*, *51*: 2102 (1979).
258. J. M. Dale, L. D. Hulett, E. L. Fuller, H. L. Richards, and R. L. Sherman, *J. Catal.*, *61*: 66 (1980).
259. S. L. T. Anderson, *J. Chem. Soc.*, *75*: 1356 (1979).
260. S. Lars, S. L. T. Anderson, and S. Jaras, *J. Catal.*, *64*: 51 (1980).
261. J. S. Brinen and A. Melera, *J. Phys. Chem.*, *76*: 2525 (1972).
262. Y. Okamoto, N. Ishida, T. Imanaka, and S. Teranishi, *J. Catal.*, *58*: 82 (1979).
263. Y. Inoue and I. Yasumori, *Bull. Chem. Soc. Jap.*, *54*: 1505 (1981).
264. Y. Okamoto, Y. Nitta, T. Imanaka, and S. Teranishi, *J. Chem. Soc., Faraday Trans. 1*, *75*: 2027 (1979).

265. H. Vinek, J. Latzel, H. Noller, and M. Ebel, *J. Chem. Soc., Faraday Trans. 1, 74*: 2092 (1978).
266. J. J. Carberry, G. C. Kuczynski, and E. Martinez, *J. Catal., 26*: 247 (1972).
267. R. L. Chin, A. Elattar, W. E. Wallace, and D. M. Hercules, *J. Phys. Chem., 84*: 2895 (1980).
268. Y. Boudeville, F. Figueras, M. Forissier, J. L. Portefaix, and J. C. Védrine, *J. Catal., 58*: 52 (1979).
269. J. S. Brinen, in *Appl. Surf. Anal.*, ASTM STP 699 (T. L. Barr and L. E. Davis, eds.), American Society for Testing and Materials, Philadelphia, 1980, p. 24.
270. S. Hoste, D. Van De Vondel, and G. P. Vanderkelen, *J. Electron Spectrosc. Relat. Phenom., 16*: 407 (1979).
271. F. Delannay, C. Defossé, B. Delmon, G. P. Menon, and G. F. Froment, *Ind. Eng. Chem. Res. Dev., 19*: 537 (1980).
272. K. Richter, B. Peplinski, H. Hebisch, and G. Kleinschmidt, *Appl. Surf. Sci., 4*: 205 (1980).
273. N. C. McDonald, in *Physical Aspects of Electron Microscopy and Microbeam Analysis* (B. M. Siegel and D. R. Beaman, eds.), Wiley, New York, 1975, p. 431.
274. C. C. Chang, *Surf. Sci., 48*: 9 (1975).
275. P. H. Holloway, *J. Electron Spectrosc. Relat. Phenom., 7*: 215 (1975).
276. C. D. Wagner and J. A. Taylor, *J. Electron Spectrosc. Relat. Phenomon., 20*: 83 (1980).
277. J. E. Castle and R. H. West, *J. Electron Spectrosc. Relat. Phenom., 18*: 355 (1980).
278. C. D. Wagner and P. Biloen, *Surf. Sci., 35*: 82 (1973).
279. S. P. Kowalczyk, L. Ley, F. R. McFeely, R. A. Pollak, and D. A. Shirley, *Phys. Rev., B9*: 381 (1974).
280. D. A. Shirley, *Phys. Rev., A7*: 1520 (1973).
281. C. D. Wagner, *Discuss. Faraday Soc., 60*: 291 (1975).
282. C. D. Wagner, *J. Electron Spectrosc. Relat. Phenom., 10*: 305 (1977).
283. C. D. Wagner, L. H. Gale, and R. H. Raymond, *Anal. Chem., 51*: 466 (1979).
284. B. J. Wood, W. E. Isakson, and H. Wise, *Ind. Eng. Chem. Prod. Res. Dev., 19*: 197 (1980).
285. P. K. Agrawal, W. D. Fitzharris, and J. R. Katzer, in *Catalyst Deactivation* (B. Delmon and G. F. Froment, eds.), Elsevier, Amsterdam, 1980, p. 179.
286. Physical Electronics Industries, Inc., *Application Note 7502*, January 31, 1975.
287. H. P. Bonzel and H. J. Krebs, *Surf. Sci., 91*: 499 (1980).
288. D. J. Dwyer and G. A. Somorjai, *J. Catal., 52*: 291 (1978).
289. M. M. Bhasin, *J. Catal., 38*: 218 (1975).

290. S. L. Swib, G. D. Stucky, and R. J. Bealtner, *J. Catal.*, *65*: 174 (1980).
291. S. L. Swibb, G. D. Stucky, and R. J. Bealtner, *J. Catal.*, *65*: 179 (1980).
292. A. N. Goldobin and V. I. Savchenko, *Kinet. Katal.*, *15*: 1363 (1974).
293. M. M. Bhasin, *J. Catal.*, *34*: 356 (1974).
294. D. M. Holloway, *J. Vac. Sci. Technol.*, *12*: 392 (1975).
295. M. P. Hooker and J. T. Grant, *Surf. Sci.*, *51*: 328 (1975).

# 7
# The Measurement of Catalyst Dispersion

JACQUES L. LEMAITRE Université Catholique de Louvain, Louvain-la-Neuve, Belgium

P. GOVIND MENON Rijksuniversiteit Gent, Gent, Belgium

FRANCIS DELANNAY Université Catholique de Louvain, Louvain-la-Neuve, Belgium

## I. INTRODUCTION

Heterogeneous catalysts used in industrial practice are usually multicomponent systems. Indeed, most industrial processes (especially those handling gaseous reactants) require catalysts exhibiting a variety of properties that can be obtained only by the combination of several phases. Besides a good catalytic activity, the following properties may be mentioned: an appropriate porous structure which, by controlling the diffusion of reactants and products, allows the control of selectivity; a suitable physical form (irregular particles, extrudates, pellets, rings, or powder) in order to minimize the pressure drop through the catalyst bed or to allow fluidized-bed operation; good crushing and attrition resistance so as to minimize catalyst losses due to dust formation; and so on.

The activity of heterogeneous catalysts is known to be mainly a surface property. It is therefore often possible to reduce the amount of active component without affecting the overall activity by increasing its surface-to-volume ratio (e.g., by spreading it onto the surface of a suitable carrier). This surface-to-volume ratio of the active component is usually referred to as its dispersion.

Optimum dispersion is of particular economic importance in the case of supported catalysts containing expensive active substances such as noble metals. Indeed, the price of such catalysts is usually charged on a double basis: price per kilogram of catalyst plus price of the precious metal contained in it. For instance, in April 1982, a typical $Pt/Al_2O_3$ reforming catalyst containing 0.6 wt % Pt per kilogram of catalyst cost about $10 for the alumina carrier plus $84 for the 6 g of platinum. A Pt/$Al_2O_3$ catalyst containing only 0.3 wt % Pt with a dispersion improved by a factor of 2 would exhibit the same activity as the former but cost only about half of the price cited above.

During the course of their working life, catalysts may suffer a more or less rapid deactivation. The deactivation process may have various causes, such as coke formation, poisoning of the active sites by deposition of impurities (S, As, Pb) present in trace amounts in the feedstock, or decrease of dispersion due to agglomeration and growth in size (sintering) of the active particles. One of the roles of the carrier may be, in the latter case, to prevent sintering by firmly anchoring onto it the particles of the active phase.

The considerations above illustrate the practical importance of dispersion measurements: they will allow the catalyst manufacturer to control the quality of his products, and the customer to choose the best catalyst at the lower cost. In addition, they can give the user some clue to the origin of deactivation and help him or her to find appropriate remedies.

Dispersion measurements are also of prime importance for scientists studying reaction mechanisms. Proper interpretation of heterogeneously catalyzed reaction kinetics requires a precise knowledge of the number of active atoms exposed on the surface. Indeed, it is by the study of the variation of the activity per exposed active site as a function of the reaction conditions that catalysts may be compared and reaction mechanisms may be disclosed.

The most common technique for measuring dispersion is the selective chemisorption of a suitable gas onto the surface of the active component. The assessment of the accuracy of this method requires, however, complementary measurements using other independent methods. In addition, chemisorption techniques are generally of little use for nonmetallic catalysts. The other major methods for dispersion measurements are based on X-ray diffraction, photoelectron spectroscopy, and electron microscopy. (Magnetic susceptibility will not be considered, as its use is restricted to catalysts containing metallic nickel as the active component.) The aim of this chapter is to introduce the principles of dispersion studies by use of these various methods and to show how the methods can be combined to give a coherent picture of the catalyst being studied.

In Sec. II the concepts of dispersion and active phase are defined in a more precise way and their relations to particle size are discussed. This section also deals with the principles of particle size analysis which are relevant to dispersion studies.

The major experimental techniques are presented in Sec. III. The aim of Sec. IV is to illustrate, on the basis of selected examples, how different techniques may complement and support each other. This section serves as a critical evaluation of the methodology to be followed for assessing the accuracy of dispersion measurements.

Finally, some recent aspects of the application of chemisorption methods to major supported catalyst systems are presented in Sec. V.

## II. CONCEPTS

### A. Definitions

#### 1. Active Phase

The catalytically active component of a supported catalyst is often concentrated in a separate phase (in the thermodynamic sense) distinguishable from the inactive carrier. This is clearly the case for supported metal catalysts, in which the active component is concentrated in metallic particles well characterized by several physicochemical techniques (electron microscopy, X-ray diffraction). The situation, however, is not always so clear. In catalysts such as $MoO_3/Al_2O_3$ (especially for low-$MoO_3$ loadings) no separate phase into which the active molybdenum is concentrated can be found by any technique. There is strong evidence that $MoO_3$ is spread onto the carrier surface in the form of a two-dimensional adlayer (e.g., Ref. 1). In such a case, the strict concept of active phase vanishes and a more general term such as "active fraction" would be more appropriate, since this concept does not contain any assumption about the physical form (three-dimensional particles or surface adlayer) of the active component.

#### 2. Dispersion

In practice, the dispersion D of the active fraction of a catalyst will be defined by the equation

$$D = \frac{N_s}{N_{tot}} \tag{1}$$

where $N_s$ is the number of the active atoms exposed at the surface and $N_{tot}$ is the total number of active atoms present in the catalyst. The values of $N_s$ and $N_{tot}$ defined in this way differ according to the experimental approach. As concerns $N_s$, it is clear that the nature of the "surface atoms" varies according to the technique. For instance, chemisorption techniques consider only those atoms actually exposed to the gas phase, while X-ray diffraction cannot distinguish these atoms situated at the solid-gas interface from those situated at a solid-solid interface (e.g., active phase-carrier interface). Obviously, the latter atoms are not active sites for the catalytic reaction. Insofar as a correlation between dispersion and catalytic activity is studied, the most relevant value of $N_s$ will be given by chemisorption, as it involves only atoms accessible to gaseous molecules.

The value of $N_{tot}$ may also differ according to the technique adopted. When using chemisorption methods, $N_{tot}$ will usually be simply the total number of potentially active atoms incorporated into the catalyst as a whole as it can be determined by bulk chemical analysis. When measuring the dispersion of supported metal catalysts by X-ray diffraction or electron microscopy, $N_{tot}$ will be the reduced fraction of the supported phase and will exclude, for instance, the atoms combined chemically with the carrier or with other inactive phases.

It follows that the definition of D given by (1) is somewhat "operational" and that D may have different meanings according to the different cases. From the point of view of catalytic reaction, the most useful value of D is, of course, the value provided by the chemisorption method. However, comparison of D values obtained by different methods will often be helpful to identify phenomena such as irreversible adsorption of the probe gas or poisoning of the active sites. In addition, it may sometimes be necessary to determine the dispersion of a phase without consideration for the catalytic activity (e.g., when it is desired to control the dispersion of the successive precursors produced in the course of catalyst manufacture).

## B. Relation Between Dispersion and Particle Size

In systems, such as supported metal catalysts, where the active fraction is present as separate particles distinguishable from the carrier, a definite relationship exists between the dispersion D and the size of the active particles.

Let V be the total volume of the active fraction (or phase) and S its surface area. Relation (1) defining dispersion may then be written as

$$D = \frac{fA}{\rho \sigma N} \frac{S}{V} \tag{2}$$

where A is the atomic weight of the active atoms, $\rho$ the specific mass (or density) of the active phase, $\sigma$ the average surface area occupied by one active atom at the surface, N is Avogadro's number, and f is the fraction of the surface of the active phase which is effectively exposed to the reactants during the catalytic reaction.

The dimension of V/S is a length that is proportional to some size characterizing the active particles contained in the catalyst. To illustrate this point, let us assume that all supported particles are identical spheres of diameter d. One calculates easily that, in such a case,

$$\frac{S}{V} = \frac{6}{d} \tag{3a}$$

In general, when particles have different sizes, one will write

$$\frac{S}{V} = \frac{g}{d_s} \tag{3b}$$

where g is a factor that depends on the shape of the particles and $d_s$ is a characteristic size, the significance of which will be discussed in more detail in Sec. II.C. Relation (2) then becomes

$$D = \frac{cf}{d_s} \tag{4}$$

with

$$c = \frac{gA}{\rho \sigma N}$$

As D may not be higher than 1, this relation is valid provided that

$$d_s = g\frac{V}{S} \geqslant \frac{fgA}{\rho \sigma N} \tag{5}$$

Below this limit, the active phase becomes a pure surface species for which, by definition, D = 1.

The concept of dispersion D is thus directly related to the concept of particle size. However, this relationship implies a precise knowledge of the nature of the active phase (its molecular weight A and its specific mass $\rho$), of its shape (through the geometric factor g), of its crystallographic structure (through $\sigma$), and of the extent of the active phase/carrier interface (through f). In addition, relations (2) and (4) become invalid even when condition (5) is fulfilled if only a fraction of the exposed atoms are actually active, owing either to an incomplete activation treatment or partial poisoning of the catalyst. In such a case, there would be no obvious relationship between dispersion and size of the active particles. The ratio of the number of catalytically active sites to the number of atoms of active component present in the catalyst is then the only useful estimate of the efficiency of the catalyst.

### C. Particle Size Analysis

The active fraction of a supported catalyst sometimes consists of particles exhibiting a very high degree of homogeneity with respect to particle size. Such a sample is said to be *monodispersed*. Most catalysts, however, exhibit a variety of particle sizes. The description of such "polydispersed" systems requires the use of statistical methods.

A detailed discussion of these methods would be outside the scope of the present chapter. Only basic principles will be presented in this section. The topics of statistical distribution functions (normal, log-normal) and statistical precision are dealt with separately in Appendixes 1 and 2, respectively. For a more detailed discussion, the reader may consult the appropriate literature [2-4].

The characterization of a "population" of particles exhibiting different sizes may follow different approaches according to the experimental techniques available. Microscopic techniques allow the determination of the size (and shape) of a discrete number of these particles. These data may serve to estimate various "average" parameters of the overall population. On the other hand, techniques such as chemisorption or X-ray diffraction provide directly one of these "average" parameters of the population. It may be shown (see Appendix 1) that the knowledge of only two such parameters may be sufficient to characterize completely the size distribution when it obeys some well-defined probability functions.

### 1. Particle Size and Shape

Supported catalyst particles are usually found to have very simple shapes: spheres or hemispheres are most common, cubes and plates less frequently observed. Therefore, only spherical particles will be considered in what follows (unless otherwise stated). The characteristic size will be simply the diameter of the spheres. A detailed discussion on how to define the size in the case of more complicated shapes may be found in Ref. 3.

### 2. Particle Size Distribution

The most direct way of characterizing a polydispersed population of particles is the measurement of the size of a fairly large number of particles chosen at random in, for instance, an electron micrograph. The number of measurements (also referred to as the "sample") must be large enough so as to be sufficiently representative of the total population. Some considerations about statistical precision will be given later (see Appendix 2). Such a large amount of data has then to be condensed to allow easier handling of the information. This operation, known as classification, consists of sorting the measured sizes into a limited number of classes (commonly 10 to 20). An example is given in Table 1, where a hypothetical set of 500 particles has been sorted into 16 classes.

Each class i is represented by its class mark and comprises a number $n_i$ of particles whose size lie between the class boundaries of the ith class. One may tabulate in this way the frequency of observation of particles of each class. This is known as the frequency distribution of the sample. One may also calculate the total surface area developed by the particles of each class (which is proportional to $n_i d_i^2$)

TABLE 1 Classification of a Set of 500 Spherical Particles into 16 Classes

| Class boundaries $\leqslant d <$ (nm) | Class mark $d_i$(nm) | Number in class $n_i$ | Fraction in class $f_{n,i}$ | Total number with $d < d_i$ | Surface fraction $f_{s,i}$ | Volume fraction $f_{v,i}$ |
|---|---|---|---|---|---|---|
| 2.25-2.75 | 2.5 | 2 | 0.003 | 2 | 0.001 | 0.000 |
| 2.75-3.25 | 3.0 | 9 | 0.018 | 11 | 0.005 | 0.003 |
| 3.25-3.75 | 3.5 | 28 | 0.057 | 39 | 0.023 | 0.013 |
| 3.75-4.25 | 4.0 | 55 | 0.111 | 94 | 0.058 | 0.039 |
| 4.25-4.75 | 4.5 | 77 | 0.154 | 171 | 0.103 | 0.078 |
| 4.75-5.25 | 5.0 | 84 | 0.168 | 255 | 0.139 | 0.117 |
| 5.25-5.75 | 5.5 | 76 | 0.152 | 331 | 0.152 | 0.141 |
| 5.75-6.25 | 6.0 | 60 | 0.120 | 391 | 0.143 | 0.144 |
| 6.25-6.75 | 6.5 | 43 | 0.085 | 434 | 0.120 | 0.132 |
| 6.75-7.25 | 7.0 | 28 | 0.056 | 462 | 0.091 | 0.107 |
| 7.25-7.75 | 7.5 | 17 | 0.034 | 479 | 0.063 | 0.080 |
| 7.75-8.25 | 8.0 | 10 | 0.020 | 489 | 0.042 | 0.057 |
| 8.25-8.75 | 8.5 | 5 | 0.011 | 494 | 0.024 | 0.034 |
| 8.75-9.25 | 9.0 | 3 | 0.006 | 497 | 0.016 | 0.024 |
| 9.25-9.75 | 9.5 | 2 | 0.003 | 499 | 0.012 | 0.019 |
| 9.75-10.25 | 10.0 | 1 | 0.002 | 500 | 0.007 | 0.011 |

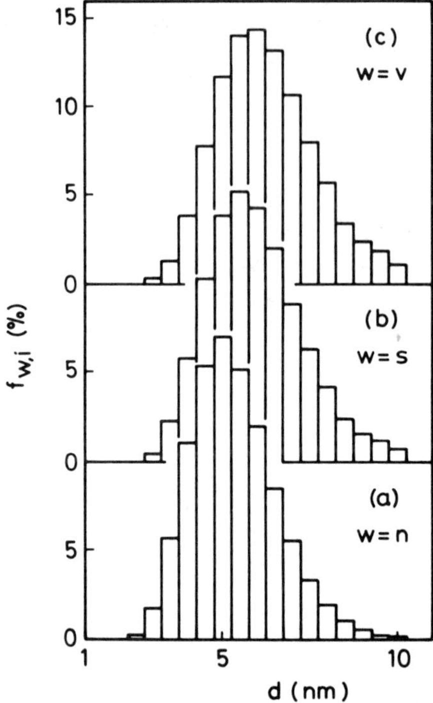


FIG. 1. Histograms of the distributions of (a) frequency $f_{n,i}$, (b) surface $f_{s,i}$, and (c) volume $f_{v,i}$ corresponding to the classification of Table 1.

or the total volume of these particles (which is proportional to $n_i d_i^3$). One then obtains the fraction of the surface area or of the volume which is due to each class. These various distributions (of frequency, surface area, or volume), as a function of the size, may be represented graphically as histograms, as shown in Fig. 1.

3. Mean Particle Size

Let us first consider only the frequency distribution of the sample. The information contained in this distribution allows the estimation of important parameters of the population. The mean and standard deviation are the most useful of these parameters. Assuming a sample of polydispersed particles exhibiting a frequency distribution $n_i(d_i)$, the *sample mean* $\langle d_n \rangle$ is defined as

$$\langle d_n \rangle = \frac{\Sigma\, n_i d_i}{\Sigma\, n_i} \tag{6}$$

where $\Sigma$ denotes the summation over all classes i. It is evident that $<d_n>$ tends to be equal to the mean (or arithmetic mean) $d_n$ of the population when the number of measured sizes tends toward infinity. This mean is also referred to as the *number-average size.*

In statistical terms, the sample mean $<d_n>$ is said to be the "estimation" of the mean $d_n$. The mean may also be defined as the *first moment about the origin,* the estimation of the nth moment about the origin being

$$<^n d> = \frac{\Sigma\, n_i d_i^n}{\Sigma\, n_i} \tag{7}$$

The sample standard deviation is defined as

$$s_n = \left[\frac{\Sigma\, n_i (d_i - d_n)^2}{\Sigma\, n_i}\right]^{1/2} \tag{8}$$

It is thus equal to the square root of the second moment of the sample about the mean. It tends toward the standard deviation $\sigma_n$ of the population when the number of measured sizes increases (i.e., $s_n$ is an estimation of $\sigma_n$).

It is often convenient to consider the logarithm of the particle size rather than the size itself. The sample mean $\ln <d_g>$ of the distribution of the logarithms of the measured sizes is thus, from (6),

$$\ln <d_g> = \frac{\Sigma\, n_i \ln d_i}{\Sigma\, n_i} \tag{9}$$

taking

$$f_i = \frac{n_i}{\Sigma\, n_i} \tag{10}$$

and applying the rules of logarithms, one obtains

$$<d_g> = \Pi\, d_i^{f_i} \tag{11}$$

where $\Pi$ denotes the product over all terms. Parameter $<d_g>$ is referred to as the *geometric mean* of the sample, $d_g$ being the geometric mean of the population.

Similarly, the *geometric standard deviation* of the sample $s_g$ may be obtained from the sample standard deviation ln $s_g$ of the logarithms of the size as

$$s_g = \exp\left[\frac{\Sigma\, n_i(\ln d_i - \ln \langle d_g \rangle)^2}{\Sigma\, n_i}\right]^{1/2} \tag{12}$$

The reader may check that $\langle d_n \rangle$ and $\langle d_g \rangle$ are not identical in polydispersed samples, by calculating these two estimations for the hypothetical distribution given in Table 1. In general, it will appear that

$$\langle d_g \rangle \leqslant \langle d_n \rangle$$

4. Average Sizes Relevant to Dispersion Studies

It was shown already that when the active phase is concentrated into separate particles, the dispersion D varies as the reciprocal of a characteristic size $d_s$ (see Eqs. 3 and 4) proportional to the volume-to-surface ratio of the active phase. When a sample of sizes has been measured by a microscopic technique, relation (3) suggests that $d_s$ may be estimated from the frequency distribution as

$$\langle d_s \rangle = \frac{\Sigma\, n_i d_i^3}{\Sigma\, n_i d_i^2} \tag{13}$$

It may easily be verified that g, in (3), is equal to 6 for both spheres and cubes when $d_i$ is the diameter of the spheres or the edge length of the cubes, respectively.

It is noteworthy that relation (13) is obtained from relation (6) by substituting $n_i d_i^2$ for $n_i$. Thus $\langle d_s \rangle$ is equal to the sample mean of the distribution of the surface area as a function of the size of the particles (Fig. 1b). For this reason, $d_s$ is usually called the *surface-average size*.

It will be seen in Sec. III that the data on dispersion provided by chemisorption, X-ray diffraction, or XPS may usually be translated into a characteristic "average" size of the populations of particles. This average will differ according to the technique as the sensitivity of each technique to the size of the particles differ according to the physical principle upon which it is based. Methods such as chemisorption or XPS, which are primarily sensitive to the surface of the particles, provide the surface-average size $d_s$. But a method such as X-ray line broadening, being sensitive to the bulk of the particles,

TABLE 2 Various Definitions of Average Particle Size

| Name | Symbol | Estimator | Techniques[a] |
| --- | --- | --- | --- |
| Number of average (or arithmetic mean) | $d_n$ | $\Sigma n_i d_i / \Sigma n_i$ | — |
| Surface average | $d_s$ | $\Sigma n_i d_i^3 / \Sigma n_i d_i^2$ | Chemisorption, XLBA, SAXS, XPS[b] |
| Volume average | $d_v$ | $\Sigma n_i d_i^4 / \Sigma n_i d_i^3$ | XLBA |
| Geometric average (or geometric mean) | $d_g$ | $\exp [\Sigma n_i \ln d_i / \Sigma n_i]$ | SAXS[b] |

[a]All the averages can be estimated from the size distribution measured by electron microscopy.
[b]As far as some conditions are fulfilled, see details in Sec. III.

TABLE 3 Various Average Sizes (nm) Estimated from the Hypothetical Distribution Presented in Table 1

| | |
|---|---|
| $s_n$ | 1.25 |
| $\langle d_g \rangle$ | 5.2 |
| $\langle d_n \rangle$ | 5.4 |
| $\langle d_s \rangle$ | 6.0 |
| $\langle d_v \rangle$ | 6.3 |

provides the so-called volume-average size $d_v$ (which is the mean of the distribution of the volume of the active fraction as a function of the size). Table 2 summarizes the various definitions of average size relevant to the various experimental techniques and shows how these averages may be estimated from a sample of sizes (measured by microscopy) for comparison between the techniques.

Table 3 presents the values of the various average sizes estimated from the hypothetical distribution given in Table 1. Significant differences between these values are found. Of course, all averages would have been identical for a monodispersed sample. The differences observed follow from the polydispersed character of the sample under study. The more spread the particle size distribution the larger would be these differences.

## III. EXPERIMENTAL TECHNIQUES

### A. Chemisorption

Chemisorption is undoubtedly the most used technique for the measurement of catalyst dispersion. Only fundamental principles and instrumental aspects will be presented in this section. More specialized considerations will be dealt with in Sec. V.

#### 1. The Physical and Chemical Aspects of the Chemisorption Method

*a. Elementary Concepts of Adsorption.* The kinetic theory of gases gives us the picture of innumerable molecules of the gas (or atoms in the case of inert gases) moving in all directions in straight lines. These molecules collide with one another and also with the walls of the containing vessel in a never-ending sequence. The molecules, which collide with the surface, may stick to it for a very short interval of time before bouncing back to the gas phase. In that case, at any instant there will be an excess of gas molecules on the surface as compared to a corresponding volume element in the bulk of the gas, as shown in Fig. 2. This excess gas on the surface is usually regarded as the adsorbed amount.

It has to be emphasized here that there are no special adsorption forces. The intermolecular forces or van der Waals forces are well known to cause the cohesion of molecules in liquids and solids, the liquefaction of gases, and the deviation of real gases from the laws of ideal gases; these very same forces also cause *physical adsorption* of a gas on a solid. Similarly, the valency forces, which lead to combinations of chemical elements to form compounds, can also cause surface combinations between elements on the surface of a solid and molecules (atoms) of a reactive gas or vapor. This is called *chemical adsorption* or *chemisorption*. If the interacting surface atom and the gas molecules more or less retain their identities, the phenomenon is generally regarded as physical adsorption. On the other hand, if the gas (or vapor) molecule splits up into atoms, radicals, or ions which are separately adsorbed on the surface atoms (or sites), or if an electron transfer or electron sharing occurs between the solid adsorbent and the adsorbate, the phenomenon is usually considered as chemisorption. The major differences between these two types of adsorption are summarized in Table 4. Detailed discussions of adsorption phenomena are given in several excellent monographs [5-7]; hence they will not be discussed any further here.

*b. Selective Chemisorption.* Physical adsorption is nonselective; for example, nitrogen can adsorb on any surface at sufficiently low temperatures (<100 K). Although the adsorption of nitrogen and other gases at low temperatures may lead to multilayer or multimolecular adsorption on a solid substance, a value for only the unimolecular coverage of the *entire* surface of the solid can be derived from the adsorption data. This is the basis of Brunauer-Emmett-Teller (BET)

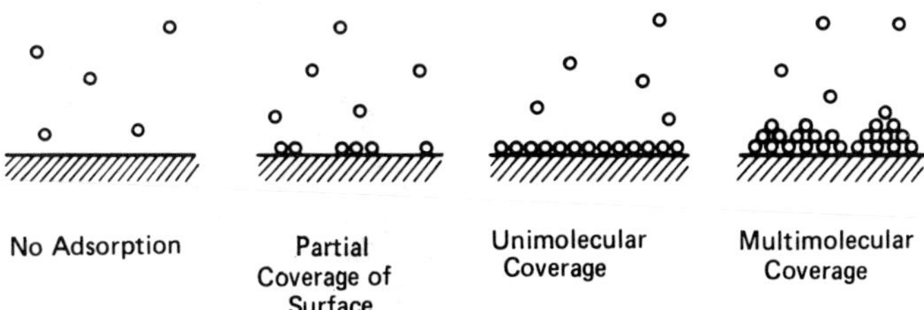


FIG. 2. Schematic representation of adsorption of a gas on a solid surface.

TABLE 4 Major Differences Between Physical Adsorption and Chemisorption

| Physical adsorption | Chemisorption |
|---|---|
| 1. Caused by van der Waals forces (no electron transfer) | 1. Caused by covalent/electrostatic forces (electron transfer/sharing occurs) |
| 2. Heat of adsorption 2 to 6 kcal/mol | 2. Heat of adsorption 10 to 200 kcal/mol |
| 3. A general phenomenon, such as the condensation of a gas | 3. Specific and selective |
| 4. Physisorbed layer removed by evacuation | 4. Removed only by evacuation and heating |
| 5. Multimolecular adsorption below the critical temperature of the gas | 5. Never exceeds a unimolecular layer |
| 6. Appreciable only below the critical temperature | 6. Often at high temperature also |
| 7. Rate: instantaneous | 7. May be fast or slow; sometimes involves an energy of activation |
| 8. Molecules adsorbed intact | 8. Dissociates into atoms, ions, or radicals |
| 9. Adsorbent not strongly affected | 9. Strongly affected (surface compound formation) |
| *10. There are many borderline cases* | |

method for the determination of the (total) surface area of finely divided solids, including microporous adsorbents or catalysts.

While the nonselective physical adsorption and the BET method were used to measure the total surface area of the entire solid, Emmett and Brunauer [8] developed specific chemisorption as a powerful tool to measure the areas of distinctly different chemical species exposed on the surface. The latter method became very useful in the case of supported metal catalysts and metal catalysts containing various promoters. An outstanding illustration of this is the classical work of Emmett and Brunauer [8] on the doubly promoted $Fe/Al_2O_3/K_2O$ catalyst for ammonia synthesis. In this case,

1. The chemisorption for $N_2$, $H_2$, $O_2$, or CO was specific for the exposed Fe surface only.
2. The chemisorption of $CO_2$ was specific for the $K_2O$ surface.
3. The difference between the total (BET) surface and the (Fe surface + $K_2O$ surface) gave the surface of $Al_2O_3$ alone.

The advent of catalytic reforming in the 1950s, using only 0.3 to 0.6 wt % of the precious metal platinum dispersed on a ($\gamma$ or $\eta$) alumina support, was a landmark in catalysis. It was soon imperative to know how well this precious metal was dispersed on the alumina. Afterall, only the exposed Pt atoms on the surface can come in contact with the hydrocarbon molecules; the Pt atoms that are inside the Pt crystallites are inaccessible to the reactant molecules and hence just wasted platinum. Furthermore, the performance of present-day reforming catalysts is so good that every exposed Pt atom on the catalyst surface effectively catalyzes the reactions of over 1 billion hydrocarbon molecules during the few years the catalyst will be in operation in a catalytic reformer plant. For optimum performance of the bifunctional reforming catalyst, a delicate balance has also to be maintained between the Pt-metal function and the acid function of the alumina. For these and other reasons a knowledge of the Pt dispersion became very valuable not only for comparison of activities of different reforming catalysts but also for periodic check on the performance of the catalyst in the plant. This problem was further highlighted when supported Pt catalysts soon found applications in other important petrochemical processes such as xylene isomerization, benzene hydrogenation (for manufacture of nylon), paraffin isomerization, and selective dehydrogenation of n-paraffins to n-olefins (for manufacture of biodegradable detergents).

Chemisorption of hydrogen on Pt is instantaneous at ambient temperature and it readily reaches a complete monolayer coverage on the exposed Pt surface. Hence the extent of the specific Pt surface could be easily measured by the $H_2$ chemisorption technique provided that the following three conditions are more or less fulfilled:

1. The H/Pt stoichiometry is assumed and a site density for H atoms on a Pt surface or the effective area per H atom on the surface is experimentally determined. The latter is usually done by a comparison of $H_2$ chemisorption with the BET surface area obtained from physical adsorption of $N_2$ or Kr on one and the same surface of pure Pt (in the form of Pt black or Pt powder).
2. The physical adsorption on the metal surface and on the support surface is negligible. (This is a reasonable assumption for $H_2$ as the adsorbate; for other gases, such as $N_2$ or CO, a correction for physical adsorption has to be subtracted from the totally measured adsorption on the composite catalyst surface; see Table 4.)

TABLE 5 Specific Chemisorption for Measurement of Metal Area

| Adsorbate | Advantages | Disadvantages | Metal | Preferred temperature (°C) |
|---|---|---|---|---|
| $H_2$ | Relatively simpler chemisorption; physical adsorption negligible; practically no adsorption on oxide carriers | 1. Possibility of dissolution, formation of hydrides<br>2. Sensitive to impurities | Pt | 0-20 |
| | | 3. Sometimes misleading results due to residual hydrogen in the catalyst after reduction at higher temperatures | Ni | −78, −195 |
| CO | Less chance for dissolution | 1. Physical adsorption at low temperatures | Pd, Pt | 25 |
| | | 2. Complications due to different structures of the chemisorbed species | Ni, Fe | −78, −195 |
| | | 3. Danger of carbonyl formation<br>4. Sensitive to impurities | Co | −78, −195 |

| | | | | |
|---|---|---|---|---|
| $O_2$ | Low adsorption on oxide carrier | 1. Physical adsorption at low temperatures | Pt, Ni | (25) |
| | | 2. Bulk oxidation at higher temperature, especially with Fe, Cr, and even Ni, Cu, Co, Pt, and Ag | Ag | (200) |
| $H_2S$<br>$CS_2$<br>Thiophene | Less danger of bulk compound (sulfide formation) | 1. Physical adsorption<br>2. Complex adsorption mechanism<br>3. Inaccessibility of very small pores | Ni | (40) |
| Dissociative adsorption of $N_2O$ | | | Cu<br>Ag | (25) |

*Source*: Adapted From Ref. 7.

3. The chemisorption of $H_2$ itself occurs without further complications like diffusion or dissolution of $H_2$ in the metal, spillover of hydrogen from the metal to the support, strong metal-support interaction, and so on. Such complications are often the cause for the deviation from ~1 of the H/Pt surface stoichiometry.

The advantages and disadvantages of using the chemisorption of $H_2$ and other gases for measurement of specific metal areas are summarized in Table 5. The limitations of the chemisorption technique, apart from those indicated in Table 5, are that most adsorbent gases are not so specific to one and only one metal. Hence this method often becomes inapplicable to multimetallic catalysts or catalysts with two or more components with rather similar chemisorption properties toward adsorbate gases. For monometallic supported catalysts, however, there is no cheaper or better alternative to specific chemisorption for measuring the metal area. Hence it is used almost universally these days. More important, comparison of catalytic activities of different catalysts (containing the same metal but in different amounts, or the same weight percent of the metal incorporated or impregnated in different ways) is meaningless unless the specific metal areas of these catalysts are also compared. This has led to the increasing use of the more quantitative kinetic term of turnover number or turnover frequency (i.e., molecules converted per exposed metal atom per unit time).

c. *Surface Titration Methods.* In 1965, Benson and Boudart [9] introduced a surface gas titration method to measure the dispersion of Pt on supported Pt catalysts. This method is based on the chemisorption of $H_2$ and $O_2$ on the exposed Pt atoms on the surface, as also on the reaction of $H_2$ with oxygen chemisorbed on Pt, and conversely the reaction of $O_2$ with hydrogen chemisorbed on Pt. All these surface reactions are carried out at room temperature. The stoichiometries of the chemisorptions and surface titrations, proposed by Benson and Boudart, are

$$Pt + (1/2)H_2 \longrightarrow Pt{-}H \qquad \text{(H chemisorption, HC)}$$

$$Pt + (1/2)O_2 \longrightarrow Pt{-}O \qquad \text{(O chemisorption, OC)}$$

$$Pt{-}O + (3/2)H_2 \longrightarrow Pt{-}H + H_2O \qquad \text{(H titration, HT)}$$

$$2Pt{-}H + (3/2)O_2 \longrightarrow 2Pt{-}O + H_2O \qquad \text{(O titration, OT)}$$

In the case of $Pt\text{-}Al_2O_3$ catalysts, the water formed is retained on the alumina and it does not interfere with the titration. With non-desiccant oxides as support (e.g., $TiO_2$) the water formed in the titration can be frozen out if necessary.

The $H_2$-$O_2$ titration method has been extended by Benson et al. [10] to measure Pd areas on supported Pd catalysts.

*d. Derivation of Metal Dispersion from Chemisorption Data.* The quantity of a gas (e.g., $H_2$, $O_2$, or CO) consumed during the chemisorption experiments discussed above (selective chemisorption, or $H_2$-$O_2$ titration) can be measured by use of the various techniques presented in the next section. The purpose of this section is to discuss briefly how dispersion may be derived from these measurements. Let U be the amount of gas consumed (in moles per gram of catalyst) and $\nu$ the stoichiometry of the reaction (i.e., the number of gaseous molecules reacting per surface atom of the metal). It follows from the definition of dispersion (relation 1) that

$$D = \frac{AU}{\nu W} \times 100\% \tag{14}$$

where W is the weight fraction of the metal in the catalyst and A its atomic weight (g/atom). In the case of hydrogen chemisorption on a supported Pt catalyst (A = 195 g/atom, $\nu = 0.5$), if $V_g$ is the volume of gas adsorbed in ml STP (1 mol = 22,400 ml STP), Eq. (14) becomes

$$D = 1.74 \frac{V_g}{W} \% \tag{15}$$

Another useful parameter that can be deduced from chemisorption measurements is the *metal surface area* per gram of catalyst

$$S_M = \nu^{-1} U N \sigma \quad m^2/g \tag{16}$$

where $\nu$ and U have the same meaning as above, N is Avogadro's number, and $\sigma$ ($m^2$/atom) is the area occupied by one surface atom. Values of $\sigma$ may be calculated from crystallographic data; some of them are given in Table 6 for metallic Pt and Ni, assuming different types of surface planes.

## 2. Experimental Techniques

*a. Volumetric Measurements.* The volumetric method with a fixed volume apparatus has been used for chemisorption measurements for the last 50 years or more. It is still the most common and popular technique. In its simplest form it is an all-glass unit consisting of a diffusion pump and a roughing pump for evacuating the catalyst sample, a gas burette for dosing the gas to the evacuated catalyst, a mercury manometer, McLeod gauge, or other pressure-measuring device, a detachable catalyst tube wherein a weighed quantity of catalyst

TABLE 6 Surface Area ($nm^2$) Occupied by Each Surface Atom in Metallic Pt and Ni for Different Sets of Crystallographic Planes[a]

| Planes | Pt | Ni |
|---|---|---|
| {100} | 0.0769 | 0.0621 |
| {110} | 0.1088 | 0.0878 |
| {111} | 0.0666 | 0.0537 |
| Average[b] | 0.0841 | 0.0679 |
| Average[c] | 0.0806 | 0.0651 |

[a]FCC structure with a = 0.3923 (Pt) or 0.3524 (Ni) nm.
[b]Assuming *same surface area* developed by {100}, {110}, and {111} planes.
[c]Assuming *same number of atoms* exposed on {100}, {110}, and {111} planes.

can be taken, and an oven to heat (calcine, reduce, etc.) the catalyst. After pretreatment and evacuation of the catalyst, a known quantity of the purified adsorbate gas is introduced into the system. When adsorption equilibrium is attained over the catalyst, the remaining gas in the system can be calculated from the pressure and the known volume of the system. The free volume or dead space in the catalyst tube and in the manometric part of the apparatus has to be determined with a practically nonadsorbable gas such as helium.

Detailed sketches and descriptions of static volumetric adsorption equipment can be seen in the monographs of Hayword and Trapnell [6], Ponec et al. [7], and Anderson [11]. Figure 3 shows a typical volumetric adsorption unit described by Lippens et al., who have also given details of the calculations involved for dead-space corrections, and so on. A static adsorption apparatus of modern design with an attached mass spectrometer described recently by Den Otter and Dautzenberg [13] is shown schematically in Fig. 4. Technical refinements include the elimination of mercury from the system, the use of greaseless stopcocks or valves, turbomolecular pumps for evacuation, more precise temperature control and pressure measurements, and so on.

In practice, the amount of gas (volume in $cm^3$ at 273 K and 1 bar pressure, or after it is converted to micromoles) adsorbed is measured at increasing pressures, with the catalyst maintained at a constant temperature. If a typical Langmuir-type adsorption isotherm is obtained (Fig. 5a), it is easy to intrapolate the isotherm to zero pressure and take the intercept on the ordinate as the amount of gas required to form a unimolecular coverage on the surface. But this method is

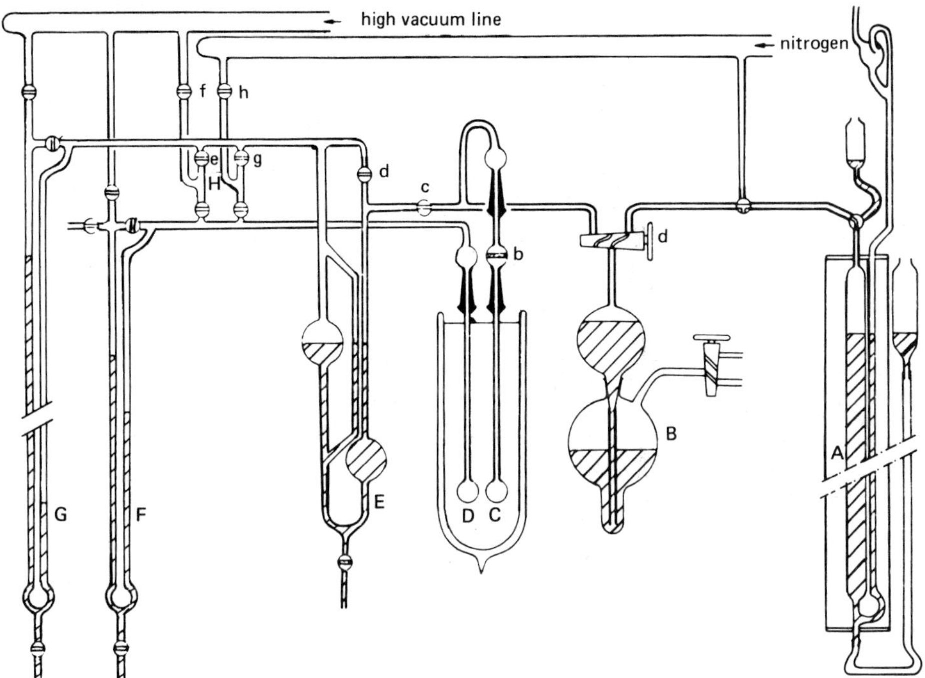


FIG. 3. Typical volumetric apparatus for adsorption measurements. A, 100-ml gas burette; B, mercury pump for transferring gas; C, bulb containing the catalyst; D, nitrogen vapor-pressure thermometer (usually only for physical adsorption measurements); E, capillary differential manometer; F and G, mercury manometers; H, pressure and vacuum locks. The high-vacuum line usually consists of a mercury or oil diffusion pump, backed by a two-stage rotary vacuum pump and a vacuum measuring device such as a McLeod gauge or Pirani/Penning gauges. (After Ref. 12.)

not always so easily applicable due to (1) the isotherm not showing a clear or nearly horizontal linear part, thereby making the intrapolation rather ambiguous, and (2) physical adsorption on the carrier, promoters, or other components of the catalysts also making a substantial contribution to the measured overall adsorption. The most commonly practiced method to overcome the two difficulties or uncertainties above is the one proposed by Emmett and Brunauer [8] in 1937 and illustrated in Fig. 5b. In this case the physically adsorbed amount is subtracted from the totally measured adsorption.

*b. Gravimetric Method.* In its principle, the gravimetric method is very similar to the volumetric method. The only difference is that

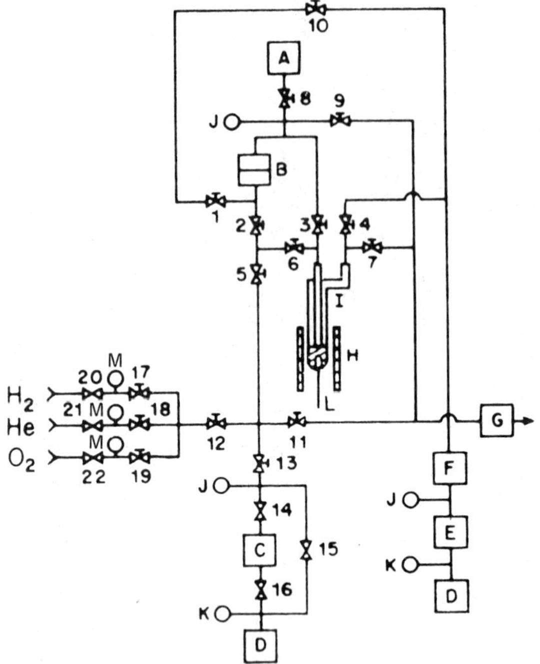


FIG. 4. Adsorption apparatus. A, Ionization pump; B, pressure transducer; C, oil diffusion pump; D, rotary vacuum pump; E, turbomolecular pump; F, mass spectrometer; G, flowmeter, H, furnace; I, quartz reactor; J, ionization gauge; K, pirani gauge; L, thermocouple; M, manometer; 1-10, high-vacuum bakable valves; 11-22, Hoke vacuum valves. (From Ref. 13.)

the amount of gas adsorbed is measured by directly weighting the sample. The early gravimetric method made use of a quartz-spring balance, the elongation of which as a function of weight could be measured accurately with a cathetometer. In the last two decades electrobalances have become quite popular; they are also commercially available.

The gravimetric system eliminates the dead-space determination with helium, which is necessary in the volumetric procedure. However, it is susceptible to vibrations. Buoyancy corrections are needed for measurements at higher pressures.

c. *Continuous-Flow Techniques*. Flow techniques and gas chromatography offer an alternative to the static volumetric or gravimetric chemisorption measurements. The advantages here are the elimination of the vacuum system and dead-space measurements, the

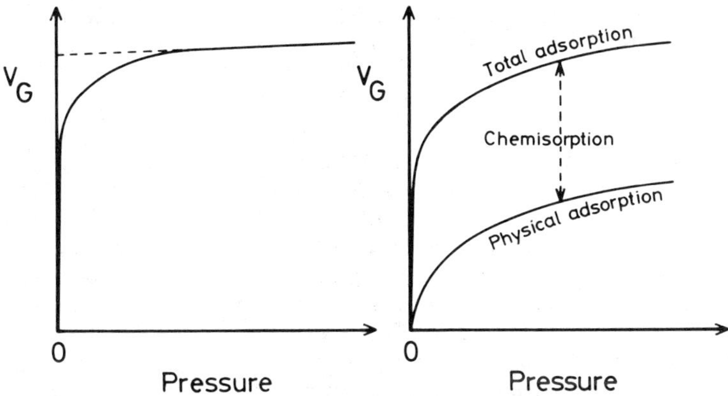


FIG. 5. Typical measurement of chemisorption: (a) intrapolation of Langmuir-type isotherm to zero pressure; (b) total adsorption at 90 K and physical adsorption at 90 K after evacuation at 195 K. The difference between the two gives the chemisorbed amount. (After Ref. 8.)

simplicity of present-day ready-made metal connections (in contrast with the all-glass systems), the speed and repeatability of the measurements, and so on. The disadvantages may be that weak chemisorption may be too reversible and hence may not be indicated, equilibrium may not be reached for slow or activated chemisorption, and so on. Comparison of data from the flow technique and the static volumetric technique will show if serious discrepancies arise due to the limitations noted above.

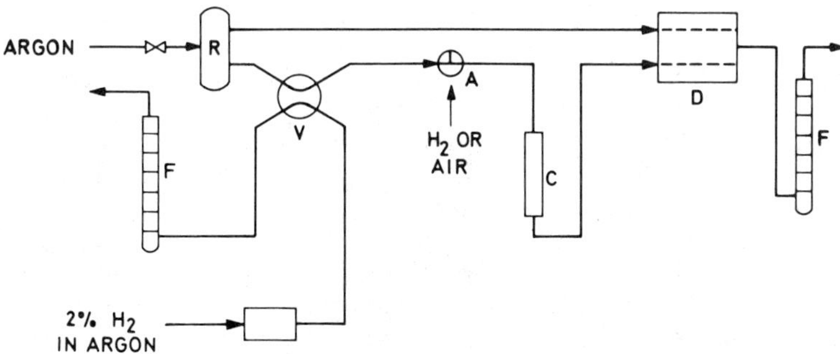


FIG. 6. Flow apparatus for chemisorption measurements. R, flow controllers; C, adsorption cell; D, thermal conductivity detector; F, soap-bubble flowmeters; V, four-way valve. (From Ref. 14.)

A simple flow apparatus, assembled from the usual hardware used in chromatographic studies and described in detail by Mears and Hansford [14], is shown in Fig. 6. The adsorption cell (10 mm o.d. × 15 cm long) can contain 10 to 20 g of catalyst. Following catalyst pretreatment, the reactor is flushed with argon. This argon stream and a 2% $H_2$ in argon stream (both 25 ml/min) can be interchanged in a four-way valve. To measure hydrogen adsorption, the flow is switched from argon to the 2% $H_2$-Ar mixture. The stream composition can be monitored by the thermal conductivity detector of a gas chromatograph until the $H_2$ content of the gas phase becomes constant. Argon purging for 15 min will then remove the reversibly adsorbed hydrogen from the support. The flow is once again switched to the $H_2$-Ar mixture to determine the dead volume plus any adsorption on the support. The difference in time for the two steps represents the hydrogen uptake by the metal catalyst alone.

The hydrogen uptake, U, in mol/g, is given by

$$U = \frac{xf_r(h_c - h_d)}{W} \frac{273}{Ta} \frac{Pa}{760} \frac{10^6}{22,414} \tag{17}$$

where $f_r$ is the flow rate of the $H_2$-Ar mixtures, x the mole fraction of $H_2$ in the mixture, $(h_c - h_d)$ the difference in breakthrough time, W the weight of the catalyst (dry basis), and Pa and Ta are the ambient pressure and temperature. Both the static and flow techniques can also be employed for surface gas titrations of the type discussed in Sec. III.A.1.c.

*d. Pulse Technique.* The pulse technique is in many respects derived from the flow technique. Buyanova et al. [15,16] have applied the gas chromatographic pulse technique for measurement of chemisorption of $H_2$ and $O_2$ on supported Ni and Pt catalysts. The results obtained by the pulse method have been found generally to be in good agreement with those from volumetric or gravimetric methods.

The Benson-Boudart gas titration of Pt surfaces has been adapted to the quicker gas-chromatographic pulse technique by Freel [17] and Menon et al. [18]. In this method a pulse of adsorbate gas is injected into the flow of inert gas over the reduced catalyst. The pulse volume is so chosen that a few pulses will be completely consumed by the catalyst bed. Knowing the pulse volume and the number of pulses consumed (= reacted + newly adsorbed on the metal surface), including fraction of pulses, the amount of gas chemisorbed by the catalyst to obtain a monolayer coverage on the exposed metal surface can be calculated.

The apparatus used for the GC pulse titration is shown schematically in Fig. 7. Only the thermal conductivity detector of the chromatograph is required here; no column for separation is employed.

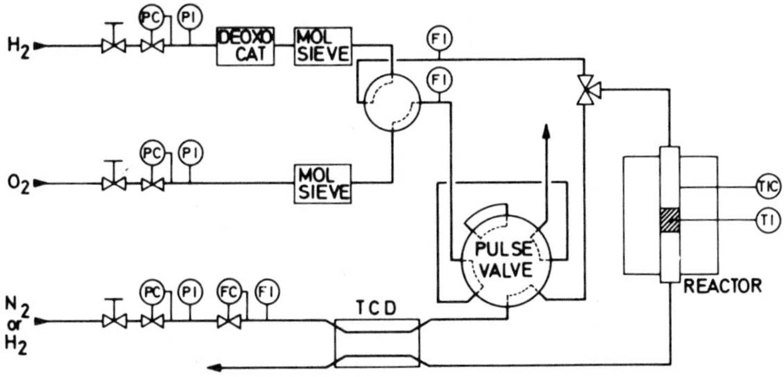


FIG. 7. Gas chromatographic setup for gas titration of metal surfaces. PC, pressure control; PI, manometer; FC, flow control; FI, rotameter; TI, thermocouple; TIC, temperature control. (From Ref. 18.)

Gas pulses (0.1 to 0.3 ml per pulse) can be sent into the carrier gas stream through an eight-way sampling valve. About 2 g of catalyst (broken into 1 mm size and calcined at 450°C for 1 h in air) is placed in the reactor. The hydrogen flow is started and the catalyst is slowly heated to 450°C, kept at that temperature for 2 h, and then cooled to room temperature in flowing hydrogen. The system is flushed with the carrier gas helium for 5 min. Oxygen pulsing is started with the catalyst at room temperature and continued at 2-min intervals until the oxygen peaks on the chromatograph are identical, indicating that no more oxygen is irreversibly adsorbed on the catalyst. Typical results of an oxygen pulse experiment are shown in Fig. 8. Knowing the volume per pulse, the amount of oxygen chemisorbed can be readily calculated. Once the Pt surface is saturated with oxygen, it can be titrated with pulses of hydrogen also, using nitrogen as the carrier gas. In practice, reproducible results can be obtained after only two or three oxygen-hydrogen cycles at room temperature. The $H_2$ titration of a Pt · · · O surface and the $O_2$ titration of a Pt · · · H surface give identical values for the chemisorbed quantity of gas and hence for the dispersion of Pt on the catalyst.

The pulse experimental setup can also be used for measurement of a specific Ni area [19]. In this case pulses of CO are sent over the catalyst at room temperature in a carrier gas stream of $H_2$ or He. Direct chemisorption of CO and not a surface titration is measured in this case. The specific metal surface area can be calculated taking the area occupied by a CO molecule on the Ni surface as 12 Å$^2$.

Another successful application of the pulse technique is the measurement of the dispersion of Pt and Re separately on the bimetallic Pt-Re-$Al_2O_3$ (Chevron-type) reforming catalyst. Menon et al. [18]

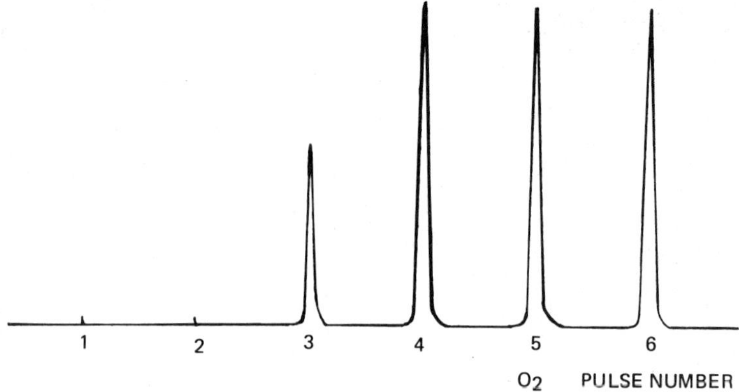


FIG. 8. Typical chromatogram for $O_2$ titration of a Pt-H surface. (From Ref. 18.)

found that, in contrast to Pt, the chemisorbed oxygen on Re could not be reduced by hydrogen at room temperature. Hence it was possible to determine oxygen chemisorption by Pt and Re separately in a Pt-Re-$Al_2O_3$ composite catalyst as follows (all at room temperature): (1) first oxygen pulsing gave chemisorption by Pt + Re; (2) subsequent reduction at 25°C converted Pt---O to Pt---H; (3) renewed oxygen pulsing gave chemisorption by Pt only; and (4) the difference between (1) and (3) gave the chemisorption by Re only. In practice, reproducible results could be obtained for step (1) after a second reduction at 450°C, and for step (3) after two or three oxygen-hydrogen cycles at room temperature. The chemisorption of $H_2$ or $O_2$ gases under the same conditions on the blank carrier alumina extrudates did not occur to any detectable extent; hence correction for the adsorption on the carrier, usual in volumetric methods, was unnecessary.

## B. X-Ray Diffraction and Scattering

### 1. Introduction

X-ray line broadening analysis (XLBA) is perhaps the oldest way to estimate the size of small crystallites, since the relationship between the latter and the width of diffraction lines was already recognized by Scherrer in 1918 [20]. Since that time, owing to the popularity of the X-ray diffraction technique and also to theoretical developments and computer facilities, XLBA has been applied in many fields, such as mineralogy, metallurgy, and ceramics. In its simplest form, it has been used for many years for characterizing heterogeneous catalysts in conjunction with chemisorption measurements [21]. More sophisticated uses of XLBA have recently led to the determination of size distributions of supported metals [22].

An alternative X-ray method for particle size determination consists of the analysis of small-angle X-ray scattering (SAXS). In a specimen, inhomogeneities in the range 50 to 500 nm will scatter X-rays exactly in the same way as atoms do. But as the sizes of the inhomogeneities are much larger than the wavelength of the radiation commonly used in X-ray diffraction analysis, the angles at which the scattering occurs are correspondingly small. With the usual copper $K_\alpha$ radiation (0.1542nm) the scattering will be confined in the region $2\theta < 2°$ ($2\theta$ is the scattering angle). The experimental separation of X-rays scattered by the specimen from the unscattered ones and those scattered by air and by the slits of the diffractometer is not an easy task.

The use of an especially designed instrument is therefore compulsory. A review of the instrumental aspects of SAXS has been made by Riley [23]. The basic theory has been developed by Guinier [24, 25] and by Fournet [26]. The first extended application in the field of heterogeneous catalysts is due to Whyte et al. [27]. The fundamental aspects of these two techniques will be outlined briefly in the following sections.

2. X-Ray Line Broadening Analysis (XLBA)

*a. Overall Description.* Scherrer [20] first showed that the broadening $\beta$ of the diffraction line corresponding to the Bragg angle $\theta$, using a wavelength $\lambda$, was related to the thickness t of the crystal in a direction perpendicular to the diffracting planes as

$$t = \frac{K\lambda}{\beta \cos \theta} \tag{18}$$

Actually, the pure diffraction broadening $\beta$ has to be derived from the experimental line breadth B by taking into account the instrumental broadening b. The latter is brought about by the imperfection of the diffractometer and is measured on a reference sample consisting of crystallites larger than 100 nm. The value of the constant factor K depends on the actual definition of $\beta$. A derivation of the Scherrer equation, together with a detailed discussion of the procedures for estimating the pure diffraction broadening $\beta$, are given in Ref. 28.

Two main definitions of $\beta$ are used: the full breadth at half maximum, $\beta_{1/2}$ (expressing $2\theta$ in radians) is the easiest to be measured; the integral breadth $\beta_i$ is the width of a rectangle having the same height and the same surface area as the observed line. The latter definition is the most fundamental one; it has been shown [28] that, irrespective of the detailed shape of the line profile, the average

TABLE 7 Values of the Scherrer Constant K

| Definition of the broadening | K |
|---|---|
| $\beta_{1/2}$, gaussian line | 0.89 |
| $\beta_{int}$ | 1.00 |

particle thickness t derived using $\beta_i$ is equal to the volume-average particle thickness $t_V$ of a polydispersed sample (see Table 2 and Sec. II.C). Values of the Scherrer constant K corresponding to the different definitions of $\beta$ are given in Table 7.

A simplified way to calculate $\beta$, knowing B and b, is given by the formula

$$\beta = (B^2 - b^2)^{1/2} \tag{19}$$

Equation (19) is valid if both the experimental and reference lines exhibit gaussian profiles. Treatments for nongaussian profiles can be found in Ref. 28.

A more detailed analysis of the X-ray line profile leads to the estimation, not only of the average crystallite size but also of their size distribution [29]. The derivation is based on the fact that if F(L) (with $L = \lambda/2 \sin \theta$) is the Fourier transform of the true line profile I(s) (with $s = 2 \sin \theta/\lambda$), then

$$\frac{d^2F(L)}{dL^2} = p_V(L) \tag{20}$$

The function $p_V(L)$ is the *volume distribution* as a function of the crystallite thickness measured in a direction perpendicular to the diffracting planes (see Sec. II.C). In other words, $p_V(L)$ represents the volume fraction of the crystallites having a thickness comprised between L and L + dL. Furthermore, it may be shown that

$$t_s = -\left[\frac{dF(L)}{dL}\right]_{L=0}^{-1} \tag{21}$$

where $t_s$ is the surface-average thickness of the crystallites (see Table 2). Relation (21) expresses that $t_s$ may be calculated from the initial slope of the Fourier transform of the line profile.

To simplify the discussion above, it has been assumed implicitly that the pure line broadening was only caused by the finite thickness of the crystallites. In fact, other causes of line broadening exist, among which the most important is the contribution of lattice strains. A complete treatment of powder diffraction data allowing for the separate estimation of particle size and lattice strains has been developed by Warren and Averbach [29]. A detailed procedure has been reported in Ref. 28. Recently, the Warren-Averbach method has been adapted to the characterization of supported metal catalysts by Ganesan et al. [22].

b. *Practical Aspects of XLBA.* Since the method rests on the analysis of X-ray diffraction lines, it is obviously restricted to the measurement of the size of crystalline particles. Therefore, XLBA can give some information on the dispersion of a supported catalyst only if it is in the form of a separate crystalline phase.

It is important to note here that the result of the application of the Scherrer formula (18) is a *crystallite thickness* (perpendicular to the diffracting planes) rather than an actual particle size. In order to derive the actual crystallite size from the thickness, it is necessary to apply a correction factor that depends on the actual shape of the crystallites and on the Miller indices of the diffracting planes. Values of the correction factor are given in Table 8 for some useful geometries [28].

Another important point to remember is that XLBA is a bulk analysis which is sensitive to all crystallites present in the sample, irrespective of their position either on the surface of the carrier or embedded in it (or of their actual accessibility to the gas phase). Therefore, the particle size estimated by XLBA might, in some cases, be smaller than the size derived from chemisorption measurements, as will be discussed in more detail in Sec. IV.

TABLE 8 Values of the Geometric Factor g, Such as $d = gt_{hkl}$

| Geometry of the crystallite | g | Definition of d |
|---|---|---|
| Sphere | 4/3 | Diameter |
| Hemisphere (basal plane parallel to hkl) | 8/3 | Diameter |
| Cube with {100} boundary faces, and: | | |
| hkl = 100 | 1 | Edge of the cube |
| 110 | 1.061 | Edge of the cube |
| 111 | 1.155 | Edge of the cube |

### 3. Small-Angle X-Ray Scattering (SAXS)

According to Guinier [24,25], provided that the diffraction angle $2\theta$ is sufficiently small, the radius of the diffraction centers (particles or pores) is related to the diffracted intensity as

$$\log_{10} I = -K'R_G X^2 \tag{22}$$

where $X = 2\theta$ is the diffraction angle (radian), I the normalized intensity ($I = 1$ for $X = 0$), $R_G$ the *radius of gyration* or the *Guinier radius* of the diffraction centers, and K' is a constant that depends on the geometry of the diffraction centers. For solid spheres,

$$K' = \frac{4\pi^2}{5\lambda^2} \log_{10} e \tag{23}$$

where $\lambda$ is the wavelength of the X-ray radiation and the other symbols have their usual meaning. The Guinier radius $R_G$ can thus be obtained from the slope $(-a)$ of $\log_{10} I$ at $X = 0$ as

$$R_G = \left(\frac{a}{K'}\right)^{1/2} \tag{24}$$

Equations (22) to (24) are valid only in the case of a dilute system consisting of identical, noninteracting, and randomly oriented diffraction centers.

In the case of supported heterogeneous catalysts, many supports contain scattering centers, such as micropores, having approximately the same size as the active particles. Since a definite interference exists between the two scattering systems (particles and pores), the contribution of the pores cannot be considered simply as a background radiation. A way to overcome this difficulty is to suppress the scattering by the pores by filling them with a liquid, called *pore maskant*, exhibiting an electronic density as close as possible to that of the catalyst support. This is due to the fact that the absolute intensity diffracted by a diffraction system, $I_{abs}$, is related to the normalized intensity I according to the equation

$$I_{abs} = I \Delta\rho_e^2 V_c^2 \tag{25}$$

where $\Delta\rho_e$ is the difference in electronic density between the diffracting centers and the continuous medium, and $V_c$ is the volume of these centers. In the case of $\eta$-alumina, for instance, a convenient pore maskant has been found to be methylene iodide ($CH_2I_2$) [27].

Care must be exercised to avoid an excess of pore maskant which would result in an increase of the background.

When the catalyst particles are polydispersed, the Guinier radius is an average radius [27] which can be estimated statistically by

$$\langle R_G^2 \rangle = \frac{\Sigma\, n_i r_i^7}{\Sigma\, n_i r_i^5} \tag{26}$$

where $r_i$ is the radius of spheres having the same volume as the particles. The volume $V_c$ in Eq. (25) is then an average volume which may be estimated by

$$\langle V_c^2 \rangle = \left(\frac{4\pi}{3}\right)^2 \frac{\Sigma\, n_i r_i^6}{\Sigma\, n_i} \tag{27}$$

Another type of average particle size is the Porod radius $R_p$ [27], which is obtained from SAXS data as

$$R_p = \frac{3}{2\pi^2} \frac{\int_0^\infty s^2 I(s)\, ds}{\lim_{s\to\infty} s^4 I(s)} \tag{28}$$

where $s = 2 \sin \theta/\lambda$ and the other symbols have their usual meanings. The Porod radius may be estimated as

$$\langle R_P \rangle = \frac{\Sigma\, n_i r_i^3}{\Sigma\, n_i r_i^2} \tag{29}$$

and thus corresponds to a surface-average radius (see Table 2).

If the distribution of the particle sizes is log-normal (see Appendix 1), it is possible to derive its parameters (geometric mean and standard deviation) from the knowledge of $R_G$ and $R_p$ [27] by using the expressions

$$\ln d_g = \ln 2R_G - 1.714 \ln \frac{R_G}{R_P} \tag{30}$$

and

$$(\ln \sigma_g)^2 = 0.286 \ln \frac{R_G}{R_P} \tag{31}$$

These relationships are easily demonstrated by considering Eqs. (28) and (29) and the properties of the log-normal distribution presented in Appendix 1. A more general theory applicable to any type of particle size distribution may be found in [30].

## C. Transmission Electron Microscopy

The principles of transmission electron microscopy and its application to the study of catalysts are detailed in Chap. 3. As concerns the observation of supported catalyst particles, the reader is especially referred to Sec. II.C. Only a brief review of the salient features will be presented here.

The concepts of polydispersion, particle size distribution, and average particle size have been dealt with in Sec. II. Some considerations about statistical precision will be found in Appendix 2. As pointed out by Flynn et al. [31], the measurement of a reliable particle size distribution from electron images is based on the three following implicit assumptions:

1. The size measured on the image is equal to the true size of the particle (multiplied by the magnification).
2. All particles have the same probability of being observed on the image, whatever their size.
3. Contrast arising from the support cannot be confused with contrast arising from the particles.

The resolving power of modern electron microscopes is currently within the range 0.5 to 0.3 nm. It has been demonstrated that isolated heavy atoms can indeed be imaged down to this size. In the case of supported catalysts, the visibility of the smallest particles will usually be hindered by the contrast arising from the support (unless the particles may be separated from the support by means an extraction replication method). The various imaging modes that may be used and the contrast effects governing the image are discussed at length in Chap. 3. Summarizing, it may be concluded that particle size distributions (measured on properly prepared electron transparent catalyst specimens) are increasingly subject to error when the proportion of particles smaller than some limiting size increases.

This limiting size depends essentially on the nature of both the supported particle and the support. Flynn et al. [31] set this limit at 2.5 nm in the case of Pt metal particles supported on $\gamma$-alumina. As explained in Chap. 3, this value may be used as a reference, allowing estimation of the limiting size relevant to other types of supported particles. The use of more amorphous supports, such as silica or carbon black, probably lowers the limit down to less than 2.0 nm.

It is worth stressing that supported particles smaller than this limit can usually be imaged. As a matter of fact, particle size distributions peaked at less than 2.0 nm are frequently found in the literature (e.g., Refs. 32 and 33). The present discussion suggests that such measurements may probably not be considered as faithful representations of the true particle size distribution. However, there is no doubt that they provide valuable qualitative estimates of the dispersion to be compared with chemisorption data. Indeed, it is worth noticing that a particle size of about 1.0 nm corresponds generally to 100% dispersion, as all atoms are exposed on the surface.

For the purpose of comparison with X-ray line broadening data, size distributions determined from dark-field images are likely to be more reliable. Indeed, the latter imaging mode gives the true *crystallite* size, whereas bright-field images provide generally the overall *particle* size (which is the size relevant to dispersion if the particle is nonporous).

The shape of the supported particles appears usually more or less spherical on electron images. The size $d_i$ may then be estimated as the diameter of the equivalent sphere. The occurrence of disk-shaped or raftlike structures has, however, been reported [32,34]. Such a type of structure maximizes the area/volume ratio. The possibility of obtaining a reliable evidence of their presence on electron images has been the subject of some controversy [35] which has enlightened the care to be exercised when interpreting contrast effects in TEM.

## D. XPS Peak Intensity Measurements

The possibility of assessing the dispersion of supported catalysts by XPS is a consequence of the surface sensitivity of this technique. Indeed, at constant loading, the number of photoelectrons $I_M$ escaping from the supported phase increases with decreasing particle size, whereas, at the same time, the XPS signal $I_S$ from the support decreases as the supported phase covers a larger fraction of the support surface. The intensity ratio $I_M/I_S$ of two peaks associated with the supported phase and with support, respectively, thus increases with increasing dispersion.

The chief merit of this method is that it can be applied to any catalytic system, without the requirement of crystallinity (as in XLBA), minimum particle size (as in TEM), or selectively adsorbing gas (as in chemisorption). This explains the extensive use of XPS intensity measurements for assessing dispersion of oxide and sulfide catalysts.

In the early works (e.g., Refs. 36 and 37), the ratio of the peak intensities was used only in a qualitative way to follow dispersion changes as a function of catalyst preparation or heat treatment. More recently, models have been developed that provide an analytical expression for the relationship between the XPS peak intensity ratio

$I_M/I_S$ and the dispersion of the supported phase [38-41]. These models presently allow a fairly reliable quantitative interpretation of the XPS data.

Details on these models may be found in Chap. 6 and in the original references. Most often, photoelectron lines with small differences in kinetic energy may be chosen for measuring $I_M$ and $I_S$. In such cases it may be considered that the inelastic mean free paths of the photoelectrons do not depend on the emitting atom but only on the type of material which scatters these electrons along their path to the surface. Defining $\lambda_M$ and $\lambda_S$ as the respective mean free paths in the supported phase and in the support, $I_M/I_S$ may then be expressed as a product of three factors:

$$\frac{I_M}{I_S} = Q_h F_S(S_S, \lambda_S) F_M(D, \lambda_M) \tag{32}$$

$Q_h$ is the intensity ratio that would be obtained if XPS was a bulk technique instead of a surface technique. It is thus also the ratio corresponding to a homogeneous solution of the two phases within each other. As the kinetic energies are similar, one may write simply

$$Q_h = \left(\frac{M}{S}\right)_b \frac{\sigma_M}{\sigma_S} \tag{33}$$

where $(M/S)_b$ is the overall bulk atomic ratio of the emitting atoms and $\sigma_M$ and $\sigma_S$ are the respective photoelectron cross sections.

The factor $F_s(S_S, \lambda_S)$ depends only on the nature of the support and on its specific surface area $S_S$. Analytical expressions for $F_S$ have been derived by representing the support as a stacking of identical sheets, spheres, or cubes [38,41]. For instance, the following expression was obtained in the case of sheets:

$$F_S = \frac{\eta(1 + e^{-\eta})}{2(1 - e^{-\eta})} \tag{34}$$

with

$$\eta = \frac{2}{\rho_S S_S \lambda_S} \tag{35}$$

where $\rho_S$ is the density of the support. The variation of $F_S$ as a function of $\eta$ according to (34) is shown in Fig. 9. It appears that $F_S = 1$ for $\eta \leqslant 1$ or $S_S \geqslant 2/\rho_S \lambda_S$.

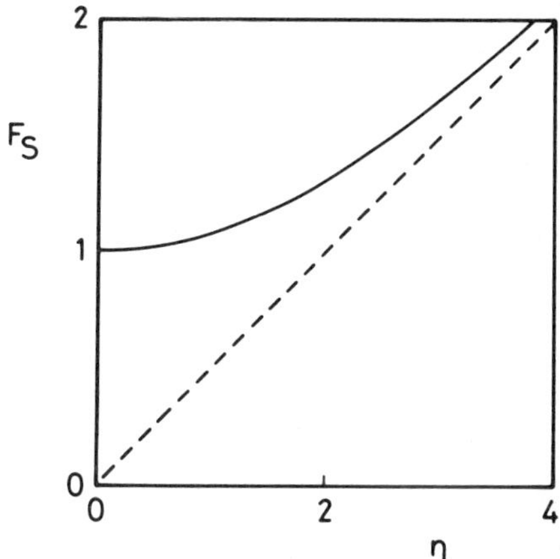


FIG. 9. Variation of the $F_S$ factor (relation 34).

The factor $F_M(D, \lambda_M)$ depends only on the nature of the supported phase and on its dispersion. Analytical expressions have been derived by assuming that the supported phase is made of identical cubes, spheres, or hemispheres [39,40]. In the case of cubes of edge d, one finds

$$F_M = \frac{1 - e^{-\alpha}}{\alpha} \tag{36}$$

with $\alpha = d/\lambda_M$. The variation of $F_M$ expressed by (36) is shown in Fig. 10. When the supported phase forms a monolayer, $\alpha \to 0$ and $F_M \to 1$ (e.g., from Eq. 36, $F_M = 0.9$ when $\alpha = 0.2$).

It was shown by Fung [39] that, in the case of polydispersion, the particle size d calculated from $I_M/I_S$ using an analytical expression for $F_M$ such as (36) is somewhat between the surface- and volume-average size. This follows from the fact that XPS is largely sensitive to the whole volume of the supported particles when $\lambda_M \geqslant d$, whereas it is mostly sensitive to the surface when $\lambda_M \ll d$. In this latter case, relation (36) reduces to $F_M = \lambda_M/d$ and the intensity ratio for a polydispersed system becomes [42]

$$\frac{I_M}{I_S} = \sum \frac{I_{Mi}}{I_S} = \sum \left(\frac{M_i}{S}\right)_b \frac{\sigma_M}{\sigma_S} F_X \frac{\lambda_M}{d_i} \tag{37}$$

As

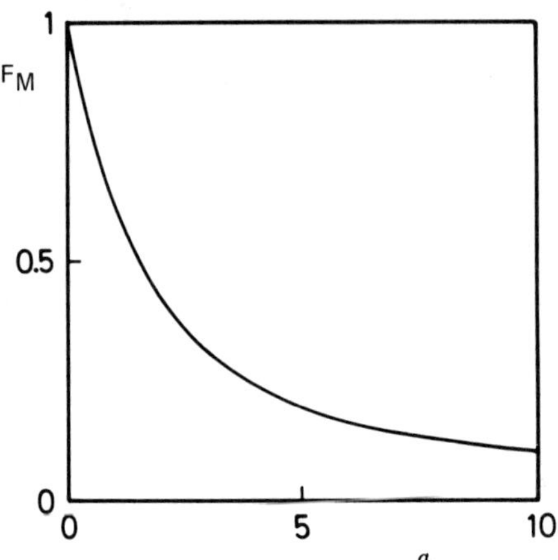


FIG. 10. Variation of the $F_M$ factor (relation 36).

$$\left(\frac{M_i}{S}\right)_b = \left(\frac{M}{S}\right)_b \frac{n_i d_i^3}{\Sigma\, n_i d_i^3}$$

one obtains

$$\frac{I_M}{I_S} = Q_h F_S \lambda_M \frac{\Sigma\, n_i d_i^2}{\Sigma\, n_i d_i^3} \qquad (38)$$

$$= \frac{Q_h F_S \lambda_M}{d_s}$$

There is no doubt that the expressions above allow convenient qualitative interpretations of the XPS data. Unfortunately, experimental studies aiming at quantitative assessment of the accuracy of this approach are still scarce. XPS has been extensively applied to the study of the dispersion of species "monoatomically" dispersed on the support. (In fact, it is often the only method available for the study of the dispersion of such species.) In such cases, experiments clearly support the variation of $I_M/I_S$ as $(M/S)_b$ (e.g., Refs. 39 and 40). The only systematic study of the influence of the surface area $S_S$ through the factor $F_S$ is the work of Defossé [41] on molybdenum oxide on alumina catalysts. Good agreement between theory and experiment was demonstrated for the sheet variant of the stacking model

(Eq. 34). The investigation of the variation of $I_M/I_S$ as a function of particle size through the factor $F_M$ requires the comparison of XPS data with particle size measurements provided by an independent method. Electron microscopy has been used by Fung [39] in the case of Pt crystallites on a silica film and by Houalla et al. [42] in the case of large NiO aggregates supported on a silica carrier. Good agreement was obtained. An example of comparison between XPS and chemisorption measurements will be dealt with in Sec. IV. More experimental support still appears necessary to establish more firmly the accuracy of the analytical expressions proposed for $F_M$.

An obstacle to the quantitative interpretation of XPS data today remains the fairly imprecise knowledge of the photoelectron cross sections $\sigma_M$ and $\sigma_S$ and electron mean free paths $\lambda_M$ and $\lambda_S$. XPS may be considered as a powerful tool for measuring relative dispersion differences within a series of similar catalysts. However, the precision of absolute measurements of the dispersion D from $I_m/I_s$ is presently most probably rather poor.

The interpretation of XPS intensity measurements may also suffer from possible limitations due to the sample itself. For instance, the supported phase may simultaneously exhibit several different forms (e.g., separate particles and monomolecular surface compound) whose contribution to the XPS signals cannot be separated. In addition, the XPS peak intensities may be strongly affected by an inhomogeneous partitioning of the supported phase within the support. The latter effect can hardly be accounted for within a model as it varies as a function of the preparation of the sample. (Grinding will tend to randomize the original partitioning [41]). Whenever possible, XPS measurement should thus be complemented by use of a method such as analytical electron microscopy, which can help to disclose heterogeneity within the sample [43-46]. A more detailed review of the use of the XPS for studying catalyst dispersion and partitioning may be found in Chap. 6.

## IV. ILLUSTRATIVE DISPERSION STUDIES

### A. Introduction

The aim of this section is to illustrate how the techniques presented in Sec. III can be used jointly for the characterization of the dispersion of practical catalysts. Before considering in detail typical experimental studies, it seems useful to propose a general scheme of the way in which dispersion is approached by the various investigation techniques. Such a scheme is presented in Fig. 11. For each technique, the nature of the primary data [step (a)], and the hypotheses involved in their interpretation [step (b)] are presented. The results are then usually expressed in terms of various average particle sizes [step (c)] except for chemisorption, where the dispersion D is directly

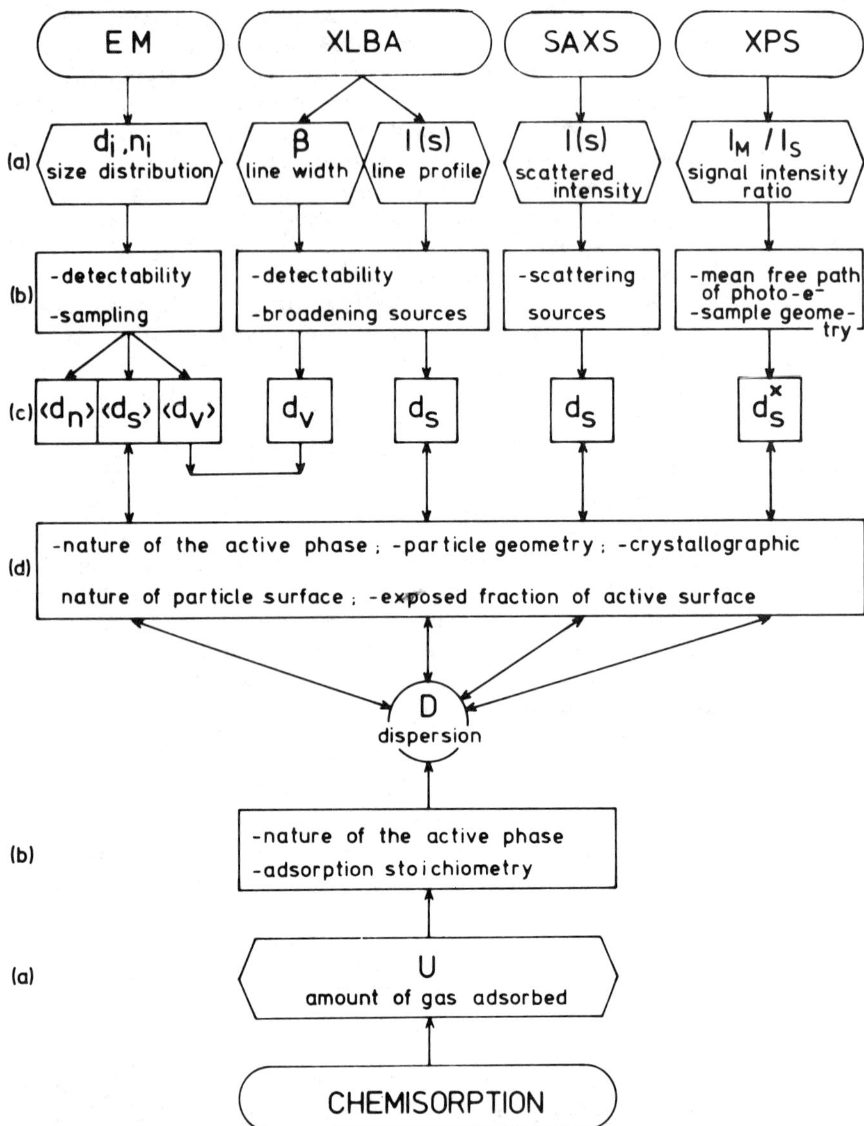


FIG. 11. General scheme of how dispersion D is approached through the various experimental methods.

obtained. Step (d) concerns the features of the system about which complementary data or hypotheses are necessary either to compare the average sizes provided by different methods or to correlate these sizes with the dispersion data obtained by chemisorption. In the case of electron microscopy, for instance, Fig. 11 shows that the primary data consist of a frequency distribution of the sizes of the catalyst particles [step (a)]. The observed particles represent correctly the whole population of particles if the sampling procedure is adequate and if no bias is brought about by detectability limits [step (b)]. Various average particle sizes are then estimated [step (c)]. The estimate of the surface average particle size $\langle d_s \rangle$ can then be correlated with the catalyst dispersion D measured by chemisorption, provided that the particle geometry, the nature of the active phase, and the fraction of its surface accessible to the gas phase are known or assumed [step (d)].

This scheme suggests that a valid comparison of dispersion values obtained from different investigation techniques is possible provided that some hypotheses are made at each step of the interpretation. Usually, these dispersion values are most easily compared by expressing them all in terms of an average particle size. Agreement is then a good indication that the set of hypotheses considered describes correctly the actual system. Discrepancies may result from incorrect hypotheses about the system [step (d)] but also from an inadequate interpretation of the primary data [step (b)]. New insight into the system under study may then be gained if the origin of the discrepancies can be disclosed.

There is always much to be learned about the catalyst when studying its dispersion by use of as many techniques as possible. However, such a comprehensive investigation is often impossible and one only requires an adequate method for routine measurements of dispersion. For metal catalysts, this method is most often based on chemisorption. Some of the "recipes" that have been proposed for application to major catalytic systems are discussed in Sec. V. The reliability of these recipes has usually been assessed in a study involving the joint use of several methods on a particular catalyst. As the similarity between catalyst samples can never be guaranteed, assessment of routine dispersion measurements by complementary techniques is always rewarding. In addition, such complementary measurements may help to disclose the origin of a deactivation phenomenon and suggest remedies.

Instead of presenting a mere summary of selected papers dealing with dispersion studies, the following subsection will show in some detail how dispersion and/or particle size estimates can be derived from the primary data reported in the original papers, using the methods presented in the preceding sections. The degree of agreement obtained among the different investigation techniques will then be discussed and our conclusions will be compared with those found in the original papers. Two systems will be examined successively in order of increasing complexity: the $Pt/SiO_2$ system, for which extensive studies have been performed using almost all the techniques presented in Sec. III, and the $Ni/SiO_2$ systems, for which detailed experimental data are available but the interpretations are not so well established.

## B. Experimental Studies

### 1. $Pt/SiO_2$ Catalysts

*a. Comparison of TEM, XLBA, and $H_2$ Chemisorption Measurements.* The early work of Adams et al. [21] will be examined first. The purpose of this work was to illustrate the applicability and limitations of electron microscopy, X-ray diffraction, and chemisorption measurements for measurement of the particle size of supported metals.

A 2.5 wt % $Pt/SiO_2$ catalyst was prepared by conventional impregnation by an aqueous solution of chloroplatinic acid (incipient wetness technique) followed by drying at 120°C and reduction in a stream of hydrogen (2 h at 210°C). The electron microscopic data are reported in Table 9.

The geometric mean and standard deviation may be estimated by applying Eqs. (9) and (12) as

$$\ln \langle d_g \rangle = 1.025 \qquad \langle d_g \rangle = 2.79 \text{ nm}$$

$$\ln^2 s_g = 0.0387$$

In the case of a log-normal distribution, $d_s$ and $d_v$ may be estimated from $\langle d_g \rangle$ and $s_g$ using Eqs. (45) and (46). These values

TABLE 9 Size Distribution of Platinum Particles

| Class mark diameter (nm) | Number in class | Frequency in class (%) |
|---|---|---|
| 1.5 | 10 | 1.0 |
| 2.0 | 111 | 11.8 |
| 2.5 | 309 | 32.8 |
| 3.0 | 300 | 31.8 |
| 3.5 | 171 | 18.2 |
| 4.0 | 32 | 3.4 |
| 4.5 | 9 | 1.0 |
| | 942 | 100.0 |

*Source:* Ref. 21.

are listed in Table 12, together with the values calculated by the authors of the original paper, using the definitions of $\langle d_s \rangle$ and $\langle d_v \rangle$ (see Table 2). The very good coincidence of these two derivations suggests that, in the present catalyst, the particles sizes are probably nearly log-normally distributed. The precision of the mean particle size, as calculated using Eq. (50), is 1.2%.

The XLBA data, namely the integral broadening and the resulting crystalline thicknesses for three different reflection planes, are presented in Table 10. In the two last columns of this table the particle sizes deduced from the crystallite thicknesses are reported, assuming that the particles are either spheres, or cubes with {100} boundary faces. Depending on the assumption made about the geometry of the particles, the calculated size varies considerably: from 3.42 (for cubes with {100} boundary faces) up to 5.04 (for spheres, using the 111 reflection).

The results obtained from hydrogen chemisorption are given in Table 11. The amount of hydrogen chemisorbed was not mentioned in the original paper; it was calculated back from the data found in the paper (metallic surface of the catalyst = 2.04 $m^2/g$; surface occupied by one $H_2$ molecule = 0.224 $nm^2$). The dispersion D may then be estimated from this calculated value ($1.51 \times 10^{-5}$ mol of $H_2$ per gram of catalyst) by use of Eq. (14), assuming that the stoichiometry of adsorption is 0.5 $H_2$ per surface Pt atom. This gives

$$D = \frac{195.1 \times 1.51 \times 10^{-5}}{0.5 \times 0.025} = 0.236$$

The average size $d_s$ is obtained in turn from relation (4). It is noted again that the particle sizes obtained depend markedly on the assumptions about the geometry of the particles (from 2.93 up to 4.77 nm).

TABLE 10 Results of XLBA ($\lambda$ = 0.1542 nm)

| Reflection khl | Integral breadth $\beta_i$ (rad) | Thickness $t_{hkl}$ (nm) | Particle size (nm) | |
|---|---|---|---|---|
| | | | $d_{cube}$[a] | $d_{sphere}$ |
| 111 | 0.0434[b] | 3.78 | 4.37 | 5.04 |
| 200 | 0.0490[b] | 3.42 | 3.42 | 4.56 |
| 220 | 0.0564 | 3.29 | 3.49 | 4.39 |

[a]Assuming {100} boundary faces.
[b]Average over two measurements.

TABLE 11 Particle Sizes Deduced from Chemisorption Measurements (nm): $d_s = fCD^{-1}$ (see Eq. 4)

| Boundary face {hkl} | Surface area per surface Pt,[a] σ $(nm)^2$ | C[b] (nm) | Particle size $d_s$ (nm) | |
|---|---|---|---|---|
| | | | Sphere | Cube[c] |
| {100} | 0.077 | 1.175 | — | 4.15 |
| {110} | 0.109 | 0.830 | — | 2.93 |
| {111} | 0.067 | 1.351 | — | 4.77 |
| — | 0.084[d] | 1.079 | 4.57 | 3.81 |

[a]From the original papcr.
[b]$C = gA/\rho\sigma N$; $\rho = 21.45\ g/cm^3$; A = 195.1; g = 6.
[c]Assuming that the basal face of the cubic particles is inaccessible to the gas (f = 5/6 in Eq. 4).
[d]Average value assuming same surface area developed by {100}, {110}, and {111} boundary faces.

Some of the sizes that have been derived from the three different techniques are compared in Table 12.

Two conclusions may be drawn from this discussion. First, owing to the variety of hypotheses that can be made about the shape of the

TABLE 12 Comparison of the Average Particle Size (nm)

| Type of average size | Electron microscopy | XLBA | | Chemisorption | |
|---|---|---|---|---|---|
| | | Cube | Sphere | Cube | Sphere |
| $d_g$ | 2.79 | — | — | — | — |
| $d_n$ | 2.84 ± 0.04 (2.85)[a] | — | — | — | — |
| $d_s$ | 3.07 (3.05)[a] | — | — | 2.93[b] | 4.57 (3.44)[a] |
| $d_v$ | 3.19 (3.15)[a] | 3.29[b] | 4.72[c] (3.79)[a] | — | — |

[a]Values proposed in the original paper [21].
[b]Assuming *five* {110} boundary faces exposed.
[c]Average of the values of the fifth column of Table 10.

particles, the nature of the exposed crystal faces, and the proportion of the surface accessible to the gas phase, a fairly broad range of particle sizes may be derived from the primary experimental data (see Tables 10 and 11).

Second, the average sizes derived from the three methods by Adams et al. [21] were in excellent agreement (~15% divergence). Table 12 shows that still better agreement (~4% divergence) is obtained when assuming cubic Pt particles exposing five {110} faces. If spherical particles are assumed, a good agreement is found only between XLBA and chemisorption, the sizes estimated by these two techniques being then about 50% in excess over the size derived from electron microscopic measurements. The comparatively larger divergence between the results of Adams et al. is due to the fact that, for XLBA, the average size retained by these authors was obtained by an improper averaging procedure. As concerns the chemisorption measurements, these authors assumed cubes having *six* exposed {110} faces. This study thus indicates that the best agreement between the various experimental techniques is obtained when comparing sizes derived using identical hypotheses about both the shape of the particles and the fraction of the metallic surface accessible to the gas phase.

*b. Comparison of XLBA, $H_2$ Chemisorption, $H_2$ Desorption, and $H_2$-$O_2$ Titration Measurements.* As a second example, the work of Uchijima et al. [47] will be presented. These authors performed a systematic comparison of hydrogen chemisorption, hydrogen desorption, and hydrogen-oxygen titration methods. Chemisorption and titration measurements were made using the pulse technique described previously by Freel [17]. Great care was exercised for purifying the gases (carrier gas was 99.999% purity argon, passed over hot copper oxide so as to remove traces of hydrogen, and then through a trap of $Cr^{2+}/SiO_2$ (2.5% Cr) so as to remove oxygen and water). This allows reduction of impurity adsorption and consequent enhancement of the reproducibility of the measurements. The amount of desorbed hydrogen was measured by monitoring the hydrogen concentration in an argon flow (using a thermal conductivity detector) while heating rapidly the catalyst from ambient up to 450°C.

The results were expressed as a percentage of dispersion D and were derived from the raw data assuming the following stoichiometries: $H_2/Pt_{surface} = 1/2$ for hydrogen chemisorption or desorption; $H_2/Pt_s = 3/2$ for $O_2$-$H_2$ titration (corresponding to the reaction

$$Pt_s\text{-}O + (3/2)H_2 \longrightarrow Pt_s\text{-}H + H_2O).$$

The catalysts studied were prepared using a wide-pore silica gel having a specific surface area of 285 $m^2/g$, a pore volume of 1.2 $cm^3/g$, and an average pore diameter of 14 nm. Pt was deposited onto the support either by impregnation with a solution of chloroplatinic acid or by ion exchange. Samples are denoted x-Ion X (or PtCl)-S (or L), where x is the metal loading, ion X (PtCl) states a catalyst prepared by the ion exchange (impregnation) method, S (L) means that a mesh fraction of 70 to 80 (120 to 140) of the gel was used in the preparation.

The results presented in Table 13 are average values when more than one measurement was available in the original paper. It is shown in Table 13 that the most reproducible results have been obtained using hydrogen chemisorption (the standard deviation ranges from 0.6% of the mean for sample 0.83-ion X-S up to 7.2% for sample 1.91-PtCl-S). The reproducibility of $H_2$ desorption measurements is fair (standard deviation = 6.4% of the mean for sample 0.83-ion X-S, 28.3% for sample 1.97-PtCl-L). The reproducibility of $H_2$-$O_2$ titration data is more difficult to estimate, owing to the limited amount of data. It seems comparable to that of $H_2$ desorption data. Comparison of the dispersion values (see the bottom of Table 13) shows that $H_2$ chemisorption and desorption results are in very close agreement, while $H_2$-$O_2$ titration gives values systematically lower than those obtained from $H_2$ chemisorption measurement (average ratio $D_t/D_h = 0.8$).

Four of the active samples have also been studied by XLBA [48]. These results are presented in Table 14, together with the particle sizes derived from XLBA and chemisorption data, assuming different geometries. It is noted that the sizes derived from $H_2$-$O_2$ titration (surface average $d_s$) tend to be slightly higher than the corresponding values derived from XLBA (volume-average size $d_v$), in contradiction to the rule (see Sec. II) according to which $d_s \leqslant d_v$. The size derived from $H_2$ chemisorption are in general compatible, whatever the underlying hypotheses, with the corresponding values obtained from XLBA. The small difference between $d_s$ and $d_v$ suggests that the distribution of the sizes is probably fairly narrow. Sample 1.91-PtCl-S is an exception; in that case the chemisorption and XLBA values are compatible only ($d_s \leqslant d_v$) if the particles are assumed to be cubes exposing five {100} boundary planes to the atmosphere. It was observed, however, that strain contributed appreciably to the X-ray line broadening of sample 1.91-PtCl-S, resulting in an underestimation of the corresponding $d_v$, so that spherical particles are also compatible with the present data.

One may conclude from the discussion above that pulse $H_2$ chemisorption at room temperature, in the present case, gives metallic particle sizes in closer agreement with those obtained by XLBA than $H_2$-$O_2$ titration. It is shown again that the best agreement between XLBA and chemisorption methods is obtained when comparing sizes derived using identical hypotheses about the geometry (shape, nature of faces exposed) of the particles and the fraction of surface accessible to the gas phase. In addition, it may be necessary to account for other causes of line broadening, such as crystal strain.

TABLE 13 Percentage Platinum Exposed in $Pt/SiO_2$ Catalysts

| Catalyst | Loading (wt % Pt) | $H_2$ chemisorption $D_h$ (%) | Desorption $D_d$[a] (%) | $H_2$-$O_2$ Titration $D_t$[b] (%) |
|---|---|---|---|---|
| 0.83-ion X-S | 0.83 | 80,8 ± 0.5[c] | 86.8 ± 5.5 | 66.6 ± 2.1 |
| 0.49-ion X-L | 0.49 | 63.6 ± 1.3 | 68.6 ± 2.7 | 56.0 |
| 0.48-ion X-S | 0.48 | 63.1 ± 1.3 | 70.0 ± 1.8 | 57.4 |
| 1.10-PtCl-L | 1.10 | 39.7 ± 0.2 | 41.5 ± 1.4 | 37.2 |
| 1.17-PtCl-S | 1.17 | 39.3 ± 1.0 | 37.9 ± 2.0 | 32.8 ± 0.2 |
| 1.48-ion X-S | 1.48 | 27.3 ± 0.3 | 25.9 ± 4.0 | 19.5 |
| 1.48-ion X-L | 1.48 | 21.5 ± 0.0 | 18.9 ± 3.8 | 14.5 |
| 1.48-ion X-LC[d] | 1.48 | 15.6 ± 0.3 | 14.4 ± 3.5 | 12.3 ± 0.3 |
| 1.91-PtCl-S | 1.91 | 6.9 ± 0.5 | 6.5 ± 1.2 | 4.8 ± 1.5 |
| 1.97-PtCl-L | 1.97 | 6.3 ± 0.4 | 6.0 ± 1.7 | 4.8 |

[a] $D_d = (0.99 \pm 0.08)D_h$.
[b] $D_t = (0.80 \pm 0.09)D_h$.
[c] Standard deviation when more than one result was available.
[d] Sample calcined in air at 441°C for 20.3 h before reduction.
*Source*: Adapted from Ref. 47.

TABLE 14 Particle Sizes of $Pt/SiO_2$ Catalysts: Comparison of XLBA, Chemisorption, and $H_2$-$O_2$ Titration Results

| | XLBA | | | | | | $d_s$ (nm) | | | | | |
|---|---|---|---|---|---|---|---|---|---|---|---|---|
| | $L_{hkl}$ (nm) | | | $d_v$ (nm) | | | $H_2$ Chemisorption | | | $H_2$-$O_2$ titration | | |
| Catalyst | 111 | 100 | 110 | a | b | c | a | b | c | a | b | c |
| 1.17-PtCl-S | 2.8 | 2.5 | 2.2 | 3.3 | 2.2 | 2.5 | 2.7 | 1.8 | 2.5 | 3.3 | 2.1 | 3.0 |
| 1.48-ion X-S | 4.2 | 3.9 | 4.1 | 5.4 | 4.1 | 3.9 | 4.0 | 2.5 | 3.6 | 5.5 | 3.6 | 5.0 |
| 1.48-ion X-L | 4.9 | 4.3 | 4.5 | 6.1 | 4.5 | 4.3 | 5.0 | 3.2 | 4.6 | 7.4 | 4.8 | 6.8 |
| 1.91-PtCl-S[d] | 12.1 | 7.9 | 10.8 | 13.7 | 10.8 | 7.9 | 15.6 | 10.1 | 14.2 | 22.4 | 14.6 | 20.4 |

[a]Spheres ($\sigma$ = 0.084 $nm^2$).
[b]Cubes with {110} boundary faces, five faces exposed to the gas phase.
[c]Cubes with {100} boundary faces, five faces exposed to the gas phase.
[d]Analysis of 222 reflections showed a contribution of strain to line broadening; all other samples were strain-free.
*Source*: Adapted from Ref. 47.

*c. Comparison of XPS and $H_2$-$O_2$ Titration Measurements.* Owing to the large amount of information available on $Pt/SiO_2$ catalysts, it is quite natural that this system was used in early studies aiming at assessing the prospects of quantitative XPS analysis of supported catalysts. The XPS and chemisorption data considered here concern 12 $Pt/SiO_2$ catalysts of different origins. These data have been published by Scharpen [36] and by Angevine et al. [49]. Some of the $H_2$-$O_2$ titration measurements presented by Angevine et al. originate from the work of Uchijima et al. [47] studied above. These data will be discussed in the light of the model presented in Sec. III.D, using the most recent data concerning XPS parameters (mean free paths and cross sections of photoelectrons). The specific contribution of XPS to the characterization of supported catalysts will appear more clearly if the experimental ratios of XPS peak intensities ($I_{Pt}/I_{Si}$) are compared with the corresponding ratios calculated on the basis of the $H_2$-$O_2$ titration results.

All the experimental data useful for the present purpose are presented in Table 15. The 12 catalysts are sorted into four series. Catalysts of series A and B were prepared using the ion exchange method; those of series C and D were obtained by impregnation. Series A and C originate from Stanford University; they were prepared by Benesi et al. [50] and the corresponding XPS data are due to Scharpen [36]. Series B and D originate from Northwestern University [47], the XPS data being due to Angevine et al. [49]. The XPS lines used for measuring $I_{Pt}$ and $I_{Si}$ were, respectively, $Pt_{4f\ 5/2,\ 7/2}$ [binding energy (BE) = 72 eV] and $Si_{2p}$ (BE = 99 eV). The incident radiation was the $Al_{K\alpha}$ line (1486 eV). The photoelectrons have kinetic energies similar enough so that one can consider that the corresponding mean free paths are equal. According to the computations of Seah and Dench [51], we choose the values $\lambda_{Pt} = 1.89$ nm and $\lambda_{SiO_2} = 3.3$ nm.

The calculation of the $I_{Pt}/I_{Si}$ ratio corresponding to the chemisorption data involves the conversion of the latter into particle sizes. This has been made using relation (4), assuming that the particles were cubic and exposed five {110} boundary faces to the gas phase. Equations (32) to (36) are then used to calculate $(I_{Pt}/I_{Si})_{calc}$. The $\sigma_M/\sigma_S$ ratio in Eq. (33) has been calculated a priori using the theoretical photoelectron cross-section values proposed recently by Goldberg et al. [52] ($\sigma_{Pt}/\sigma_{Si} = 19.8$). Other data needed for the calculations (wt % Pt, $S_S$) are listed in Table 15, the last column of which contains the calculated $I_{Pt}/I_{Si}$ ratios.

The degree of agreement between XPS and chemisorption data is best appreciated when the experimental $I_{Pt}/I_{Si}$ ratio is plotted versus the calculated one (Fig. 12). A very good correlation is found for samples from series A, except for the sample containing the highest metal loading (2.30-ion X). The experimental values for series B are

TABLE 15 Dispersion of $Pt/SiO_2$ Catalyst: Comparison of XPS and $H_2$-$O_2$ Titration Data

| Series | | Catalyst | $S_s$ ($m^2/g$) | D (%) | $d_{110}$ (nm) | $I_{Pt}/I_{Si}$ expt. ($\times 10^{-3}$) | $I_{Pt}/I_{Si}$[a] calc. ($\times 10^{-3}$) |
|---|---|---|---|---|---|---|---|
| A[b] | 1. | 0.38-ion X | 279[c] | 99[b] | 0.7 | 22[b] | 20.8 |
| | 2. | 0.53-ion X | 245[c] | 56[b] | 1.3 | 19[b] | 25.9 |
| | 3. | 1.10-ion X | 276[c] | 103[b] | 0.7 | 67[b] | 60.8 |
| | 4. | 1.50-ion X | 273[c] | 121[b] | 0.6 | 92[b] | 86.3 |
| | 5. | 2.30-ion X | 298[c] | 62[b] | 1.1 | 76[b] | 115 |
| B[d] | 6. | 0.48-ion X-S | 285[d] | 57[d] | 1.2 | 8.5[c] | 23.7 |
| | 7. | 0.49-ion X-L | 285[d] | 56[d] | 1.2 | 10.7[c] | 23.9 |
| | 8. | 1.48-ion X-S | 285[d] | 20[d] | 3.5 | 15[c] | 44.0 |
| C[b] | 9. | 0.80-PtCl | 518[c] | 34[b] | 2.1 | 47[b] | 30.6 |
| | 10. | 3.70-PtCl | 526[c] | 14[b] | 4.9 | 69[b] | 84.4 |
| D[d] | 11. | 1.17-PtCl-S | 285[d] | 33[d] | 2.1 | 26[c] | 46.7 |
| | 12. | 1.91-PtCl-S | 285[d] | 5[d] | 13.8 | 48[c] | 17.7 |

[a]Values obtained using Eqs. (32) to (36), assuming that $\sigma_m/\sigma_S = 19.8$; $F_M = 1$ for $D \geqslant 100\%$; for $D < 100$, $\lambda_{Pt} = 1.89$ nm, $\lambda_{Pt} = 1.89$ nm, $\lambda_{SiO_2} = 3.31$ nm; cubic particles exposing five {110} boundary faces.

[b]From Scharpen [36].

[c]From Angevine et al. [49].

[d]From Uchijima et al. [47].

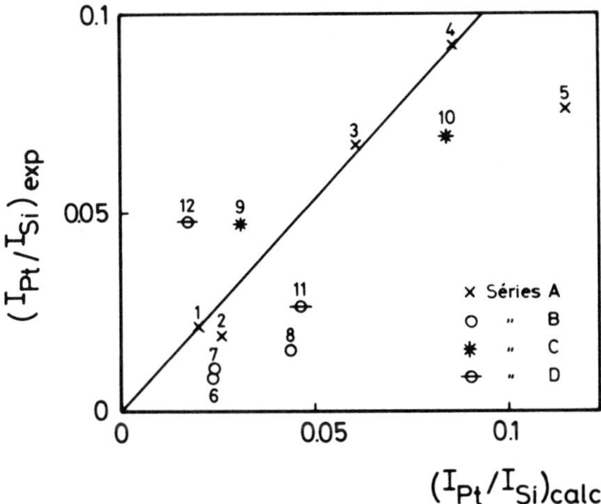


FIG. 12. Plot of the experimental $I_{Pt}/I_{Si}$ ratio versus the theoretical one calculated from the $H_2$-$O_2$ titration data using relation (32) for the 12 catalysts listed in Table 15.

equal to about 50% of the values expected from the chemisorption data. The points corresponding to series C and D are scattered irregularly away from the correlation line.

The good correlation found for series A supports the interpretation of both XPS and $H_2$-$O_2$ titration data in terms of dispersion changes. In contrast, the discrepancies observed for the other series of samples suggest that these samples are not accurately described by the chosen model. According to the comments made in the introduction of the present section, the interpretation of these discrepancies in the light of the physical principles involved in XPS measurements may bring about a refined picture of the catalysts. Unfortunately, the experimental data presented in the original papers do not allow definitive conclusions to be drawn. Only tentative explanations will be suggested here.

Two phenomena might explain the observation of experimental $I_{Pt}/I_{Si}$ ratios higher than expected from the $H_2$-$O_2$ titration data (samples 9, 10, and 12 which were all prepared by impregnation). The first would be a Pt enrichment of the outer parts of the support grains. Such an enrichment is often observed after impregnation of a high-surface-area support. In such a case, proper grinding of the grains before XPS study should tend to reduce $I_{Pt}/I_{Si}$ as a higher amount of the inner parts of the grains becomes exposed to the analysis [41]. The second phenomenon could be that the fraction of the Pt crystallites that chemisorb oxygen is lower than expected. This might be due to an incomplete reduction of the precursor oxide or to clogging of the pores preventing access of the gas phase to some fraction of the active phase. The observation of a $I_{Pt}/I_{Si}$ ratio lower than expected might, conversely, originate from a depletion of the outer parts of the support grains. Only the detailed description of the preparation of these catalysts would help to evaluate the likelihood of this hypothesis. The fact that all samples of series B exhibit the same 50% discrepancy suggests a possible systematic error in the measurements or in the interpretation of these data.

In conclusion, the specific information brought about by XPS measurements with respect to the chemisorption ones comes from the sensitivity of XPS, not only to the overall dispersion of the supported catalyst, but also to the actual repartition of the active phase in the grains of the support.

### 2. Supported Nickel Catalysts

Supported nickel catalysts have been the subject of numerous studies, only a few of which are concerned with dispersion measurements. A recent work by Mustard and Bartholomew [53] will serve here as a representative example. The authors investigated the application of $H_2$ chemisorption, XLBA, and TEM to the determination of metal crystallite sizes in $Ni/SiO_2$, $Ni/Al_2O_3$, and $Ni/TiO_2$ catalysts with a wide range of metal loadings and dispersions. $Ni/Al_2O_3$ and $Ni/TiO_2$ catalysts were prepared by impregnation to incipient wetness, whereas the $Ni/SiO_2$ catalysts were obtained from a homogeneous precipitation technique. After drying, the samples were reduced for 15 h in flowing hydrogen at 725 K. After cooling at 298 K the samples were passivated using a 1% air in $N_2$ stream, in order to prevent complete reoxidation of the pyrophoric nickel obtained after reduction when exposing the sample to air [54]. Richardson and Dubus [55] had shown previously that the nickel particle size distribution was not affected by such a passivation treatment. The reader will find full experimental details in the original papers.

The results of the particle size investigations are summarized in Table 16. It was found that $Ni/Al_2O_3$ samples were in general very difficult to analyze by TEM, owing to an insufficient contrast between the nickel crystallites and the pore structure of the alumina support. Experimental difficulties were also encountered in estimating the dispersion of $Ni/Al_2O_3$ catalysts from $H_2$ chemisorption measurements. Evidence was obtained in a separate study [56] that $H_2$ chemisorption was inhibited ($H/Ni_s < 1$) in those samples containing less than 3 wt % Ni. Accordingly, a reliable estimation of $d_s$ could only be obtained for catalysts containing more than 3 wt % metal. Concerning the use of XLBA, it was found that the most prominent peak of Ni (the 111 line) was completely obscured by a broad peak of $\gamma$-$Al_2O_3$ and that the second prominent peak (Ni 200) was detectable only for samples containing more than 15% metal. Table 16 shows that, for the $Ni/Al_2O_3$ samples, the estimates of $d_s$ obtained from $H_2$ chemisorption and TEM were generally in very close agreement, whereas the agreement between the estimates of $d_v$ by XLBA and TEM was only fair.

In the case of $Ni/SiO_2$ catalysts, the study by TEM was made easier by the excellent contrast observed between the metal particles and the support. Chemisorption measurements could be performed without an apparent problem. The precision of XLBA data was rather poor, as most $Ni/SiO_2$ catalysts contained a large fraction of particles smaller than the detection limit of the technique (estimated by the authors as about 3.0 to 4.0 nm). In the case of medium-range crystallites, XLBA was easy because of the absence of diffraction from the support. Table 16 shows that the agreement between chemisorption and TEM results is generally very good. These results also compared favorably with XLBA results for the samples containing more than 13.5% nickel.

In contrast with the systems above, crystallite sizes derived from chemisorption and TEM were in very poor agreement for the $Ni/TiO_2$ catalysts: estimates of $d_s$ from chemisorption were found to be about twice the corresponding values obtained by TEM for the fresh samples and about 30 times these values for the sintered samples. On the other hand, a reasonable agreement is found between TEM and XLBA when comparison is possible.

The discrepancy between chemisorption and the other techniques in the case of $Ni/TiO_2$ catalysts is attributed to the suppression of $H_2$ adsorption on Ni particles as a result of strong electronic interaction between these particles and the $TiO_2$ carrier. This occurs especially when the catalysts have experienced severe heat treatments in a reducing atmosphere. The suppression of the ability of $Ni/TiO_2$ catalysts to chemisorb $H_2$ has been correlated with a marked loss in their ability to catalyze the hydrogenation of CO [54]. The origin of the discrepancy between chemisorption and other techniques for the fresh $Ni/TiO_2$ catalysts might be explained by inaccuracies resulting from the assumption that particles were spherical. Indeed, TEM observations show that the metal particles are actually more like flat plates.

It may be concluded from the discussion above that dispersion measurements made using chemisorption techniques do not always correlate with other particle size measurements. This is due to modifications of the chemisorptive properties of the active fraction caused by residual hydrogen still retained in the subsurface layers of the metal catalyst, surface poisoning, hydride formation, strong metal-support interactions, and the like (for a review of such hydrogen effects in metal catalysts, see Paál and Menon [57]). Hence abnormal results obtained for metal catalysts supported on oxides such as $TiO_2$ (which itself can get reduced easily and form a hydride on the surface or in the bulk) should be regarded as typical limitations of that particular catalyst system, and not of the chemisorption technique itself.

TABLE 16 Dispersion and Particle Sizes of Supported Ni Catalyst According to $H_2$ Chemisorption, TEM, and XLBA

| | | | $d_s$[b] (nm) | | $d_v$[b] (nm) | |
|---|---|---|---|---|---|---|
| Catalyst | Treatment[a] | D (%) | Chemisorption | TEM | TEM | XLBA |
| 15% $Ni/Al_2O_3$ | Fresh | 18 | 5.4 | 3.7 | 4.6 | 4 |
| | Sintered[c] | 10 | 9.7 | 9.3 | 11 | 6.1 |
| | Sintered[d] | 10 | 9.7 | 10.0 | 12 | 6.5 |
| 23% $Ni/Al_2O_3$ | Fresh | 16 | 6.0 | 6.0 | 6.4 | 9.1 |
| 2.7% $Ni/SiO_2$ | Fresh | 52 | 1.9 | 2.9 | — | — |
| | Calcined[e] | 16 | 6.0 | 11.0 | — | — |
| 3.6% $Ni/SiO_2$ | Fresh | 37 | 2.6 | 2.7 | — | — |
| 13.5% $Ni/SiO_2$ | Fresh | 41 | 2.4 | 2.9 | 3.1 | <4 |
| | Sintered[f] | 22 | 4.4 | 4.1 | 4.5 | 3.7 |
| | Sintered[g] | 16 | 6.0 | 6.3 | 7.1 | 7.2 |

| | | | | | | |
|---|---|---|---|---|---|---|
| | Sintered[h] | 15 | 6.4 | 6.9 | 8.0 | 6.4 |
| 15% $Ni/SiO_2$ | Fresh | 19 | 5.1 | 8.1 | 9.4 | 16.0 |
| | Calcined[i] | 6 | 16.1 | 19.0 | 24.0 | 25.0 |
| 28% $Ni/TiO_2$ | Fresh | 11 | 8.8 | 5.5 | — | — |
| 15% $Ni/TiO_2$ | Fresh | 4 | 24.2 | 9.9 | 11.5 | 13. |
| | Sintered[j] | 0.1 | 967 | 32 | 35 | 28 |

[a]Calcination treatment was performed *before* the reduction step.
[b]Assuming spherical particles with = 0.068 $nm^2$/Ni atom.
[c]In $H_2$ for 72 h at 1023 K.
[d]In 3% $H_2O/H_2$ for 13 h at 1023 K.
[e]In air for 3 h at 573 K.
[f]In $H_2$ for 50 h at 923 K.
[g]In $H_2$ for 50 h at 973 K.
[h]In $H_2$ for 50 h at 1023 K.
[i]In air for 22 h at 773 K.
[j]In $H_2$ for 3 h at 1023 K.
*Source*: Adapted from Ref. 53.

In the absence of such peculiar complications of the metal-support system, dispersion values from chemisorption measurements are still the most likely to correlate with the actual performance of a given supported metal catalyst.

## V. APPLICATION OF CHEMISORPTION METHODS TO MAJOR CATALYST SYSTEMS

When the proper experimental conditions are established, chemisorption undoubtedly offers the most convenient way for routine dispersion measurements. As already mentioned, this method is more directly related to the concept of catalyst activity and can, in addition, often be combined with activity measurements within the same experimental setup. The importance of chemisorption studies in the literature of catalysis is also justified by the vital role of metal catalysts in industrial processes. It turns out that chemisorption results are often the first data to be sought for about metal catalysts; other methods will usually be involved only afterward when the complexity of the problem requires further study.

The amount of literature concerned with the application of chemisorption to the purpose of measuring dispersion is so large that a detailed review would far exceed the framework of this chapter. In view of the importance of this literature, it appears useful, however, to complement the introductory discussion of Sec. III.A by presenting a brief overview of the present state of the art about the application of chemisorption methods to various catalyst systems of practical importance. This overview should provide the reader with a key to the more specialized literature in the field.

Apart from platinum (and probably also nickel) catalysts, for which proper experimental conditions are now well established, it appears at present that the use of chemisorption on other types of catalysts often remains a matter of "recipes." This chapter would not have been complete without a brief presentation of some of these recipes.

The subject of metal dispersion measurements has also been dealt with in detail in the monographs by Anderson [11] and Ponec et al. [7] and in recent reviews by Moss [58], Farrauto [59], and Scholten [60].

### A. Some General Remarks

Although the chemisorption technique for dispersion measurements seems to be quite reliable for self-made or laboratory-made catalysts, uncertainties could arise in the case of industrial catalysts due to special additives or promoters in such catalysts. The nature of such additives is a closely guarded secret of catalyst manufacturers and is often unknown to, or even unsuspected by, research workers in the laboratories of user industries and of academic institutions. The presence of such additives may give misleading results, which in turn may lead to inadvertently wrong conclusions regarding the reliability of the chemisorption technique.

Still another basic uncertainty in studies on proprietary industrial catalysts arises from special pretreatments. For instance, the bimetallic Pt-Re-$Al_2O_3$ reforming catalyst has a very rigid and elaborate startup procedure in industrial plants. Without this special startup procedure, the bimetallic catalyst is well known to give a performance notoriously worse than that of the monometallic Pt-$Al_2O_3$ reforming catalyst. This procedure, however, is the proprietary and confidential know-how of the process licensor and/or the catalyst manufacturer, and academic research people usually have no access to it. A catalyst that is only simply calcined and reduced cannot be compared to an industrial catalyst subjected to chloriding, sulfiding, and such special pretreatments.

Surface enrichment of particular components of a catalyst may also occur during calcination, reduction, pretreatments, and the catalytic reaction itself. Such surface enrichment phenomena in catalysts have recently been reviewed by Menon and Prasada Rao [61]. Thus a knowledge of the exact chemical composition of a catalyst surface, as measured by specific chemisorption or other techniques, is of paramount importance, particularly the changes in it as a consequence of preparation methods, pretreatments, or the catalytic reaction itself. At the same time one has to be very careful not to give too much importance to the initial state of a catalyst, and when comparing results of different research teams on different catalysts subjected to varying pretreatments. Not realizing these basic limitations will only lead to finding fault with the technique.

Exposure of supported metallic catalysts to $H_2$ at high temperatures can also cause strong metal-support interactions, particularly in the case of $TiO_2$-supported Pt [62,63] and Ni [53,56] catalysts. Spillover of hydrogen from the metal to the carrier is also well known (for a review, see Ref. 64). These and other hydrogen-induced effects in metal catalysts have just been reviewed by Paál and Menon [57]. Hence they will not be discussed here any further.

## B. Overview of Major Catalyst Systems

It would be too long to make an historical review of all papers which have contributed to the progressive disclosing of all factors affecting the measurement of dispersion by chemisorption methods. Only the present state of the art will be outlined here.

### 1. Platinum

Much has already been said about supported Pt catalysts in Secs. III.A and IV. In summary, it is now well demonstrated that reliable measurements of Pt surface area may be performed by use of $H_2$ chemisorption or $H_2$-$O_2$ titration at ambient temperature.

In the case of $H_2$-$O_2$ titrations of Pt surface on supported Pt catalysts, a controversy arose during the last 15 years on the exact stoichiometry of hydrogen chemisorption/oxygen chemisorption/hydrogen titration (HC:OC:HT) to be used in the titrations (for a brief review, see Ref. 65). Much of this controversy was perhaps caused because every research group used the very first $H_2$ chemisorption on their freshly reduced catalyst as the basis for all calculations. But this first chemisorption value itself was often not reproducible since the surface was still in a rather metastable condition after the reduction. Prasad et al. [65] found that if the surface was given an annealing or "homogenizing" treatment by a few $H_2$-$O_2$ cycles at ambient temperature, it can behave normally in subsequent gas titrations. Furthermore, if the $H_2$-titer values were used as the basis for calculations after the above-mentioned $H_2$-$O_2$ cycles, the stoichiometry HC:OC:HT was always found [65] to be 1:1:3, independent of Pt crystallite size and independent of pretreatment of the catalysts. Recent studies by Menon and Froment [66,67] suggest that the residual hydrogen retained by the supported Pt catalysts after a reduction is perhaps responsible for the metastable condition of freshly reduced Pt catalysts mentioned above.

### 2. Nickel

The measurement of Ni dispersion has already been discussed in detail in Sec. IV. The specific metal area of Ni on supported Ni catalysts is measured most commonly by $H_2$ chemisorption at ambient temperatures. If the chemisorption proceeds too slowly, the temperature may be raised to 50 or 60°C. For comparative purposes, very often a single-point measurement at a pressure of about 200 torr of $H_2$ will suffice. The gas chromatographic pulse method using $H_2$, developed by Buyanova et al. [15], has also become popular for Ni [19].

For silica-supported Ni catalysts, Lohrengel and Baerns [68] have used a high-vacuum balance (Sartorius No. 4433 type) for gravimetric measurement of (1) BET surface area, (2) metal dispersion of Ni from chemisorption of CO, and (3) total nickel content by formation of nickel carbonyl when CO reacts with the catalyst at 100°C, all on the same sample of catalyst. One special advantage here is that the degree of reduction (or completeness of reduction) of the catalyst can readily be seen from the constant weight in a gravimetric system. The carbonylation experiment, however, takes over 160 h. The highly toxic nature of nickel carbonyl also requires special precautions.

### 3. Bimetallic Catalysts

The measurement of Pt and Re dispersions separately [18] in the case of the bimetallic (Chevron-type) $Pt/Re/Al_2O_3$ reforming catalyst has already been described in Sec. III.A.2.d. Quite recently, Blanchard et al. [69-71] have employed a temperature-programmed titration technique to determine Pt and Ru dispersion separately on a Pt-Ru-$Al_2O_3$ catalyst. After chemisorption of oxygen, the catalyst was heated in a stream of 5% $H_2$ in argon. Two $H_2$ consumption peaks were observed: the low-temperature peak was related to the total (Pt + Ru) atoms either alloyed or in close proximity to each other on the surface, while the high-temperature peak corresponded to the unalloyed Ru atoms on the surface.

4. Palladium

Chemisorption of $H_2$ on Pd can be complicated by the tendency of Pd to (1) dissolve hydrogen and form hydrides, (2) undergo sintering during evacuation at high temperatures, and (3) weakly chemisorb the "excess hydrogen." These problems have been reviewed by Scholten [60].

An alternative is to use the chemisorption of CO. But CO can chemisorb on Pd either in a linear form or in a bridge form, the relative proportion of the two forms being dependent on temperature, pressure, and perhaps even the metal particle size [111]. The chemisorption stoichiometry CO/Pd is 1 for the linear form and 1/2 for the bridged form. This makes it difficult to use chemisorption data for direct calculation of Pd metal area or dispersion.

Quite recently, Ryndin et al. [72] have used the $H_2$-$O_2$ titration technique to measure Pd dispersion on a variety of supported Pd catalysts. The evacuated catalyst samples were kept in a flow of $H_2$ at 573 K for 12 h, stripped with argon at the same temperature for 1 h, cooled to room temperature, and then titrated with $O_2$. The consecutive oxygen titer values are nearly identical and equal to one-half the $H_2$ uptake during the $H_2$ titration, as is indeed to be expected from the titration stoichiometry:

$$\text{Pd-H} + (3/4)O_2 \longrightarrow \text{Pd-O} + (1/2)H_2O$$

$$\text{Pd-O} + (3/2)H_2 \longrightarrow \text{Pd-H} + H_2O$$

5. Copper

The dissociative adsorption of $N_2O$ seems to be the best method for measurement of specific copper metallic surface [73,74], according to the reaction

$$\text{Cu} + N_2O(g) \longrightarrow \text{Cu-O} + N_2(g)$$

Apart from the general volumetric technique, the $N_2O$ reaction can be followed on a gravimetric sorption balance (Menon and Prasad, [75]) or by the gas chromatographic technique (Dvorak and Pasek [76]).

A mixed oxide of copper and zinc is used as an industrial catalyst for the water-gas shift reaction,

$$CO_2 + H_2O \longrightarrow CO_2 + H_2$$

In this case Sen Gupta et al. [77] have used the dissociative adsorption of $N_2O$ to obtain valuable information on the stability of the catalyst as affected by its method of preparation, nature of the support, curing temperature, conditions of reduction, and so on. Reduction in $H_2$ leads to sintering of the catalyst while the copper surface area remains practically the same. For the sample reduced at 230°C, practically all the surface is covered with Cu. Clearly, a surface reconstruction is occurring here, with zinc oxide submerging and copper spreading over the catalyst surface.

Reduction in the presence of steam causes no sintering; however, the Cu area is now lower due to a partial oxidation of the Cu metal surface by steam, as shown earlier by Sen Gupta et al. [78].

6. Silver

In industry, supported silver catalysts are used in the selective oxidation of ethylene to ethylene oxide. Silver gauze is the catalyst for the oxidation of methanol to formaldehyde, although iron molybdate catalyst has become popular for this process in recent years.

The chemisorption of oxygen at 200 to 250°C and physisorption of krypton at −196°C (BET) were employed by Meisenheimer and Wilson [79] in their studies on silver powder; the maximum oxygen coverage reported was 0.93 at 200°C and 1.2 cm $O_2$ pressure.

Scholten et al. [80] have applied the method of adsorption-decomposition of $N_2O$, successfully used earlier for Cu, to measure the specific Ag metal surface on unsupported as also $Al_2O_3$-supported Ag catalysts at 150°C.

$$2Ag + N_2O \longrightarrow Ag_2O + N_2$$

They found satisfactory agreement between the results from the $N_2O$, X-ray, and electron microscopy techniques. The general applicability of the $N_2O$ method is thus established for silver catalysts. The epoxidation on Ag catalysts is, however, believed to be caused by molecularly adsorbed oxygen species, and hence the oxygen adsorption measurement on Ag may perhaps give a more meaningful measure of the active species on the Ag catalyst responsible for the selective epoxidation of ethylene.

7. Nonmetallic Molybdenum-Containing Catalysts

As indicated in Table 17, nonmetallic catalysts containing molybdenum oxide and/or molybdates are presently of major importance in

TABLE 17 Important Molybdate Catalysts in Industry

| Catalyst type | Process to convert: |
|---|---|
| Bismuth molybdate | Propylene to acrolein<br>Propylene to acrylonitrile<br>Butene to butadiene<br>Xylene to phthalonitrile |
| Iron molybdate | Methanol to formaldehyde |
| Cobalt molybdate | Propylene to acrylic acid<br>Butene to maleic anhydride |
| Cobalt/molybdenum on alumina | Hydrodesulfurization, hydrotreating<br>Olefin metathesis<br>Processing coal and coal liquids |

many chemical and petrochemical processes. The energy crisis of the last decade and the renewed interest in coal-conversion processes also add to this importance, since these catalysts find applications not only in primary coal liquefaction processes but also in the stupendous problems of the removal of S, N, and O and metals from coal-derived liquid feedstocks (which sometimes contain even 10 times higher contents of S, N, and O than petroleum feedstocks). Hence the problem of determining the specific surface area of molybdena in supported and composite molybdate catalysts is of paramount importance today, just as the determination of specific metal surface areas was in the 1960s. It was thus tempting to elaborate a chemisorption procedure that could allow the measurement of this surface area as conveniently as for platinum. This section would not have been complete without mentioning these relatively new trends.

A method based on low-temperature oxygen chemisorption has been developed by Weller and co-workers [81-84]. After reduction of the supported molybdena catalyst at 500°C for 6 h in flowing $H_2$, the amount of oxygen selectively chemisorbed onto the reduced molybdena surface is determined (e.g., as the difference between two $O_2$ adsorption isotherms at −78°C). Absolute value of the $MoO_3$ surface area may then be obtained by comparison with an unsupported $MoO_3$ sample.

Millman and Hall [85] have employed this method to characterize the sites on incompletely reduced $MoO_3/Al_2O_3$ catalysts active for propylene hydrogenation. From a comparison of $O_2$ chemisorption and CO chemisorption on molybdena, Ramakrishnan and Weller [83] conclude that the former is to be preferred over the latter. However, the accuracy of such surface area measurements appears to be affected by the degree of reduction obtained prior to oxygen adsorption [86].

It is also worth mentioning the recent work of Tauster and coworkers [87] on the use of $O_2$ chemisorption for measuring the active surface area of $MoS_2$ in hydrodesulfurization catalysts. When chemisorption is performed under very mild conditions (dynamic oxygen chemisorption), these authors obtained a good correlation between the amount chemisorbed and the HDS activity. It is thought that such oxygen chemisorption occurs only on the edge planes of the $MoS_2$ crystallites and that only these planes are catalytically active. Further work is needed before we can make a more definite evaluation of the perspective of the application of such selective chemisorption methods to nonmetallic catalysts.

## ACKNOWLEDGMENTS

The authors are indebted to Dr. B. K. Hodnett for correcting the style of the manuscript.

## APPENDIX 1: THEORETICAL DISTRIBUTION FUNCTIONS

The size distribution of a population of particles may sometimes be closely fitted by an analytical function of the sizes. Two such functions are most commonly encountered in practice: the *normal*, or *gaussian* distribution function and the *log-normal* distribution function. They will be discussed below in more detail.

### A. The Normal Distribution

A size distribution is said to be normal or gaussian if it obeys the relation

$$f_n(x) = \sigma_n^{-1}(2\pi)^{-1/2} \exp\left[-\frac{1}{2}\left(\frac{x - d_n}{\sigma_n}\right)^2\right] \qquad (39)$$

where $f_n(x)$ represents the number fraction of particles having a size between x and x + dx, $d_n$ the (arithmetic) mean, and $\sigma_n$ the standard deviation of the distribution. Note that f(x) is maximum for $x = d_n$ and that $\sigma_n$ is a measure of the spread of the distribution. Note also that

$$\int_{-\infty}^{+\infty} f_n(x)\, dx = 1$$

Tables of

$$f(t) = (2\pi)^{-1/2} \exp\left(\frac{-t^2}{2}\right) \tag{40}$$

where

$$t = \frac{x - d_n}{\sigma_n}$$

are easily found in the literature (e.g., Refs. 2, 4, and 88). For any sample of a normally distributed population, $\langle d_n \rangle$ and $s_n$ as defined by Eqs. (6) and (8) are, respectively, the estimates of the parameters $d_n$ and $\sigma_n$ of the normal function (39).

## B. The Log-Normal Distribution

The frequency distributions of small particles do not usually follow a normal curve but are skewed toward the high $d_i$ values (e.g., see Fig. 1a). It has been demonstrated (e.g., Ref. 89) on the basis of statistical arguments that, for small particles, it is the *logarithm* of the size that should be normally distributed. This distribution is the log-normal distribution, which may be described by the function

$$f_g(x) = (\ln \sigma_g)^{-1}(2\pi)^{-1/2} \exp\left[-\frac{1}{2}\left(\frac{\ln x - \ln d_g}{\ln \sigma_g}\right)^2\right] \tag{40}$$

Estimations of $d_g$ and $\sigma_g$ in (40) are, respectively, $\langle d_g \rangle$ and $s_g$ defined by relations (9) and (12).

## C. Derivation of the Parameters of a Distribution from Experimental Data

When the analytical form of the particle size distribution is known a priori, the various average sizes defined in Table 2 are usually simple functions of the mean and standard deviation of the distribution. Let us illustrate this in the case of the log-normal distribution.

The nth moment about the origin of a continuous distribution function f(x) is defined as

$$^{n}d = \int_0^\infty x^n f(x)\, dx \tag{41}$$

This equation is the translation in terms of a continuous integration of the definition of the estimator of the nth moment given by Eq. (7).

By combining Eqs. (40) and (41), the following relationship is obtained in the case of a log-normal distribution [27]:

$$^{n}d = \exp\left[n \ln d_g + \frac{n^2}{2} (\ln \sigma_g)^2\right] \tag{42}$$

As suggested in Table 2, $d_s$ and $d_v$ may be expressed as

$$d_s = \frac{^{3}d}{^{2}d} \tag{43}$$

and

$$d_v = \frac{^{4}d}{^{3}d} \tag{44}$$

It follows from (42) to (44) that

$$\ln d_s = \ln d_g + \frac{5}{2} (\ln \sigma_g)^2 \tag{45}$$

and

$$\ln d_v = \ln d_g + \frac{7}{2} (\ln \sigma_g)^2 \tag{46}$$

By solving Eqs. (45) and (46) for $d_g$ and $\sigma_g$, the following relationships are finally obtained:

$$\ln d_g = \ln d_s - 2.5 \ln \frac{d_v}{d_s} \tag{47}$$

and

$$(\ln \sigma_g)^2 = \ln \frac{d_v}{d_s} \tag{48}$$

This shows that a log-normal distribution may be completely described if only two different average sizes are known.

One may also derive from (8), (41), and (42)

$$\frac{\sigma_n}{d_n} = \frac{\sigma_s}{d_s} = \frac{\sigma_v}{d_v} = \sqrt{\exp (\ln^2 \sigma_g) - 1} \tag{49}$$

where $\sigma_n$, $\sigma_s$, and $\sigma_v$ are the standard deviations of the distributions of frequency, surface, and volume, respectively.

Grandqvist and Buhrman [89] have shown that, indeed, the log-normal distribution constitutes an excellent approximation for many particle size distributions of supported catalysts reported in the literature. The $\sigma/d_n$ values of all the distributions compiled by these authors fall within the range $0.18 \leqslant \sigma_n/d_n \leqslant 0.38$.

## APPENDIX 2: STATISTICAL PRECISION

When measuring particle size distributions by microscopy, the question often arises of the number of measurements required in order to ensure a faithful representation of the true size distribution. Of course, this number varies as a function of the spread of the distribution. When the distribution exhibits a cumbersome profile (e.g., with several maxima), fairly large amounts are usually needed to reproduce the outlines with sufficient precision. However, the distribution of supported particles usually has a fairly simple profile. The problem is then only to determine to which precision the true average sizes of the population are determined when using the estimators proposed in Table 2.

Elementary statistical theory shows that, for sufficiently large samples, there is a 95% chance that

$$\langle d_n \rangle - \frac{1.96\sigma_n}{\sqrt{n}} \leqslant d_n \leqslant \langle d_n \rangle + \frac{1.96\sigma_n}{\sqrt{n}} \tag{50}$$

where n is the number of particle sizes measured. Table 18 gives the number of measurements required to obtain a given precision over the mean, in the 95% confidence interval, for some values of $\sigma_n/d_n$.

TABLE 18 Number of Measurements Required to Obtain a Given Precision (95% Confidence Interval)

| n | Precision[a] (% over $d_n$) | | |
|---|---|---|---|
| $\sigma_n/d_n$ | 10 | 5 | 1 |
| 0.10 | 4 | 15 | 384 |
| 0.25 | 24 | 96 | 2401 |
| 0.50 | 96 | 384 | 9604 |

[a]Precision (%) = $196\ \sigma_n d_n^{-1} n^{-1/2}$.

The precision of the estimation of $d_S$ and $d_V$ from the measured sample of size can be appreciated in a similar way by estimating the standard deviation $\sigma_S$ or $\sigma_V$ of the distributions either of surface area (Fig. 1b) or volume (Fig. 1c). [These standard deviations are merely estimated from relation (8) substituting $n_i$ by $n_i d_i^2$ or $n_i d_i^3$ and $d_n$ by $d_S$ or $d_V$.]

## REFERENCES


1. G. C. A. Schuit and B. C. Gates, AIChE J., *19*: 417 (1973).
2. E. Whalpole, *Introduction to Statistics*, Macmillan, New York, 1968.
3. P. C. Hiemenz, *Principles of Colloid and Surface Chemistry*, Marcel Dekker, New York, 1977.
4. Z. K. Jelinek, *Particle Size Analysis*, Ellis Horwood, Chichester, England, 1970.
5. J. H. de Boer, *The Dynamical Character of Adsorption*, Oxford University Press, Oxford, 1953.
6. D. A. Hayword and B. M. W. Trapnell, *Chemisorption*, Butterworth, London, 1964.
7. V. Ponec, Z. Knorr, and S. Czerny, *Adsorption on Solids*, Butterworth, London, 1974.
8. P. H. Emmett and S. Brunauer, *J. Am. Chem. Soc.*, *59*: 310 (1937).
9. J. E. Benson and M. Boudart, *J. Catal.*, *4*: 704 (1965).
10. J. E. Benson, H. S. Hwang, and M. Boudart, *J. Catal.*, *30*: 146 (1973).
11. J. R. Anderson, *Structure of Metallic Catalysts*, Academic Press, New York, 1975.
12. B. C. Lippens, B. G. Linsen, and J. H. de Boer, *J. Catal.*, *3*: 32 (1964).
13. G. J. Den Otter and F. M. Dautzenberg, *J. Catal.*, *53*: 116 (1978).
14. D. E. Mears and R. C. Hansford, *J. Catal.*, *9*: 125 (1967).
15. N. E. Buyanova, A. P. Karnaukhov, L. M. Kefeli, I. D. Ratner, and O. N. Chernyavskaya, *Kinet. Catal. (English transl.)*, *8*: 737 (1967).
16. N. E. Buyanova, N. B. Ibragimova, and A. P. Karnaukhov, *Kinet. Catal.* (English trans.), *10*: 322 (1969).
17. J. Freel, *J. Catal.*, *25*: 139, 149 (1972).
18. P. G. Menon, J. Sieders, F. Streefkerk, and G. J. M. van Keulen, *J. Catal.*, *29*: 188 (1973).
19. E. A. Verma and D. M. Ruthven, *J. Catal.*, *19*: 401 (1970).
20. P. Scherrer, *Goett. Nachr.*, *2*: 98 (1918).
21. C. R. Adams, H. A. Benesi, R. M. Curtis, and R. G. Meisenheimer, *J. Catal.*, *1*: 336 (1962).

22. P. Ganesan, H. Kud, A. Saavedra, and R. J. de Angelis, *J. Catal.*, *52*: 310, 320 (1978).
23. D. P. Riley, in *X-ray Diffraction by Polycrystalline Materials* (H. S. Speiser, H. P. Rookshy, and A. J. C. Wilson, eds.), The Institute of Physics, London, 1955, p. 232.
24. A. Guinier, *Ann. Phys. (Paris)*, *12*: 90 (1939).
25. A. Guinier, *J. Chim. Phys.*, *40*: 133 (1943).
26. G. Fournet, *Acta Crystallogr.*, *4*: 293 (1951).
27. T. E. Whyte, Jr., P. W. Kirklin, R. W. Gould, and H. Heinemann, *J. Catal.*, *25*: 407 (1972).
28. H. Klug and L. Alexander, *X-ray Diffraction Procedures for Polycristalline and Amorphous Materials*, 2nd ed., Wiley, New York, 1974, p. 618.
29. B. E. Warren and B. L. Averbach, *J. Appl. Phys.*, *21*: 595 (1950).
30. A. Renouprez and B. Imelik, *J. Appl. Crystallogr.*, *6*: 105 (1973).
31. P. C. Flynn, S. E. Wanke, and P. S. Turner, *J. Catal.*, *33*: 233 (1974).
32. D. J. C. Yates, L. L. Murrel, and E. B. Prestridge, *J. Catal.*, *57*: 41 (1979).
33. G. R. Wilson and W. K. Hall, *J. Catal.*, *24*: 306 (1972).
34. E. B. Prestridge, G. H. Via, and J. H. Sinfelt, *J. Catal.*, *50*: 115 (1977).
35. M. M. J. Treacy and A. Howie, *J. Catal.*, *63*: 265 (1980).
36. L. H. Scharpen, *J. Electron Spectrosc. Relat. Phenom.*, *5*: 369 (1974).
37. J. S. Brinen, J. L. Schmitt, W. R. Doughman, P. J. Achorn, L. A. Siegel, and W. N. Delgass, *J. Catal.*, *40*: 295 (1975).
38. C. Defossé, P. Canesson, P. G. Rouxhet, and B. Delmon, *J. Catal.*, *51*: 269 (1978).
39. S. C. Fung, *J. Catal.*, *58*: 454 (1979).
40. F. P. J. M. Kerkhof and J. A. Moulin, *J. Phys. Chem.*, *83*: 1612 (1979).
41. C. Defossé, *J. Electron Spectrosc. Relat. Phenom.*, *23*: 157 (1981).
42. M. Houalla, F. Delannay, and B. Delmon, *J. Electron Spectrosc. Relat. Phenom.*, *25*: 59 (1982).
43. F. Delannay, M. Houalla, D. Pirotte, and B. Delmon, *Surf. Interface Anal.*, *1*: 172 (1979).
44. F. Delannay, P. Gajardo, P. Grange, and B. Delmon, *J. Chem. Soc., Faraday Trans. 1*, *76*: 988 (1980).
45. M. Houalla, F. Delannay, and B. Delmon, *J. Chem. Soc. Faraday Trans. 1*, *76*: 1766 (1980).
46. F. Delannay, C. Defossé, M. Houalla, A. Lycourghiotis, and B. Delmon, in *Perspectives in Catalysis* (R. Larsson, ed.), C. W. K. Gleerup, Lund, Sweden, 1981, p. 85.

47. T. Uchijima, J. M. Herrmann, Y. Inoue, R. L. Burwell, Jr., J. B. Butt, and J. B. Cohen, *J. Catal., 50*: 464 (1977).
48. S. R. Sashital, J. B. Cohen, R. L. Burwell, and J. B. Butt, *J. Catal., 50*: 479 (1977).
49. P. J. Angevine, J. C. Vartulli, and W. N. Delgass, *Proc. 6th Int. Congr. Catal.*, Vol. 2 (G. C. Bond, P. B. Wells, and F. C. Thompkins, eds.), The Chemical Society, London, 1977, p. 611.
50. H. A. Benesi, R. M. Curtis, and H. P. Studer, *J. Catal., 10*: 328 (1968).
51. M. P. Seah and W. A. Dench, *Surf. Interface Anal., 1*: 1 (1979).
52. S. M. Goldberg, C. S. Fadley, and S. Kowo, *J. Electron. Spectrosc. Relat. Phenom., 21*: 285 (1981).
53. D. G. Mustard and C. H. Bartholomew, *J. Catal., 67*: 186 (1981).
54. C. H. Bartholomew, R. B. Pannell, and J. L. Butler, *J. Catal., 65*: 335 (1980).
55. J. T. Richardson and R. J. Dubus, *J. Catal., 54*: 207 (1978).
56. C. H. Bartholomew and R. B. Pannell, *J. Catal., 65*: 390 (1980).
57. Z. Paál and P. G. Menon, *Catal. Rev. Sci. Eng., 25*: 229 (1983).
58. R. L. Moss, in *Experimental Methods in Catalytic Research*, Vol. 2 (R. B. Anderson and P. T. Dawson, eds.), Academic Press, New York, 1976.
59. R. J. Farrauto, *AIChE Symp. Ser., 70*(143): 9 (1974).
60. J. J. F. Scholten, in *Preparation of Catalysts II* (B. Delmon, P. Grange, P. Jacobs and G. Poncelet, eds.), Elsevier Scientific, New York, 1979, p. 685.
61. P. G. Menon and T. S. R. Prasada Rao, *Catal. Rev. Sci. Eng., 20*: 97 (1979).
62. S. J. Tauster, S. C. Fung, and R. L. Garten, *J. Am. Chem. Soc., 100*: 170 (1978).
63. R. T. K. Baker, E. B. Prestridge, and R. L. Garten, *J. Catal., 59*, 293 (1979).
64. P. A. Sermon and G. C. Bond, *Catal. Rev., 8*:211 (1973).
65. J. Prasad, K. R. Murthy, and P. G. Menon, *J. Catal., 52*: 515 (1978).
66. P. G. Menon and G. F. Froment, *J. Catal., 59*: 138 (1979).
67. P. G. Menon and G. F. Froment, *Appl. Catal., 1*: 31 (1981).
68. G. Lohrengel and M. Baerns, *Appl. Catal., 1*: 3 (1981).
69. G. Blanchard, H. Charcosset, M. T. Chenebaux, and M. Primet, in *Preparation of Catalysts II* (B. Delmon, P. Grange, P. Jacobs, and G. Poncelet, eds.), Elsevier Scientific, New York, 1980, p. 197.
70. G. Blanchard, H. Charcosset, H. Dexpert, E. Freund, C. Leclerq, and G. Martino, *J. Catal., 10*: 168 (1981).

71. G. Blanchard, Thesis, Lyon, France, 1980.
72. Yu A. Ryndin, R. F. Hicks, A. T. Bell, and Yu. I. Yermakov, *J. Catal.*, *70*: 287 (1981).
73. T. J. Osinga, B. G. Linsen, and W. P. van Beek, *J. Catal.*, *7*: 277 (1967).
74. J. J. F. Scholten and J. A. Konvalinka, *Trans. Faraday Soc.*, *65*: 2456 (1969).
75. P. G. Menon and J. Prasad, *J. Catal.*, *17*: 238 (1970).
76. B. Dvorak and J. Pasek, *J. Catal.*, *18*: 108 (1970).
77. G. Sen Gupta, D. K. Gupta, M. C. Kundu, and S. P. Sen, *J. Catal.*, *67*: 223 (1981).
78. G. Sen Gupta, D. K. Gupta, and S. P. Sen, *Indian J. Chem.*, *16A*: 1030 (1978).
79. R. G. Meisenheimer and J. N. Wilson, *J. Catal.*, *1*: 151 (1982).
80. J. J. F. Scholten, J. Konvalinka, and F. Beekman, *J. Catal.*, *28*: 209 (1973).
81. B. S. Parekh and S. W. Weller, *J. Catal.*, *47*: 100 (1977).
82. H. C. Liu, L. Yuan, and S. W. Weller, *J. Catal.*, *62*: 282 (1980).
83. N. R. Ramakrishnan and S. W. Weller, *J. Catal.*, *67*: 237 (1981).
84. J. J. Garcia Fierro, S. Mendioroz, J. A. Pajares, and S. W. Weller, *J. Catal.*, *65*: 263 (1980).
85. W. S. Millman and W. K. Hall, *J. Catal.*, *59*: 311 (1979).
86. H. C. Liu and S. W. Weller, *J. Catal.*, *66*: 65 (1980).
87. S. J. Tauster, T. A. Pecoraro, and R. Chianelli, *J. Catal.*, *63*: 515 (1980).
88. H. B. Dwight, *Tables of Integrals and Other Mathematical Data*, Macmillan, New York, 1961.
89. C. G. Grandqvist and R. A. Buhrman, *J. Appl. Phys.*, *47*: 2200 (1976).

# 8

# The Measurement of Surface Acidity

PETER A. JACOBS National Fund of Scientific Research and Katholieke Universiteit Leuven, Leuven (Heverlee), Belgium

## I. INTRODUCTION

The concept of surface acidity of highly divided solids was derived originally to explain the action of acid surfaces in catalytic reactions. Acid surfaces are known to be able to generate surface carbenium ions. It is now the general belief that this occurs through proton addition to an unsaturated hydrocarbon molecule, although in the 1950s it was also accepted that it was possible to generate these ions through hydride abstraction from a saturated carbon atom. The first mechanism of carbenium ion generation requires the existence of proton-donating sites, while the second mechanism would be possible only over electron acceptor sites.

Acid catalysis is important in catalytic reforming, cracking, hydrocracking, isomerization, hydrodewaxing, alkylation, and dealkylation, to name the most important large-tonnage applications. It is therefore important to be able to measure acidity and to rank solids as possible candidates for improvement of the yields of these processes.

The aim of this chapter is to describe techniques that are able either to determine some aspects of acidity or to characterize as completely as possible the acid properties of highly divided solids, which have been used as catalysts in the processes mentioned or show some potential as candidates for new catalyst development.

## II. ACIDITY OF SOLIDS

A description of acidity in general, and surface acidity more specifically, requires the determination of the nature, the strength, and the number of acid sites. A solid acid is capable of transforming an adsorbed basic molecule into its conjugated acid form. In its most general definition an acid is an *electron-pair acceptor*. So the *Brönsted acid site* is able to transfer a proton from the solid to the adsorbed molecule. In this way an ion is generated and an ion-dipole interaction with the solid exists. The *Lewis acid site* is able to accept an electron pair from the adsorbed molecule and a coordinative bond with the surface is formed. It should be mentioned that oxidation-reduction reactions, which involve incomplete transfer of electrons from the substrate to the Lewis site, are not considered here as Lewis acid-Lewis base reactions [1].

## A. Nature of Surface Acidity

Brönsted acid sites in solids can be generated when a trivalent cation is present in tetrahedral coordination with oxygen. The most common example is aluminum. When all tetrahedral oxygen anions are shared between two cations, net negative charges are created for cations with charges lower than 4. This is schematically shown for aluminosilicates, the most common case encountered:

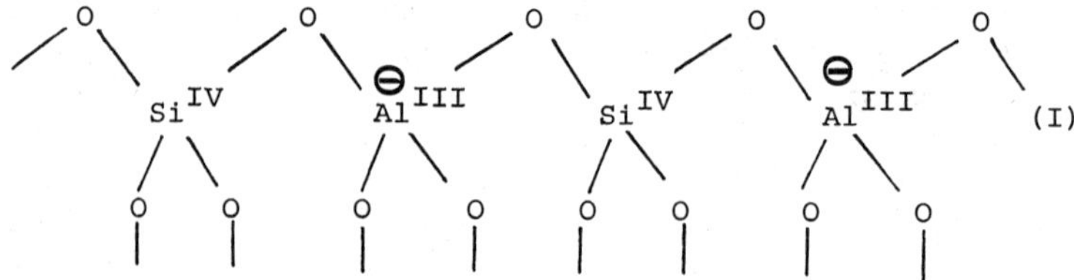


When the excess negative charges are compensated for by protons, silanol groups are formed, which can be represented as follows:

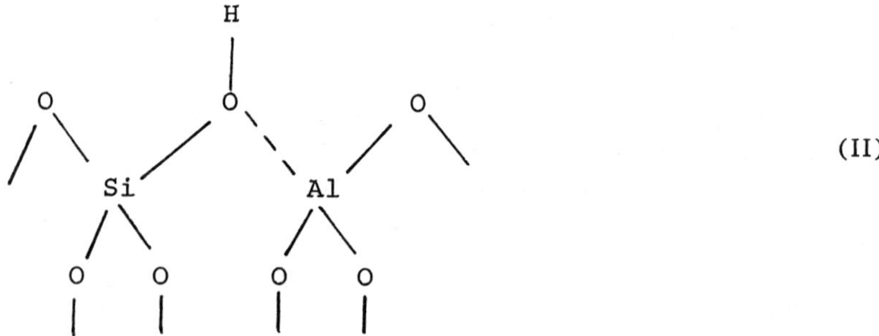


It has to be understood that in such a structure a trigonal oxygen does not exist; it indicates only that Si as well as Al retain their tetrahedral coordination. Upon interaction with a basic molecule (e.g., an olefin), the following equilibrium is established:

$$+ R\text{-}CH{=}CH_2 \rightleftarrows R\text{-}\overset{+}{C}H\text{-}CH_3 + \qquad (1)$$

Depending on the strength of the Brönsted site this equilibrium will be shifted. It seems, therefore, that surface acidity is *dynamic* in character and will be dependent on the chemical nature of both the adsorbed base and the solid. The process of isomorphic *substitution* of a tetravalent for a cation with lower valency in tetrahedral coordination may only occur locally at the surface or may be a bulk process. The latter is true for zeolites, which are crystalline aluminosilicates with quite homogeneous composition, while an example of the former is encountered with their amorphous counterparts, the silicoaluminas.

When coordinative unsaturated sites by some mechanism are generated, acid sites of the Lewis type are created which are able to accept electrons. For the silica-aluminum example, this may be schematized as follows:

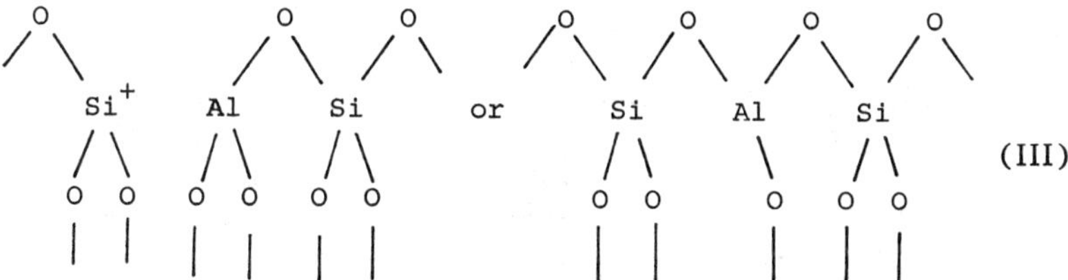


On the other hand, supported Lewis acids (e.g., $SbF_5$, $AlCl_3$, $BF_3$ on silica) behave in the same way as in solution. Zeolite cations that neutralize the lattice charge are also accessible to basic reactants and may therefore also behave as Lewis acid sites.

## B. Strength and Number of Surface Acid Sites

A given acidic solid usually does not have a single class of acidic sites, but normally shows a *large distribution of strengths* of acid sites. This may be the result of inhomogeneity in the composition of the solid, or the existence of short-range interactions or of surface structures. Moreover, most of the time both Lewis and Brönsted sites will be present in the same solid.

For all these reasons, a good method(s) must permit making all these distinctions and characterizing a surface in terms of nature, number, and strength of the acid sites. Since the ultimate goal is to characterize catalytically active solids, the measurements should be performed as closely as possible to catalytic conditons.

## III. MEASUREMENT OF ACIDITY OF SURFACES

### A. Aqueous Methods to Determine Catalyst Acidity

When aqueous methods are used, one should be aware of the following possible complications, which tend to suggest that water is not an inert medium but may affect the acid sites:

1. Addition of water at room temperature may drastically alter either the structural or textural properties of the solids or both (e.g., the structure of acid X-type zeolites will partially collapse).
2. Water may create new sites upon reaction with structural defects in oxides [2]; in this way Lewis sites may be transformed in Brönsted sites.
3. All Brönsted sites, having an acid strength higher than that of $H_3O^+$, will react with water to form $H_3O^+$, and consequently it will be impossible to discriminate among the acid strength of these sites [2].

#### 1. Ion Exchange Methods to Determine the Total Number of Acid Sites

This is a fast and suitable method to determine the number of Brönsted acid sites of a catalyst. The activated (i.e., dehydrated) acid may be neutralized with gaseous ammonia, which results in the transformation of all Brönsted sites into $NH_4$ ions, irrespective of their strength, according to

$$\text{solid-H} + NH_3 \rightleftharpoons \text{solid}^{\ominus} + NH_4^+ \tag{2a}$$

The $NH_4^+$ ion concentration can then be determined either directly by a spectroscopic method (the N-H deformation in $NH_4^+$ around 1450 to 1420 $cm^{-1}$ gives an isolated band in the infrared spectrum) or indirectly by back exchange with an excess of a second cation:

$$\text{solid}^- \, NH_4^+ + K^+ \rightleftharpoons \text{solid}^{\ominus} K^+ + NH_4^+ \tag{2b}$$

Suitable cations are $Ag^+$ or $K^+$, which generally have a high selectivity for a cation exchanger. However, the back-exchange method is not applicable to mixed-cation forms of the solid. Indeed, on the rare earth-exchanged zeolites (e.g., used as cracking catalysts), Brönsted acidity is formed through a dissociation reaction of hydration water in which only part of the cations are involved:

$$[La(H_2O)_x]^{+3}(zeolite^{\ominus})_3 \rightarrow [La(OH)(H_2O)_{x-1}]^{+2}$$

$$(zeolite^-)_2 + zeolite^{\ominus}H^+ \qquad (3)$$

2. Titration of Aqueous Slurries of the Acidic Solids

When upon slurrying an acid solid in water, the pH of the solution phase decreases, it can be titrated with a standard base to either a potentiometric or an indicator end point.

*a. Typical Procedure [3].* Ion exchange of the hydrogen ions of the acidic solid by treatment with a NaCl solution should produce an acid solution and a neutral solid:

$$\text{solid-H} + Na^+_{aq} \rightleftharpoons \text{solid}^{\ominus}Na^+ + H_3O^+ \qquad (4)$$

The combined wash waters are then titrated with NaOH in small increments.

Alternatively, acid solids may react as follows:

$$\text{solid-OH} + F^-_{aq} \rightleftharpoons \text{solid}^{\oplus} - F^- + OH^-_{aq} \qquad (5)$$

The basic solution formed on interaction with aqueous KF can be titrated with HCl. An example of both approaches is given in Fig. 1 for an ultrastable Y zeolite, the active component of industrial cracking catalysts.

*b. Limitations.* Aqueous methods should be applied with caution to water-sensitive catalysts. Hydrogen zeolites with relatively low $SiO_2/Al_2O_3$ ratios (<2.5) are certainly among them, since they may undergo partial structure collapse upon interaction with water. Silica-magnesia catalysts with excess MgO often show a basic instead of an acidic reaction (4). The situation with aqueous slurries of silica-aluminum is also rather complex. As a result of the following equilibrium [5]

$$Al_2O_3(SiO_2)_x + H_2O \rightleftharpoons 2HAlO_2(SiO_2)_x \qquad (6)$$

the end point of the slurry titrated with a strong base is continuously being reestablished upon aging.

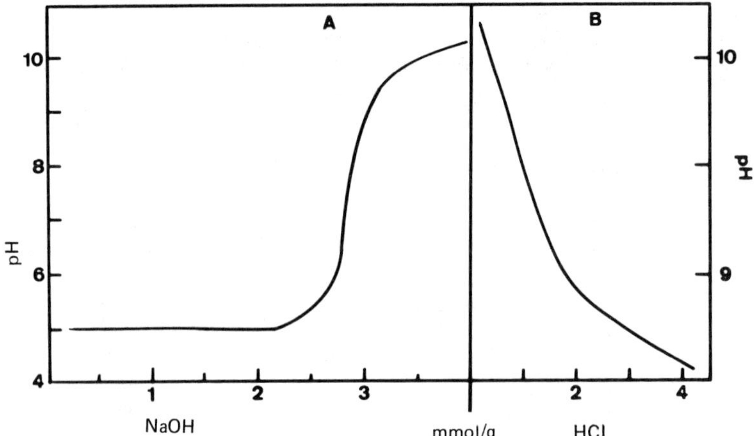


FIG. 1. Potentiometric titration curve for ultrastable Y zeolite, titrated: (A) after treatment with 3.4 mol/dm$^3$ NaCl with NaOH, 0.1 mol/dm$^3$; (B) in KF solution, 3.4 mol/dm$^3$ with HCl, 0.1 mol/dm$^3$.

## B. Amine Titration and Adsorption of Indicators for Visual Measurement of Acid Strength in a Nonaqueous Liquid Phase

This method has as major advantage that it excludes water from the system. It allows not only the determination of the total amount but also of the acid strength distribution. On the other hand, bulky molecules are handled (amines and indicators) which may be excluded sterically from part of the pores. The basic aspects of this method have been thoroughly reviewed [2,4,6-11].

### 1. The Hammett Acidity Function ($H_0$)

The extent to which in solution reaction occurs between a base (B) and a Brönsted acid to its conjugate acid ($BH^+$) is determined by the Hammett acidity function [12]:

$$H_0 = -\log a_{H^+} \frac{f_B}{f_{BH^+}} \tag{7}$$

in which $a_{H^+}$, $f_B$, and $f_{BH^+}$ represent the activity coefficients in solution of the protons, the base, and its conjugated acid, respectively. A similar relation exists when a Lewis acid (A) reacts with the base (B) to form AB:

$$H_0 = -\log a_A \frac{f_B}{f_{AB}} \tag{8}$$

in which $a_A$, $f_B$, and $f_{AB}$ are the corresponding activity coefficients. In homogeneous solution, $H_0$ can be determined by the use of a set of Hammett indicators, provided that the color of the unprotonated form is different from that of the conjugate acid form. It is assumed that at the point of color change $H_0$ is equal to the $pK_A$ of the indicator.

When applied to heterogeneous systems [13,14], the indicator in its basic form (I) is adsorbed and is converted into its conjugate ($IH^+$) by reaction with the surface acid sites. $H_0$ is then redefined as follows:

$$H_0 = -\log a_{H^+} \frac{f_I}{f_{IH^+}} \tag{9}$$

or

$$H_0 = pK_{IH^+} - \log C_{IH^+} C_I \tag{10}$$

in which $a_{H^+}$, $f_I$, and $f_{IH^+}$ are now the activity coefficients in the heterogeneous system of the species indicated. $C_I$ and $C_{IH^+}$ are the concentrations, again in the heterogeneous system of the indicator, in basic and acid form. $pK_{IH^+}$ is the negative logarithm of the equilibrium constant of the following surface reaction:

$$I + H^+ \rightleftharpoons IH^+ \tag{11}$$

Since $pK_{IH^+}$ is known only for aqueous solutions, this value is also used for heterogeneous systems. The basic assumption in applying the $H_0$ function to solids is that the $pK_{IH^+}$ value of the indicator in both systems is equal [11]. It is also clear from what precedes that the method does not distinguish Lewis from Brönsted acid sites.

The most common $H_0$ indicators, which span a $pK_A$ range between +6.8 and −14.5, together with their color changes and acid strength in terms of weight percent $H_2SO_4$, are given in Table 1.

### 2. The $H_R$ Acidity Function

Arylmethanols are able to react with $H^+$ in the following specific way:

TABLE 1 Hammet ($H_0$) Indicators for the Measurement of Acid Strength

| Indicator | $pK_A$ | $H_2SO_4$ (wt %) | Color[a] Base form | Acid form | References |
|---|---|---|---|---|---|
| Neutral red | +6.8 | $8 \times 10^{-8}$ | Y | R | 4, 7, 8, 11 |
| p-Ethoxychrysoidin[b] | +5.0 | — | Y | R | 4, 8, 11 |
| Methyl red | +4.8 | $8 \times 10^{-6}$ | Y | R | 7, 8, 11 |
| 4-Phenylazo-1-naphtylamine[b,c] | +4.0 | $5 \times 10^{-5}$ | Y | R | 4, 7, 8, 11 |
| Aminoazoxylene | +3.5 | — | Y | R | 4, 7, 8 |
| p-Dimethylaminoazobenzene[b] | +3.3 | $3 \times 10^{-4}$ | Y | R | 4, 7, 8, 11 |
| 4-Aminoazobenzene[b] | +2.8 | — | | | 11 |
| 2-Amino-5-azotoluene | +2.0 | $5 \times 10^{-3}$ | Y | R | 4, 7, 8 |
| 1,4-Diisopropylaminoanthraquinone | +1.7 | — | B(V) | R | 4, 8, 11 |
| 4-Phenylazodiphenylamine[b] | +1.5 | 0.02 | Y | V | 4, 7, 8, 11 |
| 4-Dimethylaminoazobenzene[b] | +1.2 | 0.03 | Y | R | 4, 7, 8, 11 |
| Crystal violet | +0.8 | 0.1 | B | Y | 7, 8 |

| | | | | | |
|---|---|---|---|---|---|
| p-Nitrobenzeneazo-(p'-nitro)-diphenylamine | +0.4 | — | O | V | 4, 7, 8, 11 |
| o-Chloroaniline | −0.2 | — | | | 4 |
| Chloro-o-nitroaniline | −0.9 | — | | | 4, 11 |
| 4-Nitrodiphenylamine[b] | −2.4 | — | | | 11 |
| Dicinnamalacetone | −3.0 | 48 | O | R | 4, 7, 8, 11 |
| 4-Nitroazobenzene[b] | −3.3 | — | | | 11 |
| Benzalacetophenone | −5.6 | 71 | C | Y | 4, 7, 8, 11 |
| 4-Bromacetophenone | −6.4 | — | | | 11 |
| Anthraquinone | −8.2 | 90 | C | Y | 4, 7, 8, 11 |
| 2,4,6-Trinitroaniline[b] | −9.3 | — | C | Y | 11 |
| p-Nitrochlorobenzene | −12.7 | — | C | Y | 15 |
| m-Nitrochlorobenzene | −13.2 | — | C | Y | 15 |
| 1,4-Dinitrotoluene | −13.7 | — | C | Y | 15 |
| 2,4-Dinitrofluorobenzene | −1.45 | — | C | Y | 15 |

[a]Y, yellow; R, red; B, blue; V, violet; O, orange; C, colorless.
[b]Only with this set can a reproducibility better than ±0.005 mmol/g be obtained (Ref. 11).
[c]Butter yellow.

TABLE 2 Arylcarbinol Indicators ($H_R$) for Measuring Acid Strength

| Indicator | $pK_A$ | $H_2SO_4$ (wt %) | References |
|---|---|---|---|
| 4,4',4"-Tridimethylaminotriphenylmethanol[a] | +9.36 | $4.37 \times 10^{-10}$ | 11 |
| 4,4'-Bisdiethylaminotriphenylmethanol[a] | +7.90 | $1.26 \times 10^{-8}$ | 11 |
| 4,4'-Bisdimethylaminotriphenylmethanol | +6.90 | $8 \times 10^{-8}$ | 11 |
| 4,4'-Bisdimethylaminodiphenylmethanol[a] | +5.61 | $2.45 \times 10^{-6}$ | 11 |
| 4-Dimethylaminotriphenylmethanol | +4.75 | $1.71 \times 10^{-5}$ | 11 |
| 2,2',2",4',4"-Pentamethoxytriphenylmethanol | +1.82 | 0.5 | 11 |
| 4,4',4"-Trimethoxytriphenylmethanol | +0.82 | 1.2 | 2, 4, 8, 11 |
| 4,4'-Dimethoxytriphenylmethanol | −1.24 | 16 | 11 |
| 4-Methoxytriphenylmethanol | −3.40 | 32 | 11 |
| 4,4',4"-Trimethyltriphenylmethanol | −4.02 | 36 | 2, 4, 8, 11 |
| 4-Methyl-triphenylmethanol | −5.24 | 41 | 11 |

| | | | |
|---|---|---|---|
| 4,4'-Dimethoxydiphenylmethanol | −5.71 | 44 | 11 |
| 4,4',4"-Tri-t-butyltriphenylmethanol | −6.50 | 47 | 11 |
| Triphenylmethanol | −6.63 | 48 | 2, 4, 7 ,8 11 |
| 4,4',4"-Trichlorotriphenylmethanol | −7.74 | 54 | 11 |
| 4,4'-Dimethyldiphenylmethanol | −10.40 | 64 | 11 |
| 3,3',3"-Trichlorotriphenylmethanol | −11.03 | 68 | 2, 4, 8, 11 |
| 2,2'-Dimethyldiphenylmethanol | −12.45 | 72 | 11 |
| Diphenylmethanol | −13.30 | 77 | 2, 4, 7, 8, 11 |
| 4,4-Dichlorodiphenylmethanol | −13.96 | 80 | 11 |
| 4,4',4"-Trimnitrotriphenylmethanol | −16.27 | 88 | 2, 4, 8, 11 |
| 2,4,6-Trimethylbenzyl alcohol | −17.38 | 92 | 2, 4, 7, 8, 11 |

[a]Give dark color in interaction with, e.g., zeolites, as a result of oxidation or decomposition.

$$ROH + H^+ \rightleftharpoons R^+ + H_2O \tag{12}$$

The $H_R$ function is defined as follows [16]:

$$H_R = pK_{R^+} - \log \frac{C_{R^+}}{C_{ROH}} \tag{13}$$

$$H_R = -\log a_{H^+} + \log a_{H_2O} + \log \frac{f_{R^+}}{f_{ROH}} \tag{14}$$

The notations are similar to those derived for the $H_0$ function and the same restrictions are encountered when the method is applied in heterogeneous systems. Nevertheless, the reaction is more specific and the molecular structure of the $H_R$ indicators is more uniform than that of the $H_0$ indicators. The commonly used $H_R$ indicators, together with their $pK_A$ and strength in percent, $H_2SO_4$ are listed in Table 2.

3. Procedure for Acid Strength Measurement with $H_0$ or $H_R$ Indicators

The dry acid solid is suspended in a nonaqueous solvent and titrated with a base (e.g., an amine) using an adsorbed indicator ($H_0$ or $H_R$) to establish the end point. The resulting number of sites is that whose acid strength is greater or equal to that of the indicator used. If a number of indicators with different strength are used on separate samples, an acid-strength spectrum can be derived. Essentially, this method of titration is by successive additions of amine to separate samples, followed by indicator addition after the acid-base equilibrium has been established [17,18].

Typically [19], 2 g of the catalyst is dehydrated and divided into about 200-mg samples. These samples are transferred into preweighted screw-cap vials of about 15 $cm^3$ in such conditions that water readsorption can be excluded. The solids are immediately covered with about 1 $cm^3$ of dry benzene. Then increasing aliquots of n-butylamine in benzene (0.3 to 0.5 molar) are added to the vials from a 10-$cm^3$ graduated burette. The samples are shaken overnight in tightly capped vials. To small amounts of each suspension are added a few drops of a 0.1% solution of each indicator in benzene, and after further equilibration the end point is determined.

4. Precautions and Standardization of Parameters

When the *color change* [11] of the $H_0$ indicators can be accurately determined, a reproducibility better than 0.005 mmol/g can be obtained (see Table 1).

TABLE 3 Steric Effects on Total Acidity Measured by Various Amines

| Nature of base | Van der Waals diameter (nm) | Total acidity: Silica[a] ($\mu$mol/$m^2$) | Total acidity: NaY[b] (mmol/g) | Total acidity: NaMOR[c] (mmol/g) |
|---|---|---|---|---|
| n-Butylamine | 0.547 | 2.673 | 2.825 | 0.537 |
| n-Hexylamine | 0.603 | 1.952 | 2.184 | 0.165 |
| n-Octylamine | 0.650 | 1.498 | 1.752 | 0.095 |
| sec-Butylamine | 0.552 | 2.471 | 2.771 | 0.267 |
| tert-Butylamine | 0.558 | 2.087 | 2.107 | 0.196 |
| Dibutylamine | 0.656 | 1.237 | 1.648 | 0.054 |
| Dihexylamine | 0.731 | 0.945 | 1.091 | 0.045 |
| Dioctylamine | 0.694 | 0.721 | 0.906 | 0.036 |
| Tributylamine | 0.734 | 0.750 | 0.878 | 0.019 |
| Trihexylamine | 0.825 | 0.480 | 0.843 | 0.010 |
| Trioctylamine | 0.898 | 0.274 | 0.266 | 0.002 |

[a]From Merck, 764.5 $m^2$/g.
[b]Zeolite with tridimensional cage system, 13.2 nm in diameter.
[c]Mordenite-type zeolite consisting of elliptical monodimensional pores (0.7 × 0.58 nm).
*Source*: After Ref. 11.

The *titer of amine solutions* [11] may change with storage time; only freshly prepared solutions should be used.

Titrations with $H_R$ indicators are particularly sensitive toward residual *physisorbed water* [11]; with hydrophilic catalysts (as some zeolites), the presence of strongly held water may result in an overestimation of the surface acidity.

Ultrasonic treatment [11] of the suspensions to reduce the equilibration time should be avoided since particle fragmentation and indicator decomposition may occur.

Recommended *solvent* for the method is *n-heptane* [11]. Benzene in some cases may not be the expected inert dispersing liquid, since hydrogen-bond formation of the surface hydroxyls may occur with the $\pi$ electrons of benzene. n-Paraffins are preferred and n-heptane should be selected over n-hexane as a result of its lower volatility. *Steric effects* [11] caused by the size of the amine are the limiting factor in the application of the method (Table 3).

In some cases [2], "acid" colors may be produced by processes other than proton addition; NaY zeolite, which is inactive for cracking reactions, shows an appreciable total acidity (Table 3). The same is true to a minor extent for pure alumina [2].

5. Relation Between Acid Strength Measured with $H_0$ and $H_R$ Indicators

Values for $H_0$ and $H_R$ on the same solid are based on two different surface reactions, which are unsufficiently understood [11]. Combination of Eqs. (9) and (14) gives

$$H_R = H_0 + \log a_{H_2O} - \log \frac{f_{ROH} f_{IH^+}}{f_{R^+} f_I} \qquad (15)$$

This indicates that for this comparison the activity of water at the surface should be taken into account. Since this quantity is unknown, $H_R$ and $H_0$ are at best arbitrary quantities to set an acidity scale. The same numerical values do not refer to identical acid strengths, but may be related to a common reference, the acid strength of aqueous sulfuric acid (Fig. 2). Although direct comparison between $H_0$ and $H_R$ is restricted to water, there exists a surprising agreement for the strong acidity of Y zeolites determined by the two sets of indicators. This was considered to be an argument for the existence of solids with the properties of polar solvents [20].

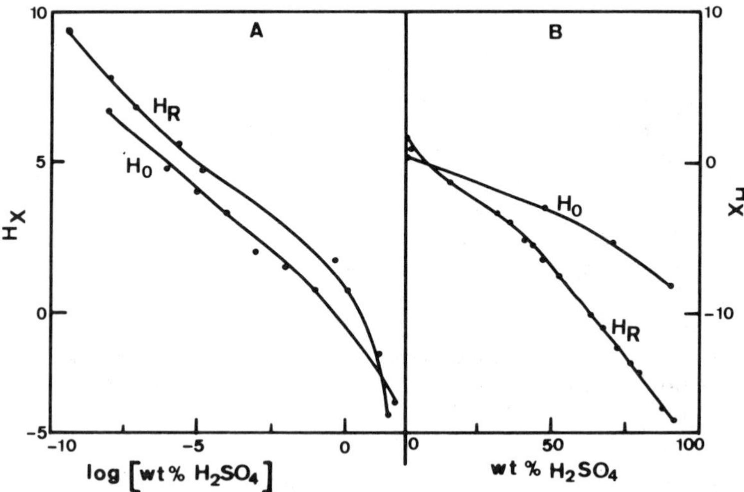


FIG. 2. $H_R$ and $H_0$ values against the acid strength of aqueous $H_2SO_4$ solutions for (A) weak acidity and (B) medium and strong acidity.

6. Application of the Indicator Method

The reproducibility of the $H_0$ indicator method is illustrated in Fig. 3. The acid strength distribution as determined by two different authors is given on zeolites LaY and CaY. For the high acid strengths, the agreement is remarkably good. The large discrepancies at the lower acid strengths probably reflect the presence of physisorbed water in the system.

The range of acid strengths determined for solids with acid character by several research groups is listed in Table 4. When these solids are ranked according to their acid strength, an order will be obtained which is distinctly different from their catalytic properties in acid-catalyzed reactions. It is the author's experience that for, for example, acid cracking of long-chain paraffins the following sequence is obtained:

mounted superacids > zeolites > mixed oxides ≈ clays

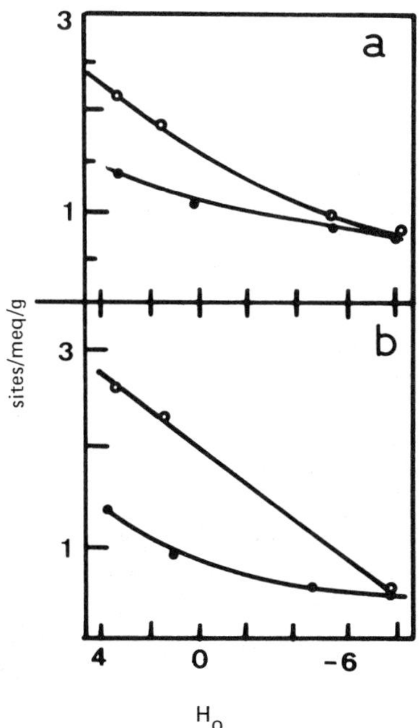


FIG. 3. Comparison of the distribution of acid strength by the $H_0$ indicator method over LaY zeolite (a) and CaY zeolite (b). (From Ref. 22, open circles, and Ref. 10, closed circles.)

TABLE 4 Range of Strength of Acid Sites Determined by $H_0$ Indicators

| Type of solid | $H_0$ range | References |
|---|---|---|
| Clays | | |
| H-kaolinite | −3.0 to −5.6 | 8, 18 |
| H-montmorillonite | −5.6 to −8.2 | 8, 18 |
| Mixed oxides | | |
| $SiO_2$-$Al_2O_3$ | < −8.2 | 8, 18 |
| $SiO_2$-MgO | 6.8 to −3.0 | 8, 18 |
| $Al_2O_3$-$B_2O_3$ | < −8.2 | 8, 18 |
| $TiO_2$ | +6.8 to 1.5 | 7, 8 |
| ZnS | +6.8 to 3.3 | 7, 8 |
| Mounted superacids | | |
| $SbF_5SiO_2Al_2O_3$ | < −13.75 | 15 |
| $SbF_5Al_2O_3$ | < −13.16 | 15 |
| $SbF_5TiO_2SiO_2$ | < −13.16 | 15 |
| Zeolites | | |
| H-mordenite | +3.3 to −3.0 | 21 |
| H-ZSM-5 | +3.3 to −3.0 | 21 |
| H-Y | +3.3 to +0.8 | 21 |
| Phosphates | | |
| Cr-phosphate | +1.5 to −8.2 | 31 |
| Zr-phosphate | +3.3 to −3.0 | 31 |
| $NH_4$-phosphate | +1.5 to −5.6 | 31 |

It is therefore important to realize that the acid strength measured by the indicator method is not necessarily identical to that seen by a reactant molecule in an acid conversion.

The application of the $H_R$ indicator method for silica-aluminas with variable composition is illustrated in Fig. 4. The authors [23] note that between the total acidity determined this way and the figure obtained from cation exchange capacity measurements, there is only satisfactory agreement for samples with $Al_2O_3$ content higher than 50%. This mismatch between both techniques is not understood in detail but is associated with the modifications the samples undergo in the presence of water [23].

## C. Amine Titration and Indicator Adsorption for Spectroscopic Measurement of Acid Strength

The use of visual indicators in the amine-titration method may have drawbacks on the accuracy of the method: (1) the color of the acid

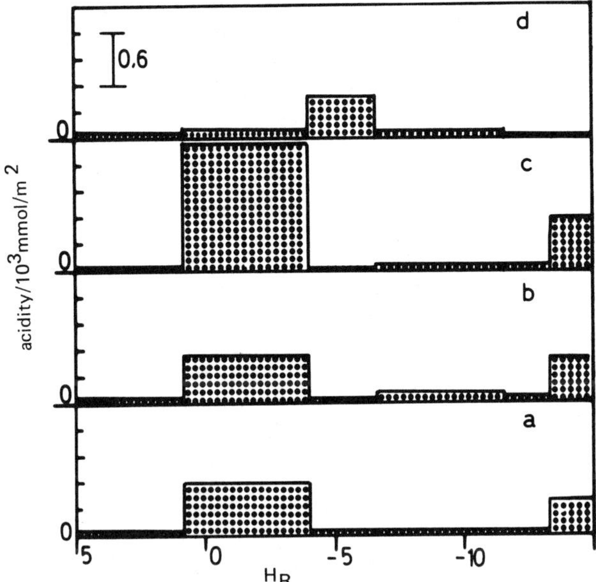


FIG. 4. Brönsted acid strength distribution measured with $H_R$ indicators for silica-aluminas with varying composition: (a) $0.15Al_2O_3SiO$; (b) $0.40Al_2O_3SiO_2$; (c) $0.60Al_2O_3SiO_2$; (d) $0.85Al_2O_3SiO_2$. (After Ref. 23.)

form may mask that of the basic form [2] or (2) the "acid" color of the indicator may be caused by processes other than just proton addition [2,19]. Indeed, physical absorption of the indicator may cause a bathochromic shift to longer wavelengths [19]. This may produce the typical color of the protonated indicator and would result in a significant overtitration if the reaction is not followed spectroscopically.

Therefore, with the use of the ultraviolet indicators given in Table 5, the end point of the titration may be determined spectrophotometrically. In the same way, a set of fluorescent indicators may be used [27]. The spectrophotometric method will provide more quantitative information than visual observation of the color changes. Nevertheless, the possible discrepancy between $pK_A$ values of the indicator in aqueous solution and adsorbed on a solid with high specific surface will remain unchanged. The spectrophotometric method also allows the direct determination of $C_{IH^+} + C_I$ (Eq. 10), that is, the concentration on the solid of the indicator in its basic and acid form. For a constant value of the amount of base added, the $H_0$ value should not vary with the nature of the indicator used. In fact, it was observed that plots of $H_0$ against the amount of base added for different in-

TABLE 5 Ultraviolet Spectrophotometric $H_0$ Indicators and Their Absorption Bands

| Compound | $H_0$ | Wavelength (nm) | | References |
|---|---|---|---|---|
| | | Base | Acid | |
| Butter yellow | +3.3 | 400 | 520 | 22 |
| p-Nitroaniline | +1.1 | 323 | 380 | 24 |
| o-Nitroaniline | −0.2 | 378 | 270 | 25 |
| p-Nitrodiphenylamine | −2.4 | 350 | 440 | 26 |
| 2,4-Dinitroaniline | −4.4 | 310, 365 | 235 | 19 |
| Benzalacetophenone | −5.6 | 300 | 400 | 22 |
| 2,4,6-Trinitroaniline | −9.3 | 320, 390 | 340, 420 | 19 |
| p-Nitrotoluene | −10.3 | 260 | 340-380 | 22 |
| Nitrobenzene | −11.3 | 252 | 280 | 24, 26 |
| 2,4-Dinitrotoluene | −12.8 | 230 | 260-310 | 22 |

dicators lie on distinct curves and do not coincide as expected [7,28]. This discrepancy seems to be the result of [7]:

The difference in molecular structure of the indicator
The specific activity of the indicator used
The color change mechanism

It is therefore recommended to select indicators with analogous chemical structure.

## D. Determination of Overall Brönsted Acidity in the Presence of Physisorbed Water

The $H_0$ or $H_R$ titration method was shown to be sensitive to residual physisorbed water (see, e.g., Fig. 3). During the sample handling procedure after activation, it is extremely difficult to avoid the readsorption of traces of water, particularly when hydrophilic samples (e.g., high-alumina zeolites of the type X and Y) are handled. A gentle method has been developed to take this into account [29,30]. The method combines a reaction with $LiAlH_4$, a Karl Fischer (KF) titration, and a determination of the sample weight loss upon calcination.

The weight loss upon calcination determines the sum of the physisorbed and chemically held water. Chemically sorbed water thermally is desorbed as follows:

$$\text{solid-(OH)}_2 \rightleftharpoons H_2O + \text{solid} = 0 \qquad (16)$$

Therefore, the sample weight loss corresponds to the weight of physisorbed water and the 18/34 part of the weight of the hydroxyl groups.

The Karl Fischer titration is a very *fast* and quantitative reaction of water with iodine, $SO_2$, and pyridine in methanol solution. If the titration is carried out in excess reactant [29], and the curve extrapolated to time zero, a possible slow reaction of surface hydroxyl groups and methanol is excluded.

Lithium aluminum hydride reacts with water and acidic OH groups as follows:

$$LiAlH_4 + 2H_2O \rightarrow LiAlO_2 + 4H_2 \tag{17}$$

$$LiAlH_4 + solid - (OH)_4 \rightarrow LiAlO_4 - solid + 4H_2 \tag{18}$$

A $LiAlH_4$ solution in diethylene glycol diethyl ether is added to a bottle containing the zeolite under hydrogen atmosphere. The hydrogen generated during the reaction is determined volumetrically. It is recommended that a blank experiment be carried out and that eventually the data be corrected.

By combining the three measurements, the Brönsted acidity can be determined in two independent ways (Table 6):

$$OH_{calcination} - OH_{KF}$$

or

$$OH_{LiAlH_4} - OH_{KF}$$

This combined method is very efficient to determine the total number of potential Brönsted acid sites, although it gives no indication of the distribution of their strength. However, it may verify figures of total acidity obtained by either the cation exchange or the indicator method. Moreover, the method is particularly useful in microporous catalysts, where part of the pores (or cages) are inaccessible toward hydrocarbons and $LiAlH_4$. In the case of Y-type

TABLE 6 Determination of OH Groups in Presence of Physisorbed Water

| Method | OH species measured |
|---|---|
| I. Calcination | Water (physically + chemically held) |
| II. KF | Physically held water |
| III. $LiAlH_4$ | Water and hydroxyl groups |

zeolites (used to prepare cracking catalysts), it was shown [29] that the $LiAlH_4$ reaction is able to discriminate between OH groups in the supercages and the sodalite cages. The latter are inaccessible toward hydrocarbons.

### E. Calorimetric Determination of the Heat of Immersion and Heat of Adsorption

This procedure involves the sudden immersion of a solid in a liquid and a precise measurement of the heat liberated by a calorimeter. This heat is an integral heat of reaction and corresponds to the *heat of immersion*. Figure 5 shows the heat of immersion of methanol on HNaY catalysts with different proton content. It is correlated with the rate of toluene ethylation. A good correlation exists for low and medium proton contents, although for the very high proton contents the catalytic activity increases much faster than the heat of immersion. The advantage of such method is that the heat of immersion of the reactants for a given reaction can be determined in the precatalytic temperature region, although as Fig. 5 shows, this does not necessarily allow us to predict the catalytic properties.

The determination of *differential heats of adsorption* can also be carried out using sensitive microcalorimeters. Usually, the heat of adsorption is expressed as a function of the amount of adsorbate admitted or of the surface coverage. Therefore, measurement of both

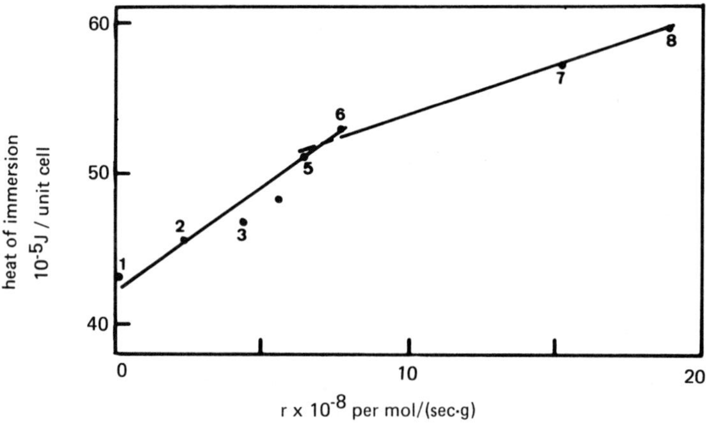


FIG. 5. Heat of immersion of NHaY zeolites in methanol against the ethylation rate (r) of toluene with ethanol. The sample numbers refer to the proton fraction of the total cations ($H^+/Na^+ + H^+$): 1, 0; 2, 0.35; 3, 0.48; 4, 0.60; 5, 0.72; 6, 0.77; 7, 0.87; 8, 0.98. (After Ref. 32.)

the heat evolved upon adsorption and the amount adsorbed is required and the calorimeter has to be connected to ancillary equipment for the determination of adsorbate quantities [33]. This is most commonly done in *heat-flow or conduction calorimeters* of the Tian-Calvet type [33-37]. These calorimeters are *quasi-isothermal* throughout the experiment, since the reaction heat is easily transferred through a mechanically defined path to a surrounding heat sink. This heat-conductor facilitates heat transfer so that all other heat leaks become negligible [33]. Tian's equation governs heat exchange in such a system:

$$\frac{dQ}{dt} = p\ \Delta T + \frac{\mu\ dT}{dt} \tag{19}$$

dQ/dt is the rate at which the heat is adsorbed or liberated, $\mu$ the heat capacity of the calorimeter cell and its contents, p the heat transfer coefficient between the cell and its surroundings, $\Delta T$ the temperature difference between the calorimeter cell and the shield of the cell, and $\mu$ dT the heat liberated or adsorbed in the cell during time dt for which the cell temperature changes by dT. In a heat-flow calorimeter, p remains constant during the experiment and the equation may be used to analyze the data from both fast and slow processes [33].

An example of the differential heat of ammonia sorption on H-zeolites at different coverages is given in Fig. 6. When differential heats of adsorption are determined calorimetrically by successive introduction of doses of adsorbate on an energetically heterogeneous sur-

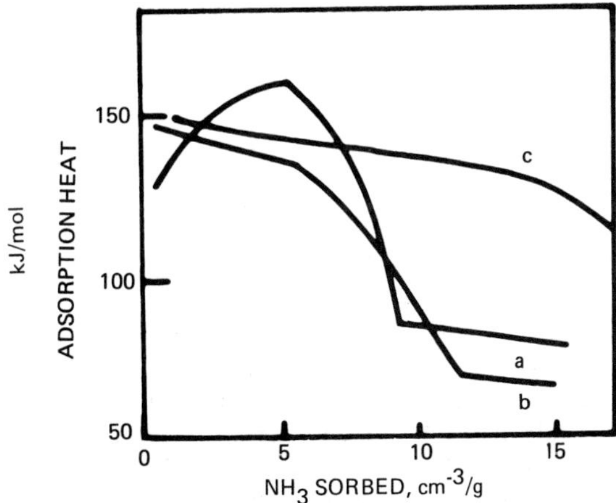


FIG. 6. Differential heat of adsorption of ammonia at 416 K on: a, HZSM-5 zeolite (from Ref. 35); b, another type of HZSM-5 zeolite (from Ref. 36); and c, H-mordenite (from Ref. 35).

face, the strongest sites are preferentially covered, which results in a gradual decrease of the heat with the coverage (Fig. 6, b and c). Therefore, maxima in such curves (Fig. 6, a) are unusual for chemisorption processes since only in case of physisorption, are they indicative of lateral interaction of adsorbate molecules. In the present case, they reflect [35] one of the following:

A faulty calorimetric procedure
Mass-transfer limitations
Immobile adsorption
Nonuniform distribution of the acid sites in the catalyst pores

### F. Temperature-Programmed Desorption (TPD) of Chemisorbed Bases

This technique is a gas chromatographic variant of the flash-filament desorption technique used in surface science [38], which as such is applicable only to metal surfaces kept in high vacuum so that readsorption is negligible. A practical catalyst can be examined in an instrument which essentially is a gas chromatograph with a thermal conductivity-type detector [39,40]. The heating rate of the furnace should be programmable and the chromatographic column is replaced by a reactor containing the catalyst in a shallow bed (less than 1 cm in length) in order to eliminate chromatographic separation along the column. When the desorption temperature is linearly increased, the rate of desorption will show a maximum with temperature or time. In ideal conditions (i.e., when no readsorption of gas takes place during desorption and when the molecules are adsorbed on a homogeneous surface without mutual interactions) the temperature at which the peak maximum appears ($T_M$) is related to the activation energy of desorption ($E_d$) [38-40]:

$$2 \log T_M - \log \beta = \frac{E_d}{2.303RT_M} + \log \frac{E_d a_m}{Rk_0} \tag{20}$$

in which $\beta$ is the rate of linear temperature increase, $a_m$ the amount adsorbed at saturation, and $k_0$ the preexponential factor in the expression of the rate of desorption. When $\beta$ is varied, $T_M$ will shift and a plot of $2 \log T_M - \log \beta$ versus $1/T$ will permit determination of $E_d$ if the kinetics of desorption are first order. Although the surface heterogeneity, large surface areas, and microporosity present in real catalysts cause deviations from this ideal behavior, each TPD peak represents a group of sites whose energy distribution is continuous in a finite range [38].

In Fig. 7 are shown schematic results from this method using ammonia as chemisorbed base and formally assuming that ideal condi-

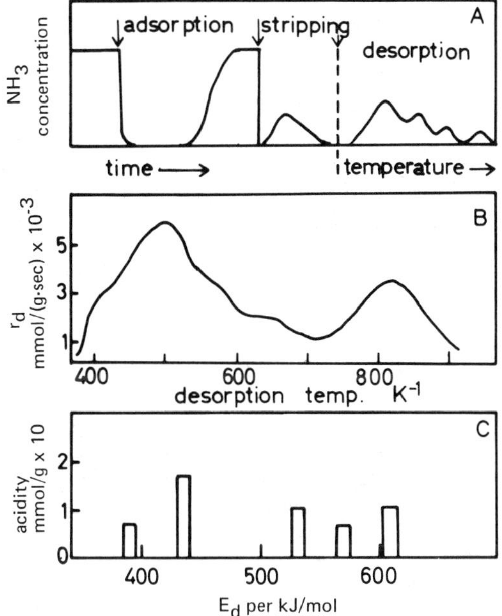


FIG. 7. Temperature-programmed desorption of ammonia from acid catalysts: (A) schematic drawing of the ammonia concentration at the column exit during the whole experiment; (B) actual desorption curve from a sample of HZSM-5 zeolite (desorption rate is 4 K/min): (C) acid strength spectrum (activation energy of desorption, $E_d$, against concentration).

tions exist. Figure 7A shows the variation of the chromatographic trace representing the ammonia concentration in the carrier gas during the saturation period (at ambient temperature and using a $He/NH_3$ gas mixture), the stripping period (at ambient temperature with He as carrier), and during the desorption (linear temperature increase in helium). Figure 7B shows a practical TPD curve obtained on a HZSM-5 catalyst (used, e.g., to transform methanol into gasoline), and Fig. 7C gives the acid strength distribution, derived for the same catalyst using the procedure outlined above. It should be noted that a wide selection as to the nature of the base is possible, although for catalysts with narrow pores and bulky bases, diffusion effects may disturb the picture. For zeolites, the decomposition of $NH_4^+$ ions in some sites may be delayed as a result of a very favorable coordination [46]. Therefore, in microporous solids, the acid-strength spectrum will be determined to some extent by the geometry of the base. It is also evident that the nature of the acid sites cannot be determined this way.

If this method is applied in a discontinuous way (i.e., performing desorption from partially covered samples), the change of the activation energy of desorption with the surface coverage can be determined [41-43]. For solids with a broad spectrum of strengths of sites, this incomplete coverage will increase the danger of readsorption during desorption and give rise to "apparent" values of $E_d$ which are difficult to compare. Therefore, multiplicity of desorption spectra may as well be induced by the existence of different desorption mechanisms as by different adsorption states [49]. The dependence of the desorption mechanism on the mobility of the adsorbed species will increase with their surface density. To overcome this, it is preferable gradually to poison the acid sites. This in case of Brönsted acid sites can be done conveniently by back exchange with group IB cations. This method has been demonstrated to be particularly useful for acid zeolites [44].

### G. Gas-Chromatographic Measurement of the Heat of Adsorption of Weak Bases at Different Degrees of Prepoisoning with a Strong Base [8,9,45]

Provided that a base is available which at partial site coverage is sufficiently strongly adsorbed that the acid sites are selectively blocked according to their strength, the heat of adsorption of a weaker base on the sites uncovered by the strong base can be determined at different degrees of surface coverage. These measurements can be done in catalytic conditions using a column of catalyst poisoned to a different extent. The retention volume ($V_R$) of the weaker base is determined in a certain temperature range:

$$V_R = (t - t_0) \frac{T_c}{273} \frac{3}{2} \frac{(P_i/P_o)^2 - 1}{(P_i/P_o)^3 - 1} \frac{F}{W} \tag{21}$$

in which $T_c$ is the column temperature; t and $t_0$ are the retention times of an adsorbable and nonadsorbable component, respectively; F/W is the carrier gas flow rate per unit weight of catalyst; and $P_i$ and $P_o$ are the pressure at the column inlet and outlet, respectively. Benzene and pyridine have been used as the two basic probe molecules. From the temperature dependence of the retention volume of benzene, its heat of adsorption can be determined. The variation of this heat with the degree of poisoning with pyridine (or other strong bases) is also representative for the acid-strength spectrum.

The specificity of this method is dependent on the nature of the base. The selectivity of pyridine toward Brönsted sites in the presence of Lewis acid sites is not pronounced, while with 2,6-dimethylpyridine the Brönsted sites are titrated first on zeolites [47], and on alumina there still exists a pronounced degree of site specificity [48].

## H. Acidity and Infrared (IR) Spectroscopy

### 1. Separate Determination of Total Lewis and Brönsted Acidity

Numerous studies appeared on the interaction between surfaces and basic molecules by IR. The subject has been thoroughly reviewed [9,50-53] and references to the original research papers can be found therein. Pyridine is the favored molecule to study the Brönsted and Lewis acidity of a solid separately, since Lewis (IV) and Brönsted (V) held pyridine can easily be distinguished by their IR spectrum.

solid-O ⊖⊕ HN (pyridinium ring) ≡Al:N (pyridine ring)

(V) (IV)

The vibrational modes used to make the distinction between (I) and (II) are shown in Table 7. The determination of the Lewis and Brönsted sites then requires the application of *quantitative IR spectroscopy*. This is easily done provided that a relatively thin self-supported wafer (~5 to 10 mg of material per square centimeter of wafer) can be pressed from the solid. This wafer is then suspended in a cell, which allows degassing and thermal treatment of the wafer [50-53]. The spectrum of adsorbed pyridine can even be scanned at elevated wafer temperatures, provided that the spectrometer design is such that the radiation emitted by the hot sample is not modulated. If the spectrum is scanned in the absorbance mode, a consistent baseline can be drawn tangent to the spectral areas of low absorption. The application of the integrated form of Beer's law,

$$B = c\ell \int_{\gamma} \varepsilon_{\gamma}^{(a)}\, d\gamma \qquad (22)$$

TABLE 7 Assignment of Vibrational Modes of Pyridine (Py) Adsorbed on Brönsted and Lewis Acid (L) Sites

| Vibrational mode | $PyH^+$ | $Py{:}L^a$ |
|---|---|---|
| 8a $\nu CC(N)$ ($A_1$) | 1655s | 1595vs |
| 8b $\nu CC(N)$ ($B_1$) | 1627s | 1575m |
| 19b $\nu CC(N)$ ($B_1$) | 1550m | 1455-1442s |
| 19a $\nu CC(N)$ ($A_1$) | 1490vs | 1490s |

[a]vs, very strong; s, strong; m, medium intensity.

in which B is the peak area (in absorbance × $cm^{-1}$ units), c the concentration of the adsorbed species (in μmol/g), ℓ the wafer thickness (in g/cm), γ the wavenumber ($cm^{-1}$), and $\int_\gamma \varepsilon_\gamma^{(a)}$ the apparent integrated extinction coefficient (in cm/μmol). The concentration of species in a given IR peak can be calculated provided that its integrated extinction coefficient is known. It is easily shown that [54]

$$\frac{(\int_\gamma \varepsilon_\gamma^a)_L}{(\int_\gamma \varepsilon_\gamma^a)_B} = \frac{2(B_L^{T_1} - B_L^{T_2})}{B_B^{T_2} - B_B^{T_1}} \tag{23}$$

in which the subscripts L and B refer to a specific IR band for Lewis or Brönsted held pyridine, respectively (e.g., at 1450 and 1550 $cm^{-1}$, respectively), and the indices $T_1$ and $T_2$ refer to the two calcination temperatures of the catalyst. The ratio of the concentration of Lewis (L) and Brönsted (B) sites is then

$$\frac{[L]}{[B]} = \frac{B_L}{B_B} \frac{(\int_\gamma \varepsilon_\gamma^a)_L}{(\int_\gamma \varepsilon_\gamma^a)_B} \tag{24}$$

### 2. Interaction of Surface Hydroxyl Groups with Hydrogen-Bond Acceptor Molecules

The absolute value of the stretching frequency of surface hydroxyl groups (i.e., of Brönsted acid sites) tends to be a rather insensitive probe for acid strength, although recently for zeolites, its fundamental frequency was found to be dependent both on the chemical composition of the material and on the geometry of the pore (or cage) in which it is vibrating [55]. Moreover, from measurement of the overtones of these stretching frequencies [56], it is clear that the anharmonicity factor of the stretching vibration of a diatomic O-H group does not differ significantly from one sample to another.

$$\gamma_{o\to n}^{OH} = n\gamma_e^{OH} - n(n+1)\gamma_e^{OH} x_e^{OH} \tag{25}$$

where $\gamma_e^{OH}$ is the harmonic frequency of the OH stretching vibrations, n the overtone considered, and $x_e^{OH}$ the parameter of anharmonicity. This anharmonicity factor measures the curvature of the potential function at the bottom, describing the diatomic vibrator:

$$x_e^{OH} = \frac{\gamma_e^{OH}}{4D_e} \tag{26}$$

$$D_e = D_0 + \frac{1}{2\gamma_e^{OH}} \tag{27}$$

$$U_{(r)} = D_e[1 - e^{-\alpha(r-r_e)}]^2 \tag{28}$$

Equation (27) is the Morse potential function, $D_0$ the dissociation energy of the OH bond, $r_e$ the OH bond length at equilibrium, and $\alpha$ is a constant.

Although the absolute measurement of the fundamental and overtone frequencies of the OH bond gives no information about the acid strength of the Brönsted site involved, the frequency shifts of these vibrations upon interaction with hydrogen-bond acceptor molecules are more informative in this respect. This interaction can be quantified as follows:

$$\Delta\gamma = \frac{3qE}{4r(2\mu)^{1/2}D^{1/2}} \tag{29}$$

where $\Delta\gamma$ is the frequency shift of the hydroxyl group upon interaction with a hydrogen-bond acceptor molecule, q the dipole charge, E the electric field component along the O-H axis, $\mu$ the reduced mass, and D the dissociation energy of the OH bond. These frequency shifts have been shown to provide a convenient hydrogen-bond-strength estimate [46,57,58] and consequently an estimation of Brönsted acid strength. Indeed, a significant correlation exists between the frequency shift of the H-bond donor and its proton donating power [58].

For hydrogen bonding in solution [58], the frequency shifts of two H-bond donors R-XH and R'-X'H with various acceptors are usually compared by plotting the relative frequency shifts of the two donors ($\Delta\gamma/\gamma_0$ and $\Delta\gamma'/\gamma_0'$) against each other, $\gamma_0$ and $\gamma_0'$ being their fundamental stretching frequency. When the proton bearing atoms are the same, this relation is linear:

$$\frac{\Delta\gamma}{\gamma_0} = a + b\,\frac{\Delta\gamma'}{\gamma_0'} \tag{30}$$

The slope of such a plot, commonly referred to as a BHW plot (after the authors who first used it [59]), is therefore an estimate of the H-bonding strength of R-XH compared to R'-XH [58].

A correlation between the value of the BHW slope and the $pK_A$ of various proton donors is given in Fig. 8. A confident correlation exists in the range 0 to 10 $pK_A$. For higher acid strengths, extrapolated values have to be used. Even in case the relation of the BHW slope to a $pK_A$ value cannot be made, the BHW parameter is very

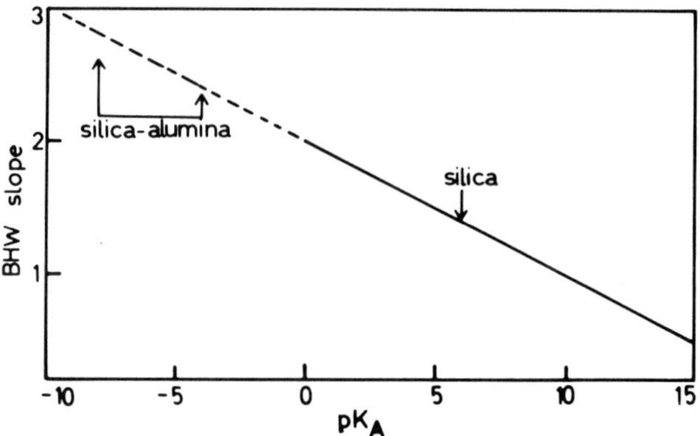


FIG. 8. Correlation between BHW slope of various OH containing proton donors against their $pK_A$ in water. (After Ref. 58.)

useful for the estimation of an overall acid strength. Its determination is very easy, since it requires only the measurements of the OH frequency shifts of a series of proton acceptors upon interaction with the catalyst OH groups and with, for example, phenol as reference. The major advantage of the method is that the reactant molecules can be tested and used in the catalytic transformation in which one is interested.

## I. Miscellaneous Spectroscopic Methods

These are methods that are either not of general applicability or require not generally accessible equipment, but which in a particular case may provide interesting information on the acidity of catalysts.

### 1. Electron Spin Resonance (ESR)

Upon $\gamma$ irradiation of zeolites, hydrogen atoms are released which are characteristic of the hydroxyl groups in their lattice [60]. They can be trapped (e.g., at 77 K) and detected by ESR spectroscopy. It seems now that the trapping strength is dependent on the type of zeolite [36]. The mechanism of formation and trapping of H atoms can be schematized as in Eq. (31).

The ESR signal of NO adsorbed on zeolites shows a hyperfine structure (with a hyperfine splitting of roughly 13 G) attributed to the interaction of the unpaired electron with an aluminum nucleus [36, 61]. Such a signal characterizes strong Lewis acid centers [62].

The formation of charge transfer complexes upon adsorption of organic bases upon Lewis acid sites can also be followed by ESR. Perylene, anthracene, naphthalene, and benzene adsorbed on acid

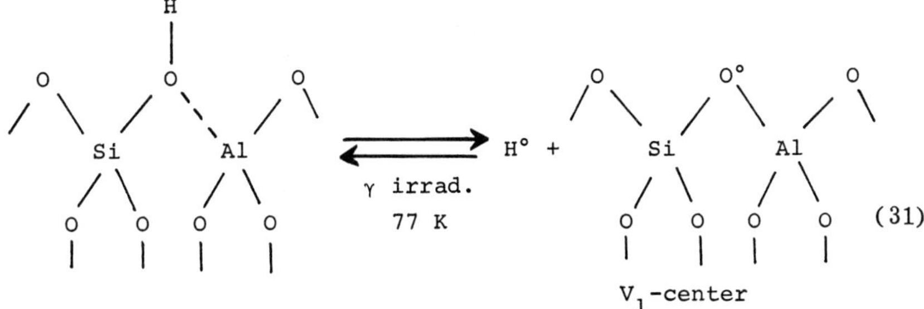


zeolites at elevated temperature are ionized by electron transfer between the organic base and electron acceptor sites of the Lewis type [36,62]. This is a unique method to determine the spectrum of acid strength of Lewis acid sites, just by using a series of bases with different ionization potential. The number of $A^-D^+$ species formed in such a reaction is governed by Mulliken's theory [63]:

$$N = N_0 e^{(-I-A-W)/kT} \tag{32}$$

where D is the electron donor and A the electron acceptor; and W, A, and I are the dissociation energy of the complex $A^-D^+$, the electron affinity of the acceptor, and the ionization potential of the donor, respectively.

### 2. Ultraviolet (UV) Spectroscopy

Molecules such as anthraquinone, triphenylcarbinol, N,N-dimethylaniline, pyridine, and triphenylmethane upon interaction with Brönsted or Lewis acid sites are transformed into carbenium ions or radical cations, respectively. Others, such as benzene and cumene, are ionized only after UV irradiation. The nature and concentration of these species can be followed with UV spectroscopy [64]. The adsorption of a series of well-selected bases therefore permits determination of an acid-strength spectrum.

### 3. Nuclear Magnetic Resonance (NMR) Spectroscopy

All previous methods neglect an important characteristic of acidity, its *dynamic* character. Acid strength in such a context can be defined as the *lifetime* of the complex formed upon interaction of an acid site with a reactant molecule. Both the number of Brönsted sites interacting with a substrate ($n_A$) and the mean residence time or proton correlation times ($\tau_c$) of these protons on their respective oxygen anions can be determined by NMR spectroscopy. The ratio $n_a/\tau_c$ is a measure of the overall Brönsted acid strength of a solid [65], that is, the shorter $\tau_c$, the more mobile the proton. The overall acid

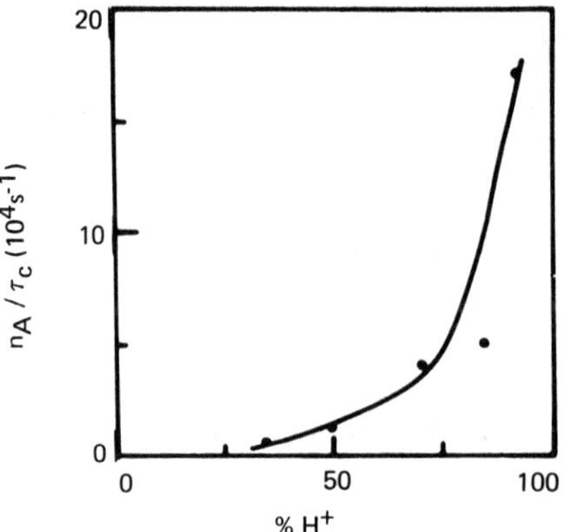


FIG. 9. Overall acid strength of HNaY zeolite calcined in deep-bed geometry as determined by NMR spectroscopy against residual Na content. $n_A$, number of acid sites; $\tau_c$, residence time of the protons on the surface oxygen atoms in the presence of pyridine. (After Ref. 65.)

strength will increase with increasing $n_a/\tau_c$ ratio: at constant number, with decreasing $\tau_c$ or increasing proton mobility; at constant $\tau_c$, with increasing number of acid sites.

Such measurements have been reported on H-Y zeolites with different residual $Na^+$ content and activated in so-called "deep-bed" sample geometry [65], which is close to the packing in an actual reactor. The proton transporting vehicle was pyridine. The results are shown in Fig. 9. The sudden increase in acid strength at high proton contents is consistent with the catalytic behavior in acid-catalyzed reactions (see Fig. 5) and could not be derived from the heat of immersion measurements.

Correlation times $\tau_c$ can be derived from an Arrhenius plot of the transverse relaxation time $\tau_2$ of the OH groups. To do so, the transition of the temperature-independent to the temperature-dependent part of the plot has to be determined. This can be done with an accuracy of only ±10% [66].

## J. Use of Model Reactions for Determination of Surface Acidity

### 1. Determination of the Initial Apparent Turnover Frequency

There is considerable weight of evidence now that in hydrocarbon transformations, the Brönsted acid sites are the primary seat of activity [67-70]. Therefore, in the following discussion, only the action of protonic acid sites will be considered. Lewis acid sites are considered important insofar that through direct interaction with Brönsted sites, the strength of the latter may be changed [61]. If catalysts are to be compared, it should be stressed that both the strength and number of the Brönsted sites may vary. If this comparison is done via a catalytic test reaction, it is important to note that the rate of activity decay or the rate of poisoning may change with the catalyst. It is therefore necessary to measure an *initial apparent turnover frequency*. The turnover frequency of the Brönsted sites represents the average catalytic efficiency of the acid OH groups. It is commonly determined by dividing the initial reaction rate by the *total* number of acid sites. The *actual* number of acid sites ($C_s$) can only be determined using absolute rate theory in very specific conditions. For example, the rate of an acid-catalyzed unimolecular reaction (r) that follows zero-order kinetics is given by

$$r = C_s \frac{kT}{h} e^{-E_a/RT} \tag{33}$$

where $E_a$ is the activation energy and k, h, and R are the Boltzmann, Planck, and gas constants, respectively. Although it is realized now that the absolute number of active sites may be far below the total number of Brönsted sites [71], measurement of the apparent turnover frequency (as defined above) is a very useful index for the catalytic efficiency of an acid solid and permits comparison of solids with a wide variety of physical and chemical properties [55].

### 2. Determination of Initial Rates of Reaction

In typical acid catalysts, initially the activity shows a very fast decay followed by a slower decrease for longer time on-stream. As a result, determination of the initial activity requires measurements at short intervals after the catalyst comes on-stream. Such an interval is for an on-line analysis of the reactor exit determined by the sample analysis time. So initial rates can be determined only with sufficient accuracy for noncomplex reactions which require only a short analysis time, unless the 16-loop Valco valve [72] is used to store the samples. So sampling can be done at short intervals and the analysis can be done afterward.

### 3. The Actual Number of Active Sites and the True Turnover Number

It is common knowledge that some molecules can be transformed over weaker Brönsted acid sites than can others. A comprehensive list of typical transformations arranged in a sequence requiring increasing acid strength (and therefore higher reaction temperatures) and being catalyzed by a decreasing fraction of the overall Brönsted acid sites is given in Table 8. All these reactions can be utilized as quick tests for the acid strength, although it remains a "superficial and dirty test" of the carbonium-ion-generating power of a solid [73].

TABLE 8 Minimum Brönsted Acid Strength Required for the Acid-Catalyzed Conversion of Some Reactants

| $H_R$ required | Reaction type | Reference | Estimate of fraction of active sites |
|---|---|---|---|
| < +4 | Alcohol dehydration | 9 | ~1 |
| < +0.82 | Cis-trans isomerization of olefins | 23 | ~1 |
| < −6.63 | Double-bond migration | 23 | — |
| < −11.63 | Skeletal isomerization | 23 | — |
| < −11.5 | Cracking of alkylaromatics | 9 | 0.05-1 |
| < −16.0 | Cracking of alkanes | 9 | $1 \times 10^{-4}$ |

It should also be realized that during dehydration reactions, the steam formed might alter the physical and chemical properties of the catalyst or may function as a strong and competitive sorbent for the active sites. For the cumene cracking reaction in particular, it is clear that only if for each catalyst the reaction is studied sufficiently in detail "may we one day be able to map the activity and site distribution of cracking catalysts." The latter would require an understanding of the mechanism, kinetics, and deactivation behavior.

The determination of the *true* number of active sites allows us to determine a true turnover number, provided that the initial reaction rate is known. This can be done using a catalytic titration [74]. During such a procedure, the amount of base required to poison catalytic activity is determined for a model reaction. The minimum amount of base required to remove activity gives an indication of the number of sites. From the slope of the activity versus amount of added base curves, the acid strength is gauged [74]. Base effectiveness for poisoning of cumene cracking over silica-alumina catalysts was found to decrease in the following order [75]:

quinaldine > quinoline > pyrrole > piperidine > decylamine
> aniline

Experimentally, this can easily be done by alternating pulses of reactant and poison. This method requires a poison which selectively interacts with the Brönsted centers according to their strength. A homogeneous distribution of the poison over the catalyst bed is better achieved by increasing the time interval between pulse additions or by raising the sample temperature shortly after each pulse addition [74]. The effectiveness of an amine for the selective titration of Brönsted acids in the presence of Lewis sites is enhanced considerably when the coordination of the reactive N atom is hindered by substitution. 2,6-Dimethylpyridine is a much more selective reagent than the unhindered amine, pyridine [47].

### 4. An Ideal Test Reaction: The Isomerization-Hydrocracking Pattern of n-Decane

Deactivation of cracking catalysts may be avoided by addition of a hydrogenation function and by performing the reaction in the presence of hydrogen. Therefore, the conversion of hydrocarbons on Pt-loaded acid catalysts in the presence of hydrogen will not suffer from deactivation. In order to gather as much information as possible on reaction routes, the chain length of the reactant paraffin should be as high as possible. Separation of most of the isomers by high-

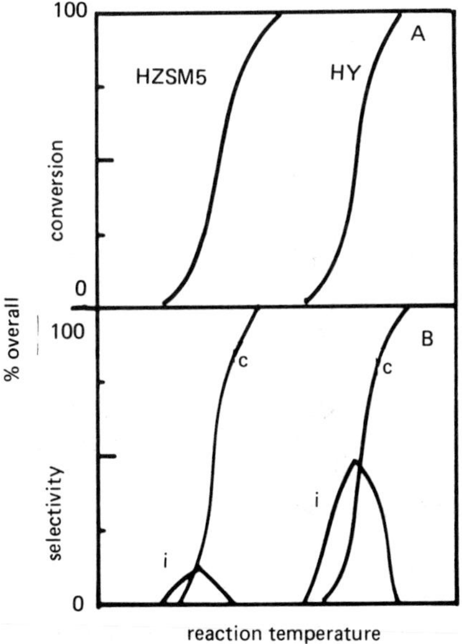


FIG. 10. Schematic representation of n-decane conversion in hydrogen over HY and HZSM-5 impregnated with Pt: (A) overall activity and (B) overall selectivity for i, isomerization, and c, hydrocracking.

resolution capillary chromatography is still possible for n-decane, but not for hendecane.

The classical bifunctional mechanism for n-decane conversion may be depicted as follows [46]:

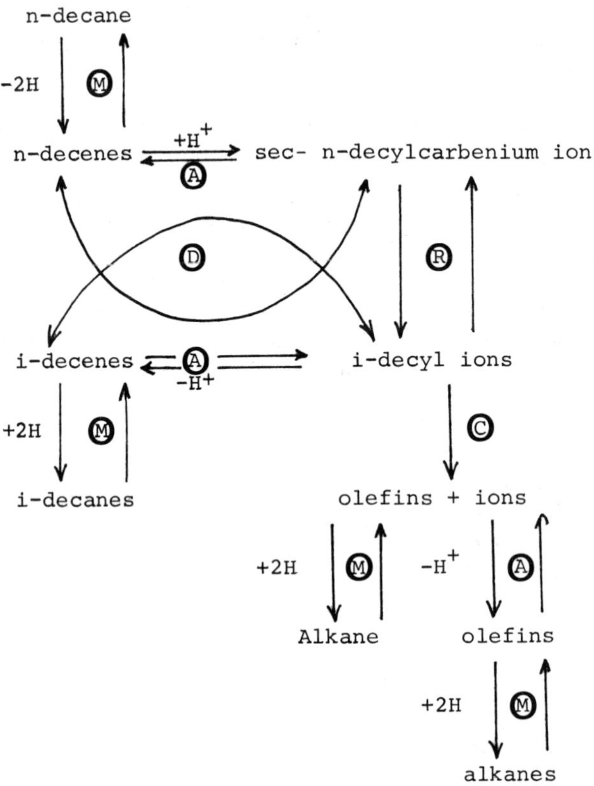


in which M represents the hydrogenation-dehydrogenation equilibrium reactions occurring on the metal phase, B the carbenium ion formation on acid sites through proton addition to the olefins, D the competitive sorption-desorption processes of alkenes and carbenium ions, R the rearrangement of carbenium ions, and C the cracking of carbenium ions. The selectivity between isomerization (R) and cracking (C), which are consecutive processes, is entirely determined—all other factors remaining unchanged (step D)—by the lifetime of the carbenium ions, stronger Brönsted sites will produce longer-living ions and will favor hydrocracking. Moreover, from the initial activity it will be possible to determine apparent turnover numbers. If some OH groups are located in sterically hindered sites, it will be evident from the product distribution of the n-decane isomers. For open structures, equilibrium is obtained between the methylnonanes and ethyloctanes. The latter is no longer true if shape-selective constraints exist.

The catalytic behavior of Pt on HY zeolites and on HZSM-5 zeolites is illustrative of all this [46]. The overall activity and selectivity for both catalysts are represented schematically in Fig. 10. Both zeolites are prepared so as to have the same number of surface OH groups. The catalytic picture indicates that the HZSM-5 zeolite is, on the average, the solid with the strongest acidity.

## IV. CONCLUSIONS

A single method does not exist which would be able to determine the acid spectrum of a solid (i.e., nature, strength, and number of acid sites) in conditions comparable to those in which the solid is used as a catalyst. All methods measure only certain aspects, and therefore the application of as many as possible methods is desirable. If only a limited number of tests can be applied, they should be judiciously selected in terms of the acidity aspect, which is considered to be most relevant for a particular catalytic application.

## ACKNOWLEDGMENT

The author is grateful to NFWO (Belgium) for a permanent research position as Senior Research Associate as well as for financial support.

## REFERENCES

1. B. D. Flockhart and R. C. Pink, *J. Catal.*, *8*: 293 (1967).
2. H. A. Benesi and B. H. C. Winquist, *Adv. Catal.*, *27*: 98 (1978).
3. D. W. Breck and G. W. Skeels, *Proc. 6th Int. Congr. Catal.*, Vol. 2 (G. C. Bond, P. B. Wells, and F. C. Tompkins, eds.), The Chemical Society, London, 1977, p. 645.
4. M. S. Goldstein, in *Experimental Methods in Catalytic Research* (R. B. Anderson, ed.), Academic Press, New York, 1968, p. 361.
5. A. G. Oblad, T. H. Milliken, Jr., and G. A. Mills, *Adv. Catal.*, *3*: 199 (1951).
6. M. W. Tamele, *Discuss. Faraday Soc.*, *8*: 270 (1950).
7. K. Tanabe, *Solid Acids and Bases*, Academic Press, New York, 1970.
8. L. Forni, *Catal. Rev.*, *8*: 65 (1973).
9. P. A. Jacobs, *Carboniogenic Activity of Zeolites*, Elsevier, Amsterdam, 1977, p. 33.

10. W. Kladnig, *J. Phys. Chem.*, *80*: 262 (1976).
11. K. K. Unger, U. R. Kittelman, and W. K. Kries, *J. Chem. Tech. Biotechnol.*, *31*: 435 (1981).
12. L. B. Hammett, *Physikalische Organische Chemie*, Chemie Verlag, Weinheim, West Germany, 1973, p. 263.
13. C. Walling, *J. Am. Chem. Soc.*, *72*: 1164 (1950).
14. H. A. Benesi, *J. Am. Chem. Soc.*, *78*: 5490 (1956).
15. H. Hattori, O. Takahashi, M. Takagi, and K. Tanabe, *J. Catal.*, *68*: 132 (1981).
16. N. C. Deno and A. Schriesheim, *J. Am. Chem. Soc.*, *77*: 3051 (1955).
17. O. Johnson, *J. Phys. Chem.*, *59*: 827 (1955).
18. H. A. Benesi, *J. Phys. Chem.*, *61*: 670 (1957).
19. D. Atkinson and G. Curthoys, *Chem. Rev.*, 475 (1981).
20. P. A. Jacobs, *Carboniogenic Activity of Zeolites*, Elsevier, Amsterdam, 1977, pp. 71-72.
21. S. Namba, N. Hosonuma, and T. Yashima, *J. Catal.*, *72*: 16 (1981).
22. M. Ikemoto, K. Tsutsumi, and H. Takahashi, *Bull. Chem. Soc. Jap.*, *45*: 1330 (1972).
23. J. P. Damon, B. Delmon, and J. M. Bonnier, *J. Chem. Soc., Faraday Trans. 1*, *73*: 372 (1977).
24. M. Robin and K. N. Trueblood, *J. Am. Chem. Soc.*, *79*: 5138 (1957).
25. H. P. Leftin and M. C. Hobson, *Adv. Catal.*, *14*: 115 (1963).
26. J. C. D. Brand, *J. Chem. Soc.*, 997 (1950).
27. E. P. Parry, *J. Catal.*, *2*: 371 (1963).
28. J. Kobayashi, *Nippon Kagaku Zasshi*, *84*: 21 (1963); *82*: 288 (1961); *80*: 1399 (1959).
29. L. Moscou and M. Lakeman, *J. Catal.*, *16*: 173 (1970).
30. L. Moscou, *Adv. Chem. Ser.*, *102*: 250 (1971).
31. J. B. Maffat, *Catal. Rev. Sci. Eng.*, *18*: 199 (1978).
32. B. Coughlan, W. M. Carroll, P. Kavanagh, and J. Nunan, *J. Chem. Tech. Biotechnol.*, *31*: 1 (1981).
33. P. C. Gravelle, *Catal. Rev. Sci. Eng.*, *16*: 37 (1977).
34. K. Tsutsumi, Hong Qui Koh, S. Hagiwara, and H. Takahashi, *Bull Chem. Soc. Jap.*, *48*: 3576 (1975).
35. A. Auroux, P. Wierzchowski, and P. C. Gravelle, *Thermochim. Acta*, *32*: 165 (1979).
36. J. C. Vedrine, A. Auroux, V. Bolis, P. Dejaifve, C. Naccache, P. Wierzchowski, E. G. Derouane, J. B. Nagy, J. P. Gilson, J. H. C. Van Hooff, J. P. Van den Berg, and J. Wolthuizen, *J. Catal.*, *59*: 248 (1979).
37. A. Auroux, V. Bolis, P. Wierzchowski, P. C. Gravelle, and J. C. Vedrine, *J. Chem. Soc., Faraday Trans. 1*, *75*: 2544 (1979).
38. Y. Amenomiya, *Chem. Tech.*, *6*: 21 (1972).

39. R. J. Cvetanovic and Y. Amenomiya, *Adv. Catal.*, *17*: 103 (1967).
40. R. J. Cvetanovic and Y. Amenomiya, *Catal. Rev.*, *6*: 21 (1972).
41. M. D. Navalikhina, B. V. Romanovskii, K. V. Topchieva, and V. V. Demkin, *Kinet. Catal.*, *13*: 306 (1972).
42. K. V. Topchieva and K. S. Tkhoang, *Russ. J. Phys. Chem.*, *47*: 1185 (1973).
43. H. S. Thouang, K. V. Topchieva, and B. V. Romanovskii, *Kinet. Catal.*, *15*: 934 (1974).
44. H. Itoh, T. Hattori, and Y. Murakami, *Chem. Lett.*, 1147 (1981).
45. M. D. Navalikhina, B. V. Romanovskii, and K. Topchieva, *Kinet. Katal.*, *12*: 145 (1971); *13*: 231 (1972).
46. P. A. Jacobs, J. A. Martens, J. Weitkamp, and H. K. Beyer, *Discuss. Faraday Soc.* (Nottingham), 353 (1981).
47. P. A. Jacobs and C. F. Heylen, *J. Catal.*, *34*: 267 (1974).
48. H. Knözinger and H. Stolz, *Ber. Bunsenges. Phys. Chem.*, *75*: 1055 (1971).
49. M. Smutek, S. Cerny, and F. Buzek, *Adv. Catal.*, *24*: 343 (1975).
50. R. P. Eischens and W. A. Pliskin, *Adv. Catal.*, *10*: 1 (1958).
51. L. H. Little, *Infrared Spectra of Adsorbed Species*, Academic Press, New York, 1966, and references therein.
52. M. L. Hair, *Infrared Spectroscopy in Surface Chemistry*, Marcel Dekker, New York, 1967, and references therein.
53. J. W. Ward, in *Zeolite Chemistry and Catalysis* (J. A. Rabo, ed.), ACS Monograph 171, American Chemical Society, Washington, D.C., 1976 p. 118, and references therein.
54. J. W. Ward, *J. Catal.*, *11*: 272 (1968).
55. P. A. Jacobs, *Catal. Rev. Sci. Eng.*, *24*: 415 (1982).
56. L. M. Kustov, V. Y. Borovkov, and V. B. Kazansky, *J. Catal.*, *72*: 149 (1981).
57. J. Datka, *J. Chem. Soc., Faraday Trans. 1*, *77*: 511 (1981).
58. P. G. Rouxhet and R. E. Semples, *J. Chem. Soc., Faraday Trans. 1*, *70*: 2021 (1974).
59. L. J. Bellamy, H. E. Hallam, and R. L. Williams, *Trans. Faraday Soc.*, *54*: 1120 (1958).
60. A. Abou-Kais, J. C. Védrine, J. Massardier, G. Dalmai-Imelik, and B. Imelik, *J. Chim. Phys.*, *69*: 561 (1972).
61. J. H. Lunsford, *J. Phys. Chem.*, *72*: 4163 (1968).
62. Y. Ben Taarit, C. Naccache, and B. Imelik, *J. Chim. Phys.*, *70*: 728 (1973).
63. P. A. Jacobs, *Carboniogenic Activity of Zeolites*, Elsevier, Amsterdam, 1977, pp. 42-43.
64. P. A. Jacobs, *Carboniogenic Activity of Zeolites*, Elsevier, Amsterdam, 1977, p. 41.

65. D. Freude and H. Pfeifer, *Proc. 5th Int. Conf. Zeolites* (L. V. Rees, ed.), Heyden, London, 1980, p. 732.
66. H. Pfeifer, *NMR and Relaxation of Molecules Adsorbed on Solids*, NMR—Basic Principles and Progress, Vol. 7, Springer-Verlag, Berlin, 1972.
67. H. H. Voge, *Catalysis, 6*: 407 (1958).
68. R. M. Kennedy, *Catalysis, 6*: 1 (1958).
69. F. E. Condon, *Catalysis, 6*: 43 (1958).
70. A. G. Oblad, G. A. Mills, and H. Heinemann, *Catalysis, 6*: 341 (1958).
71. R. W. Maatman, *Catal. Rev., 8*: 1 (1973).
72. *The Chrompack Guide to Chromatography*, Chrompack, Middelburg, Holland, 1981 p. 107.
73. A. Corma and B. W. Wojciechowski, *Catal. Rev. Sci. Eng., 24*: 1 (1982).
74. H. A. Benesi and B. H. C. Winquist, *Adv. Catal., 27*: 114 (1978).
75. G. A. Mills, E. R. Boedeker, and A. G. Oblad, *J. Am. Chem. Soc., 72*: 1554 (1950).

# Index